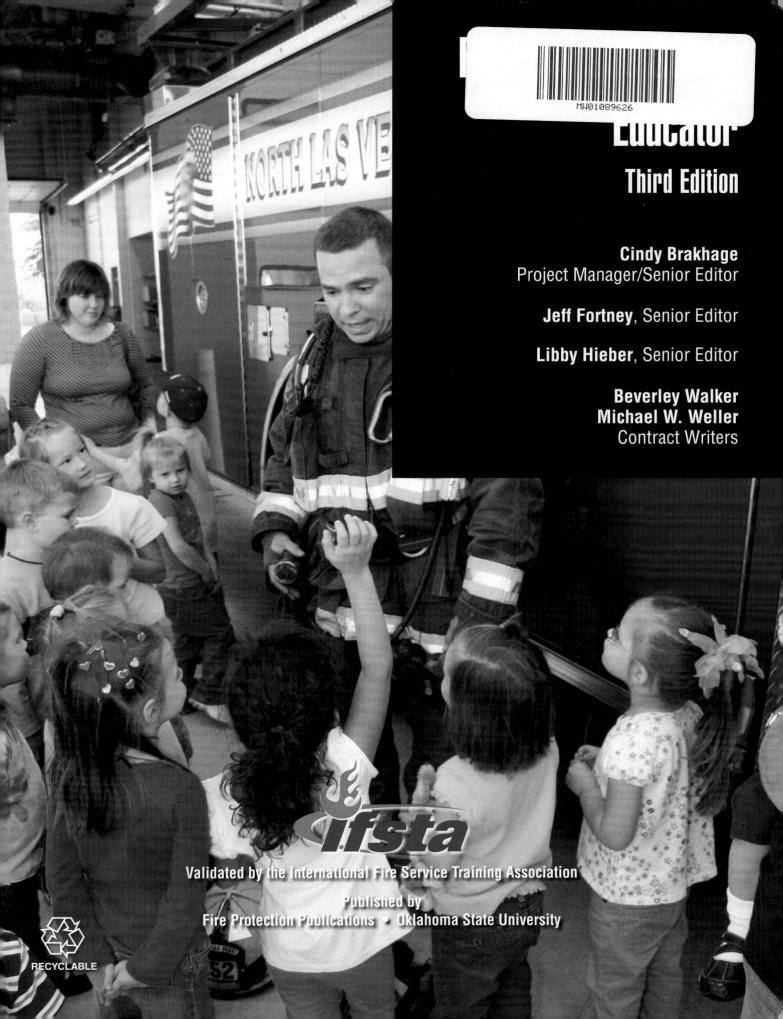

Educator

Third Edition

Cindy Brakhage
Project Manager/Senior Editor

Jeff Fortney, Senior Editor

Libby Hieber, Senior Editor

Beverley Walker
Michael W. Weller
Contract Writers

Validated by the International Fire Service Training Association

Published by
Fire Protection Publications • Oklahoma State University

RECYCLABLE

The International Fire Service Training Association

The International Fire Service Training Association (IFSTA) was established in 1934 as a *nonprofit educational association of fire fighting personnel who are dedicated to upgrading fire fighting techniques and safety through training.* To carry out the mission of IFSTA, Fire Protection Publications was established as an entity of Oklahoma State University. Fire Protection Publications' primary function is to publish and disseminate training texts as proposed and validated by IFSTA. As a secondary function, Fire Protection Publications researches, acquires, produces, and markets high-quality learning and teaching aids as consistent with IFSTA's mission.

The IFSTA Validation Conference is held the second full week in July. Committees of technical experts meet and work at the conference addressing the current standards of the National Fire Protection Association® and other standard-making groups as applicable. The Validation Conference brings together individuals from several related and allied fields, such as:

- Key fire department executives and training officers
- Educators from colleges and universities
- Representatives from governmental agencies
- Delegates of firefighter associations and industrial organizations

Committee members are not paid nor are they reimbursed for their expenses by IFSTA or Fire Protection Publications. They participate because of commitment to the fire service and its future through training. Being on a committee is prestigious in the fire service community, and committee members are acknowledged leaders in their fields. This unique feature provides a close relationship between the International Fire Service Training Association and fire protection agencies, which helps to correlate the efforts of all concerned.

IFSTA manuals are now the official teaching texts of most of the states and provinces of North America. Additionally, numerous U.S. and Canadian government agencies as well as other English-speaking countries have officially accepted the IFSTA manuals.

ISBN 978-0-87939-396-0   Library of Congress Control Number: 2010942508

Third Edition, Third Printing, August 2019   *Printed in the United States of America*

10   9   8   7   6   5   4   3

If you need additional information concerning the International Fire Service Training Association (IFSTA) or Fire Protection Publications, contact:

Customer Service, Fire Protection Publications, Oklahoma State University
930 North Willis, Stillwater, OK 74078-8045
800-654-4055   Fax: 405-744-8204

For assistance with training materials, to recommend material for inclusion in an IFSTA manual, or to ask questions or comment on manual content, contact:

Editorial Department, Fire Protection Publications, Oklahoma State University
930 North Willis, Stillwater, OK 74078-8045
405-744-4111   Fax: 405-744-4112   E-mail: editors@osufpp.org

Chapter Summary

Table of Contents

List of Tables

Preface

The third edition of **Fire and Life Safety Educator** provides the educator with the knowledge to support successful performance as a fire and life safety educator and a juvenile firesetter intervention specialist as addressed in NFPA® 1035, *Standard for Professional Qualifications for Fire and Life Safety Educator, Public Information Officer, and Juvenile Firesetter Interventionist Specialist*. The manual also meets the learning outcomes of the National Fire Academy's Fire and Emergency Services Higher Educator (FESHE) noncore course *Fire and Life Safety Educator*.

Acknowledgement and special thanks are extended to the members of the IFSTA validating committee who contributed their time, wisdom, and knowledge to the development of this manual.

IFSTA Fire and Life Safety Educator, Third Edition
IFSTA Validation Committee

Committee Chair
Dena Schumacher
Education Specialist, Fire/Life Safety
Champaign Fire Department
Champaign, Illinois

Contract Writers

Beverley Walker
Lieutenant of Public Education
Hall County Fire Services
Gainesville, Georgia

Michael W. Weller
Fire Prevention Officer
Hagerstown Fire Department
Hagerstown, Maryland

Committee Members

Bruce Evans
EMS Chief
North Las Vegas Fire Department
North Las Vegas, Nevada

Christopher Garrett
Deputy Chief
Owasso Fire Department
Owasso, Oklahoma

Dayna Hilton
Public Fire and Life Safety Educator II
Johnson County RFD #1
Clarksville, Arkansas

Angela Mickalide
Director of Education and Outreach
Home Safety Council
Washington, D.C.

Patricia Mieszala
Consultant/Educator
Burn Concerns
Burbank, California

Rob Ross
Department of Public Safety
Middletown, Connecticut

Terry Spoor
Instructor
Southeast Community College
Lincoln, Nebraska

Much appreciation is given to the following individuals and organizations for contributing their time, photographs, or information that was instrumental in the development of this manual:

Aaron Nichols

Addilee, Alysia, Joriann, and Lizzy Thiriot

Al Oliva

Amber, Kalven, and Kassidy Gibbons

Andrea Nichols

Angela Mickalide

Annie and Linda Miller

Ashley Sellers

Ashley Watts

Bradley Fuchs

Brendyn Sellers

Brettan Thomas

Brett, Melissa, Caden, and Tanner Noakes

Brian Clingenpeel

Bruce, Debora, and Oliver Evans

Candace Willhite

Carl Noftsger

Carl Thomas

Cary Cdeman

Chad Payne

Cherlynn Thomas

Christopher Garrett

Chris Van Dyke

Cinda Seamon

Danny Speaks

Dave Statter 911

Deanna Pelton

Debbie Ryan

Debora Hahn

Denise Childress

Dylan Murray

Edna Merrick

Elizabeth Bush-Iabichello

Gary Fortney

Gerry Penney

Ginger Warner

Greg Scheiling

Hannah, Isabella, and Isiah Warner

Jacklynn Gilmore

James Free

James Heflin

Jeffrey Varga

Jennifer and Jesse Frank

Jonah and Julia Willhite

Joshua Nichols

Julianna Thomas

Kevin Walsh

Kimberly, Lindsey, and Braden Cleveland

Kody Savage

Mary Dickinson

Mason Watts

Melissa, Kayla, and Tanner Hardman

Melissa Nichols

Michael Weller

Nancy Smith

Patricia Mieszala

Robert, Megan, and Mariah Collins

Robert Ross

Ronald Campbell

Sean and Mara Fortney

Stacie Durham

Steven Ward

Tanna Prince

Terry Spoor

The Columbus Dispatch

Thomas Petty

W. O. Green

Brunswick Fire Department, Brunswick, ME
  Fire Chief Clark Labbe

Colorado Springs Fire Department, Colorado Springs, CO
  Brianna Goodwin
  Fire Marshall Brett Lacey

xvii

Federal Emergency Management Agency
  Liz Roll

Fire Factor, Champaign Fire Department, Champaign, IL
  Dena Schumacher

Fireman's Fund Insurance Company
  Kelly Hill

Fire Protection Publications
  Andrea Haken
  Cathey Wollenberg
  Cindy Finkle
  Cindy Rice
  Joy Kotey
  Libby Hieber
  Matthew Johnson
  Robin Balderson
  Tara Gladden

Fire Protection Publications Research Division
  Nancy Trench
  Tom Hughes

Glendale (AZ) Fire Department
  Dr. Janet A. Boberg

Hahira (GA) Fire Department
  Lt. Michael J. Kufrovich

Hall County Fire Services, Gainesville, GA
  Lieutenant Beverley Walker

Johnson County RFD #1, AR
  Dayna Hilton
  Sparkles

KOSU Radio Station, Stillwater, OK
  Rachel Hubbard

Massachusetts Fire Academy, Stow, MA
  Michael McLeieer

New Orleans Fire Department Photo Unit, New Orleans, LA
  District Chief Chris Mickal

North Las Vegas Fire Department, North Las Vegas, NV
  Beverly Bolton
  George Arting
  James Frater
  Kevin Brame
  Lenny Mayorga

Oklahoma Fire Service Training, Stillwater, OK
  Ruth Collert

Oklahoma State Fire Marshall's Office, OK
  Donny Howard

Perkins Fire Department, Perkins, OK
  Alec Barta
  Captain Bruce Davis

Perkins-Tryon Schools, Perkins, OK
  Bailee Hall
  Barbara Gnagy, Teacher
  Beth Oyster, Teacher
  Braden Fielding
  Brady Wells
  Breanna Sutherland
  Cashtin Craycraft
  Chance Alley
  Cheyenne Drigg
  Colton Hill
  David Cline
  Dylan Hoxsie
  Felipe Dorame
  Gabrielle Bostian
  Gabrielle Woodard
  Hannah Collier
  J. Cody Lewis
  Jessica Gnagy
  Joshua McFee
  Kolten Dotter
  Lane LaBorde
  Logan Harris
  Mariah Thomas
  Marlee Lowe
  Matlin McCray
  Niki Shoemaker
  Scottie Fielding
  Trevor Johnson
  Virginia Hemphill

Portland Fire and Rescue, Portland, OR
  Donald Porth, Public Education Officer

Renaissance Assisted Living Facility, Stillwater, OK
  Ethel Mae Myers
  George Carney
  Louise Smith
  Madge Bolt
  Mignon Thomas
  Wanda Legako
  Wanda Newport

Seattle Fire Department, Seattle, WA
  Fire Marshall John Nelsen

Stillwater Fire Department, Stillwater, OK
  Chief Marion Blackwell
  Assistant Chief Rex Mott
  Fire Marshall Trent Hawkins
  A. J. Westermier
  David Westfall
  Dick Giles (retired)
  Kathleen Bird
  Mike Wilda

Rudy Osborn
Steve Sylvester
Thomas Wise
Todd Jones

Stillwater Police Department, Stillwater, OK
  John Stanberg

University Medical Center, Las Vegas, NV
  Julie Rabeu, R.N.

Last, but certainly not least, gratitude is extended to the following members of the Fire Protection Publications staff whose contributions made the final publication of this manual possible.

Fire and Life Safety Educator, 3rd Edition, Project Team

Project Manager
Cindy Brakhage, Senior Editor

Editors
Libby Hieber, Senior Editor
Leslie Miller, Senior Editor

Illustrators and Layout Designer(s)
Ann Moffat, Coordinator, Publications Production
Errick Braggs, Senior Graphic Designer

Photographer
Jeff Fortney, Senior Editor

Technical Reviewer
Ed Kirtley

Production Coordinator
Ann Moffat

IFSTA Projects Coordinator
Ed Kirtley

Editorial Staff
Elkie Burnside, Graduate Research Assistant
Gabriel Ramirez, Research Assistant
Tara Gladden, Editorial Assistant

The IFSTA Executive Board at the time of validation of the **Fire and Life Safety Educator** manual was as follows:

IFSTA Executive Board

Executive Board Chair

Jeffrey Morrissette
State Fire Administrator
Commission on Fire Prevention and Control
Windsor Locks, Connecticut

Vice Chair

Paul Valentine
Fire Marshal
Village of Mount Prospect Fire Department
Mount Prospect, Illinois

Executive Director

Chris Neal
International Fire Service Training Association
Stillwater, Oklahoma

Board Members

Stephen Ashbrock
Fire Chief
Madeira & Indian Hill Joint Fire District
Cincinnati, Ohio

Roxanne Bercik
Assistant Chief
Los Angeles Fire Department
Los Angeles, California

Bradd Clark
Fire Chief
Owasso Fire Department
Owasso, Oklahoma

Dennis Compton
Chairman
National Fallen Firefighters Foundation
Mesa, Arizona

Frank Cotton
Battalion Chief
City of Memphis Fire Department
Memphis, Tennessee

George Dunkel
Consultant
Scappoose, Oregon

John W. Hoglund
Senior Instructor
Maryland Fire & Rescue Institute at the
 University of Maryland
College Park, Maryland

John Judd
Institution of Fire Engineers
Moreton in Marsh, United Kingdom

Wes Kitchel
Captain
Santa Rosa Fire Department
Santa Rosa, California

Dr. Lori Moore-Merrell
Assistant to the General President
International Association of Fire Fighters
Washington, DC

Randy Novak
Bureau Chief
Iowa Fire Service Training Bureau
Ames, Iowa

Dena Schumacher
Education Specialist, Fire/Life Safety
Champaign Fire Department
Champaign, Illinois

Introduction

Introduction Contents

Introduction

The American Paradigm of Fire is a term that exemplifies a potentially lethal attitude displayed by citizens: Fire cannot or will not happen to me. Unfortunately, fire does affect millions of Americans each year by claiming lives and causing injuries. Despite technological advancements in the field of fire prevention, America still exhibits one of the most expensive and deadly fire problems in the free world. "The American Paradigm of Fire" could be easily modified to "The American Paradigm of Preventable Injury" as the same mind-set applies to nearly every type of incident resulting in injury or death.

The third edition of **Fire and Life Safety Educator** provides the educator with knowledge to support successful performance as a fire and life safety educator as addressed in NFPA® 1035, *Standard for Professional Qualifications for Fire and Life Safety Educator, Public Information Officer, and Juvenile Firesetter Intervention Specialist.* In addition, the manual meets the learning outcomes of the National Fire Academy's Fire and Emergency Services Higher Education (FESHE) non-core course *Fire and Life Safety Educator.* New to the **Fire and Life Safety Educator** manual is the addition of two levels: Juvenile Firesetter Intervention Specialist I and Juvenile Firesetter Intervention Specialist II. In all, the third edition covers five levels of the standard:

- Fire and Life Safety Educator Level I: Chapters 2-6
- Fire and Life Safety Educator Level II: Chapters 7-11
- Fire and Life Safety Educator Level III: Chapters 12-16
- Juvenile Firesetter Intervention Specialist I: Chapters 17-20
- Juvenile Firesetter Intervention Specialist II: Chapters 21-25

Today's fire and life safety educators perform an ever-expanding range of services that often transcend all levels of NFPA® 1035. While the tasks of an educator new to the profession may initially be limited to delivery of pre-written lessons, he or she will likely assume future responsibilities that include developing programs, budgeting, and leadership roles. Therefore, it is wise to read this manual in sequential order and in its entirety over time.

Chapter 1 explains the various levels of requisite knowledge and skills that are needed to meet each level of the standard. **Appendix A** of the manual provides text references for the specific job performance requirements (JPRs) that are outlined in each level of NFPA® 1035. The chapters address information in the same sequence as required in the standard.

Fire and Life Safety Educator is a user-friendly document that should be part of every educator's library. The IFSTA fire and life safety committee has designed this manual to serve as a credible resource for information that will empower the reader with knowledge to address the challenge of preventing fire and injury.

Purpose and Scope

The goal of this manual is for it to be the first document on a public educator's bookshelf, a document that defines the knowledge of the public educator's profession, and a "ready reference" of public education knowledge. The manual is intended to *educate* the educator rather than to *train* the educator. In this way, the educator will be able to apply his or her knowledge and skills to many different areas all under the "umbrella" of injury prevention and control. The manual focuses on all-risk education. This edition is intended to assist in preparing the individual for certification to the Fire and Life Safety Educator I, II, and III and Juvenile Firesetter Intervention Specialist I and II levels of NFPA® 1035 *Standard for Professional Qualifications for Fire and Life Safety Educator, Public Information Officer, and Juvenile Firesetter Intervention Specialist*, 2010 edition.

NFPA® Codes and Standards

One of the basic purposes of IFSTA manuals is to allow fire service personnel and their departments to meet the requirements set forth by NFPA® codes and standards. These NFPA® documents may be referred to throughout this manual. Applicable NFPA® job performance requirements are referenced at the beginning of each chapter.

Key Information

Various types of information in this manual are given in shaded boxes marked by symbols or icons. See the following definitions:

Case History

Case History boxes present information analyzing an actual event. The event can be summarized and analyzed, with investigative results and lessons learned presented.

Information Box

Information boxes are need-to-know information that provide information that is emphasized, highlighted, or separated from the main text.

What This Means to You

Information presented in the text and synthesized into an example of how the information is relevant to (or will be applied by) the intended audience, essentially answering the question, "What does this mean to you?"

Summary

Summary boxes summarize chunks of information presented within chapter sections. They can appear at the end of a section or within a section as necessary.

Key Term

A **key term** is formatted bold, red in the text. It emphasizes key concepts, technical terms, or ideas that the reader needs to know. The definitions for the chapter key terms are at the end of each chapter.

FLSE Level I Educators: On the Front Line of Community-Risk Reduction

Chapter Contents

Key Terms

Job Performance Requirements

This chapter provides information that addresses the following job performance requirements of NFPA® 1035, *Standard for Professional Qualifications for Fire and Life Safety Educator, Public Information Officer, and Juvenile Firesetter Intervention Specialist*, 2010 edition.

NFPA® 1035 references

2.3.1

FESHE Objectives

Fire and Emergency Services Higher Education (FESHE) Objectives: *Fire and Life Safety Education*

1. Differentiate between Public Education, Public Information and Public Relations/Marketing.

2. Demonstrate the need for establishing fire and life safety education as a value within the fire service culture.

FLSE Level I Educators:
On the Front Line of Community-Risk Reduction

Learning Objectives

After reading this chapter, students will be able to:

1. Outline the evolution of fire and life safety education in America.

2. Articulate how fire and life safety education integrates into the overall process of community risk reduction. (NFPA® 1035, 2.3.1, 5.2.4)

3. Identify challenges to reducing fire and preventable injury. (NFPA® 1035, 5.3.1)

4. List sources of higher education for the fire and life safety educator. (NFPA® 1035, 5.3.1)

5. Explain the process of effective community risk reduction.

6. Identify why leadership is an essential component of successful community risk reduction.

7. Define the five categories used in each level of NFPA® 1035. (NFPA® 1035, 5.4.1)

8. Explain why fire and life safety educators should strive to meet NFPA® 1035. (NFPA® 1035, 5.4.1)

Chapter 1
FLSE Level I Educators: On the Front Line of Community-Risk Reduction

Case History

Before the early 1970s, somewhere between 8,000 and 12,000 people were being killed annually in residential fires throughout the United States. This disparity of estimation was due to the lack of a national fire incident reporting system.

By 1972, the federal government, under the direction of President Richard Nixon, had studied America's fire problem and produced a landmark report entitled *America Burning*. The report called for an integrated approach to fire prevention using a combination of preventive interventions.

It took until the mid-1980s for residential fire deaths to fall to an annual occurrence of between 4,000 and 6,000. Over the next twenty-plus years, this rate would drop to 3,000 at times but spike as high as 4,500. According to the United States Fire Administration (USFA), 3,320 civilians lost their lives as the result of fire in 2008.

While this manual is titled **Fire and Life Safety Educator**, its content promotes using a broad spectrum of integrated strategies to prevent or mitigate community risk through public education, technology, and leadership.

Reducing risk and the occurrence of incidents is not an easy task. Effective risk reduction requires knowledge, skill, experience, and leadership. Success does not simply happen. Successful risk reduction is realized through the commitment of individuals, organizations, and the community at large that follow an organized process to reach set goals.

Fire and life safety education is a key component of community-risk reduction. The fire and life safety educator works as part of a community team along with code inspectors, fire investigators, firefighters, health officials, teachers, and others committed to reducing the fire problem in the community. In the team, fire and life safety education activities work to change the beliefs and behaviors of citizens resulting in less risk and fewer fires and injuries.

This chapter provides an overview of community-risk reduction with a focus on fire and life safety education, the challenges fire and life safety educators face in reducing risk, and proven solutions that can be applied in any community. Also included is the rationale explaining why fire and life safety educators should pursue standards of excellence in community-risk reduction.

NOTE: When referring to the three levels of fire and life safety educators, the following terms are used: Level I is *educator;* Level II is *manager;* and Level III is *administrator.*

Fire and Life Safety Education: Past, Present, and Future

Public fire education by the North American fire service began in the late 1800s.[1] By 1909, Franklin H. Wentworth, a young member of the **National Fire Protection Association (NFPA®)** staff, was recruiting "correspondents" in cities across the continent. These correspondents received a series of fire prevention bulletins to place in local papers as news items. The NFPA® took fire safety education seriously as evidenced by the following:

● Creation of Sparky the Fire Dog® in 1954[2]

● Publication in the 1960s of "Reaching the Public" in the *Fire Journal*

● Development of the Learn Not to Burn™ program in the mid-1970s[3] with public service announcements starring Dick Van Dyke

Fire and Life Safety Education: 1970s

In the early 1970s the United States government estimated that approximately 12,000 citizens were being killed annually in fires.[4] To address the problem, the National Commission on Fire Prevention and Control was established. Its 1973 report, *America Burning,* made many recommendations. Among them were the following:

● Place greater emphasis on fire prevention.

● Provide better training for firefighters.

● Educate the American public about fire safety.

● Improve the safety of living environments through design and materials.

● Improve the fire protection features of buildings.

● Enhance research into how and why fires occur.

Through these milestone recommendations, the **United States Fire Administration (USFA)** and the **National Fire Academy (NFA)** were created. Building codes, standards, and built-in fire protection began to improve. Fire experience research was enhanced dramatically and eventually led to the development of the National Fire Incident Reporting System (NFIRS), which will be discussed in Chapter 9.

A monumental lifesaving development occurred in the early 1970s as a result of America's space program. Driven by the need to protect astronauts, NASA helped develop a product to alert those aboard a spacecraft to a fire in progress: the smoke alarm.

While first-generation smoke alarms were battery-powered, the need for consumers to replace batteries encouraged the development of electric-powered alarms. Along with this development came the country's first standard for smoke alarms. Many states soon initiated laws requiring installation and maintenance of smoke alarms in homes. Deaths and injuries from fire began to drop quickly.

The early 1970s found firefighters providing an increasing number of educational programs at schools and holding fire station open houses during fire prevention week. In 1974, the NFPA® published a report entitled *A Study of Motivational Psychology Related to Fire Preventive Behavior in Children and Adults*[5] that encouraged fire and life safety educators to focus on positive prevention messages directing people how to prevent fire and what to do if it occurred.

Also in 1974, the federal government conducted the first-ever project dedicated to the study of juvenile firesetting. This study served as catalyst for a national focus on the subject. This focus was expanded in the 1980s, 1990s, and continues today.

By the end of the decade, the USFA and the NFA were offering a number of advanced training programs on how to reduce fire risk in the community. NFPA® established a professional qualification standard for fire prevention education officers, and the **International Fire Service Training Association (IFSTA)** published the manual **IFSTA 606, Public Fire Education** in 1979.

The USFA, NFA, NFPA®, IFSTA, and the Consumer Product Safety Commission (CPSC) provide quality professional guidance in the field of risk reduction. For example, USFA has a section on its web page linking the reader with institutions offering degree programs in fire and life safety domains. In today's era of technology, educators conduct Internet research to locate current data and information from credible sources such as those previously referenced.

Fire and Life Safety Education: 1980-2000s

By the early 1980s, fire and life safety educators were becoming an integral part of many fire departments and state agencies. Meanwhile, a number of states were enhancing training and networking opportunities by conducting their own statewide fire and life safety education conferences. State training academies were beginning to develop certification programs for fire and life safety educators based on the NFPA® professional qualification standard.

At the same time, educators were helping vendors create higher quality prevention materials. Notable accomplishments in public education during the 1980s included pilot-testing of instructional materials, performing market research, evaluating program results, and "reaching the hard-to-reach."[6] In many communities, the occurrence of preventable injuries exponentially outnumbered fire-related incidents. Many organizations with shared responsibility for both fire and EMS began addressing the leading causes of fire and unintentional injury. Astute fire and life safety educators examined both local data and information released by credible national sources, such as the Centers for Disease Control (CDC), to better understand root causes of preventable injury.

In the latter 1980s, the federal government again convened committees to study why America's fire problem continued to be one of the worst among developed countries. Since 1973, the recommendations from *America Burning* have been revisited twice: In 1987 through *America Burning Revisited*[7] and in 2000 with the publication of *America at Risk*.[8] Reading these titles provides important background information of fire-prevention efforts in the United States. Although over thirty years have passed, the recommendations of *America at Risk* still echo the core suggestions of *America Burning*:

- Educate people on causation and prevention.
- Use improved built-in protection.
- Adopt more stringent fire codes.
- Provide timely and adequate emergency response.

This era also saw fire and life safety educators integrating their efforts even deeper into the area of community-risk reduction. While education remained the root of prevention, credible national organizations such as USFA, NFA, and NFPA® continued advocating the integration of prevention strategies such as technology, codes, and standards. Educators responded positively to the challenge with many forming partnerships that encouraged local decision-makers to adopt higher-order preventive interventions such as residential fire sprinklers.

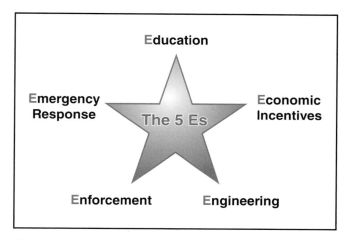

Figure 1.1 The five interrelated integrated prevention interventions.

Community-Risk Reduction and Integrated-Prevention Interventions

Community-risk reduction (CRR) is the process of preventing the occurrence of fire, injury, and property loss. While public education is the foundation of reducing community risk, effective and sustained success is best realized through use of combined prevention interventions **(Figure 1.1)**. In the next chapters, the following **integrated prevention interventions** are referred to as the **Five Es**.

1. **Education**: Teaching people about a risk issue and how to prevent it. Enlightening decision-makers about comprehensive risk solutions.

2. **Engineering**: Using technology and built-in protection in prevention strategies.

3. **Economic incentives**: Financial incentives that promote use of technology as a prevention intervention.

4. **Enforcement**: Codes and standards that require use of technology. Penalties for irresponsible behavior exhibited by hosts of risk.

5. **Emergency response**: Rapid and effective response to the occurrence of incidents.

Throughout the latter half of the 1980s and into the 1990s, shrinking budgets for fire departments forced officials to find partners to help maintain **risk-reduction initiatives**. Accountability and evaluation of fire and life safety education programs were emphasized. In 1990, TriData Corporation released its study *Proving Public Fire Education Works*.[9] The study provided examples of successful programs which could be modeled by localities. It also provided a solid rationale explaining why educators should strive to measure the effectiveness of prevention efforts.

In an era of latchkey children, substance abuse, and AIDS, the public demanded classroom instruction in many important subjects — each of which competed with fire and life safety education for classroom time. As a result of these challenges, fire and life safety educators continued to strengthen partnerships with schools, businesses, hospital burn centers, and local government as a way to extend their outreach into the community.

The 1990s saw many fire and life safety educators placing an even greater emphasis on overall injury prevention (community-risk reduction). Two notable risks that affected many communities were fall-related injuries to older adults and drowning deaths by young children. Many organizations expanded community outreach by offering comprehensive school-based programs, free smoke alarm programs, and home safety visitations. Some communities used burned homes as interactive classrooms to allow citizens a reality-based examination of how to prevent fire incidents. Effective educators were capitalizing on a wide variety of windows of opportunity to enhance safety education in the community **(Figures 1.2a and 1.2b)**.

The most effective fire and life safety educators were also examining relationships of how gender, community demographics, and diversity among populations contributed to local fire and injury problems. The following list includes some of their findings:

- Data identified the male gender continuing to exhibit a higher occurrence of morbidity and mortality from preventable injury.

- The southern portion of the United States experienced higher numbers of casualties from fire and burn injury.

- People living in poverty were at higher risk as compared to those having greater financial means.

- Diversity among cultures created challenges to reducing risk as the number of languages spoken in many communities continued to grow.

Figure 1.2a A home safety visitation for an older adult.

Figure 1.2b A fire and life safety educator testing a fire alarm in a residence.

Risk Watch©

The NFPA® was again at the forefront of both fire and injury prevention by debuting its new *Risk Watch©* program in 1998. The program addressed the eight leading areas of unintentional injury involving children. Champion Management Teams were created that included a coalition of community partners such as law enforcement, education, health, and fire. *Risk Watch©* was pilot-tested over a three-year period in six communities. Pretests and posttests revealed its impact by documenting knowledge gain.

The late 1990s saw the federal government and the NFPA® Center for High Risk Outreach take a closer look at who was at greatest risk from fire in America. *Solutions 2000* was a symposium attended by advocates for high-risk populations who examined fire safety challenges of groups statistically identified as being most at risk due to age, physical condition, or social circumstances. This symposium led to fire safety recommendations focusing on the following populations:

- Young children under age 5
- Older adults
- People with disabilities

Solutions 2000

As result of the *Solutions 2000* recommendations, the National Fire Academy created curriculum to help educators address risk among those at highest risk from fire. The course included Federal Emergency Management Agency (FEMA) supplementary material on high-risk populations.

The recommendations of *Solutions 2000* were revisited in 2001 as professionals reconvened to discuss national progress being made on fire issues affecting the populations at greatest risk. While progress had been made, the advancement of codes, standards, and built-in protection were identified as areas still needing greater focus.

NOTE: The United States Fire Administration created the Prevention Advocacy Resources and Data Exchange (PARADE) program that provides fire and life safety educators access to fire prevention and protection information through the USFA Web site **(Figure 1.3)**.

Interestingly, many of the recommendations identified in the *Solutions* reports mirrored those identified through the *America Burning* series. It was again emphasized that while education remained

Figure 1.3 The USFA's Prevention Advocacy Resources and Data Exchange (PARADE) Web site.

the root of prevention, effective mitigation required use of combined prevention interventions such as technology, standards, and codes. Further, the recommendations suggested a "shared responsibility" on the part of the government, emergency services, advocacy groups, corporate industry, and society at large in the war against fire.

Many national corporations rose to the challenge of helping local communities fight preventable injuries. Perceptive educators formed partnerships with their retail, business, and industrial community and therefore strengthened prevention efforts.

The late 1990s and early twenty-first century saw school-based education reflecting the government's call for schools to focus on basic skills such as reading, math, and science. As a result, state and provincial education authorities required students to meet specific benchmark scores on standardized tests. Consequently, many educators became reluctant to give up their classroom time to outside programs. It became more difficult for fire and life safety educators to have access to students for the delivery of fire and injury prevention presentations.

Comprehensive injury prevention programs such as *Risk Watch* correlated lesson objectives with the state educational standards. Teachers could integrate the curriculum in the classroom to produce measurable benchmarks of performance that correlated with required health and other subject curriculum objectives. Many progressive fire and life safety educators followed the example set by the NFPA® by collaborating with local school officials to integrate life safety education into the essential curriculum.

On a solemn note, the 1990s also saw an increase in violent behaviors. The massacre at Columbine High School proved that no community is immune from violence. That fact continues to be reinforced, as evidenced by the 2007 mass shootings at Virginia Tech. Also in the 1990s, organized terror emerged as a driving force for another evolution of community-risk reduction.

Fire is often used as a weapon of terror. Arson is now the leading cause of multi-death fires in the U.S.[10] FBI death crime reports identify that 55 percent of all arson arrests are under age 18.

The twenty-first century has seen challenges for our country and educators alike. The U.S. has been struck by a number of disasters, some natural, others manmade. Natural disasters such as hurricanes, floods, and tornadoes threaten as well as terrorism and war, which have forever changed the threat-free lifestyle we once enjoyed.

Fire and Life Safety Education: The Future

Today's fire and life safety educators are preparing citizens to help prevent and respond to emergencies of all types. Disaster Preparedness and Homeland Security are two areas where local leadership is essential. The development of **Community Emergency Response Teams (CERT)** together with volunteer groups such as **Fire Corps** and Citizens Corps may strengthen risk-reduction efforts at the local level. While challenging, events of the twenty-first century give many new opportunities to expand fire and life safety education programs.

Not forgotten in the twenty-first century is America's fire problem as collaborative mitigation efforts continue at the national level. The formation of the Public-Private Fire Safety Council is one such example. The council is a partnership of federal agencies and nongovernment organizations coordinating a national effort to eliminate residential fire deaths by the year 2020.

The Impact of September 11, 2001

The tragic events of September 11, 2001, forever changed the U.S. and how people view the emergency services. Important to the subject of this publication is the way that the American people began to view the notion of preparedness — being prepared for emergencies, big and small.

Many success stories were seen on 9/11 as a result of pre-planning by business owners and safety personnel. Mandatory participation in emergency action training and drills had occurred in many companies after the first bombing of the World Trade Center in 1993. Citizens began to realize that fire and life safety educators had been a driving force behind initiating a cultural change that encouraged people to understand that being prepared for trouble was an important and achievable goal.

In honor of the brothers and sisters who serve in public safety (and those who perished on September 11, 2001) a huge debt of gratitude is owed for instilling the importance of prevention and preparedness; not just for community members, but for members of the emergency services as well.

Courtesy of Lt. Beverley Walker, Hall County Georgia Emergency Services

Thanks, in part, to the **American Paradigm of Fire**, the national fire death rate has reached a plateau that we have not been able to move below in nearly a decade. While early efforts of the council were focusing on the enhancement of residential smoke alarm operability, probable long-term solutions will surely include comprehensive education, use of improved technology, codes, standards, and supportive incentives coupled with efficient emergency response **(Figure 1.4)**.

Fire and Life Safety Education: A Chronological History

The fires listed in **Table 1.1** drew national attention because they resulted in large losses of life. Each incident was studied by nationally recognized agencies to identify factors contributing to the magnitude of the tragedy. Large-loss fires are often case-studied by agencies such as the National Fire Protection Association, the U. S. Department of Labor's Occupational Safety and Health Administration, the U.S. Fire Administration, and others.

Figure 1.4 Firefighters fighting a residential fire. *Courtesy of Dick Giles.*

Table 1.1
Lessons Learned From Major Fires

Date	Fire	Deaths	Lessons Learned
1942	Coconut Grove Nightclub	492	Overcrowding; the role of interior finish; lack of adequate exits; difficulty in exiting
1958	Our Lady of Angels School	95	Storage of combustible materials; lack of teacher training in emergency response; lack of practiced fire drills; difficulty in exiting
1977	Beverly Hills Supper Club	165	Lack of evacuation and planning practice; importance of early detection; difficulty of exiting
1980	MGM Grand Hotel	85	Smoke travel in high-rise buildings; evacuation from high-rise buildings; the need to teach people when to evacuate and when to "defend in place" (stay where they are)
2003	Station Nightclub	100	Improper interior use of pyrotechnics; combustible interior furnishings; importance of automatic detection, reporting and suppression equipment; the importance of an emergency action plan; employee and patron training in emergency action

The study of major loss of life events often leads to conclusions that improvements are needed in the areas of public education, use of technology, or the creation or enforcement of standards and codes. In each of the previously listed incidents, the need for better use of combined preventive interventions was identified.

The combined use of preventive interventions to include the Five Es (Education, Engineering, Economic incentives, Enforcement, and Emergency response) is recognized as the most effective strategy to mitigate risk. This strategy not only applies to mitigating large-loss events, but also to the wide-range of preventable incidents that threaten populations protected by members of the fire service at the local level.

Federal Agencies

The federal government continues to offer localities support for reducing the occurrence of fire. The following federal agencies also support risk-mitigation initiatives:

- FEMA has distributed billions of dollars to organizations that demonstrated financial need for local risk-reduction initiatives through the Assistance to Firefighters Grant Program. In 2009 alone, at the development time of this manual, FEMA appropriated $775 million through this grant.

- U.S. Consumer Product Safety Commission has focused fire safety research dollars in areas such as furniture flammability standards and smoke alarm technology.

- Centers for Disease Control and Preventions' *National Center for Injury Prevention and Control* studies injury causation and helps fund strategies to reduce the occurrence of preventable incidents.

- Healthy People 2010 is managed by the Office of Disease Prevention and Health Promotion under the U.S. Department of Health and Human Services and is another example of federal action to mitigate preventable injury and promote citizen well-being. This initiative challenges individuals, communities, and professionals to collectively take specific steps to ensure that good health, as well as long life, are enjoyed by all. Healthy People's goals for injury prevention are categorized in two groups: unintentional and intentional causation.

The unintentional injury group includes focus on the following:

- Falls
- Fires
- Poisonings
- Motor vehicle crashes
- Pedestrian incidents and firearms

The intentional injury group includes the following:

- Firearms
- Physical
- Domestic violence
- Assaults (including sexual)
- Aggressive adolescent behavior

The initiative encourages preventive action through use of combined interventions. At development time of this manual, the Healthy People initiative was on track to reach many of its proposed goals. While some areas need improvement (violence prevention and fall injury to the elderly), overall progress is encouraging.

As fire and life safety educators examine the present and look toward the future, the twenty-first century is, to say the least, an interesting and exciting place to be. Technology, society, and communities are constantly changing. Fire and life safety educators must keep up with a changing world to consistently and effectively reduce risk.

Community Demographics

From a geographic perspective, some areas of the country remain rural while others have exploded in suburban sprawl. As many older cities enjoy redevelopment, others remain challenged by aging infrastructure. Socially, the gap between those with and without adequate economic resources continues to widen. From a population perspective, baby boomers of retirement age will enlarge the older adult population exponentially over the next 20 years. Spending some time with local community planners will help educators in identifying what their community's demographics will look like in the future.

An ever-diversifying culture also presents challenges to fire and life safety educators. The following factors can make it a difficult task to reach people with information about prevention:

- Many languages are spoken in numerous urban and suburban areas of the country. Even in rural areas, English may be spoken as a second language by many residents.

- Literacy is another issue that demands attention from the fire service as prevention strategies are planned and initiated. Although our country is the most prosperous in the free world, 93 million adults with low literacy skills have resided in the U.S. for years and are *not* recent immigrants.

- Learning disabilities (often exacerbated by stimuli such as today's fast-paced world) are also challenges that must be considered and addressed.

- Security and privacy are two major concerns. People want to feel safe in their home and community. They are also less tolerant of intrusions into their personal environment such as web-generated SPAM and telemarketing.

- The advancement of technology is arguably one of the greatest factors driving the speed of our complex world. High-tech machines that create instant world-wide communication are not just a reality, but a necessity in most households. Thanks to the Internet, satellite TV and radio, the media outlets can be thousands of miles away thus competing with the outreach of "hometown" media. Automated answering equipment has replaced people in many organizations. Interactive reality-based entertainment is not only enjoyed by consumers, it's expected.

Interactive gaming, high-definition television, and more expensive lifestyles are examples of how society often places a higher degree of importance on entertainment over safety. These factors, combined with a society forced to multitask as a way of life, creates competition for people's attention and resources.

Technology Revolution

While the technology revolution has created its share of challenges for educators, it is also responsible for some very positive changes. The Web has created more opportunities to deliver comprehensive risk-reduction messages to both the local community and worldwide. It has offered opportunities for the fire and life safety educator to network with educators around the world as well as to research information.

Technology has enhanced protective equipment such as smoke alarms, monitoring equipment, automatic fire suppression systems, and automobile safety systems (**Figures 1.5 and 1.6, p. 16**). Many consumers are recognizing the cost-effectiveness of prevention and requesting built-in fire protection as standard equipment in new construction. Automotive air bags and seat belts are now standard equipment on new vehicles (**Figures 1.7 and 1.8, p. 16**).

Study on Fire and Life Safety Education

While advancements in risk mitigation have been steadily improving throughout the past four decades, much work remains. In 2007, the **Home Safety Council (HSC)** teamed with the Center for Injury Research and Policy at the Johns Hopkins Bloomberg School of Public Health to conduct the first ever study on fire and life safety education. The survey benchmarked fire and life safety educational services provided by the U.S. fire service. It assessed the state of educational

The World Wide Web

The World Wide Web provides an excellent opportunity to promote risk mitigation. A well-designed Web page can provide valuable fire and life safety messages, information on specific programs, department contacts, and links to other related sites.

A plethora of resources are available for learning about the development of web pages. Many community colleges and private vendors offer courses on Web page design. There are also many forms of assistance online.

An example of a site providing assistance is the University of Maryland at College Park's, "How to make a Web site." This site provides the basics needed to get started.

A caution on Web page design: You never get a second chance to make a good first impression. An organization's Web page is often the first thing that a consumer sees when seeking information. It is essential to produce a professional user-friendly site that provides accurate and current information.

Courtesy of Dayna Hilton; Johnson County RFD # 1 Arkansas

Figure 1.5 A fire and life safety educator presenting information about smoke alarms.

Figure 1.7 Automobile air bags have proven effective in saving lives and preventing injuries.

Figure 1.6 The main control valve and water flow alarm of a residential sprinkler system.

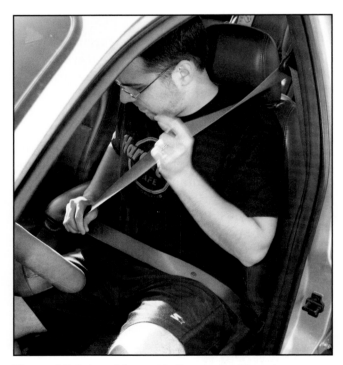

Figure 1.8 Automobile seat belts are also lifesaving devices.

programming and identified needs for training and additional resources.

The report conducted by the Home Safety Council and John's Hopkins clearly indicates a desire from leaders of America's fire service to enhance prevention activities in their home community. If this desire is

to become reality, it will require a commitment from those in positions of authority (chiefs, administrators, political leaders, and other decision-makers) who have the power to dedicate resources and facilitate organizational priorities. Many communities are rising to that challenge.

Chief executive officers in Richmond (Virginia) and Owasso (Oklahoma) are two examples of leaders with vision who are championing prevention as a core value displayed by their organizations. Both cities have embraced the concept of "Village Fire Departments" whereby staff members from fire stations take ownership for their service areas.

The Need for Credibility and Competence

As society moves faster, people expect higher levels of consumer service and competent trained professionals to deliver it. As an educator, it does not matter whether you are a volunteer or career practitioner. What matters is that you perform the job in a competent, ethical, and professional manner. Current risks and emerging trends must be addressed in an accurate and timely manner. Using up-to-date information and practicing sound delivery methodologies is essential. This is why it is important to meet performance standards. NFPA®1035 *Standard for Professional Qualifications for Fire and Life Safety Educator, Public Information Officer, and Juvenile Firesetter Intervention Specialist,*[11] is a standard that fire and life safety educators should strive to meet. **NFPA® 1035** addresses the following levels:

- **Fire and Life Safety Educator I.** Those who have demonstrated the ability to coordinate and deliver existing educational programs and information.

- **Fire and Life Safety Educator II.** Those who have demonstrated the ability to prepare educational programs and information to meet identified needs.

- **Fire and Life Safety Educator III.** Those who have demonstrated the ability to create, administer, and evaluate educational programs and information.

- **Public Information Officer.** Those who have demonstrated the ability to conduct media interviews, prepare news releases, and advisories. (**NOTE:** Please see IFSTA's manual, **Public Information Officer**, for information on the duties and challenges faced by this profession. The PIO level is not addressed in this manual.)

- Juvenile Firesetter Intervention Specialist I. Those who have demonstrated the ability to conduct an intake and interview with a firesetter and his or her family using prepared forms and guidelines and who, based on program policies and procedures, determines the need for referral for counseling, and implements educational **intervention strategies** to mitigate effects of firesetting behavior.

- **Juvenile Firesetter Intervention Specialist II.** Those who have demonstrated the ability to manage juvenile firesetting intervention program activities and the activities of the Juvenile Firesetter Intervention Specialist I.

NFPA® has long been recognized as the organization that sets professional qualification standards for the emergency services. NFPA® 1035 grew from a document dated 1977 that grouped public educators with inspectors and investigators. Notably absent from the earlier standard was a place for nonemergency service educators. NFPA® 1035 came to fruition in the mid-1980s and has been enhanced multiple times since. The 2010 edition of this standard includes professional qualifications for safety educators, public information officers, and juvenile firesetter intervention specialists. In many organizations, the same person may perform all three roles or closely interact with those who perform one or more of the jobs.

NFPA® 1035 not only outlines the overall expected proficiencies of a fire and life safety educator, public information officer, and a juvenile firesetter intervention specialist, it also categorizes each level into five areas:

- General Requirements
- Administration
- Planning and Development
- Education and Intervention
- Evaluation

Within these categories are job performance requirements (JPRs). JPRs outline the knowledge, skills, and proficiencies educators should exhibit to meet the various levels of the standard. For the benefit of the reader, text references to the various levels of the standard are provided in Appendix A of this manual.

NFPA® 1035 sets the professional qualification standards for fire and life safety educators, public information officers, and juvenile firesetter intervention specialists. It is not, however, a certifying body. NFPA® does not certify someone as a Fire and Life Safety Educator I, II, or III. Two organizations in the U.S. — the International Fire Service Accreditation

Congress (IFSAC) and the National Board on Fire Service Professional Qualifications (Pro Board) — accredit certification programs offered by state training academies, government agencies, universities, and similar institutions.

Many states have developed curricula to address the NFPA® 1035 standard. Such curricula may include testing as specified by the local certifying agency. At the time of the writing of this manual, 20 municipalities including states and provinces have adopted fire and life safety education certification. Several have also adopted juvenile firesetter intervention specialist certification **(Figure 1.9)**.

The Process of Effective Community-Risk Reduction

There are two critical components of successful risk reduction that must be covered in the introductory chapter of this manual:

1. The importance of following an organized process to reduce risk

2. Why the unified effort of leaders, managers, and followers is essential to an effective risk-reduction process

Information about the process of effective risk reduction and leadership are included in the introduction because without them successful risk

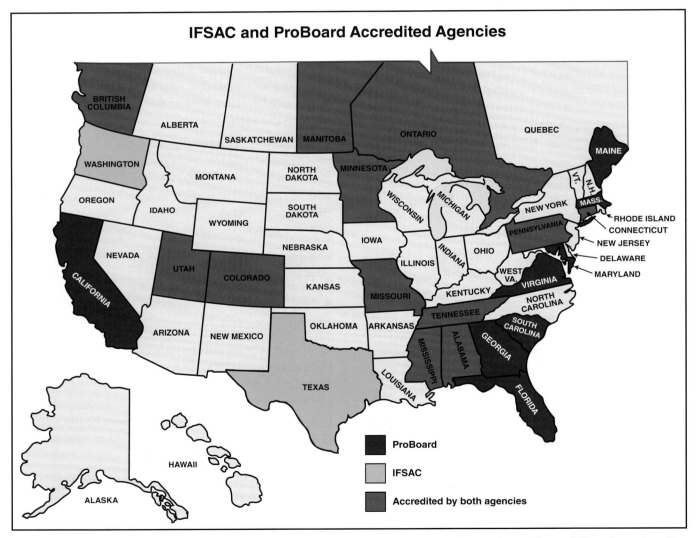

Figure 1.9 IFSAC and Pro-Board accredited agencies in the U.S. and Canada that have adopted fire and life safety education certification.

reduction is often difficult, if not impossible, to realize. **Community-risk reduction** is a process that involves an entire community, but it starts with an individual. Whether you deliver programs, develop community-based initiatives, or help set public policy for risk reduction, you must understand the big picture of how to get the job done effectively and comprehensively.

The Catalyst

Behind every successful risk-reduction effort is a catalyst with the desire and ambition to reduce preventable injuries. Some catalysts hold positions of rank such as chiefs and administrators; others carry no official title. What sets catalysts apart from others is their vision of why and how community risk should be addressed. They also exhibit the drive needed to pursue such aggressive actions.

Being a catalyst for reducing risk can but does not have to be a lonely endeavor. Often, a catalyst may decide to act alone, fearing peer pressure or lack of support from leadership. Acting alone is a very dangerous strategy that can lead to ineffective efforts, stress, burnout, and even health challenges for the fire and life safety educator. To be successful and not compromise personal well-being, the most successful strategy is to follow an organized process to reduce risk.

The first step the catalyst should take is to become credible in the area of community-risk reduction. Reading this IFSTA manual is an excellent way to expand knowledge base. Organizations such as the NFPA® and USFA are nationally recognized authorities that offer material on how to develop, implement, lead, and evaluate community-risk reduction **(Table 1.2)**.

Table 1.2	
The Process of Effective Community-Risk Reduction (CRR)	
Term	**Description**
Catalyst for Community-Risk Reduction	An individual who considers prevention a core mission of his/her organization and is willing to initiate actions in support of risk mitigation.
Organizational Support	Members of the organization consider prevention a core mission of the organization and demonstrate behaviors that support risk mitigation.
Community Support	The community at-large believes they have a personal responsibility for their safety. The public and groups demonstrate behaviors that support risk reduction.
Planning and Evaluation	The organization convenes a planning team to study leading local risks and develop mitigation strategies. The team commits to evaluating the development, implementation, delivery, and results of all mitigation strategies.
Use of Integrated Preventive Interventions (5 Es)	All risk mitigation strategies include a combination of integrated preventive initiatives to include: Education, Engineering, Enforcement, Economic Incentives, and Emergency Response.
Resources to Support Risk Reduction Process and Preventive Interventions	Basic tools to support the fire and life safety educator/risk reducer; resources to support all levels of preventive interventions.

Additionally, many government materials are free. The National Fire Academy offers an excellent series of courses that provide higher education on the subject of reducing community risk. Many universities now offer curricula and Web-based courses as well.

Having background knowledge in community-risk reduction is essential to building credibility on the subject. The catalyst will use that credibility as he or she pursues the next step in the process — gaining organizational support for reducing community risk.

Organizational Support

Just as effective fire suppression and emergency medical operations require teamwork, so does risk reduction. Organizational support for reducing risk does not "just happen." It is cultivated by catalysts who understand their community, its risks, and potential risk solutions. It also requires that fire and life safety educators have a good understanding of their organizations and be able to identify leaders whose support is essential to any organizational effort **(Figure 1.10)**. These leaders will not only be officers but they will also be non-ranking people who have influence over others. Gaining their support is an important early step in the risk-reduction process.

Source: *When In Doubt, Lead, Part 3*, Dennis Compton

Figure 1.10 Fire and life safety educators need to be knowledgeable about the fire and life safety mission.

Good communication from the catalyst to his or her organization is absolutely essential to gaining cooperation. If the catalyst wants help, potential collaborators must understand a problem, how it affects them, why they should participate, and how the effort will be accomplished. They also need resources to get the job done and feedback that provides reports on progress. People and organizations want to know, "What is the benefit for the work being asked of us?"

As the catalyst evaluates the best strategy to attain an organizational buy-in, it is helpful to understand the difference between leaders, managers, and followers. The talents and cooperation of all three are essential to successful prevention efforts.

Leaders

Leaders are often people who are dissatisfied with simply maintaining the status quo. They are motivated visionaries who see the potential of what things could be and how to get there. They are good communicators who can rally a team by using a strong rationale for why a cause should be pursued. They then work collaboratively with the team to achieve goals through measurable benchmarks of success. Leaders have trust in their team members and get things accomplished by empowering others.

Effective leaders build credibility among peers by doing what they say they will do when they say they will do it. They show honesty, trustworthiness, integrity, and respect toward others in the process. Good leaders are subject-matter experts on their cause, always willing to help others advance and succeed. Most importantly, they roll up their sleeves and are not afraid to help with less desirable tasks in order to get a job done.

While leaders may sound like "knights in shining armor" by description, even people with innate leadership abilities can face challenges. Because leaders are often very creative people, they may become bored with monitoring day-to-day events, details, and other small (though critical) components of a risk-reduction process. This is where managers fit in as important members of the team.

Managers are often task-oriented people who thrive on monitoring details. They enjoy tracking progress and excel at helping a team meet established benchmarks in a timely manner. A quality manager could be summarized as an "organized organizer."

As with leaders, effective managers earn credibility among team members by treating people fairly and doing their fair share of activity.

Even the best managers can exhibit challenging behavior. Due to their innate drive to reach goals on time, managers can sometimes lose sight of the humanistic side of teamwork by inadvertently neglecting their "people skills." They may also lose sight of the "big picture" because of attention to minute detail.

Followers

Many people simply are not interested in leading or managing a project. However, they may be excellent followers who will respond positively to dynamic leadership and fair management. Without effective followers, any comprehensive risk-reduction effort is doomed to fail. As a rule, people will follow good leadership and management if they are provided with the following:

- Knowledge, understanding, and belief that they have a stake in an issue and that their assistance will help resolve the issue

- Adequate training and encouragement that they can accomplish the task

- Awareness of how their role will assist in addressing the issue

- Adequate resources to get the job done

- Empowerment to make decisions and work independently if they choose to do so

- Feedback and support on their actions

- Rewards for their efforts

The point of highlighting the various roles that people perform in organizations is this: It is important to identify, understand, and utilize the talents of everyone in the organization when addressing community risk. While support for efforts must come from the top, it must also be present throughout the entire organization as well. There is a place for everyone. Organizations that consistently perform the best are those that identify each member's forte, allowing those strengths to be used to their maximum potential. Not everyone wants to be in charge of something or to speak in public. However, each person has strengths that can be maximized toward a common organizational goal. Success is realized by recognizing talent and structuring efforts accordingly.

An organization that supports reducing risks by willingly committing time, people, and money has reached a milestone: It has institutionalized community-risk reduction as a core organizational value. Success is likely if the organization creates a well-designed plan to address risk and receives support from the community.

Community Support

As with organizational support, help from the community is essential to the success of reducing risk. Examining risk carefully, educators will find that the roots of fire and preventable injury are often found in underlying social, environmental, cultural, and economic factors. The occurrence of incidents such as those created by unattended cooking fires and candle neglect can be attributed to forgetfulness or distraction. However, potentially lethal situations such as disabled smoke alarms or children with access to lighters are examples of people not taking personal responsibility for their actions and ultimate destiny. While educational campaigns directed at human behavior provide a good foundation for prevention, the ultimate solutions involve the integration of prevention interventions such as the use of technology, standards, codes, and supporting incentives.

No single organization has enough people, time, or money to single-handedly address comprehensive risk issues. Involving the community in problem identification, solutions, and outreach is essential. Often the best solutions come from the target populations that are experiencing a particular risk issue.

The ultimate aim of this profession is for risk reduction to become an institutionalized community value. Like organizations, communities that value risk reduction invest resources in the form of people, time, and money.

An important first step in gaining community support is to make sure constituents are aware of and understand an organization's mission and its services. It sounds easy given the variety of communication media currently available. However, as more information is available, it becomes challenging to ensure people receive, remember, and act on what is being disseminated. Many of the current progressive organizations conduct community surveys to find out what constituents know about their local emergency services. Marketing professionals are good partners to help educators determine how to best reach the local community.

Enlisting support from a broad base of stakeholders will help with development of effective risk-reduction strategies. Once interest is expressed by an appropriate number of people, they may use resources that already exist to enable their group to become effective members of a CERT.

Planning and Evaluation

Planning and evaluation are used together to reach goals of reducing risk. Any process or intervention that is included in a plan must be evaluated because the wider community will want to know the point of investing efforts into a project that may not produce visible results. Leaders, managers, followers, stakeholders, and the community must know the progress that has been made on risks being addressed.

Developing, implementing, and evaluating a plan to reduce risk is a **five-step planning process**.

Step 1: Examine local data to identify leading causes of risk.

— Select the risk to be addressed.

— Develop a community-risk profile that includes a problem statement explaining what is wrong, who is at risk, and why.

Step 2: Identify and recruit partners who will comprise a community planning team.

Step 3: Work to create an intervention strategy. The planning team examines the sequence of events causing the greatest number of incidents that are being addressed.

— Identify places within the sequence where risk interventions may be used.

— Examine potential target populations and locations for interaction.

— The needed resources are noted and an evaluation strategy is developed.

Step 4: Pilot-test the intervention strategy, adjust accordingly, and implement.

— Refine timetables for completion.

— Market and expand the strategy as needed.

Step 5: Monitor the intervention strategy.

— Continue to collect and analyze incident experience data.

— Modify interventions as necessary.

— Report results to team members, the sponsoring organization, and the community.

Developing, implementing, and evaluating risk reduction requires work and patience. While outreach may be realized quickly, impact such as knowledge

Ethics for Fire and Life Safety Educators

The preservation of human life, freedom from injury, and the protection of valuable property depend upon the careful and thorough execution of the duties of fire and life safety education. Fire and life safety educators recognize the value of their work, whether performed on a full-time or part-time basis. In recognition of the importance of performing their work correctly, fire and life safety educators pledge themselves to the highest standards of professional and ethical conduct which includes a commitment to the following:

1. Achieving and maintaining professional competency.
2. Advancing the professional competency of other fire and life safety educators through networking and mentoring.
3. Teaching only those subjects which the fire and life safety educator is qualified to teach.
4. Preparing for each presentation as if a life in the audience depends upon it.
5. Evaluating program results honestly.
6. Continually improving programs and presentations.
7. Using only current and accurate material and information, including statistics.
8. Performing the duties of fire and life safety education with integrity.
9. Respecting the work of other educators, through the courtesies of crediting their ideas and materials where appropriate and through compliance with copyright laws.
10. Recognizing when your own conduct does not fully meet this canon of ethics, and resolve to improve.

gain and behavioral changes may take months or even a year or more to occur. Outcome in the form of fewer incidents may not be seen for several years. However, measurable and sustained outcome is more likely to be realized by communities that invest the time and resources into attacking risk through a well-designed process.

Resources

Resource allocation is another essential component of effective risk reduction. Fire and life safety educators cannot effectively reduce community risk without basic tools. Basic tools for reducing risk include the following:

- Professional attire and required protective equipment and personal safety equipment
- Reliable transportation dedicated to risk reduction
- Current technology and communications media such as a computer, software, Internet access, audiovisual equipment, cellular phone, portable radio, and other tools
- Dedicated work space and equipment storage area
- Intervention equipment and supplies such as teaching tools, smoke alarms, and installation kits
- When applicable, access to human resources such as staff to assist with program delivery and community outreach

While the organizations that fire and life safety educators represent should provide them with basic tools needed to function effectively, the community at large should also accept responsibility by contributing its share of resources. Organizations and communities that have institutionalized support for risk reduction will make such commitments. This can save money over the long term by preventing incidents which allows our colleagues, constituents, and communities to enjoy a safer life.

Chapter Summary

Risk reduction has progressed dramatically over the past century. Deaths from fire have been reduced, and technology is being employed in the campaign against preventable injury. Success, in part, is credited to those directly involved with loss prevention— fire and life safety educators. However, as evidenced by stagnant fire death rates and rising property loss, much work remains for educators.

Effective fire and life safety educators understand the organization they represent and the community being served. Quality educators follow a proven process to mitigate risk by bringing their organizations and communities together so that everyone becomes part of the solution. They recognize that solutions require more work than simply teaching people what to do. Education is used as a foundation for solutions. It is backed by integrated interventions.

Effective prevention efforts can help build organizational and community equity for risk reduction. Positive results often lead to increased levels of resources being allocated for prevention.

Fire and life safety educators and their community partners are the frontline leaders of community-risk reduction in America. Those most effective at their trade are continually striving for excellence though education and integrated interventions. USFA, NFA, NFPA®, and IFSTA are agencies committed to helping educators reach those goals. These organizations actively develop resources geared toward specific types of risks.

Education and experience help create professional credibility. For that reason, the remainder of this manual provides comprehensive information on how to meet the multiple performance levels of the standard.

Review Questions

1. How does fire and life safety education support the process of community-risk reduction?

2. How has the fire safety education function changed since 1973?

3. What are the challenges to reducing fires and preventable injuries?

4. What are sources of training in the area of fire and life safety education?

5. What are the elements of a successful fire and life safety education program?

6. What is the role of leadership in an effective fire and life safety education program?

7. What are the five categories found in each level of the NFPA® 1035 standard?

8. What is the benefit of meeting the requirements for fire and life safety educators found in the NFPA® 1035 standard?

Key Terms

American Paradigm of Fire — A belief held by many people that fire cannot or will not happen to them.

Community Emergency Response Teams (CERT) — Groups of people within neighborhoods, community organizations, or the work place who are trained by the emergency services in basic response skills.

Community-Risk Reduction — The process of addressing the larger issue of preventable injury that is occurring in a community. The process involves identifying leading risks and creating mitigation strategies through the use of integrated prevention interventions.

Economic Incentives — Used to support the prevention interventions. Examples of positive incentives include reduced insurance premiums for buildings having fire-resistive construction, sprinklers, and automatic notification systems. Examples of negative incentives would be fines for violating fire codes.

Education Interventions — Designed to raise awareness, provide information, impart knowledge, and ultimately produce a desired behavior. Education provides a foundation for the entire prevention intervention system.

Emergency Response — Because risk will never be completely eradicated, communities must have an adequately staffed, trained, and equipped emergency response system.

Enforcement Interventions — All the ways in which people are required to act to mitigate risk. Examples related to fire safety include ordinances, laws, and building codes that require the installation of smoke detection and sprinkler systems.

Engineering Interventions — Modifications made to vehicles, products, materials, and processes to make them less hazardous, or to alter an environment to make it safer.

Fire and Life Safety Educator I — Those who have demonstrated the ability to coordinate and deliver existing educational programs and information.

Fire and Life Safety Educator II — Those who have demonstrated the ability to prepare educational programs and information to meet identified needs.

Fire and Life Safety Educator III — Those who have demonstrated the ability to create, administer, and evaluate educational programs and information.

Fire Corps — A national program in which citizen advocates assist fire departments with nonoperational roles.

Five-Step Planning Process — A nationally recognized process proven to be successful in guiding risk-reduction efforts.

Home Safety Council (HSC) — A national non-profit organization solely dedicated to preventing home-related injuries. HSC helps facilitate national programs and partnerships to educate people of all ages to be safer in and around their homes.

Integrated Prevention Interventions — Process of combining education, technology, codes, standards, and supporting incentives to address community risk. Commonly referred to as the Five Es of Intervention.

International Fire Service Training Association (IFSTA) — An organization of personnel dedicated to upgrading the training and skills of emergency services personnel and allied professionals.

Intervention Strategy — The action plan that describes how a risk-reduction initiative will be implemented and evaluated.

Juvenile Firesetter Intervention Specialist I — Those who have demonstrated the ability to conduct an intake and interview with a firesetter and his or her family using prepared forms and guidelines and who, based on program policies and procedures, determine the need for referral for counseling, and implement educational *intervention strategies* to mitigate effects of firesetting behavior.

Juvenile Firesetter Intervention Specialist II — Those who have demonstrated the ability to manage juvenile firesetting intervention program activities and the activities of Juvenile Firesetter Intervention Specialist I.

National Fire Academy (NFA) — Through its courses and programs, this federal agency works to enhance the ability of emergency service providers and allied professionals to deal more effectively with fire and related emergencies.

National Fire Protection Association (NFPA®) — A private nonprofit organization that works to reduce the worldwide burden of fire and other hazards. The organization develops and advocates use of consensus codes, standards, research, training and education.

NFPA® 1035 — Document outlining the Job Performance Requirements that can be used to determine whether an individual possesses the skills and knowledge to perform as a public or private fire and life safety educator.

Public Information Officer — Those who have demonstrated the ability to conduct media interviews, prepare news releases, and advisories. (**NOTE:** Please see IFSTA's manual, **Public Information Officer**, for information on the duties and challenges faced by this profession. The PIO level is not addressed in this manual.)

Risk-Reduction Initiative — A fire or life safety program that targets a specific issue and audience(s) and is terminated when program goals are achieved.

United States Fire Administration (USFA) — This federal agency works to reduce death and economic losses due to fire and related emergencies. The organization provides public education, training, technology support, and data initiatives to educators and the public at large.

Chapter 1 Notes

Risk Watch® is a registered trademark of the National Fire Protection Association, Inc., Quincy, MA 02269.

Solutions 2000. North American Coalition for Fire and Life Safety Education. September, 1999.

Process of Community Risk Reduction. National Fire Academy Risk Reduction Curriculum.

Public Fire Education Planning – A Five Step Process. Federal Emergency Management Agency. August, 2002.

1. See Pam Powell, "Firesafety Education: It's Older Than You Think," *Fire Journal*, May 1986.

2. *Sparky*® is a registered trademark of the National Fire Protection Association, Quincy, MA 02269.

3. *Learn Not to Burn*® is a registered trademark of the National Fire Protection Association, Inc., Quincy, MA 02269.

4. *America Burning.* National Commission on Fire Prevention and Control. May, 1973.

5. Richard Strother, Foreword to the unpublished report, *A Study of Motivational Psychology Related to Fire Preventive Behavior in Children and Adults*, National Fire Protection Association, 1974.

6. Ann Kulenkamp, Barbara Lundquist, and Philip Schaenman, *Reaching the Hard-to-Reach: Techniques from Fire Prevention Programs and Other Disciplines*, TriData Corporation, October 1994.

7. *America Burning Revisited.* United States Fire Administration; Federal Emergency Management Agency. December, 1987.

8. *America at Risk.* Federal Emergency Management Agency. March, 2000.

9. Proving Public Fire Education Works. TriData Corporation, 1990.

10. Data sources: NFPA®, Fire Analysis and Research Division, Quincy, MA. USFA, Fire Data Center. Emmitsburg, MD.

11. NFPA® 1035, *Professional Qualifications for Public Fire and Life Safety Educator*, Copyright ©2005, National Fire Protection Association, Quincy, MA 02269.

FLSE Level I Educators: Getting Started

▪ Chapter Contents

Key Terms

Job Performance Requirements

This chapter provides information that addresses the following job performance requirements of NFPA® 1035, *Standard for Professional Qualifications for Fire and Life Safety Educator, Public Information Officer, and Juvenile Firesetter Intervention Specialist*, 2010 edition.

NFPA® 1035 References

5.1.1

Learning Objectives

After reading this chapter, students will be able to:

1. Diagram the organizational structure of a fire department. (NFPA® 1035, 5.1.1)

2. Describe the procedure for reporting an emergency. (NFPA® 1035, 5.1.1)

3. Explain the dynamics of fire behavior. (NFPA® 1035, 5.1.1)

4. Describe the parts of firefighter protective clothing, and clarify the purpose of each piece. (NFPA® 1035, 5.1.1)

5. Explain the operation and purpose of basic fire protection systems and devices. (NFPA® 1035, 5.1.1)

6. Discuss human behavior in a fire, and how it relates to fire and life safety education. (NFPA® 1035, 5.1.1)

7. Explain the different hazard classifications, identification, and correction. (NFPA® 1035, 5.1.1)

8. Describe the injury process, various categories of injuries, and how unintentional injuries can be prevented.

9. Identify the various types of disasters, both manmade and natural, that can affect the safety and health of community members.

10. Explain the importance of professionalism, personal image, and public relations in the role of the fire and life safety educator. (NFPA® 1035, 5.1.1)

Chapter 2
FLSE Level I Educators: Getting Started

Case History

In April 2007, Harris Interactive conducted a survey on behalf of the Home Safety Council to determine the public's level of awareness of dangers in the home relating to injury. The results found that while a majority of the adults in the United States think about home safety, very few actually take action to make their homes safer. While eighty-two percent (82%) of the adults surveyed indicated that they were very knowledgeable or somewhat knowledgeable about what could be done to make their home safer, only about one-third (36%) were able to name a safety action that they had already taken. Over one-quarter of those surveyed said that they were not worried that an injury might occur in their home.

These findings led to the conclusion that there is a definite need for additional education to increase the level of awareness about the leading cause of home injuries. Many of the 20,000 deaths that result from home-related injuries can be avoided with the proper education and simple behavioral modifications.

It is the job of the fire and life safety educator to increase the level of knowledge of the public about fires and unintentional injuries. Before this can happen, the nature of fire and injuries needs to be understood. The information in the following chapter provides a foundation for sound preventative actions and behaviors for a fire and life safety educator to present in the educational process.

Source: Home Safety Council, 2007.

The role of a fire and life safety educator in the community risk-reduction process is one of great significance. Over the years, education and instruction in the areas of fire and life safety for community members has risen to a level of importance, both in the fire service and in the community. Some departments may still have progress to make in this area, but most departments are performing some kind of community education whether it is at the shift level or with an individual whose sole responsibility is fire and life safety education.

As was indicated in the previous chapter, the NFPA® standard for Fire and Life Safety Educator distinguishes between the different levels of educators based upon the knowledge, skills, and abilities required for the job:

- The Fire and Life Safety Educator I, or Level I educator, is tasked with the delivery of educational presentations and information. The Level I educator provides the foundation for community risk-reduction initiatives.

- The Fire and Life Safety Educator II, or Level II manager, is responsible for the preparation of educational programs to meet needs that have been identified in a particular community.

- The Fire and Life Safety Educator III, or Level III administrator, is responsible for the creation, administration, and evaluation of educational programs and information.

Certainly, the role of the Fire and Life Safety Educator I is critical. In some small or volunteer departments, one individual may be responsible for the activities at all three levels. The Level I educator is a delivery person, an individual who is delivering vital and lifesaving information.

The profession of a fire and life safety educator is an extremely rewarding one. There are different ways to fight fire: Firefighters use water, and educators use words. Just as with the shift firefighter who possesses a wide range of knowledge and expertise in a variety of fields and continuously studies and trains, the Level I fire and life safety educator must have a wide range of knowledge and expertise about a variety of subjects, including understanding of instructional roles, learning characteristics, learning theories, and educational methodologies.

In any comprehensive risk-reduction program, education is the root of prevention. In the previous chapter, the Five Es, components of the prevention process were covered. All five components are certainly important. But it seems that education is a key component for success. Smoke alarms can be installed, but if individuals are not educated about their maintenance, they will be less than effective. Bike helmets can be provided free of charge, but if children are not educated on the importance of using them and wearing them properly, their effectiveness will be lessened.

This chapter provides necessary information for the beginning educator and also gives resources and references for further study. Much of the information contained in this chapter will be more inclusive than would be shared with most audiences. For some, such as those with a fire service background, this text will serve as a review of many of the basics. For those coming into this career from outside the fire service, valuable insight is given into the world of fire, the fire service, and the people whose lives are affected by fire.

In the field of fire and life safety education, power is necessary to transform and change each individual's attitude and behavior. Therefore, a firm knowledge in a wide range of subjects will provide the needed power to facilitate change. Armed with this knowledge, the informed and educated fire and life safety educator can make a difference in his or her community.

Fire Department Organization and Structure

For those individuals new to the fire service, an understanding of the basic organization and structure of a traditional fire department is in order. Though organizational structure will vary from department to department depending on the size of the department and the community or area served, a basic structure is common to all departments. The basic structure consists of the following:

- Fire chief as the head of the organization
- Assistant chief or deputy chief
- Shift commanders
- Station officers
- Company officers
- Driver/operators
- Firefighters
- Administrative staff, usually consisting of a prevention division, training division, and a maintenance or quartermaster division **(Figure 2.1)**

Some departments will have a more complicated and expanded structure, while others will have fewer officers. The job of fire and life safety educator may fall under the prevention or training division or may report directly to the assistant chief or chief.

Fire departments operate under a chain-of-command management system. **Chain of command** is the pathway of responsibility from the highest level of the department to the lowest. **Unity of command** exists in most departments, meaning each individual reports to only one supervisor, though ultimately everyone reports to the chief **(Figure 2.2)**.

Within the department is an operations or suppression division and an administrative or staff division. The operations division consists of firefighters in the stations staffing the fire apparatus. Administrative staff includes the chief, assistant chief, and, in some

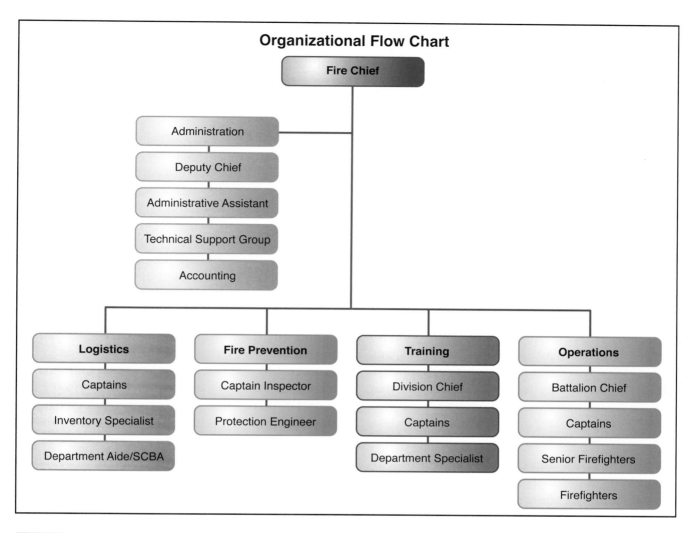

Organizational Flow Chart

Fire Chief

Administration

Deputy Chief

Administrative Assistant

Technical Support Group

Accounting

Logistics

Captains

Inventory Specialist

Department Aide/SCBA

Fire Prevention

Captain Inspector

Protection Engineer

Training

Division Chief

Captains

Department Specialist

Operations

Battalion Chief

Captains

Senior Firefighters

Firefighters

Figure 2.1 An example of a fire department organizational chart.

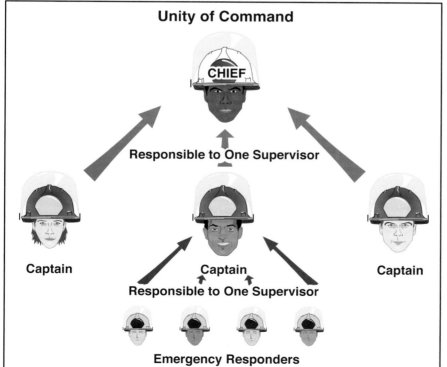

Unity of Command

CHIEF

Responsible to One Supervisor

Captain

Captain

Captain

Responsible to One Supervisor

Emergency Responders

Figure 2.2 An illustration depicting the idea of Unity of Command.

instances, a fire marshal and training officer. Again, larger departments will have a larger administrative staff.

Suppression personnel are divided into companies, which is a group of firefighters assigned to a particular piece of apparatus or to a particular station. Usually, there is a company officer, an apparatus operator, and one or more firefighters. (**NOTE:** This company makeup will vary from department to department.)

The prevention division in a fire department consists of a fire marshal, fire prevention officers or inspectors, fire investigators, fire and life safety educators, and fire protection engineers. In some departments, especially smaller departments, an individual may be responsible for multiple duties. Larger departments may have a division for each responsibility. Prevention is generally responsible for the enforcement of fire codes, review of plans for new construction, investigation of fire causes, and fire and life safety education. In some departments, the individuals handling the prevention function may be sworn personnel. Other departments make use of civilian personnel for any or all of the functions of the prevention division.

The training division consists of a training officer and one or more instructors. This division is responsible for the training and continuing education of the firefighters within the department. Some states and provinces have requirements for in-service training in order for firefighters to maintain their certifications. Many training divisions use adjunct instructors or instructors who are outside of the training division, yet trained as instructors in a certain field or specialty.

The fire and life safety educator needs to have an understanding of the organizational structure of the department for which he or she is working. Protocols usually exist for the scheduling, notification, and use of engine companies, or other fire department personnel. The fire and life safety educator should have a working knowledge of this process.

Reporting an Emergency

Emergency reporting is a standard component to many fire and life safety education presentations. While most people believe this is common knowledge, this is not always the case. The process may vary from community to community, but the concepts are the same everywhere.

In most communities, to reach emergency responders, individuals call a three-digit number: 9-1-1. In other communities, there may be a seven-digit number. Some communities have state-of-the-art communications centers, while others may have the emergency number routed to the local sheriff's office or police station.

Some communities may have an enhanced system: When the call arrives at the communications center, the address of the caller will appear on a screen, which assists in the dispatch process. Other centers may not have the benefit of this technology. Cell phones, Internet, and cable service telephone providers may not interface with this equipment, which means that it is imperative that individuals know their address and the location of the emergency.

When the call is received at the communications center, the telecommunicator will record the information concerning the nature of the emergency **(Figure 2.3)**. The information is either entered into a computer or hand-written for transfer to the appropriate dispatcher. The dispatcher will then notify the appropriate units (usually by a fire station alarm) of the call, the nature of the call, and its location.

For the fire and life safety educator, education concerning emergency reporting will revolve around when to call the emergency number and when to dial a nonemergency number. Those who are reporting emergencies need to know what information they will be asked such as name, address, and nature of the emergency. The caller will need to remain on the line until the dispatcher advises the person to disconnect. Many times in situations involving medical emergencies, the communications staff will remain on the phone with the caller and provide vital

Figure 2.3 A telecommunicator receiving an emergency call.

instructions for care, such as the steps in performing cardiopulmonary resuscitation (CPR).

Residents must also be informed about the emergency response process and how units are dispatched to an emergency scene. Level I educators must become familiar with the system and process in their community for reporting emergencies.

The Dynamics of Fire

For the Level I fire and life safety educator, a thorough understanding of the phenomenon of fire is imperative. By grasping the dynamics of fire and understanding its nature, the educator can speak confidently on the subject and enable the audience to make sense of the important fire and life safety actions and behaviors being presented.

According to the IFSTA **Essentials, 5th Edition**,[1] fire can take a variety of forms, but all involve a heat-producing chemical reaction between some type of fuel and oxygen or oxidizer. When anything burns, heat is generated faster than it can be dissipated, and this causes a significant increase in temperature.

While the terms fire and **combustion** are often used interchangeably, in reality fire is a form of combustion. To put it simply, fire is a rapid process, which is self-sustaining, that produces heat and light, and requires oxygen and fuel.

The Fire Triangle and the Fire Tetrahedron

While the **fire triangle** is useful for explaining smoldering or nonflaming combustion, it does not always provide a complete picture of fire behavior **(Figure 2.4)**. Therefore, the fire triangle has largely been replaced by the **fire tetrahedron**, which more accurately explains flaming combustion **(Figure 2.5)**. Flaming combustion is a condition that includes a chemical-change reaction that occurs during the burning process. The fire tetrahedron is composed of the following four elements:

- Fuel
- Oxygen
- Heat
- Self-sustained chemical reaction

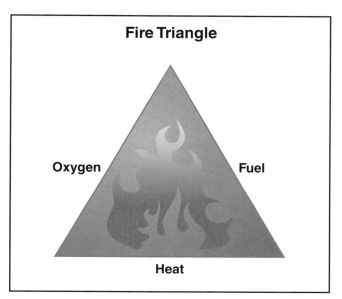

Figure 2.4 The fire triangle represents nonflaming combustion.

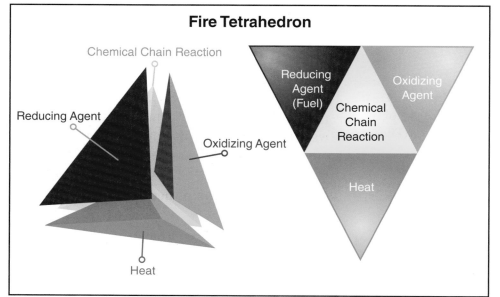

Figure 2.5 The fire tetrahedron represents flaming combustion.

Each element of the fire tetrahedron must be in place for flaming combustion to occur. If heat, fuel, or oxygen is removed from a fire, it will be extinguished. If the self-sustained chemical reaction of flaming combustion is inhibited or interrupted, flaming combustion will cease, although the fire may continue to smolder depending on the characteristics of the fuel.

Fuel

Fuel is the substance that is being oxidized or burned in the combustion process. It comes in one of three forms: solid, liquid, or gas. Some fuels are solids such as wood, paper, and cloth. Other fuels come in a liquid state such as paints, paint thinners, oils, and greases. Some fuels are in a gaseous state such as propane and natural gas. All fuels must be in the form of gases in order to ignite. Solids achieve this through a process called **pyrolysis**, where the solid fuel is heated to the point that it releases fuel gases. Liquids produce fuel gases through vaporization, turning the liquid into gases through heating. The most dangerous fuels are gaseous in their natural state and therefore already in the condition required for ignition.

Oxygen

Oxygen is a necessary component for the creation and support of fire. The air around is considered the primary source of oxygen, although there are other agents (oxidizing agents) that can produce oxygen during a chemical reaction. Normally, air consists of about 21% oxygen; however, combustion can be supported at levels as low as 14%. Oxygen is a gas that supports combustion when combined with a fuel. Oxygen itself is not combustible.

Heat

Heat is the third requirement for combustion. Heat provides energy for the fire, causes pyrolysis of the solid fuels, and causes vaporization of liquids **(Figure 2.6)**. Heat causes the following:

- Ignition
- Continuous production of fuel gases
- Combustion
- Rapid spread of fire

The following text discusses the types of heat sources.

Chemical heat. Chemical heat is the most common source of heat in combustion reactions. Examples of chemical heat are the burning of matches and spontaneous combustion (also referred to as self-heating). A ball of oil-soaked rags thrown into a corner can, under the right conditions, create enough heat to cause ignition.

Electricity. Electricity is also a common heat source. Electrical heat can occur through a variety of means:

- Overload or overcurrent occurs when the current flowing through a conductor exceeds its design limits and the conductor (or wiring) overheats.
- Resistance heating occurs when the electric current flows through a conductor. Some appliances are designed to make use of resistance heating **(Figure 2.7)**.
- An arc is a high-temperature discharge across a gap or through a medium. When there is an electrical arc, particles are formed and they splatter away from the point of arcing. This is referred to as *sparking*.
- Other electrical heat sources include static electricity and lightning.

Mechanical heat. Mechanical heat can be generated by friction or compression. The movement of two surfaces against each other can result in heat or sparks being generated. Simply rubbing two sticks together can create enough heat to ignite fuel. Heat of compression is generated when a gas is compressed.

Nuclear heat. Nuclear heat occurs by the splitting of atoms (fission) or the combining of atoms (fusion). The sun's heat is a product of fusion and thus is a form of nuclear energy.

Self-Sustaining Chemical Reaction

The fourth and final component of the tetrahedron, the self-sustaining chemical reaction, is a result of the fuel, heat, and oxygen combining in a very specific way. It is this chemical reaction, given enough of the other components, that is responsible for the spread of fire and the devastating nature of uncontrolled fire.

Fires can be extinguished by the removal of one of the components:

- Heat can be removed from the fire with water or chemical agents **(Figure 2.8)**.
- Oxygen is removed from a kitchen grease fire when baking soda or a lid is applied.

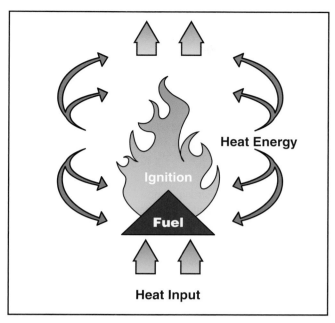

Figure 2.6 Heat sustains the combustion process.

Figure 2.7 An electric heater operates on the principle of resistance heating.

- Wildland fires are controlled through the process of removing the fuel, which is readily available in the form of trees and other natural growth.

To the fire and life safety educator, this knowledge will prove invaluable in the preparation and presentation of fire and life safety programs. Having an understanding of the components of fire gives the Level I educator the ability to explain, with clarity, fire prevention concepts and messages to the average person.

Figure 2.8 Firefighters using water to remove the heat of a fire.

The Products of Combustion

The products of combustion are heat, smoke, and light. This may seem very simple. But it is deceptive in that two of these can be and often are very deadly. Fire victims almost never burn to death — they are killed by the toxic gases and heat produced by the fire.

Heat

Heat from the fire can cause burn injuries, damage to respiratory tracts, dehydration, and heat exhaustion to those without the proper protection. Though the heat from a fire is a danger to anyone directly exposed to it, the real killer in fires is smoke.

Smoke

Smoke consists of gases, vapors, and unburned particles of fuel, which are often toxic and present a significant threat to human life. Some of the more common fire gases include carbon monoxide (CO), hydrogen cyanide (HCN), and carbon dioxide (CO_2). Other hazardous gases in smoke include acrolein, hydrogen chloride, acetaldehyde, and formaldehyde, to name a few **(Table 2.1, p. 36)**.

Carbon monoxide. Carbon monoxide (CO) is a colorless, odorless gas and the most common by-product of combustion. CO combines with the hemoglobin in blood, decreasing the body's ability to carry oxygen. CO is frequently cited as a cause of death for fire fatalities, both civilian and firefighter.

Table 2.1
Common Products of Combustion and Their Toxic Effects

Acetaldehyde	Colorless liquid with a pungent choking odor, which is irritating to the mucous membranes and especially the eyes. Breathing vapors will cause nausea, vomiting, headache, and unconsciousness.
Acrolein	Colorless-to-yellow volatile liquid with a disagreeable choking odor, this material is irritating to the eyes and mucous membranes. This substance is extremely toxic; inhalation of concentrations as little as 10 ppm may be fatal within a few minutes.
Asbestos	A magnesium silicate mineral that occurs as slender, strong, flexible fibers. Breathing of asbestos dust causes asbestosis and lung cancer.
Benzene	Colorless liquid with a petroleum-like odor. Acute exposure to benzene can result in dizziness, excitation, headache, difficulty breathing, nausea, and vomiting. Benzene is also a carcinogen.
Benzaldehyde	Colorless-to-clear yellow liquid with a bitter almond odor. Inhalation of concentrated vapor is irritating to the eyes, nose, and throat.
Carbon Monoxide	Colorless, odorless gas. Inhalation of carbon monoxide causes headache, dizziness, weakness, confusion, nausea, unconsciousness, and death. Exposure to as little as 0.2% carbon monoxide can result in unconsciousness within 30 minutes. Inhalation of a high concentration can result in immediate collapse and unconsciousness.
Formaldehyde	Colorless gas with a pungent, irritating odor that is highly irritating to the nose; 50–100 ppm can cause severe irritation to the respiratory track and serious injury. Exposure to high concentrations can cause injury to the skin. Formaldehyde is a suspected carcinogen.
Glutaraldehyde	Light-yellow liquid that causes severe irritation of the eyes and irritation of the skin.
Hydrogen Chloride	Colorless gas with a sharp, pungent odor. Mixes with water to form hydrochloric acid. Hydrogen chloride is corrosive to human tissue. Exposure to hydrogen chloride can result in irritation of skin and respiratory distress.
Isovaleraldehyde	Colorless liquid with a weak, suffocating odor. Inhalation causes respiratory distress, nausea, vomiting and headache.
Nitrogen Dioxide	Reddish-brown gas or yellowish-brown liquid, which is highly toxic and corrosive.
Particulates	Small particles that can be inhaled and deposited in the mouth, trachea, or the lungs. Exposure to particulates can cause eye irritation and respiratory distress (in addition to health hazards specifically related to the particular substances involved).
Polycyclic Aromatic Hydrocarbons (PAHs)	PAHs are a group of over 100 different chemicals that generally occur as complex mixtures as part of the combustion process. These materials are generally colorless, white, or pale yellow-green solids with a pleasant odor. Some of these materials are human carcinogens.
Sulfur Dioxide	Colorless gas with a choking or suffocating odor. Sulfur dioxide is toxic and corrosive and can irritate the eyes and mucous membranes.

Source: *Computer Aided Management of Emergency Operations (CAMEO)* and *Toxicological Profile for Polycyclic Aromatic Hydrocarbons.*

Hydrogen cyanide. Hydrogen cyanide (HCN) is produced in the combustion of materials containing nitrogen, such as polyurethane foam, which is used in furniture and bedding. Hydrogen cyanide prevents the body from using oxygen at the cellular level.

Carbon dioxide. Carbon dioxide is not toxic like hydrogen cyanide and CO; it simply displaces oxygen. It also stimulates the respiratory system, which increases the respiratory rate of the victim.

Many individuals do not understand the hazardous nature of smoke and its lethal effect. They believe the heat from the fire and the flames are of a greater concern. Fire and life safety educators must stress the facts about smoke and dispel the myths surrounding this product of combustion. Rolling out of bed and crawling low under smoke are actions that must be emphasized for individuals to successfully exit a fire-involved building.

The Development of Fire

Ignition occurs when the components of the fire tetrahedron come together, which starts the process of fire. Heat is transmitted beyond the object first ignited, and *established burning* begins. Once established burning has occurred, the fire will continue to grow and spread.

From this point, the fire will continue through several stages of development **(Figure 2.9)**. Because the development of fire is complex and dependent on many factors, all fires may not develop through each of these stages. These stages describe the development of a compartment fire as a fire event within an enclosed room or space inside a building without

any suppression activities. Fire is a dynamic event that is complex and influenced by many variables. The stages of fire are as follows:

- Incipient stage
- Growth stage
- Fully developed stage
- Decay stage

Incipient Stage

The **incipient growth stage** is where the four components of the fire tetrahedron come together, and ignition occurs. At this point, the fire is small and generally confined to the material of first ignition. Radiant heat warms adjacent fuels and continues the process of pyrolysis. The temperature is only slightly above ambient, and the products of combustion are in a low concentration. During this phase, occupants can safely escape, and the fire can be controlled or extinguished with a fire extinguisher.

Growth Stage

As the fire moves from the incipient phase to the **growth stage**, the smoke and fire gases begin to rise, being confined by the ceiling. This transition can happen very quickly. During the growth phase, the fire gases begin to spread out until they reach the walls. At this point, the deadly fire gases begin to layer down through the compartment or room of fire origin. Thermal layering will occur, which is the tendency of gases to form layers according to temperature.

The temperature during this phase has risen to grave extremes, with the hottest being at the ceiling. The cooler air will be at floor level, but even that will be extremely dangerous.

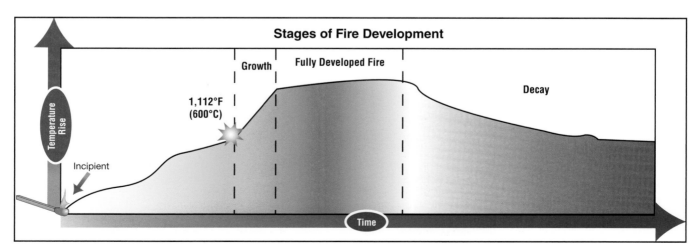

Figure 2.9 The stages of fire development.

Flashover Stage

Flashover represents the transition from the growth phase into the fully developed stage of fire. (**NOTE:** Flashover is not a specific event such as ignition that always occurs.) When flashover occurs, all combustibles within the compartment or room are involved. Simultaneous ignition occurs of all the combustible contents in the area, causing burning from floor to ceiling. Temperatures can reach 900° to 1,200°F (482°C to 649°C). Occupants who have not evacuated will not be able to survive. Even firefighters wearing protective clothing are at extreme risk of death or injury.

Fully Developed Stage

At the **fully developed stage**, all the contents of the space are involved in fire (**Figure 2.10**). Maximum heat is being released, ventilation is affecting the behavior of the fire, and gases are flowing into adjacent spaces or compartments. These gases will ignite as they travel into other areas.

Decay Stage

As the fire consumes the fuel, the heat release rate will decline. The fire will be controlled by the amount of fuel remaining at this time. The amount of fire will diminish as the amount of fuel diminishes. The remaining embers will continue to result in high temperatures for some time.

Backdraft is explosively rapid combustion that can occur during the **decay stage**. In a ventilation-controlled environment, high temperatures are usually present, but the oxygen level is quite low. Increasing the oxygen content in the room, simply by opening a door or window, can have very explosive and dangerous effects. The violence of a backdraft is usually dependent on the

amount of confinement of the fire (**Figure 2.11**). Firefighters are taught to look for signs and conditions that might indicate a possible backdraft condition prior to ventilating a structure.

The fire and life safety educator can examine the stages of fire and understand the logic and reasons for several preemptive fire safety behaviors:

- Limiting the amount of combustible items in a room or residence is a wise practice because fire development is dependent upon the amount of available fuel.

- Sleeping with bedroom doors closed limits the exposure to smoke and superheated gases during a fire.

- Closing doors to a fire room when exiting a building will help slow the fire's progress by limiting ventilation and oxygen to the fire; closed doors can serve as barriers to the heat and smoke damage caused by fire.

- Crawling low under smoke is the only hope for escape in a smoke-filled room, as the air above the floor will be superheated and contain fire gases that will kill.

Firefighter Personal Protective Equipment

One of the items unique to the fire service is the protective equipment worn by firefighters. The general public, and especially children, will ask many ques-

Figure 2.10 An example of a fully developed fire. *Courtesy of District Chief Chris Mickal, New Orleans (LA) FD Photo Unit.*

Figure 2.11 Improper ventilation for the conditions may result in a backdraft.

tions about the gear and will want to see a firefighter get into the gear. As a matter of fact, it is important for children to see a firefighter in his or her full gear, in hopes of preventing fear or avoidance on the part of that child during an emergency.

Fire and life safety educators with a fire service background will be able to handle this educational piece knowledgeably. For others who may not be as familiar, the following section serves as an introduction to this equipment and its uses in fire and life safety education presentations.

A firefighter's protective clothing is referred to as *bunker gear* or *turnout gear*. The phrases result from the historical fact that firefighters would keep their gear by their beds, or bunks, ready to "turn out" of their bunks at night to respond to emergency calls. Full protective clothing for emergency operations consists of several pieces, as listed below:

● *Helmet* — protects the head from impact and other head injuries.

● *Protective hood* — made out of a fire-resistant material; it protects portions of the firefighter's face, ears, neck, and other areas not covered by the helmet, collar, or other equipment.

● *Protective coat and pants* — protect the trunk and limbs against cuts, abrasions, and burn injuries. These items protect from direct flame contact, hot water and vapors, and other hazardous conditions. Keep in mind that these items are not entirely "fireproof." They will withstand the heat and flames for a period of time and then will begin to fail.

● *Gloves* — protect hands from cuts, wounds, and burn injuries.

● *Boots* — protect the feet from burn injuries and puncture wounds.

● *Self-contained breathing apparatus (SCBA)* – protects the face and lungs from toxic smoke and other products of combustion. There are several parts: the harness, regulator, low pressure hose, high pressure hose, cylinder, and facepiece or mask. The cylinder contains compressed air and can last from 15 minutes to 1 hour, depending on the size of the cylinder and the physical condition of the wearer.

Fire and life safety educators can use the interest that the public has in a firefighter's protective clothing as an educational tool. Firefighters dressed in full protective gear may frighten children. Therefore, children need to understand what the gear is and, more importantly, its role in a firefighter's safety. Making a comparison between a child's clothing and the firefighter's clothing can be instrumental in conveying the importance of escaping a fire. Children need to view the firefighter as a friend and helper.

Several guidelines for showing protective gear are as follow:

- *Put on the gear in front of the children.* A firefighter fully clothed in turnout gear and wearing an SCBA should never enter a room of children, especially young children. This will only frighten them.

- *Try to use clean gear because the cleanliness of the gear is an issue.* If it is not possible to have clean gear, try to limit the child's contact with it.

- *Avoid technical explanations and jargon, even with older children.* Protective clothing "keeps the firefighter safe." Focus on the job of the gear and not the operation or construction of it. Adults may be more interested in the technical aspect, but they will want to know how much it costs and how much it weighs, more than how it works.

It is incumbent upon the fire and life safety educator to become familiar with the firefighter's full protective clothing — its individual pieces, construction, and use. This can be an integral part of educational presentations, especially with children, and must be handled appropriately for the optimum impact and effectiveness.

Fire Protection Systems and Devices

Fire protection systems and devices is a broad topic that covers many classes and textbooks. The purpose of this section is to introduce some of the fire protections systems that exist in residential, commercial, health care, multi-use, and manufacturing facilities. This information will enable the educator to answer questions and offer explanations to the public when necessary.

Residential Fire Protection Systems

A wide variety of systems and devices protect a residence and its occupants from the hazards of fire. There are smoke alarms powered by a 9-volt or lithium battery or household current, complex alarm systems that are local or monitored, as well as residential sprinkler systems.

Introduced in the 1970s, working smoke alarms in residences are credited with cutting a person's risk of dying in a fire by half. Today, there are many types and varieties of smoke alarms. The important aspects are the approval of the alarm by a certified testing facility and the alarm's location and maintenance. It is not the educator's job to recommend a certain type of alarm; however, it is the educator's job to stress proper maintenance and the actions to be taken when the alarm sounds.

Smoke alarms work by detecting the particles of fuel in smoke. Two types of alarms can be used: photoelectric and ionization.[2]

Photoelectric alarm. **Photoelectric alarms** work with a light source and a photoelectric cell. Inside the area to be monitored is a beam of light that is projected onto the photoelectric cell. When smoke obscures the path of the light, the alarm sounds. Another way that photoelectric alarms work is when the light beam inside the chamber is scattered in all directions and hits the photoelectric cell, causing the alarm to activate **(Figure 2.12)**.

Ionization alarms. **Ionization alarms** contain a small particle of radioactive material that ionizes the air within the detection chamber **(Figure 2.13)**. When smoke with its particulate matter enters the chamber, the ionization level is reduced, sounding the alarm.

It is generally understood that ionization alarms typically respond faster to flaming fires than smoldering ones. They also automatically reset when the chamber is cleared. Photoelectric alarms will respond faster to smoldering fires than ionization alarms. Photoelectric alarms, by most accounts, are generally a little more expensive than ionization alarms. Units that are designed with both types of chambers may be purchased as well and are known as *dual-sensor alarms.*

Smoke-alarm technology has evolved tremendously since the first alarms were developed. They are being designed to meet the special needs of individuals, families, and households in order to provide an effective means of notification for all. For those individuals who are deaf or hard of hearing, smoke alarms have been developed that use a strobe light or vibrating device to alert the occupant of possible fire dangers **(Figure 2.14)**. There are alarm devices that allow a parent or caregiver to record emergency instructions in their own voice for children who might not be awakened by conventional alarm sounds. This message will be activated when the alarm is activated. In addition, alarms with "hush buttons" are available that allow an occupant to silence an alarm in case of accidental activation. The purpose is to discourage individuals from removing the battery or attempting to disable the alarm when it is activated by means other than a hostile fire or smoke. There are smoke alarms that are self-charging, some that use wireless technology to provide interconnection of the alarms, and some that can be tested using the remote control from one's television.

New alarms are being introduced regularly. It is the responsibility of the Level I educator to stay currrent with emerging technology and fire codes relating to smoke alarms and their operation. Manufacturers and safety experts work to design the most effective and efficient alarms for the varying lifestyles and needs of individuals. In addition, educators need to exercise caution when responding to questions about which alarm is best. It is not prudent to recommend a particular make or model of alarm. Educators should provide information about the variety of alarms available so that individuals can determine which alarm is best suited for their needs. Most importantly, individuals should be apprised of the importance of certification from a Nationally Recognized Testing

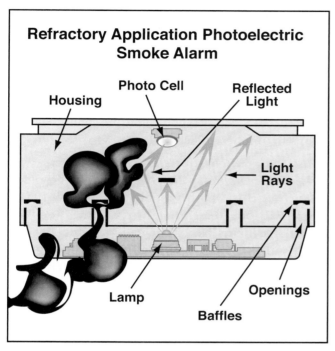

Figure 2.12 The operating principle behind refractory photoelectric smoke alarms.

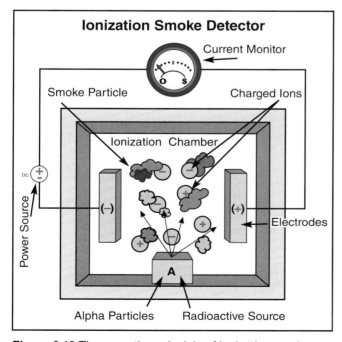

Figure 2.13 The operating principle of ionization smoke alarms.

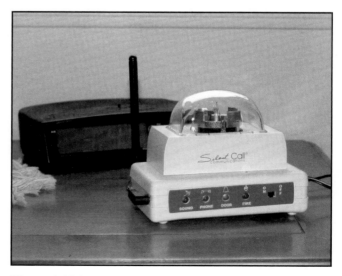

Figure 2.14 An example of a smoke alarm for individuals who are deaf or hard of hearing.

Laboratory (NRTL), such as Underwriters Laboratory (UL) or FM Global, and the effective maintenance of the alarm that is being used **(Figure 2.15)**.

The public needs to know the following facts about smoke alarms:

- *Smoke alarms may be interconnected, either by wired or wireless technology.* When one alarm sounds, they all will sound. Some jurisdictions and occupancies require that residential alarms be interconnected (See NFPA® 72).

- *Alarms may be powered in a variety of ways.* They can be connected to the wiring in the home (hardwired). This type should be equipped with a battery backup in case of a power outage. Alarms may be battery powered. Most common are alarms that are powered by 9-volt batteries. However, smoke alarms may be powered by a ten-year lithium battery that does not need changing. Lithium powered smoke alarms still need to be checked in accordance with the manufacturer's instructions.

- *Homes need to have at least one smoke alarm outside of the sleeping areas.* A two-story home will require one alarm on each level to achieve a minimum level of coverage. Further, it is recommended that each bedroom be equipped with a smoke alarm to enhance protection; most especially if occupants sleep with bedroom doors closed.

- *The manufacturer's instructions are the best source of information for placement and maintenance of smoke alarms.* It is recommended that smoke alarms be checked and maintained regularly in accordance with manufacturer's instructions.

- *An estimated 96% of the homes in the U.S. today have smoke alarms, but about 20% of those are not working.* This is due to dead, missing, or disconnected batteries. Of course these alarms will not operate in a fire. When working with the public, smoke alarm testing and maintenance are always a major fire and life safety message for educators.

- *Smoke alarms have a life of about ten years.* Manufacturers are now recommending that the entire alarm unit be replaced after ten years.

- *It is important to stress the behavior that needs to take place upon the alarm's activation: get out of the house!* Too many people want to investigate and will look to see what the problem is and then valuable time is lost for evacuation of the residence. This message is second only to the message for smoke-alarm maintenance, especially for children: If the alarm sounds, get out!

Automatic Fire Suppression Systems

Automatic sprinkler systems consist of a series of sprinklers arranged so that the system will automatically distribute a sufficient quantity of water or agent to either extinguish or confine a fire. A series of piping in the ceiling or wall supply the water and the sprinklers protrude through the ceiling or wall **(Figure 2.16)**. Some may be *complete sprinkler systems*, which protect the entire building or *partial*

Figure 2.15 This smoke alarm has been tested by UL and FM Global.

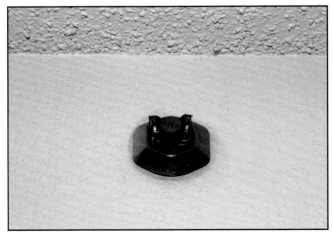

Figure 2.16 A wall-mounted sprinkler from a residential sprinkler system.

sprinkler systems, which protect only high-hazard areas, exit routes, or areas required to be protected by local codes.

The following section is an introduction to these systems, both residential and commercial. While commercial fire sprinkler systems have been around for some time, residential sprinkler systems are now being required in areas across the country and will continue to be a part of new construction, as well as existing construction.

An automatic fire suppression system has many components and can be quite complex. The following are a few simple points that the public needs to understand: Sprinkler systems are heat-activated, as opposed to smoke alarms that are activated by smoke. Therefore, only the sprinkler in the area closest to the fire will activate. If the fire is not contained by the activation of one sprinkler, then a second one will activate based upon the heat spread. Many people believe that if one sprinkler activates, they all will. This is simply not true!

- Sprinklers must be allowed to operate properly. They cannot be obstructed by stock or product that is stacked to the ceiling or by items that are hanging from them.

- Some people believe that residential sprinkler systems are very expensive. In fact, a residential sprinkler system can be installed during the construction process for the same cost as upgrad-

ing the carpet, and the same is true for retrofitting existing homes.

- Sprinklers, both residential and commercial, are designed to control fires quickly and with as little water as possible.

- The combination of residential sprinklers and smoke alarms in a residence will reduce an individual's chances of dying in a fire by 82%.

- If a fire is extinguished by the fire department, they will use 8½ times the amount of water that the sprinkler will need to control and extinguish the fire.

There is some basic terminology relating to sprinkler systems with which the fire and life safety educator should be familiar **(Figure 2.17)**. **Sprinklers**

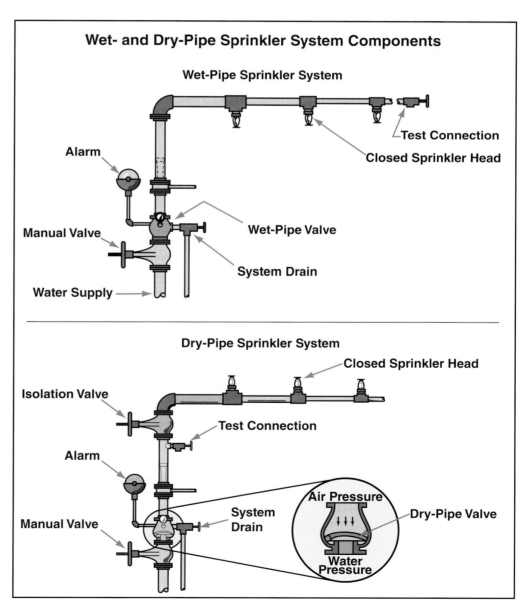

Figure 2.17 Common components of an automatic sprinkler system.

discharge water after the release of a cap or plug that is activated by a heat-responsive element. The sprinkler is attached to piping in the ceiling or wall referred to as *branch lines*. These branch lines are attached to cross mains, which are attached to the feed main. This is the main supply of water and is attached to the **riser**, which is the vertical piping coming straight from the water supply. Other parts of the system include the fire department connection, alarm check valve, sprinkler control valve, and main drain. The **fire department connection (FDC)** is just that, a connection where the fire department can connect hoselines to provide additional water supply to the sprinkler system when it is activated. The **alarm check valve** is used to test the operation of the water flow alarm. The sprinkler control valve is used to turn off the water to the system for maintenance, replacement of sprinklers, and to interrupt its operation such as when the fire is extinguished. The main drain allows the water to be drained from the system for maintenance purposes.

Sprinklers can be classified into different categories depending upon their application:

- A **wet-pipe system** contains water under pressure at all times and is the simplest and easiest to maintain. It is used in areas that are not subject to temperatures below 40°F (4°C) **(Figure 2.18)**.

- A **dry-pipe system** is used in locations where piping may be subjected to temperatures below 40°F (4°C). In this system, air under pressure replaces the water in the system. In a fire, when the sprinkler activates, the air from the system escapes first, and this allows the water to enter the system **(Figure 2.19)**.

Residential sprinkler systems are installed in one- and two-family dwellings. This type of system prevents full-room involvement in the room of the fire's origin and allows the occupants a chance to escape. Sprinklers for residential systems can be both conventional and decorative models. These systems can be attached to a public water supply or a dwelling's private domestic water supply.

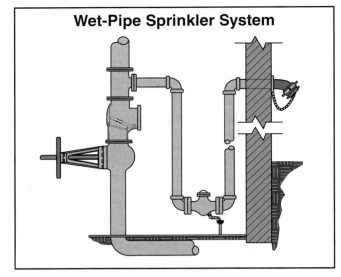

Figure 2.18 An illustration of a wet-pipe sprinkler system.

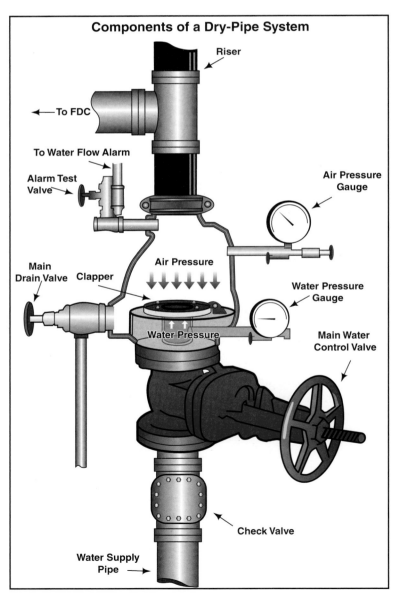

Figure 2.19 An illustration showing how a dry-pipe system uses air pressure to prevent water from entering the system until a sprinkler is activated.

What This Means to You

As a fire and life safety educator, you may encounter significant opposition to the promotion of residential fire sprinklers. Much of the opposition stems from lack of education and understanding on the part of the general public. Therefore, you must be armed with facts about residential sprinklers:

Myth: Sprinklers are unsightly.

- *Fact*: All residential sprinklers come in colors to match ceiling and wall colors and can be recessed or partially recessed.

Myth: The sprinklers may go off accidentally.

- *Fact*: Loss records of FM Global Research show that the probability of a sprinkler discharging accidentally due to a manufacturing defect is only 1 in 16 million sprinklers per year in service.

Myth: Sprinklers will leak.

- *Fact*: Sprinkler systems are under the same pressure as the plumbing system but are tested at 2-3 times higher pressure during installation.

Myth: If one sprinkler goes off, they all go off. Then, you've really got a mess!

- *Fact*: Sprinklers are designed to react to temperatures in each room individually. Normally, only the sprinkler over the fire will activate. Data show that in residential scenarios, usually one sprinkler will control a developing fire; in commercial buildings, as few as three sprinklers will do the job.

Myth: They cause water damage!

- *Fact*: Tests conducted by the Los Angeles Fire Department and the US Fire Administration showed that damage caused by water in a sprinklered fire is substantially less than damage caused by fire department hose streams in an identical unsprinklered fire and far less than damage caused by a fire which escapes early detection and suppression.

Myth: Sprinklers are just too expensive to install.

- *Fact*: With the development of quick-response sprinkler systems which can be supplied by a home's domestic water supply, a 2,000 square-foot home under construction can be affordably protected by a quick-response sprinkler system, and an older home of comparable size can be retrofitted for about 50 percent more. ***The cost is 1-2% of the home cost — about as much as to upgrade the carpeting***. More importantly, there are numerous cost-saving benefits of sprinkler systems in construction code options and insurance discounts, which will offset the cost of installation.

Myth: Residential sprinklers do not save lives.

- *Fact*: The evidence on this point is overwhelming:

  — There has not been a single residential fire fatality in a residence with a sprinkler system in either Napa, California, or Cobb County, Georgia, since the inception of those programs.

  — There has not been a single fire fatality in Prince George's County, Maryland, in a building with a sprinkler system.

  — Scottsdale, Arizona, credits sprinkler systems with saving up to 52 lives since the ordinance passed in 1985.

Source: "Residential Sprinklers, Myth and Fact." United States Fire Administration, December 28, 2006.

Fire and life safety educators need to have a working knowledge of basic sprinkler system operation, particularly residential sprinklers. Both commercial and residential fire sprinklers save lives. They have proven their value time after time. Many jurisdictions are promoting the use of residential sprinklers, and legislation exists in municipalities and counties that require residential sprinklers in new home construction.

The National Fire Protection Association (NFPA®) estimates that approximately 80% of all fire fatalities occur in residential occupancies. This is one reason why residential fire sprinklers make so much sense. Even though the basic technology is the same, there are differences in a residential system and a system designed for commercial occupancies. These changes were made to decrease cost and to enhance their effectiveness in the residential setting. For more information on residential sprinklers, visit the web site for the Home Fire Sprinkler Coalition: www.homefiresprinkler.org.

Portable Fire Extinguishers

Fire and life safety educators will frequently be asked questions or asked to make presentations about portable fire extinguishers. The Level I educator should understand their operation and be familiar with the topic in order to answer questions and provide explanations on the subject.

Many fire departments provide hands-on training with fire extinguishers. Some will use an actual fire in a controlled environment, while others make use of a variety of fire simulators. Educators should be aware of the regulations and policies of their agency or organization relating to this type of training. Topics such as the cleanup of the agent, **liability of injury**, and environmental concerns need to be discussed with the agency leaders prior to implementing a hands-on training program for fire extinguishers.

Standard for Portable Fire Extinguishers, NFPA® 10, categorizes fires based on the fuel involved. Fire extinguishers are classified according to the type of fire that they will extinguish. The five classifications of fires are listed below:

- *Class A.* These fires involve common or ordinary combustibles, such as wood, paper, cloth, and rubber. The fire extinguishers for this type of fire would include water-based, multipurpose, or dry chemical.

- *Class B.* These fires involve flammable liquids, such as gasoline, paints, paint thinners, and grease. Types of extinguishers for these fires include carbon dioxide, dry chemical, AFFF (aqueous film forming foam), and clean agent.

- *Class C.* This type of fire involves energized (or charged) electrical equipment. This would include household appliances, manufacturing equipment, and any other fuel that requires electricity. Types of extinguishers include carbon dioxide, dry chemical, and clean agent.

- *Class D.* These fires involve combustible metals. Examples include magnesium, titanium, and other such metals. The only extinguisher that is effective on this type of fire is a dry powder extinguisher.

- *Class K.* These fires typically occur in kitchens. The fuels for these fires include vegetable cooking oils or shortenings. The extinguishing agent for Class K extinguishers is an alkaline mixture that contains potassium citrate, potassium carbonates, or a combination in water.

All extinguishers are labeled according to the type of fire they will extinguish, either with letters and geometric shapes or picture-symbols **(Table 2.2)**. In addition, some extinguishers will have numbers associated with the letter designation. The number is indicative of the size of fire that the extinguisher will control. As a rule of thumb, the higher the number, the larger the amount of fire that can be controlled or extinguished with that particular extinguisher. These numerical ratings are assigned by (UL) through its testing and rating procedures.

For commercial purposes, codes govern the number, types, and sizes of extinguishers that will be found in a facility. Factors that affect this include the type of occupancy of the building, the size of the facility, the number of people in the facility, and the building's contents. Extinguishers are required to be mounted in easy-to-reach areas that are easily visible to the building's occupants and easily accessible in the exit pathways.

Most codes require that commercial extinguishers receive inspection and service annually. Certain types of extinguishers, both commercial and residential models, will have a gauge indicating a state of readiness that needs to be monitored **(Figure 2.20)**. Extinguishers should be easily accessible, not hidden behind furniture, in closets, or in other out-of-reach areas.

Types of Fire Extinguishers

As previously indicated, there are a variety of types of extinguishing agents available for the different classifications of fire. Not all extinguishers will work on all classifications of fire, and there is no single extinguisher that will work on all five classifications.

Dry chemical extinguishers are often referred to as multipurpose extinguishers or A-B-C extinguishers and are the most common type of extinguisher. Some are rated for Classes A, B, and C, while others are rated only for Class B and Class C, depending on the contents. The most commonly used dry chemicals include sodium bicarbonate, potassium bicarbonate, potassium chloride, and monoammonium phosphate.

Table 2.2
Classification of Fire

Class Name	Letter Symbol	Image Symbol	Description
Class A or Ordinary Combustibles	A — Ordinary Combustibles		Includes fuels such as wood, paper, plastic, rubber, and cloth.
Class B or Flammable and Combustible Liquids and Gases	B — Flammable Liquids		Includes all hydrocarbon and alcohol-based liquids and gases that will support combustion.
Class C or Electrical	C — Electrical Equipment		This includes all fires involving energized electrical equipment.
Class D or Combustible Metals	D		Examples of combustible metals are: magnesium, potassium, titanium, and zirconium.
Class K or Kitchen	K		Includes unsaturated cooking oils in well-insulated cooking appliances located in commercial kitchens.

Figure 2.20 A fire inspector checking the readiness of a fire extinguisher.

The agents used are nontoxic and very effective in containing or extinguishing a small fire. However, they can create a powdery mess or cause damage to delicate equipment. Dry chemical extinguishers can be either handheld or wheeled units. Most handheld units will have a gauge that will indicate that the unit is in working order **(Figure 2.21, p. 48)**.

Carbon dioxide (CO_2) extinguishers may be found in handheld units and wheeled units as well. These extinguishers are effective in extinguishing Class B and Class C fires. With CO_2 extinguishers, carbon dioxide is stored as a liquefied compressed gas and when discharged, changes into a gaseous form, displacing the oxygen and extinguishing the fire. As opposed to dry chemical extinguishers, carbon dioxide extinguishers have a large horn on

Figure 2.21 An example of a dry chemical fire extinguisher.

Figure 2.22 A CO_2 fire extinguisher.

the end of a discharge hose and are filled according to weight, so there is no gauge to indicate readiness **(Figure 2.22)**.

Clean agent products, such as halon, have long been used for the protection of sensitive electrical equipment, such as computers and delicate production machinery. These products, when used, produce toxic components and should always be used in well-ventilated areas. Halogenated products are no longer being produced because of their ozone-depleting potential. However, these extinguishers still exist, and other alternative products have replaced them. Some of these products include Halatron, FM-200, and Inergen **(Figure 2.23)**. (For more information consult NFPA® 2001, *Standard on Clean Agent Fire Extinguishing Systems.*)

The newest fire extinguishing agent is that contained in a Class K extinguisher. As previously indicated, the agent is a mixture of potassium acetate,

potassium citrate, or potassium carbonate in water. When discharged, the agent creates a soapy foam mixture that provides faster and safer extinguishment of fires involving commercial kitchen fires.

Other, less common extinguishing agents include:

- Pressurized water extinguishers which contain water or Class A foam mixed with water. These extinguishers are designed for Class A fires only. Water extinguishers may be mixed with AFFF for use on Class B fires.

- Dry powder extinguishers are designed for Class D fires. These are special extinguishing agents that have been designed and developed for the extinguishment of burning metals.

Figure 2.23 An example of a clean agent fire extinguisher. *Courtesy of Ansul Corporation.*

Using the Handheld Extinguisher

The fire and life safety educator may be called upon to provide information on the proper use of handheld extinguishers, both in work and residential environments. The mnemonic "PASS" has been used as a universal method for fire extinguisher use.

- **P** — Pull the pin, which is the locking mechanism for the extinguisher.
- **A** — Aim the nozzle low at the base of the fire, standing approximately 4-6 feet (1.2 m to 1.8 m) away.
- **S** — Squeeze the handle to allow the agent to be released.
- **S** — Sweep the nozzle from side to side, covering the entire fire area with the extinguishing agent **(Figure 2.24)**.

Fire extinguishers must be properly serviced and maintained. While anyone can inspect an extinguisher, those providing service and maintenance must be properly trained and certified. Inspections may include the following:

- Making sure the extinguisher is in its proper location
- Ensuring that access is not obstructed
- Checking the tag to determine if maintenance is up-to-date
- Examining the horn or nozzle for obstructions
- Making sure that locks and tamper seals are intact

Service will be needed based upon local code requirements. Some extinguishers need to be emptied, cleaned, checked, and refilled periodically. In addition, some cylinders must be periodically hydrostatically tested.

Probably the most important information that the Level I educator can convey to an audience is the following:

- When to use the extinguisher
- How to use the extinguisher
- When *not* to use the extinguisher

Figure 2.24 The PASS system helps personnel operate a fire extinguisher properly and safely.

Fire extinguishers are designed for use in the early stages of fire development. A fire that is confined to a trash can, small area, or to one item will be easily extinguished with a handheld unit. Of course, the individual using the extinguisher must know the proper operation of the extinguisher and be able to evacuate the area quickly if the use of the extinguisher is unsuccessful.

If the fire is spreading quickly or if there are evacuation issues (mobility impairment, small children in the area, large travel area to exit), then the fire extinguisher should not be used. Many individuals do not understand the limitations of handheld extinguishers, and it is the responsibility of the fire and life safety educator to convey this information.

Other Fire Protection Systems and Devices

While it is impossible to list and describe all the different types of fire protection systems in this chapter, there are others that are worth mentioning for the Level I educator. Automatic detection and alarm systems will be found in businesses and commercial occupancies. In addition to smoke detection technology, these systems may have heat detectors, gas-sensing detectors, and flame detectors. Some of this same technology may be found in residences as well.

Heat detectors will send a signal to the alarm system when there is an increase in the temperature in an area, based upon the particular unit and system settings. Heat detectors activate late in a fire's development and should not be used in a residential setting to alarm residents of a fire or smoke in the home. Level I educators need to be able to explain to the public the difference in technology and the importance of smoke alarms in the residential setting **(Figure 2.25)**.

Gas-sensing detectors respond to changes in the environment. The most common is the carbon monoxide (CO) detector. CO is an odorless, colorless gas that displaces the oxygen in the blood. In the home, carbon monoxide is most commonly found when heating and cooking, or when other appliances are served by natural or propane gas. Vehicles running in garages or improperly vented fireplaces can also be the source of CO in the home. CO alarms will activate when the CO levels build up in the home. The fire and life safety educator must be able to explain the differences in smoke alarm technology and CO alarm technology. CO alarms are certainly not a replacement for a smoke alarm. Today, units can be purchased that are dual alarms; that is, they contain both smoke detection chambers and CO detection.

Evacuation systems are those that allow people to escape during a fire or other emergency. These systems include exit lighting and signage, fire escapes, panic hardware, fire stairs, and doors **(Figure 2.26)**.

Figure 2.26 An exit hallway with an emergency exit light and a door equipped with panic hardware.

Figure 2.25 A fire and life safety educator explaining the operation of a heat detector.

The Level I educator must convey the importance of these systems and stress the need for unobstructed and easily identified exits. More importantly, there must be an emphasis on rapid and quick evacuation when the alarm sounds, which results through proper practice of fire drills.

Fire Hazards

A **fire hazard** is a condition that encourages a fire to start or increases the extent or severity of a fire. The following text discusses the types of fire hazards:

- **Common fire hazards** — Those that are prevalent in almost all occupancies and encourage a fire to start **(Figure 2.27)**.

- **Personal fire hazards** — Common hazards that are caused by the unsafe acts of individuals. Personal fire hazards are a result of attitudes and behaviors that the Level I educator must seek to change.

- **Special fire hazards** — Those that arise from, or are related to, the particular process or operation in an occupancy. Commercial and manufacturing occupancies present special hazard situations depending on the contents, use of flammable liquids, high-piled storage of materials, and processes using volatile substances **(Figure 2.28)**. In addition, public assembly occupancies present special hazards due to the number of people present, insufficient or blocked exits, storage of materials in paths of egress, or interior furnishings.

- **Target hazards** — Properties where there is a great potential for loss of life or property loss if a fire erupts. Occupancies such as these include lumberyards, shopping centers, hospitals, theaters, nursing homes, and schools, to name a few **(Figure 2.29)**.

Many times facilities or buildings may be labeled with hazard warning signs, and the fire and life safety educator may need to interpret these for the general public. NFPA® 704, *Standard System for the Identification of the Hazards of Materials for*

Figure 2.28 High-rack storage of materials is a type of special fire hazard.

Figure 2.27 Excessive trash buildup is a common fire hazard.

Figure 2.29 A hospital is an example of a target fire hazard.

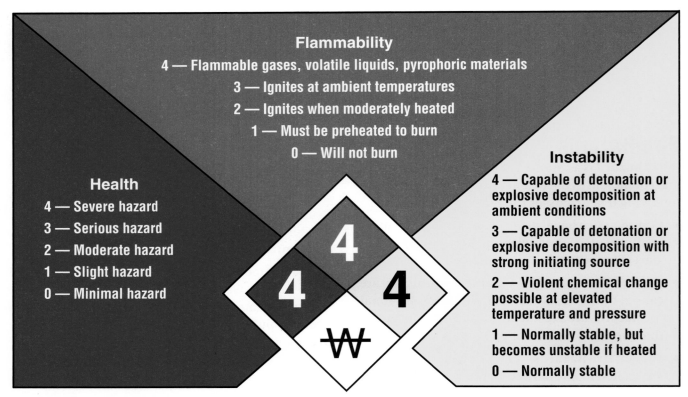

Flammability
4 — Flammable gases, volatile liquids, pyrophoric materials
3 — Ignites at ambient temperatures
2 — Ignites when moderately heated
1 — Must be preheated to burn
0 — Will not burn

Health
4 — Severe hazard
3 — Serious hazard
2 — Moderate hazard
1 — Slight hazard
0 — Minimal hazard

Instability
4 — Capable of detonation or explosive decomposition at ambient conditions
3 — Capable of detonation or explosive decomposition with strong initiating source
2 — Violent chemical change possible at elevated temperature and pressure
1 — Normally stable, but becomes unstable if heated
0 — Normally stable

Figure 2.30 Key to the NFPA® 704 numerical ratings.

Emergency Response, is the basis for markings on the buildings, but it does not include the marking or placarding of vehicles.

The NFPA® 704 label identifies three kinds of hazards: health, flammability, and instability. Each category is numbered 0 to 4, indicating the severity of the hazard classification **(Figure 2.30)**. The higher the number, the more severe the hazard. The hazard classifications are noted in a diamond-shaped marker or sign, divided into four sections:

- The blue section indicates the health rating.
- The red section indicates the flammability rating.
- The yellow section indicates the instability rating.
- The white section contains information about special considerations, such as "no water" or "radioactive."

Dynamics of Human Behavior

Human behavior is at the root of almost all fires, injuries, and deaths. This behavior is the result of an individual's attitude and the information that he or she brings to aid in the decision-making process. It is the fire and life safety educator's job to provide the appropriate information so that attitudes can be changed and decisions made based on fact instead of myth.

The study of human behavior in fires, while dating back to the early 1900s, was most productive in the United States and the United Kingdom in the 1970s to mid-1980s. Much information has since been gained by interviews with fire personnel at the time of the fire. The study of the actions of individuals involved with fire should affect the educational process employed by fire and life safety educators.

The fire and life safety educator carries a serious responsibility to provide sufficient education and instruction so that individuals will make the proper decisions during each phase of the emergency. From recognition of the threat to the commitment and reassessment phases, an individual's training and education will affect the decision-making process. The Level I educator's role is to provide accurate, informative, and crucial instruction so that the proper decision will be made in an emergency.

Certain factors may affect a person's decision-making process during a residential fire. The fire and life safety educator should be aware of these factors and discover ways to overcome these barriers:

- Past experience with fire will cause an individual to make certain assumptions and expectations about the fire that may not always hold true.

- A lack of information or perhaps erroneous information will lengthen the decision-making process. With effective education, cues and decisions can be made in advance.

- Culture may influence role expectations, such as male versus female, and parent versus child. Culture may also influence the perception of the seriousness of the fire.

- Physical environment of the residence, including the size, familiarity, and layout may influence the cues and behaviors of the occupants.

- An individual's physical condition will influence the decision-making process. As well, those individuals with physical challenges or impairments may have limited options.

- Distractions may influence those in the building or residence. For example, if there are small children in the house, this may distract the parent or caregiver from making the proper decision.

Research is currently underway to determine how humans respond when confronted with fire situations. Existing research[3] has identified the following behaviors that are common in residential fires:

- Notifying others that the house is on fire.

- Searching for the fire in the residence.

- Calling the fire department from inside the home.

- Getting dressed.

- Leaving the house.

- Getting the family together and preparing to leave together.

- Fighting the fire.

- Leaving the area of the fire and retreating to another part of the structure.

Do People Really Panic?

When examining the behavior of individuals involved in a fire, the assumption is always made that these individuals panic and that panic leads to bad choices. The media and movie industry tend to show that fire and panic are closely related. Research shows that, in fact, the opposite is true.

In early studies, *panic* was defined as a sudden and excessive feeling of alarm or fear that leads to extravagant and injudicious efforts to secure safety. More recent studies define panic as a behavior that is fear-induced, that is nonrational, nonadaptive, and nonsocial, leading to reduced possibilities for a group to escape. Studies on human behavior during fires have found that irrational or illogical response was not present, and individuals were quick to help others, often at great personal risk.

During a fire, individuals will develop a feeling of stress. The intensity of this stress is dependent on information available and the success of decisions already chosen. In fact, people are often lethargic in response to a fire alarm, ignoring or delaying their response to the initial cues of an emergency. While an individual receiving ambiguous and incomplete cues about a fire will experience an increase in the level of stress, panic in the form of irrational behavior is rare during fires.

This increased level of stress during an incident's development is not abnormal or negative; in fact, it is often what spurs an individual to action. Decision-making during stress can lead to a narrowing of attention and a reduced number of options. Therefore, an evacuation plan that has been well-rehearsed and practiced is easier to apply.

Fire and life safety educators must remember that strategies or behaviors chosen in fire situations that are unsuccessful are not necessarily irrational or illogical to the individual involved. Individuals who do not have sufficient information about the proper actions to take will make choices based upon the information they have. It is the job of the fire and life safety educator to make sure that individuals involved in a fire have all information they need to make the proper choices before they are confronted with this emergency.

Source: Proulx, G. *Cool Under Fire*. Fire Protection Engineering, October 28, 2002;

Keating, P.J. "The Myth of Panic," Fire Journal, May, pp. 57-61.

- Doing nothing.
- Having someone else call the fire department.
- Gathering personal property.

In one study, only 28% of Americans said that their first action would be to leave a burning building. Another concern is that over half of those surveyed who were 65 years of age or older (who are statistically a high-risk group) would first call the fire department when confronted with a fire situation.

In looking at this research, it is apparent that proper and effective fire and life safety education can make a huge difference in the decisions made during fire emergencies. It is the Level I educator's job to provide proper information and education that will positively affect the decision-making process, both in preventing a fire and in reacting to its occurrence.

Unintentional Injuries[4]

Community-risk reduction is an all-encompassing term for the many educational and prevention services provided by a fire agency. A fire and life safety educator delivers information related to fire as well as injuries. Some agencies may be involved in disaster preparedness and safety. Fire agencies have the responsibility and obligation to prevent any type of emergency to which they might respond, or at least to mitigate the damages that might be incurred. Many fire departments serve as either the EMS provider for their community or have taken on the responsibility as a first responder for medical and injury emergencies. It is the Level I educator's responsibility and obligation to provide information on more than fire-related issues, such as overall community safety and the prevention of unintentional injuries.

Unintentional injuries have been a leading cause of death for individuals in the United States for decades. According to the Centers for Disease Control and Prevention (CDC), unintentional injuries are the leading cause of death for persons between the ages of 1 and 44. More than 400 people die of injuries every day in the United States, with at least 58 of those being children. More children die or are seriously hurt from injuries than from all childhood diseases combined. The majority of those injury-related deaths are a result of motor vehicle crashes.

Permanent Disabilities

Unintentional injuries that result in permanent disabilities are also a significant problem. In 2004, approximately 29.6 million people were treated for an injury at a hospital's emergency department, of which 2 million were severe enough to require hospitalization. Approximately 50,000 children experience unintentional injuries annually that result in a permanent disability. Approximately 10,000 of those are disabled due to a traumatic brain injury. Young children experience the greatest impact from these severe injuries in that they will require years, or even a lifetime, of medical care or rehabilitation. This creates a tremendous social and financial burden for families, communities, and society as a whole. The savings from preventing injury, as compared to treating it, are dramatic **(Table 2.3)**.

Table 2.3 Annual Approximation of People Receiving Permanent Disabilities	
Population	**Approximate Number**
Treated at Hospital Emergency Rooms	29.6 million
Requiring Hospitalization	2.0 million
Children With Unintentional Injuries	50,000
Children Disabled Due to Traumatic Brain Injuries	10,000

Based on 2004 statistics.

Older Adults

While children are usually the main focus of unintentional injury information and prevention, older adults are also at a high risk for injury issues. Falls are the leading cause of injury-related death for Americans 65 years and older. Each year, about 35 to 40% of adults 65 and older fall at least once. Many of the falls result in hip fractures, which can lead to nursing home care or even death. Nearly half of those older adults who survive a hip fracture never regain full mobility.

Another problem for older adults is motor vehicle crash injuries. Age-related decreases in vision, cognitive functions, and physical impairments may affect the driving ability of some older adults, which contributes to a greater risk for death and injuries resulting from motor vehicle crashes.

Unintentional Injuries Versus Accidents

Unintentional injuries are not simply "accidents." The term *accident* indicates that these events are unexpected and could not have been anticipated or prevented.[5] In almost all situations, the opposite is quite true. Unintentional injuries are describable, predictable, and preventable occurrences. Unintentional injuries are definable and correctable events that result from carelessness, lack of knowledge, or both.

Intentional and Unintentional Injuries

An *injury* is described as physical damage to an individual produced by the transfer of energy, such as kinetic, thermal, chemical, electrical, or radiant energy. Injuries can also result from the absence of essentials, such as oxygen and heat. Injuries can be blunt or penetrating, intentional or unintentional. The term *mechanism of injury* refers to the method or manner in which the injury occurs, or main source of the injury.

Injury Triangle/Haddon's Matrix

Dr. William Haddon, an engineer and physician who was a pioneer in injury research, designed a tool using the injury triangle that looks at injuries and their prevention. The variables for the injury triad include the three legs of the injury triangle, which Dr. Haddon refers to as the host (human), agent (vehicle), and environment **(Figure 2.31)**:

- The *host* refers to the person suffering the injury.
- The *agent* represents the thing or person (the vehicle) that carries the energy to cause the injury.
- The *environment* is the overall setting or context in which the injury takes place.

The interaction of these three variables allows the injury to occur. As with the fire triangle, by looking at each component separately, researchers can identify a pattern of injury and thus provide input into the overall prevention of injuries.

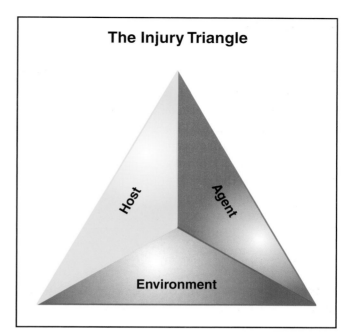

Figure 2.31 Dr. Haddon's Injury Triangle.

Injury prevention is about reducing the incidence and severity of injuries. It is about reducing the likelihood of being hurt, the number of people who are hurt, and the seriousness of the injury received. Injury prevention can occur at any one of the phases of prevention — primary, secondary, or tertiary prevention. **Primary prevention** works to stop an injury from occurring, while **secondary prevention** works to reduce the seriousness of an injury when and if it does occur. Tertiary prevention works to reduce the disability immediately after an injury has occurred by providing adequate medical treatment and appropriate rehabilitation.[6]

Haddon's Matrix uses the three variables of the injury triangle and cross-references these with three phases, or parts, of an injury event. These phases are pre-event, event, post-event:

- Pre-event factors can create or prevent the potential for injury. Pre-event factors can lead to primary prevention measures.
- Event factors are those that occur at the moment of mishap that increase or decrease the potential for injury. The discovery of these factors leads to secondary prevention measures.
- Post-event factors are those factors or conditions that influence the result of the injury and can lead to work to discover areas for tertiary prevention.

The environmental factors can be broken down into two categories: physical and sociocultural.

Examining these phases and factors together results in the matrix found in **Table 2.4**. By using this matrix, it is possible to determine feasible prevention interventions that include the Five Es of Prevention (discussed in Chapter 1). It is from the examination of the risk factors in conjunction with the phases of the injury event that appropriate and practical prevention measures can be developed.

Haddon's Matrix can be a difficult concept to grasp, but it is a valuable tool for injury prevention specialists. It is commonly used in the public health arena for disease prevention and is very applicable to the work of injury prevention **(Table 2.5)**.

Occurrence and Nature of Injuries

The occurrence of the injury and the nature of the injury are often a product of a variety of factors, including age, gender, socioeconomic status, and drug or alcohol use. The specific types of injuries may be based upon geographic location, on the demographics of the population involved, and the culture of the members of the community.

Older adults and young children experience higher rates of home injury or death than the general population. Factors relevant to their specific stages of development make them vulnerable for unintentional injuries. Children become injured while exploring their environment, which is a normal behavior because they lack the judgment to avoid dangers and risks. Older adults experience more injuries due to a deterioration of balance and mobility. For older adults, rehabilitation poses its own difficulties.

Table 2.4
Haddon's Basic Matrix

	Human/Host	Agent/Vehicle	Physical Environment	Sociocultural Environment
Pre-Event				
Event				
Post Event				

Table 2.5
Example of Haddon's Matrix - (COMPLETED)

	Human/Host	Agent/Vehicle	Physical Environment	Sociocultural Environment
Pre-Event	Driver ability, Driver training	Maintenance, brakes, installation of child restraint, restraint inspection programs	Roadway condition, signage, correct installation of child seat, right seat for the child	Attitude toward speeding, alcohol and driving and use of restraint for every trip
Event	Human tolerance to crash forces, correct use of child restraint seat	Crash worthiness of vehicle (e.g. crush space), worthiness of restraint; airbag deployment	Presence of fixed objects near roadway, unsecured objects within the vehicle	Enforcement of mandatory seat belt and child restraint use
Post Event	General health of crash victims	Reduced possibility of post crash fire	Availability of timely emergency response	Public support for trauma care and rehabilitation

Source: Queensland Health, 2008

While there are a variety of ways that injuries can occur, the most common causes of unintentional injuries can be categorized as follows:

- Motor vehicle crashes (including motorized sporting equipment such as scooters and four-wheelers)
- Falls
- Poisonings
- Bicycle and other wheel-related sports (including bikes, skateboards, roller blades, and other nonmotorized sporting equipment with wheels)
- Fires and burns
- Drownings

The following information will provide the reader with a foundation of information on the most common injury issues experienced by communities. This information is basic and meant to provide a background of knowledge for the Level I educator. In most communities, there are agencies and organizations that specialize in a particular injury area, or areas. As will be discussed in Chapter 4, the Level I educator must seek out these organizations for expertise and partner with them to promote viable and workable injury prevention strategies and techniques.

Motor Vehicle Crashes

Motor vehicle crashes are the leading cause of death for people from age 1 until about age 44. In 2005, over 43,000 people were killed in traffic-related crashes. Approximately 119 people die daily: one death every 12 minutes. According to Safe Kids Worldwide, 1,800 children are killed in motor vehicle crashes annually and another 280,000 are injured.

Child Occupant Protection

According to the National Highway Traffic Safety Administration (NHTSA), in the year 2005, all 50 states and the District of Columbia had child occupant protection laws, as well as safety belt laws. These laws vary widely in age requirements, exemptions, enforcement procedures, and penalties. Usage rates vary from state to state and depend upon public attitude, enforcement practices, legal provisions, and public education programs.

The use of child restraint seats has greatly decreased the number of traffic-related injuries and fatalities for younger children. However, traffic crashes still remain the number one cause of unintentional injuries and death for children age 14 and under. In 2000, Safe Kids Worldwide found that 56% of children ages 14 and under who were fatally injured in a crash were completely unrestrained. A study conducted by the Safe Kids Worldwide program in 2002 found that 14% of children age 14 and under were riding completely unrestrained.

Older children are more likely to be unrestrained than younger children. In the same study, it was found that 33% of the children were using the wrong restraint based upon their age and size. Older children are more likely to be in the wrong restraint than

younger children, with older children using the vehicle's seat belt when a belt-positioning booster would be more appropriate. It is a proven fact that caregivers who fail to protect children who are riding in a vehicle are putting them at great risk for injury in a crash.

Fire and life safety educators should become informed on the various types of child safety seats and the proper use of them. At the time of this publication, Safe Kids Worldwide, in conjunction with the NHTSA, oversees a national training class that covers an in-depth study on child safety seats, the proper seat for each age child, and the proper installation methods for seats (Table 2.6, p. 58). In addition, Level I educators need to know about the laws in their state that relate to the use of child safety seats in vehicles.

Alcohol-Related Motor Vehicle Crashes[7]

Another area of concern regarding motor vehicle crashes is driving while under the influence of drugs and alcohol. Many fire and EMS departments work with local law enforcement agencies in presenting staged crash reenactments for high school students. These demonstrations show the dramatic affects that driving while intoxicated can have. For current reports and statistics regarding alcohol-related motor vehicle crashes, visit the National Highway Traffic Safety Administration's Web site at www.nhtsa.gov/

Falls

Falls are the leading cause of nonfatal injury among all age groups. Older adults and young children are most susceptible to fall injuries.[8] Falls account for an average of 5.1 million injuries and nearly 6,000 deaths each year. More than half of the deaths caused by unintentional falls occur in the home.

Death rates associated with falls increase with age. The older an individual, the more likely it is that an unintentional fall will lead to death. Falls can occur by falling on or off steps, slipping, tripping, or stumbling in the home. Falls may also occur when working on ladders or outside the home.

For children, falls in the home can result from climbing on furniture, using baby walkers, and attempting to go up or down stairs. Fall injuries

Table 2.6
General Child Seat Use Information
Buckle Everyone. Children Age 12 and Under in Back!

	Age/Weight	Seat Type/Seat Position	Usage Tips
Infants	Birth to at least 1 year **and** at least 20 pounds.	Infant-Only Seat/rear-facing or Convertible Seat/used rear-facing. ***Seats should be secured to the vehicle by the safety belts or by the LATCH system.***	• Never use in a front seat where an air bag is present. • Tightly install child seat in rear seat, facing the rear. • Child seat should recline at approximately a 45 degree angle. • Harness straps/slots at or below shoulder level (lower set of slots for most convertible child safety seats). • Harness straps snug on child; harness clip at armpit level.
	Less than 1 year/ 20-35 lbs.	Convertible Seat/used rear-facing (select one recommended for heavier infants). ***Seats should be secured to the vehicle by the safety belts or by the LATCH system.***	• Never use in a front seat where an air bag is present. • Tightly install child seat in rear seat, facing the rear. • Child seat should recline at approximately a 45 degree angle. • Harness straps/slots at or below shoulder level (lower set of slots for most convertible child safety seats). • Harness straps snug on child; harness clip at armpit level.
Preschoolers/ Toddler	1 to 4 years/ at least 20 lbs. to approximately 40 lbs.	Convertible Seat/forward-facing **or** Forward-Facing Only **or** High Back Booster/Harness. ***Seats should be secured to the vehicle by the safety belts or by the LATCH system.***	• Tightly install child seat in rear seat, facing forward. • Harness straps/slots at or above child's shoulders (usually top set of slots for convertible child safety seats). • Harness straps snug on child; harness clip at armpit level.
Young Children	4 to at least 8 years/unless they are 4'9" (57") tall	Belt-Positioning Booster (no back, only) or High Back Belt-Positioning Booster. ***NEVER use with lap-only belts—belt-positioning boosters are always used with lap AND shoulder belts.***	• Booster used with adult lap and shoulder belt in rear seat. • Shoulder belt should rest snugly across chest, rests on shoulder; and should NEVER be placed under the arm or behind the back. • Lap-belt should rest low, across the lap/upper thigh area—not across the stomach.

Source: *National Highway Traffic Safety Administration*

affecting children occur on playground equipment, including both public and residential playgrounds. For children, especially those from ages 1 to 4, falls result from natural curiosity and learning experiences.

Injuries resulting from falls include bruises, fractures, and head trauma. For older adults, falls are the most common cause of traumatic brain injuries. For many fire departments and EMS agencies, responding to incidents of falls is a large percentage of their emergency and nonemergency responses. Even if older adults are not injured in the fall, they may still need assistance in getting back on their feet or into their beds.

For fall prevention among children, interventions include the use of safety devices, such as safety gates on stairs, moving furniture away from windows, and removing baby walkers from the home. On playgrounds, all children should be properly supervised and use age-appropriate equipment. Maintenance of playground equipment is an important preventive factor as well.

Prevention measures among older adults include the installation of grab bars in bathrooms, proper lighting in hallways and stairwells, use of nonslip rugs and mats throughout the house, and the use of a step stool with a grab-bar for reaching. In addition, older adults should be encouraged to maintain a regular exercise program and see their health care providers (include an eye doctor) regularly.

Poisonings

It is estimated that 4 million poisonings occur every year in the United States. At least 75% of those receive some type of medical treatment. The remaining 25% are handled through the poison centers. In 2005, 32,691 people died as a result of poisoning. Approximately 72% of those deaths were caused by unintentional poisonings.

A poison is any substance that is harmful when ingested, inhaled, or absorbed through the skin. Effects of a single exposure may be immediate or delayed, and some poisons work in small doses while others require repeated exposure to cause harm. The majority of poisonings (78.4% in 2007) occur as a result of ingestion of a poisonous substance. Other poisonings are caused by insect stings, environmental exposure, and inhalation.

The majority of all poisonings are unintentional. That is, the person taking or giving a substance does not mean to cause harm. According to the National Poison Data System,[9] in the year 2007, 83.2% of all poisonings were unintentional. Unintentional poisonings include the use of drugs or chemicals taken for recreational purposes or the excessive use or exposure to drugs or chemicals for non-recreational purposes.

NOTE: Almost 20% of all poisonings in the United States were intentional, meaning that the individual taking or giving the substance intended to cause harm through suicide or assault by poisoning.

Unintentional poisonings are second only to motor vehicle crashes as a cause of death due to intentional injury. Drugs are the main cause of unintentional poisoning deaths, and pain medications are the most common poison. According to the CDC[10] children are most affected by unintentional poisonings from prescription or over-the-counter medications. Other typical poisons include cosmetics, personal care products, and cleaning substances.

While children younger than six are involved in more than 50% of the poisonings reports, they account for just 2% of the fatalities. Those most at risk of poisoning deaths include adults and older adults. Seventy percent of all poison fatalities occur in adults age 20 to 59. In addition, while adults age 60 and over account for just 5% of all poison exposures, they account for over 16% of all poison fatalities.

Childhood poisoning deaths are lower due to protective factors such as the use of child-resistant packaging, a decrease in the use of aspirin for fever, and an increase in poison education. The introduction of a nationwide, toll-free poison center number has also increased access to certified poison control centers.

Fire and life safety educators may obtain poison prevention educational curriculum from one of the 61 certified poison control centers in the United States. Prevention programs advocate taking such measures as the following:

- Turning on lights when administering medications
- Reading the labels
- Keeping products in their original containers
- Posting the number to the poison center near the telephone

The Most Common Poisons Among Children

- Cosmetics and personal care products
- Cleaning substances
- Pain medicine/fever-reducers
- Coins, thermometers
- Plants
- Cough and cold preparations
- Art, craft, and office supplies
- Vitamins
- Antimicrobials

The Most Common Poisons Among Adults

- Pain medicines
- Sedatives, antipsychotics
- Cleaning substances
- Antidepressants
- Alcohols
- Chemicals
- Pesticides
- Cardiovascular drugs
- Fumes, gases, vapors
- Stimulants and street drugs

Source: "Quick Facts on Poison Exposure in the United States." American Association of Poison Control Centers, 2008.

Poison Control Center Enhancement and Awareness Act

In February 2000, Congress passed the Poison Control Center Enhancement and Awareness Act (Public Law 106-174). As a result of this law, funding was provided for a nationwide toll-free number. The toll-free number, **1-800-222-1222**, is operated by the American Association of Poison Control Centers through a Cooperative Agreement with the Centers for Disease Control and Prevention (CDC) and Health Resources and Services Administration (HRSA).

- Keeping drugs and other medications in medicine cabinets and out of the reach of children
- Returning household products to a secure storage area immediately after use

These are but a few of the recommended measures for the prevention of unintentional poisonings. Level I educators should consult their area's poison center for more information.

Bicycle and Other Wheel-Related Sports Injuries

While the information in this category is generally referring to the use of bicycles, it also includes equipment such as wheeled nonmotorized vehicles, tricycles, and unicycles powered solely by pedals. The NHTSA[11] uses the term *pedal cyclists* to identify individuals in this category. In this section, information using the term *bike* or *bicycle* can apply to the use of all wheeled sports equipment.

In 2006, there were 773 deaths attributed to bicycles. This accounts for 2% of all traffic fatalities during the year. Pedal cyclists accounted for 13% of all nonmotorist traffic fatalities. There were 44,000 injuries related to the use of wheeled or pedaled equipment. The average age of pedal cyclists killed in traffic crashes was 41 years old. To contrast, in 1996 the average age of those injured was 23. Pedal cyclist fatalities occur more frequently in urban areas, at nonintersection locations, between the hours of 5:00 and 9:00 p.m., during the months of June, July, and August.

According to Safe Kids Worldwide, more than 70% of children ages 5 to 14 ride bicycles. This age group rides 50% more than the average pedal cyclists and accounts for 14% of all pedal cyclists killed in traffic crashes and nearly half of all bicycle-related injuries.[12] Children ages four and under are more likely than older children to be injured in nonstreet locations, such as a driveway, garage, or yard.

Head injury is the leading cause of death in bicycle crashes. Approximately 70% of all fatal bicycle crashes involve head injuries. Nearly half of the children age 14 and under who were hospitalized for bike-related injuries were diagnosed with a traumatic brain injury (TBI).[13] Older children are more likely to experience a TBI than younger children. A TBI can have a serious long-term effect on the quality of life for these children and their families and communities.

The most common safety device for preventing traumatic brain injury among pedal cyclists is a helmet (**Figure 2.32**).[14] Bicycle helmets are 85-88% effective in lessening the seriousness of head and brain injuries, or preventing them altogether. Proper use of a bike helmet is the single most effective way of reducing head injuries and fatalities resulting from bicycle crashes.

Despite this fact, only about 20-25% of all bicyclists wear helmets. It has been cited that universal bicycle helmet use by children ages 4 to 14 would seriously decrease the number of head, scalp, and facial injuries that occur annually. Surveys show that helmet use is lowest among children ages 11 to 14. Children give the following reasons for not wearing helmets every time they ride:

- Helmets are uncomfortable.
- They do not feel "cool" wearing a helmet.
- Parents do not require their children to wear them.

Correct fit and proper positioning of a bike helmet are essential to its effectiveness. Helmets that fit poorly or are worn tipped back on the head do little to protect against head injury in a crash.

The enactment of laws requiring the use of bicycle helmets is the most effective way to increase bicycle helmet use. As of 2006, twenty-one states and the District of Columbia, as well as numerous municipalities, had enacted age-specific bicycle laws. Most of these laws cover cyclists under the age of 16. At the time of this publication, fourteen states have no state or local helmet laws.

Design and Proper Fit for a Bike Helmet

The U.S. Consumer Product Safety Commission has developed safety standards for bicycle helmets, and only helmets that meet those standards should be used. A properly designed helmet has the following design elements:

- Stiff outer shell designed to distribute impact forces and protect against sharp objects
- Energy-absorbing liner
- Chin strap and fastener to keep the helmet in place
- Lightweight, cool, and fits comfortably

The helmet should sit on top of the head in a level position, and it should not rock forward and backward or side to side. The helmet should fit snug on the head, but not so tightly that it is uncomfortable. The helmet straps must always be buckled but not too tightly.

Source: Safe Kids Worldwide

In addition to the use of bicycle helmets, pedal cyclists need to learn the rules of the road and obey the traffic laws. Many cycle-related fatalities are associated with:

- Riding onto a street without stopping
- Turning left
- Swerving into traffic that is coming from behind
- Running a stop sign
- Riding against the flow of traffic

Most of the information presented refers to the use of bicycles. As indicated, it applies to those individuals that use any type of "wheeled sport" equipment. This includes skateboards, Rollerblades, scooters, and the variety of recreational equipment that is available. The effect is the same whether the fall is from a bicycle or a skateboard — both can result in a traumatic brain injury, which can lead to paralysis or death, or other serious injury. Level I educators need to become familiar with the helmet laws that govern their community and partner with agencies and organizations that work to prevent injury and death among pedal cyclists.

Figure 2.32 Bicycle helmets can prevent traumatic brain injury.

Drownings

In 2005, the CDC[15] lists that there were there were 3,582 fatal unintentional drownings in the United States. Drowning is the second leading cause of unintentional injury-related death to children ages 1 to 14. For each child that drowns, four more are hospitalized for near-drowning, and four are treated in hospital emergency rooms. Near-drownings can cause brain damage that results in long-term disabilities ranging from memory problems and learning disabilities to a permanent vegetative state.

When thinking of drowning, most people visualize swimming pools and lakes as the potential water hazards. However, standing water presents a serious hazard both inside and outside the home. Young children are especially vulnerable to drowning risk areas inside the home such as toilets, bathtubs, and five-gallon buckets.

Drowning is a Quick and Silent Killer

In the time is takes to:
- Cross the room for a towel (10 seconds), a child in a bathtub can become submerged.
- Answer the phone (2 minutes), that child can lose consciousness.
- Sign for a package at your front door (4 to 6 minutes), a child submerged in the bathtub or pool can sustain permanent brain damage.

Source: "Preventing Accidental Injury: Water." Safe Kids Worldwide

In a 2004 report that reviewed statistics relating to drowning, it was found that 39% of all drownings occurred in pools (14% residential, 7% community and 18% of known type, including those at hotels and clubs). Open bodies of water (such as lakes, rivers, and ponds) accounted for 37%, and 18% occurred in and around the home, in places such as bathtubs, buckets, and spas. Reviews determined that younger children (ages 4 and under) were most likely to drown in home settings (26%) and pools (44%), while drownings among children ages 5 to 14 occurred most often in open-water sites (51%).

Several risk factors contribute to the number of drownings each year. The first factor is a lack of supervision as well as a lack of barriers, such as pool fencing. A second factor that contributes to drowning incidents is recreational boating. Most individuals who drown in boating incidents are not wearing personal flotation devices. Almost half of the boating incidents involve open motor boats, and a quarter of the incidents involve personal watercraft.

A major factor in adult drowning is the use of alcohol. Alcohol use is involved in about 25 –50% of adolescent and adult drowning deaths. In addition, alcohol was reportedly involved in about one-third of all reported boating fatalities.

Personal Flotation Devices (PFD)

In pools and natural bodies of water, the use of personal floatation devices (PFD) greatly increases the chances of surviving a potential drowning incident. The United States Coast Guard has established standards for personal floatation devices, or life jackets. At this time, all states (with the exception of Hawaii) have laws that govern the wearing of personal floatation devices while boating. However, actual use statistics are very low, particularly among adults.

According to a 2005 study conducted by the United States Coast Guard, the overall use rate of personal floatation devices is 24%. From ages 0-5, the wear rate is 93%, but the use rate greatly decreases as individuals get older, leading to an adult use rate of 10%. Interestingly, wear rates are high for both adults and children when operating or using personal watercraft (jet skis).

A variety of PFDs are available, based upon the type of water and water activity being undertaken. PFDs are designed specifically for open seas, lakes, and pools, in addition to those for swimming, boating, and skiing. PFDs should be properly fitted to the individual who will be using the device. An ill-fitting PFD can be just as deadly as none at all. Parents should recognize the difference betweem PFDs and toys when it comes to life safety. Air-filled or foam toys, such as "swimmies," "noodles," rafts, or inner tubes are no replacement for PFDs.

Use of a PFD does not replace adult supervision as a measure for reducing the incidence of drowning. Designation of a responsible adult to watch young children swimming or playing around water is imperative. While supervising children in the water, adults should not be participating in any other activities such as reading, talking on the phone, texting, or mowing the lawn.

Fencing around pools is another important tool for drowning prevention. The pool area should be completely separated from the house and yard. Fencing should be at least four feet high and use self-closing and self-latching gates that open outward, and have latches that are out of a child's reach.[16]

Drowning Prevention Programs

Drowning prevention programs are needed even if there is not a large body of water or ocean near a community. Water safety issues are regionally or geographically based. Many individuals vacation at beaches or lakes, and educators can provide safety information before the vacation season. For some communities, it may be the local public pool that is the problem; for others, it is the large lake used for fishing or boating. There may even be small ponds, lakes, creeks, or rivers that are used for recreation or to simply cool off in the heat of the summer. In many areas of the country, private pools are common features for homes or condominiums. In others, the biggest drowning issue may be inside the home. There does not have to be a prominent body of water nearby for drowning to be an issue. All water sources present a drowning risk.

For the Level I educator, becoming familiar with the local water safety issues is important, and finding organizations or agencies to serve as partners in water safety programs is essential. Partnerships assist the educator in working to prevent the local drowning issues.

Burns

In the United States, approximately 2.4 million burn injuries are reported each year.[17] Health care publications, such as the *Journal of Burn Care & Rehabilitation*, report that approximately 500,000 of those injuries are severe enough to be treated by medical professionals, while 40,000 of those injured are hospitalized. Of those hospitalized, 20,000 have major burns involving at least 25% of their total body surface. Between 8,000 and 12,000 patients with burns die, and approximately one million will sustain substantial or permanent disabilities resulting from their burn injury.[18]

Burns are one of the most expensive, catastrophic injuries to treat. For example, a burn of 30% of total body area can cost as much as $200,000 in initial hospitalization costs and physicians fees. For extensive burns, there are additional significant costs that include charges for repeat admissions for reconstruction and rehabilitation.

The two groups most at risk are children from the ages of newborn to about 5 years old and older adults over the age of 65. In fact, in the youngest group, scald injuries are the leading cause of accidental death in the home. Serious injury is also possible from the least recognized sources: A child exposed to 140°F (60°C) water from a bathroom or kitchen faucet for three seconds can sustain a third degree burn.[19]

For older adults, the National Burn Information Exchange reports that after the age of 60, the risk of burn injury is greater than at any time since childhood. Sources of injury for older adults include hot liquid scalds, ignition of clothing, heaters, radiators, and trips and falls on hot pipes.

When the skin is exposed to excessive heat, electricity, or corrosive chemicals, the resulting tissue damage is referred to as a *burn*.

- Thermal burns are caused by radiation, flame contact, excessive heat from fire, steam, hot liquids, or hot objects.
- Chemical burns are caused by various acids, bases, and caustic chemicals.
- Electrical burns are caused by contact with alternating current, direct current, or lightning.
- Light or radiation burns are from ultraviolet lights (including direct sunlight), nuclear sources, or intense light sources.

Burns are categorized[20] according to the severity of tissue damage, as follows:

- **Superficial burns** or first-degree burns involve the outer layer of skin (epidermis). The skin may be red. It may also hurt when touched. A first-degree burn is most often a mild burn and will usually heal in a few days.

- **Partial-thickness burns** or second-degree burns are deeper and more severe. These burns extend to the layer of skin below the epidermis (called the dermis). The skin may be red, swollen, and blistered. There is much pain when the skin is touched.

- **Full-thickness burns** or third-degree burns are the deepest. Full-thickness burns damage all layers of skin and may also damage muscles, bones, and tendons. The skin is tough or leathery, and the burn site appears pale and charred. It may look white, brown, black, or red. There may be no sensation in the area because the nerve endings are destroyed. These burns will not heal without medical care and will require surgical skin grafts.

Calculating the Amount of Skin Burned

Overall, burn severity is a measurement of the depth and the size of the burn. The seriousness of a burn injury depends on how deep the injury is and how much of the body has been burned. Different systems have been developed to estimate the percentage of total body surface area (TBSA) that has been burned.

Rule of Nines. One of the more common systems is known as the Rule of Nines. To approximate the percentage of burned surface area, the body has been divided into eleven sections: Head, right arm, left arm, chest, abdomen, upper back, lower back, right thigh, left thigh, right leg (below the knee), left leg (below the knee). Each of these sections takes about nine percent of the body's skin to cover it; thus, this is referred to as the Rule of Nines **(Figure 2.33)**. Added together, these sections account for 99 percent. The genitals make up the last one percent.

To apply the Rule of Nines. Add up all the areas of the body that are burned deep enough to cause blisters or worse (second- or third-degree burns). For example, the entire left arm and the chest covered in blisters would be 18 percent. Partial areas are approximated. For example, the face is only the front half of the head and would be considered 4.5 percent. The most important thing to remember about the Rule of Nines is that it is used in the field to quickly determine if victims need to go to a specialty burn center. Once the victim is in a burn center, more advanced techniques will be used to determine the exact surface area that has suffered burns.

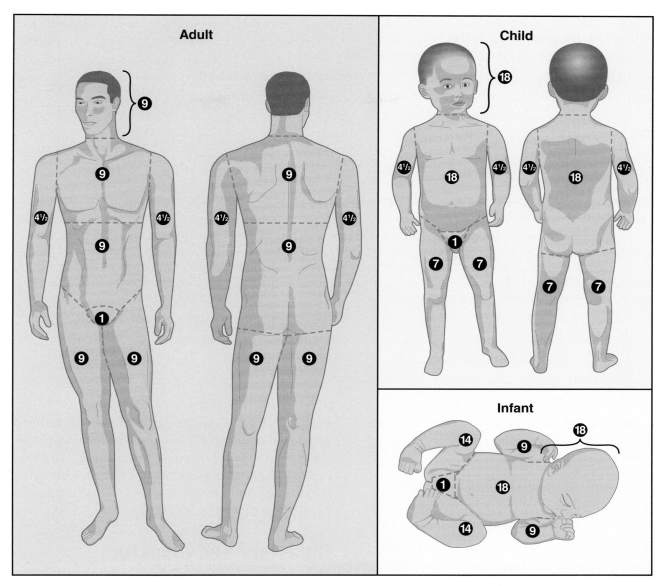

Figure 2.33 The Rule of Nines.

Location of the Burn

Burn location can be just as important as depth and extent of the burn. Certain burns, because of their size, location, or effect on the victim, are considered critical and require immediate medical attention. Critical burns include the following:

- Burns of any kind on the head, neck, hands, feet, or genitals
- Burns caused by fire, chemicals, explosion, or electricity
- Partial- or full-thickness burns covering more than 10% of the victim's body
- Burns on a child or older adult

Burn Care for Thermal, Chemical, and Electrical Burns

The first step in caring for burns is to stop the burning process.

Use the following steps to care for a thermal burn:

- Wet down or smother the burning areas if clothing is involved with fire.
- Cool burns with running water for about five minutes.
- Cover the area with a dry dressing and seek medical attention if warranted.
- Do not use cold water or pack the areas with ice. This can cause hypothermia and shock.

Burn Center Referral Criteria

Burn injuries that should be referred to a burn center include the following:

- Partial-thickness burns of greater than 10% of the total body surface area.
- Burns that involve the face, hands, feet, genitalia, perineum, or major joints.
- Third-degree burns in any age group.
- Electrical burns, including lightning injury.
- Chemical burns.
- Inhalation injury.
- Burn injury in patients with pre-existing medical disorders that could complicate management, prolong recovery, or affect mortality.
- Any patients with burns and concomitant trauma (such as fractures) in which the burn injury poses the greatest risk of morbidity or mortality. In such cases, if the trauma poses the greater immediate risk, the patient's condition may be stabilized initially in a trauma center before transfer to a burn center. Physician judgment will be necessary in such situations and should be in concert with the regional medical control plan and triage protocols.
- Burned children in hospitals without qualified personnel or equipment for the care of children.
- Burn injury in patients who will require special social, emotional, or rehabilitative intervention.

Source: American Burn Association

Use the following steps to care for a chemical burn:

- Use running water to wash away the chemical and irrigate the effected region.
- Remove contaminated clothing and jewelry.
- Brush away as much of the chemical as possible in the case of a dry chemical.
- Continuously apply flowing water to the area.
- Deliver or request medical attention for the injured individual.

Electrical burns require special care and treatment. Before providing care or assistance, it is important to determine if the power source has been disconnected. Once the source of the electricity has been secured, the individual can be examined. Burns resulting from electricity can result in serious muscle damage and organ failure, including cardiac arrest.

Burn prevention measures will be discussed in later chapters. Be aware that young children and older adults are more susceptible to burn injuries. Special attention needs to be provided to these audiences and their caregivers when discussing burn prevention and care.

NOTE: The information provided here serves as a brief introduction to the more common areas of unintentional injury. These injury areas are certainly not all of the injury issues that might be encountered by a Level I educator. There may be local injury issues that will take precedence over these. The Level I educator must research the risk issues in his or her community to determine where the attention for prevention should be focused.

Disasters and Disaster Preparedness

Both natural and man-made disasters are frequent occurrences, and most fire departments are involved in disaster response. In the years since the tragedy of September 11, 2001, federal, state, and local agencies have promoted the idea of disaster preparedness for both natural and man-made events. Measures can be taken by individuals and households to be prepared for disasters and to mitigate the effects of disasters when they occur. In some communities, the fire chief also serves as the local Emergency Management Director, and residents look to fire and life safety educators to provide information concerning the steps for disaster preparedness. It is the responsibility of the Level I educator to be familiar with the disasters that might reasonably occur in his or her community and to be able to provide audiences with measures for preparation and mitigation.

This section discusses basic information concerning disaster preparedness and presents the most common disaster situations that can affect a community. Preparedness measures are discussed in later chapters. This information is developed from publications of the Federal Emergency Management Agency (FEMA) and the United States Department of Homeland Security.

Types of Disasters

Disasters can be divided into three categories: natural hazards, technological hazards, and terrorism. Even though these categories of disaster are different, many of the measures for preparedness are similar. There may be some hazard-specific measures that need to be taken.

Natural Hazards

Natural hazards, often referred to as Acts of God, are events that at times can be predicted and sometimes not. People cannot prevent these disasters from occurring. They can, however, minimize the dangers associated with these events and mitigate the damages done. These hazards threaten lives, property, and assets.

Natural hazards are usually geographically located. They tend to occur repeatedly in the same areas due to specific patterns or characteristics of an area. The most common natural hazards are floods, hurricanes, tornadoes, wildfires, and earthquakes. Other natural hazards include landslides, tsunamis, and winter storms. Many times, one hazard will lead to or cause another; that is, hurricanes can lead to flooding, and earthquakes can cause landslides.

Floods

Floods are one of the most prevalent natural hazards in the United States. Floods may affect only a small, local area or may be large enough to affect an entire river basin or multiple states **(Figure 2.34)**.

Not all floods are alike. In some situations, the waters rise slowly. But flash floods can develop quickly; sometime in a matter of-minutes. Flooding can occur when a dam breaks or a levee is breached. Even small streams, creeks, gullies, and dry streambeds can flood during times of heavy rains. Most standard homeowners insurance policies do not cover flood damage, although flood insurance policies are available in most areas.

Figure 2.34 Flooding in New Orleans caused by Hurricane Katrina. *Courtesy of District Chief Chris Mickal, New Orleans (LA) FD Photo Unit.*

Individuals need to understand and prepare for the dangers associated with floods. Walking through flood water is dangerous, especially if the water is moving. Driving through flooded areas can cause a loss of control or stalling of the vehicle. Vehicles can float in one foot of water. Two feet of rushing water can carry away a vehicle.

The following terms will help to identify the level of immediate risk to citizens from natural hazards:

Watch: Conditions have developed that make the event possible. Watches are often issued for weather conditions such as tornados and floods.

Warning: The event has been sighted or will likely occur soon.

Tornadoes

Tornadoes are violent storms that are born out of powerful thunderstorms. Tornadoes cause death and major destruction. Each year, many people are killed or seriously injured by tornadoes despite advance warning. Some of these individuals did not hear the warning, while others received the warning but did not believe a tornado would actually affect them.

Tornadoes are found most frequently in the United States east of the Rocky Mountains during the spring and summer months. In an average year, 800 tornadoes are reported nationwide, resulting in 80 deaths and over 1,500 injuries. In the southern states, peak

Figure 2.35 The damage path of a tornado. *Courtesy of FEMA/Liz Roll.*

tornado occurrence is in March through May, while peak months in the northern states are during the summer.[21]

A tornado is a rotating, funnel-shaped cloud that extends from a thunderstorm to the ground. The winds of a tornado can reach 300 mph (483 kph). Damage paths can measure in excess of 1 mile (1.6 km) **(Figure 2.35)**. Before a tornado hits, the winds may die down and the air may become very still. They are often preceded by a dark, greenish-colored sky, large hail, a large, dark cloud, and a loud roar. Tornadoes generally occur near the edge of a thunderstorm.

Individuals in danger of being struck by a tornado should take cover in a basement, storm cellar, or a "Safe Room." Individuals living in manufactured homes should immediately evacuate and seek other shelter, as this type of construction offers little protection from these violent events.

Hurricanes

A hurricane is a type of tropical cyclone, which is accompanied by thunderstorms and a counterclockwise circulation of winds near the earth's surface. Hurricanes can cause catastrophic damage to coastlines and move several hundred miles inland. Winds can be in excess of 155 miles (249 km) per hour. Hurricanes can also cause the development of tornadoes and microbursts, create storm surges on the coast, and cause extensive damage from heavy rainfall. Hurricanes produce widespread heavy rains. Excessive rains can trigger flooding, mud slides, and flash flooding.

All of the Atlantic Coast and Gulf of Mexico areas are subject to hurricanes. Parts of the southwestern United States and the Pacific Coast experience heavy rains and storms due to hurricanes off the Mexican coast. The main season for the occurrence of hurricanes is June to November.

Hurricanes are classified into five categories, depending upon their wind speed, central pressure, and damage potential **(Table 2.7)**. Category Three hurricanes are considered major, though Categories One and Two can still produce serious danger.

Individuals living in areas prone to hurricanes and tropical storms should keep trees and shrubs around their homes well-trimmed and be prepared to secure their homes and boats. Families should have an evacuation plan in place and practice it regularly.

Earthquakes

An earthquake is the sudden movement of the earth caused by an abrupt release of strain that has accumulated over many years. They are caused by the huge plates that form the earth's surface as they move slowly over, under, and around each other. Sometimes these plates get locked together with neither being able to move. Eventually, the pressure builds up and the plates suddenly break free, causing a series of vibrations that travel through both plates. Earthquakes can cause many deaths and injuries and extensive property damage (FEMA).[22]

The area most prone to earthquakes is the Pacific coastal states. There are also hazard areas located in the central United States near the Missouri/Kentucky/Tennessee borders, as well as the coastal area of South Carolina **(Figure 2.36, p. 70)**.

Earthquakes can produce aftershocks, which are earthquakes of a similar or lesser intensity that follow the main earthquakes. When an earthquake occurs off land, it can trigger a tsunami — a series of enormous waves, also referred to as *seismic sea waves*. These can move at a speed of 100 mph (161 kmh) and smash into land with waves as high as 100 feet (30 m).

Wildfires

An average of 106,400 wildfires break out every year, consuming over 4 million acres (1.61874 hec) of land. Individuals who live in remote valleys or hillsides or near forests with thick vegetation may be subject to

Table 2.7
Hurricane Scale (Saffir-Simpson Scale)

Category One	• Minimal damage, mainly to unanchored manufactured homes, vegetation, and signs.
	• Winds will range from 74-95 mph.
	• Storm surge will reach 4-5 feet.
Category Two	• Moderate damage, including all manufactured homes, roofs, small crafts, and flooding.
	• Winds will range from 96-100 mph.
	• Storm surge of 6-8 feet.
Category Three	• Extensive damage, including small buildings. Low-lying roads will be cut off.
	• Winds will range from 111-130 mph.
	• Storm surge will be 9-12 feet.
Category Four	• Damage will be extreme, with roofs destroyed, trees down, roads cut off, manufactured homes destroyed.
	• Winds will range from 131-155 mph.
	• Storm surge will be 13-18 feet.
Category Five	• Catastrophic damage will occur. Most buildings will be destroyed, vegetation destroyed, major roads cut off, and homes flooded.
	• Winds will exceed 155 mph.
	• Storm surge will be greater than 18 feet.

Source: *Federal Emergency Management Agency*

the ravages of wildfires. Wildfires can be triggered by lightning or accidents, or can be intentionally set. Dry conditions during certain times of the year and in particular parts of the country increase the possibility of a wildfire. Wildfires spread quickly and often take weeks and months to control **(Figure 2.37, p. 70)**.

Billions of dollars are spent annually to suppress wildfires. Wildfires increase the potential for landslides and flooding. In addition, they destroy wildlife, water sheds, and scenic vistas.

Wildland fires often begin unnoticed. They can spread very quickly, igniting trees, brush, undergrowth, homes, and other structures in their path. Fires that burn along the ground are referred to

as *surface fires*. Those that move quickly by jumping along the tops of trees are called *crown fires*.

Homeowners can help protect their residences by keeping lawns trimmed, leaves raked, and the roof and rain gutters free of leaves and dead limbs. Firewood should be stored away from the home. By thinning the trees and brush near the residential and business areas, a defensible space can be created.

Technological Hazards
Technological hazards involve hazardous materials incidents and nuclear power plant failures. Usually, there is little or no warning of these incidents. The number of technological incidents is increasing, mainly due to the increased number of hazardous materials and the human error that can occur when these materials are being handled.

The following overview of common disasters is just a small portion of information that the Level I educator will need in order to answer questions and provide presentations on the steps to technological disaster preparedness. Every educator needs to examine his or her community to determine which hazards exist or are likely to occur. Each educator needs to be able to provide the appropriate information in response to citizen requests.

Hazardous Materials Incidents
Hazardous materials are found in every jurisdiction, community, workplace, and modern household. Incidents involving these materials can be caused by factors such as human error, package failure, and transportation accidents. Emergency personnel must be aware of the potential for hazardous materials

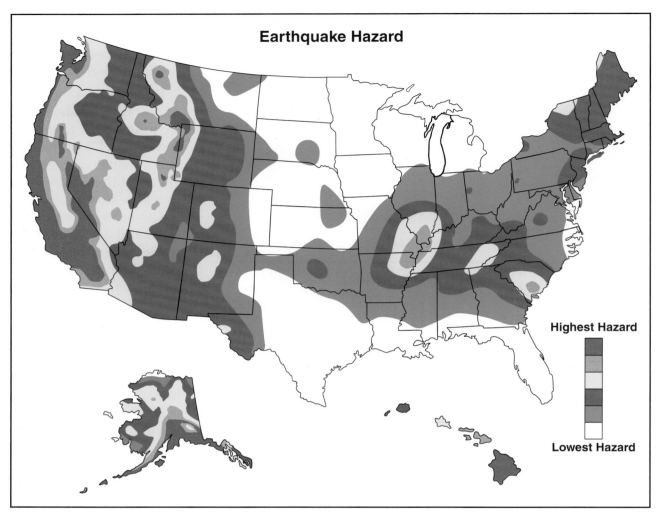

Earthquake Hazard

Highest Hazard

Lowest Hazard

Figure 2.36 Earthquake hazard zones. *Compiled from USGS data.*

Figure 2.37 This wildland fire was a small part of a larger fire that covered many square miles.

to be involved in fires, explosions, and criminal or terrorist activities.

Citizens should be encouraged to contact their local emergency planning agency to gather more information about the particular hazards in their area and how they will be notified of an emergency event. Communities have a variety of ways of notifying residents of hazardous materials incidents such as emergency sirens, local government cable and radio stations, and even door-to-door notification. Governmental agencies must develop an emergency plan for their communities that will enable them to prepare for and respond to these emergencies.

Nuclear Power Plants

Nuclear power plants operate in most states in the country and produce about 20% of the nation's power **(Figure 2.38)**. They use the heat generated from nuclear fission to convert water to steam, which powers generators to produce electricity.

The Nuclear Regulatory Agency keeps a close watch on these facilities, regulating their construction and operation. However, accidents can still occur, causing dangerous levels of radiation to enter the environ-

Figure 2.38 An example of a nuclear power plant.

ment, affecting the health and safety of those living in the area of the facility.

The potential danger from an event at a nuclear facility is the exposure to radiation. There can be radiation exposure to the body, inhalation of radioactive materials, and ingestion of these harmful agents. A danger to crops, livestock, and water supplies also exists.

Local governments have emergency plans in place should an event occur at a nuclear power facility. A warning siren or some other notification will be activated. Instructions on what procedures to take will be given to citizens through an emergency alert system on local radio and television stations. Residents in these areas should inform themselves of the recommended emergency procedures so they will be ready to act should an emergency occur.

Terrorism
On September 11, 2001, the U.S. witnessed the horrific results of an act of terrorism. Since that time, much attention has been given to terrorism and the actions that individuals can take to be prepared should such events occur again.

Terrorism is the use of force or violence against persons or property in violation of criminal laws. Its purpose is to intimidate, coerce, or extract a ransom. The goal of terrorism is to create fear among the public, to convince people that the government is powerless to prevent acts of terrorism, and to get immediate publicity for the cause being promoted by the terrorists.

Acts of terrorism include:
- Assassinations
- Kidnappings
- Hijackings
- Bomb scares and bombings
- Cyber attacks
- The use of chemical, biological, nuclear, and radiological weapons

Terrorists may target certain areas for their acts. These targets include military and government facilities, airports, large cities, public gatherings, water and food supplies, and other high-risk areas.

The U.S. Department of Homeland Security has developed an advisory system to provide a national framework to disseminate information regarding the risk of acts of terrorism. This system is designed to provide information to authorities (federal, state, and local), the private sector, and the American people. The system uses a set of graduated threat levels, which elevate as the risk of the threat increases. These conditions may be for a localized area or may cover the entire nation. When the threat level increases, government agencies (federal, state, and local), businesses, and schools implement a corresponding set of measures to reduce the vulnerability or increase the protection for the people in these areas.

The Dynamics of the Educator
The role of a fire and life safety educator carries with it a huge responsibility to remain up-to-date on technology and messages, to be informed about all matters involving the fire department in the community, and to give accurate and valid information when asked. The Level I educator is a front-line representative of the fire department and may be the only person from the fire department the public will see and meet, except during emergency situations.

The fire and life safety educator should understand the importance of the following items:
- Knowing what it takes to create fire
- Practicing good housekeeping and inspection practices that can keep the fuels separated from heat sources
- Understanding why the concept of "stop, drop, and roll" is effective in extinguishing clothing fires

- Keeping space heaters at least 3 feet (0.9 m) from any fuel items such as matches, lighters, candles, and other open flames

The role of public relations goes hand-in-hand with public education. In fact, the two are interconnected and often overlap. By providing the community with information on fire prevention and safety, the fire organization is viewed in a positive light by members of the community. The Level I educator can act as a liaison between the community and the fire organization, promoting goodwill and cooperation.

It is incumbent upon the Level I educator to always represent the department in a professional and educated manner. This includes everything from appearance and dress to behaviors and actions. The Level I educator is the front-line person for the department and must never forget to represent this noble and honored profession in the manner in which it should be represented. Values such as honor, integrity, trust, and loyalty are attached to the fire service and the profession of fire fighting, and nothing less is expected from the Level I fire and life safety educator.

Chapter Summary

The technical information required for a Level I fire and life safety educator is quite varied and broad. The fire and life safety educator is ethically and morally bound to grasp these concepts and put them to use in the job in order to effectively fulfill his or her mission to the community. Staying on top of new technology, getting more in-depth and current information than is provided here, and reviewing existing information is a continuing part of the role of the successful and effective Level I fire and life safety educator. Familiarity with the subject matter provides confidence and the ability to be better prepared in the community.

Review Questions

1. What is the organizational structure of a typical fire department?
2. What is the proper process for reporting an emergency?
3. Describe how a fire develops, beginning with ignition through the consumption of the available fuel.

4. What is included in the firefighter's protective clothing ensemble?
5. What is the benefit of a home having a working smoke alarm?
6. What is the difference in operation between an ionization and photoelectric smoke alarm?
7. How does a typical fire sprinkler system operate?
8. What is the difference between common, special, and personal fire hazards?
9. What human behaviors are common when a person is confronted with a fire situation in their home?
10. What is the difference between an unintentional injury and an accident?
11. What are the three categories of disasters?
12. Why is a professional image, acting with integrity, and being well-skilled critical to the success of a fire and life safety educator?

Key Terms

Alarm Check Valve — Type of check valve installed in the riser of an automatic sprinkler system that transmits a water flow alarm when the water flows in the system.

Backdraft — Explosively rapid combustion that occurs with an increase in ventilation in an environment with high heat, large volumes of smoke, and limited oxygen.

Chain of Command — Pathway of responsibility from the highest level of the department to the lowest.

Combustion — An exothermic chemical reaction that is a self-sustaining process of rapid oxidation of a fuel, that produces heat and light.

Common Fire Hazards — Those that are prevalent in almost all occupancies and encourage a fire to start.

Decay Stage — Heat release rate is declining and the amount of fire diminishes as the fuel diminishes.

Dry-Pipe Sprinkler System — Fire sprinkler system that consists of closed sprinklers attached to a piping system that contains air under pressure.

Fire Department Connection (FDC) — Point at which the fire department can connect into a sprinkler or standpipe system to boost water flow in the system.

Fire Hazard — A condition that encourages a fire to start or increase the extent or severity of the fire.

Fire Tetrahedron — Heat, oxygen, fuel, and the self-sustained chemical reaction.

Fire Triangle — Heat, oxygen, and fuel — the components of fire.

Flashover — Rapid transition between the growth and fully developed fire stages during which all surfaces and objects within a space have been heated to their ignition temperature and flame breaks out almost at once over the surface of all objects in the space.

Full Thickness Burns (Third-Degree)— Those involving all the layers or skins, and may damage the muscle, bone or underlying organs.

Fully Developed Stage — All combustible materials in the compartment are burning and releasing the maximum amount of heat possible.

Growth Stage — The fire is developing within the compartment, drawing air into the plume above the fire, and spreading heat to other fuels in the compartment.

Incipient Growth Stage — The fire is developing within the compartment, drawing air into the plume above the fire, and spreading heat to other fuels in the compartment.

Ionization Smoke Alarm — Uses a tiny amount of radioactive material to ionize air molecules as they enter the detection chamber.

Liability of Injury — Legal responsibility and accountability for an act or process related to a program.

Partial Thickness Burns (Second Degree) — Those involving several layers of skin.

Personal Fire Hazards — Common hazards that are caused by unsafe acts of individuals.

Photoelectric Smoke Alarm — Uses a photoelectric cell coupled with a light source to detect smoke particulate.

Primary (or Universal) Prevention — Promotes the well-being of an already healthy population through activities designed to prevent events that might result in injuries or property loss. It also seeks to enhance well-being by reinforcing healthy behaviors and discouraging lifestyles that may eventually lead to injury or illness.

Pyrolysis — Chemical decomposition of a substance through the action of heat.

Riser — Vertical water pipe used to carry water for fire protection systems aboveground.

Secondary (or Selective) Prevention — Seeks to mitigate or modify events to reduce their severity. It targets high-risk conditions and populations.

Special Fire Hazards — Those that arise from or are related to the particular processes or operation in an occupancy.

Sprinkler (or Sprinkler Head) — Water flow device in a sprinkler system.

Superficial Burns (First Degree) — Those involving only the outer layer of skin.

Target Hazards — Those properties where there is a great potential for loss of life or property loss if a fire erupts.

Unity of Command— Management system in which an individual reports to only one supervisor.

Warning — Signifies that the event has been sighted or will likely occur soon.

Watch — Conditions have developed that make the event possible. Watches are often issued for weather conditions such as tornados and floods.

Wet-Pipe Sprinkler System — Fire-suppression system that is built into a structure or site; piping contains either water or foam solution continuously; activation of a sprinkler causes the extinguishing agent to flow from the open sprinkler.

Chapter 2 Notes

1. IFSTA **Essentials,** 5th Edition, 2008, OK, Fire Protection Publications.

2. National Institute of Standards and Technology. *Statement for the Record, August 6, 2007.* As presented to Boston City Council Committee on Public Safety.

3. Society for Fire Protection Engineers. "Initial Reaction to fire may endanger people more." Fire Engineering. July 27, 2007.

4. Centers for Disease Control and Prevention. Statement for the Record on Unintentional Injury and Death by Mark L. Rosenberg, M.D. May 5, 1998. Found at http://www.hhs.gov/asl/testify/t980505b.html, January 16, 2008.

5. American College of Surgeons. Injury Prevention. Presentation by the Subcommittee on Injury Prevention and Control. Found at http://www.facs.org/trauma/injuryprevent.pdf. January, 2008.

6. Queensland Health. Child Injury Prevention. Found at http://www.health.qld.gov.au/chipp/what_is/definitions.asp. January 17, 2008

7. National Highway Traffic Safety Administration.

8. Centers for Disease Control and Prevention.

9. Bronstein, Spyker, Cantilena, Green, Rumack, Heard. "2007 Annual Report of the American Association of Poison Control Centers' National Poison Data System: 25th Annual Report." Clinical Toxicology, 46; 10, 938-940.

10. Centers for Disease Control and Prevention. 2005.

11. National Highway Traffic Safety Administration. Bicyclist and Other Cyclists. DOT HS 810 802. 2006.

12. Safe Kids Worldwide. Injury Facts: Bike Injury. Found at http://www.usa.safekids.org/tier3_cd.cfm?content_item_id=1010&folder_id=540. January 19, 2008.

13. Safe Kids Worldwide. Study of TBI and Wheel-Related Sports. May, 2002.

14. National Highway Traffic Safety Association. Bicycle Helmet Use Laws. DOT HS810 886W. January 2008.

15. Centers for Disease Control and Prevention. Water Related Injuries: Fact Sheet. Found at http://www.cdc.gov/ncipc/factsheets/drown.htm. January 19, 2008.

16. Safe Kids Worldwide.

17. Runyan, Carol W., et al. Unintentional Injuries in the Home in the United States. American Journal of Preventive Medicine. 2005:28(1). pp. 73-79

18. American Burn Association. 2006. *Practice Guidelines for Burn Care*. Found at http://www.ameriburn.org

19. Park, Jimmy, MS, RN, Research Coordinator, The Burn Center at Arkansas Children's Hospital.

20. University of Maryland Medical Center. *Burns.* Found January 24, 2008 at http://www.umm.edu/altmed/articles/burns-000021.htm

21. National Oceanic and Atmospheric Administration.

22. Federal Emergency Management Agency. *Are You Ready?* Emmitsburg, MD: 2004.

FLSE Level I Educators: Administration

Chapter Contents

Key Terms

Job Performance Requirements

This chapter provides information that addresses the following job performance requirements of NFPA® 1035, *Standard for Professional Qualifications for Fire and Life Safety Educator, Public Information Officer, and Juvenile Firesetter Intervention Specialist*, 2010 edition.

NFPA® 1035 References

5.2.1

5.2.2

5.2.3

FLSE Level I Educators: Administration

Learning Objectives

After reading this chapter, students will be able to:

1. Explain the purpose and benefits of documentation of fire and life safety education activities. (NFPA® 1035, 5.2.1)

2. Properly prepare documentation of fire and life safety education activities, determining the information that is appropriate and pertinent to the report. (NFPA® 1035, 5.2.1)

3. Properly prepare activity reports for fire and life safety education activities with information that is appropriate and pertinent to the report. (NFPA® 1035, 5.2.1)

4. Properly design and maintain a work schedule, so that all activities are scheduled and accomplished without conflict. (NFPA® 1035, 5.2.3)

5. Identify community resources, services, and organizations in order to properly refer the public to the proper resource when necessary.

Chapter 3
FLSE Level I Educators: Administration

Case History

The Colorado Springs (CO) Fire Department's Community Services section regularly visits local schools to teach young audiences how to respond in emergency situations. During the 2008-2009 school year, the department's fire and life safety educators visited 224 kindergarten classes in 82 schools and instructed 4,296 kindergarten students and 347 adults in fire and life safety education.

Through a 40-minute classroom visit, students learned about important topics such as matches and lighters, smoke alarms, escaping from a fire, 9-1-1, "firefighters are our friends," what EXIT means, and more. The presentation format included hands-on activities, strong visual aids, and characterizations including Sparky and Sniffer the Smoke alarm. Twenty-five percent of the schools visited were also given a pretest and posttest to help document any increase in fire safety knowledge as well as to identify areas in need of improvement.

Each educator documented his or her work within these schools in a number of ways. First, classroom presentations were documented in each educator's electronic calendar. Details such as the school contact, phone number, address, presentation times, and expected audience size were recorded. This information was vital not only for preparation for these presentations but also in the event an educator was unavailable or delayed, schools were closed due to inclement weather, or a substitute educator was needed.

After each school visit, the educator compiled the following data in an Excel database: school name; number of students, adults, and classes; name of the educator who presented the program; and any applicable test results. This database was vital in reporting to supervisors the progress being made in schools.

In the spring of 2009, the database proved to be even more important as it demonstrated the value and necessity of fire and life safety programs for school-age children. In April, a five-year-old boy and his sister discovered a medical emergency situation at their home requiring them to call 9-1-1. The boy was able to clearly give dispatchers his name and address just as he had learned at school during a presentation by the Colorado Springs Fire Department. In a separate incident in May, a set of five-year-old twin boys discovered smoke coming from their kitchen and were able to alert their family and get everyone outside to safety just as they too had recently learned at a fire and life-safety presentation at their school.

The phrase "if you didn't write it down, it didn't happen" may be a familiar one, especially to those individuals who have ties to the emergency medical field. Many occupations require detailed documentation of all activities related to their job. In the field of community-risk reduction, the documentation of activities is an important element of success.

The responsibilities of an effective fire and life safety educator are many and varied. The job is more than just making presentations for educational purposes. As indicated in the previous chapter, staying up-to-date on fire and life safety issues, as well as remaining current on issues relating to fire fighting and suppression takes time on the part of a Level I fire and life safety educator. Networking and developing partnerships are other important responsibilities of the effective community educator and are discussed in the next chapter.

One function that is often overlooked by a Level I fire and life safety educator is the administrative responsibilities of the job, such as documentation of activities, preparation of a work schedule, and assistance with questions and requests from the public. Office chores such as these may seem especially cumbersome to the fire and life safety educator who is usually very active and outgoing. However, such chores are an important part of the job and will make things much easier for the busy Level I educator.

All areas of the fire service are required to provide documentation to upper management and the political powers in charge, for example:

- Training officers must document activities of fire department personnel in order to maintain certifications.

- Inspectors must provide documentation of inspections performed and citations written.

- Operations personnel must provide documentation of each call to which they are dispatched, whether it is an emergency or nonemergency call.

- Paramedics and emergency medical technicians must complete patient care reports.

Fire and life safety educators are no different than those in the other divisions of the fire agency. Without proper documentation, there is no record of the work being performed and therefore no means to justify monies at budget time or the need for additional personnel. Without any records of the work being performed, there is no evidence of the effectiveness of risk-reduction activities. Documentation of work and activities may also assist with potential grant funding and increased funding from outside sources, such as businesses.

The importance of administrative activities, including proper work scheduling and activity reporting, cannot be underestimated in the field of community-risk reduction. Administrative duties as well as program preparation and delivery are vital components of the role of the Level I educator. Documentation is a piece of the program evaluation process, which is discussed in this chapter as well as later chapters. Documentation of activities conducted also assists in providing accurate evaluation results. Providing the appropriate amount of time for administrative tasks is part of the work of the successful Level I educator **(Figure 3.1)**.

Figure 3.1 Meetings are part of administrative work for which time must be scheduled.

Purpose and Benefits of Proper Documentation

Documentation of fire and life safety education programs is more than just paperwork. The purpose and benefits of properly documenting activities of the fire and life safety educator and programs that are conducted are numerous and increase the effectiveness of a community's programs.

In government agencies, staffing and funding decisions are made based upon evidence of need and cost-effectiveness. Departments or divisions will fare much better in the budgeting process if they keep accurate documentation of activities and the effectiveness of those activities. In order to receive a continuation or increase of funding or staffing, fire and life safety educators must provide documentation and evidence of the magnitude of the risk-reduction activities being performed.

Through the use of documentation of risk-reduction activities, the Level I educator can form a database of contacts in the community. This list can serve as a referral source when responding to citizen requests that are outside the ability of the fire organization. The database can also serve as a network for contacts or partners when researching and developing new programs in the community.

Documentation of fire and life safety education programs serves as a form of evaluation. Process evaluation determines that a community risk-reduction program is providing the desired service by indicating the nature of the service and naming the recipients of this service. Documentation helps program evaluators determine if the target audience of the programs is being reached and to what extent. This knowledge will enable the program developers to modify or adjust the program objectives and activities to ensure that the intended audience is being reached to the greatest extent possible.

Because most of the educator's work is performed away from the office or station, documentation provides evidence of the work that is being accomplished. There may be times when the Level I educator will have to justify the time spent on a particular project or time spent away from the office. Having documentation of programs, as well as documentation of activities surrounding those programs, will serve as proof of the work that the educator is doing in the community.

All in all, documentation is a vital part of the fire and life safety educator's responsibilities. It provides valuable information for program planners, evaluators, and agency decision-makers.

Documentation Information

The fire and life safety educator needs to document two basic areas:

- Individual activities of the fire and life safety educator

- Information about the programs and activities that are conducted in the community by the Level I educator

The following text examines the components of these different types of reports.

Educator's Activity Report

Documentation of the activities of a fire and life safety educator basically consists of a daily record of work that is being performed. There is more time invested in delivering a risk-reduction presentation than simply providing the presentation. The educator's activity report should include the following:

- Time and efforts surrounding preparation
- Planning
- Development
- Evaluation of risk-reduction activities

This record of activity can be in the simple form of a time sheet. While it certainly does not have to be a detailed account of every minute of every day, it should account for the majority of the educator's time spent at work. Activities to document include:

- Receiving and making phone calls
- Responding to e-mails and other correspondence
- Attending staff meetings
- Networking and attending meetings outside the department
- Performing research
- Training, preparation, and planning for presentations
- Critiquing and evaluating programs

Some educators may serve a dual role in the fire department, such as inspector, investigator, or operations firefighter, or have other activities that need documentation as well.

A variety of ways can be used to document the educator's work activities. Educators must find a form and format that works best for the organization and will be beneficial to them. Electronic calendars and journals can be used; the information in these electronic devices can often be downloaded into a spreadsheet format or transferred to an electronic organizer, such as a PDA or smart phone, for use by the educator in the field **(Figure 3.2)**. The fire organization may require the use of an electronic

Figure 3.2 New technologies, such as smart phones and PDAs, make scheduling easier.

log. Some educators find it easier and more accessible to use a print calendar to record the activities of each day's work.

Whatever system is used, each educator needs to find the way that works the best for his or her purpose and the organization. The system needs to account for the time and energy that the educator spends doing the work that is assigned. Oftentimes, supervisors and other leaders do not understand exactly what is involved in a task or the amount of time that it takes to accomplish it. Through documentation of daily activities, each educator can provide a source for educating those in charge about the duties of the educator and the time that it takes to perform the duties of the job effectively and efficiently.

Level I educators should share the documented information with their supervisors. Sharing the information can assist in helping administrators understand the nature of the job and what is actually being done in the area of fire and life safety education. Most of the Level I educator's work is community-based, so it is outside of the observations of administrators or supervisors. If the documentation of activities is shared, those in charge will be more aware of the scope and value of the work that is being done.

Activity Report for Presentations

While keeping records of the individual activities of the Level I educator is important, nothing can be more important than keeping accurate records of fire and life safety presentations. Documentation starts at the scheduling of the presentation and follows until its completion. This process is invaluable when it comes to evaluation of the risk-reduction programs being conducted in the community (**Figure 3.3**).

To understand the documentation process for presentations, it is important to know how these activities fit into the overall community risk-reduction process.

- A **presentation** is a single delivery of fire and life safety information. A presentation can also be called a *lesson*.

- A **lesson plan** is nothing more than a guide for making an educational presentation.

- A **curriculum** is a series of lessons, or presentations, which are designed to reach an educational goal. This approach employs only the education portion of the risk-reduction strategy.

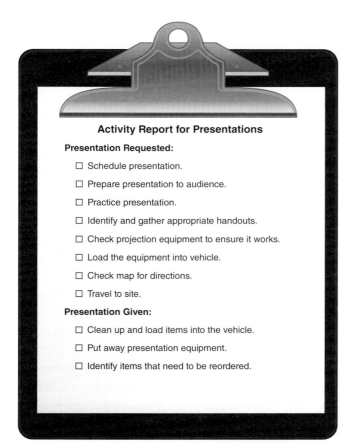

Activity Report for Presentations

Presentation Requested:

☐ Schedule presentation.

☐ Prepare presentation to audience.

☐ Practice presentation.

☐ Identify and gather appropriate handouts.

☐ Check projection equipment to ensure it works.

☐ Load the equipment into vehicle.

☐ Check map for directions.

☐ Travel to site.

Presentation Given:

☐ Clean up and load items into the vehicle.

☐ Put away presentation equipment.

☐ Identify items that need to be reordered.

Figure 3.3 Documentation should be carefully planned.

Presentations made by the Level I educator may be a single presentation on a single subject, or they may be a part of a series of presentations, or curriculum, such as those that might be used in the elementary or primary school setting.

- A **risk-reduction program** is a series of presentations and activities that is designed to impact a common risk-reduction goal and incorporates multiple intervention strategies (the five Es). An example of a risk-reduction program would be a smoke alarm program, where educational presentations are delivered, smoke alarms are checked and installed as needed, and ordinances requiring smoke alarms are adopted and reinforced.

- A **risk-reduction strategy** is a series of integrated programs designed to impact a common goal. An example of a risk-reduction strategy is the overall effort of the fire department to reduce the incidents of fires and fire deaths.

Presentations are the foundation of risk-reduction strategies in the community; therefore, the documentation of these events is of utmost importance for the evaluation and determination of the success of these strategies. The responsibility for this documentation falls directly on the Level I educator, and the importance of proper documentation cannot be underestimated.

Documenting the Activity

Documentation of the activity begins with the scheduling of the presentation or event. The Level I educator should gather information concerning the presentation from the individual who is making the request or responsible for scheduling the activity. By recording the information about the event before its occurrence, it allows the information to be passed along to an engine company or station as a reminder. The information can also be passed to a substitute educator in the event of an emergency or illness on the part of the educator originally responsible for handling the event.

The educator should gather basic information about the proposed presentation. Date, time, and location are, of course, critical informational pieces. The age of the target audience and size of the group will be important as well, which are discussed in later chapters. The individual scheduling the event may desire a specific topic for the presentation, and this needs to be determined at the time it is scheduled.

The educator should also document the length of time available for the presentation and any special information (such as special needs of the audience, unusual arrangements, and the like). This information can be used by the Level I educator to properly prepare for the presentation, as well as the documentation of the event once it has taken place.

Gathering Information for a Presentation

It is important to gather as much information as possible about a proposed presentation to meet the needs of the audience. This helps with scheduling, documenting, and evaluating the event. Information to be gathered before a presentation includes the following:

- Date and time of presentation
- Location of the presentation (be specific): name of requesting organization, address, address for presentation (if different) and the room number
- Name of contact person, telephone number, e-mail, etc.
- Topic for presentation (if there is a specific topic requested)
- Age of audience
- Number of individuals participating
- Length of presentation
- Any special information — special needs of audience or unusual facility arrangements
- Date of request

Once the presentation has taken place, the remainder of the information can be documented. This information includes the following:

- Actual topic of the presentation and its length
- Number of people who attended and the breakdown by age for better accounting
- Time involved in the delivery of the presentation
- Materials distributed or equipment used at the presentation
- Comments, feedback, or suggestions received at the time of the presentation

After the presentation has been documented, this information can be used for other types of reports or documentation. Reports may be required concern-ing the programs or risk-reduction strategies being used in the community to combat a particular risk or problem. Reports of this nature will enable those evaluating programs to ensure that the information is reaching the target audience and will also assist in determining if the information is being processed or applied.

Many fire departments will require a monthly activity report from the various departments or divisions within the organization. This information is compiled into a departmental monthly report, which in turn is compiled into an annual report for the fire agency. The annual report for the fire agency is a very important document in many jurisdictions, as decisions concerning budgeting and personnel are based upon the information presented in the annual report.

While the Level I educator will most likely not be responsible for preparing a monthly report, there should still be an understanding of the information that is contained in this document. It is simply a compilation of all the activity reports from the risk-reduction division or from those divisions that have the responsibility for risk-reduction initiatives. Monthly reports can include the number of presentations delivered and the number of individuals contacted. Documentation of the type of audiences, that is, school class, church group, or civic club is beneficial information to include. In addition, the amount of materials distributed for all the presentations needs to be compiled for inventory purposes and replacement.

Monthly reports may also include other activities of the fire prevention or risk-reduction division. These can include community events, such as health fairs and festivals, where individuals are reached with information on an informal basis. The monthly report may also contain information on other related activities, such as juvenile firesetter intervention programs, training classes, number of smoke alarms installed or checked, and other tasks relating to risk-reduction strategies and interventions in the community.

Managers compile the data from the reports of individual presentations into a monthly report, which is then compiled into an annual report and may be presented to a city council, county commission, or other governing body. Annual reports may become public documents, available on an agency's web page or published in the local paper. These reports can be useful documents to provide to a department's sponsors for risk-reduction events or activities. The proper documentation of risk-reduction activities allows this information to be integrated into the other activities of the fire department that are included in these reports. It demonstrates how risk-reduction initiatives fit into the overall mission of the fire department and shows that risk-reduction activities are supported by the organization. While one success story is certainly worthwhile, success stories compiled over a year's time can illustrate the far-reaching effects of risk-reduction programs and provide for increased focus and attention by governmental managers and the community.

For the short amount of time that it takes to document programs and presentations, the data provided is very valuable when it comes to the future of risk-reduction programs. Proper documentation of activities, presentations, and events is paramount to success of future undertakings in the risk-reduction field and should not be overlooked or short-changed.

The Educator's Work Schedule

Once a community is aware of the fire and life safety activities being conducted by the fire department, a huge demand may be placed on the educator's time. A critical element for the Level I educator is the importance of creating and managing a standard work schedule. This is in reference to how those hours of work are used and how to gain the greatest benefit from them **(Figure 3.4)**.

The main focus of the Level I educator is just that — educating the community on risk-reduction initiatives. This includes making presentations, delivering programs, and assisting with other risk-reduction activities. However, there must be some "down time" or office time available to take care of preparation, scheduling, and evaluating programs. Before establishing a standard work schedule, the Level I educator needs to take into account certain considerations. In establishing priorities, the educator must consider the priorities of the organization and develop an understanding of the organization's overall risk-reduction strategy. This will assist in scheduling programs that are in line with the mission and vision of the organization.

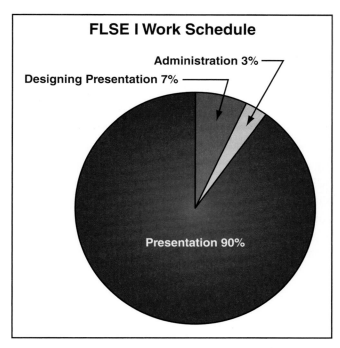

Figure 3.4 An approximation of the division of time spent by a fire and life safety educator in performing official tasks.

Knowing the Supervisor's Expectations

A supervisor's expectations will be a factor in the establishment of a work schedule. A supervisor may expect his or her staff to report to the office at the beginning of the day, instead of going directly into the field. Similarly, the educator may be asked to report to his or her supervisor at the conclusion of the workday. The supervisor may have other expectations that need to be understood and considered when developing a standard work schedule.

Working a Part-Time Schedule

If the Level I educator is performing risk-reduction activities on a part-time basis, other required duties may be assigned in addition to the education function:

● Cover response units

● Perform suppression or EMS activities

● Handle administrative duties

These duties will have to be included as a part of the work schedule.

Performing Everyday Duties

A component of every workday should include time for returning telephone calls and responding to e-mails. This can often be a time-consuming set of tasks, but it is important. Every attempt should be made to return calls or e-mails on the same day that they are received. Requests for presentations and risk-reduction activities carry a certain priority. Without handling those requests, the educator may have more office time than desired! Take advantage of e-mail and voice mail whenever possible. Many activities and events can be scheduled without ever speaking directly to the individual coordinating them.

The work schedule should provide time for reading mail, memos, newsletters, periodicals, and other publications that will keep the educator in touch with what is happening in the fire department, the community, and the risk-reduction arena. In any organization, a certain amount of time must be devoted to staying current with certifications and other training requirements.

When developing a work schedule, select consistent times and days each week to be available in the office or station. If colleagues know that Monday is a scheduled administrative day, then meetings, conferences, and other updates can be coordinated on that particular day. In larger departments where there is more than one individual performing education functions, the work schedule may need to be coordinated among all the members of the division or work group.

Allowing Time for Presentations

The majority of the Level I educator's time will be spent in the field delivering risk-reduction presentations. This is especially true for those educators who are employed full-time. The Level I educator must become a master at scheduling, maximizing the use of the time available without overloading the schedule or producing scheduling conflicts. There should also be coordination of scheduling of risk-reduction activities between station personnel and the risk-reduction educator to avoid conflicts there as well **(Figure 3.5)**.

Establishment and coordination of a daily schedule assists the Level I educator in scheduling risk-reduction activities. Once a basic work schedule is established, it is important to commit to it as much as possible. There may be times when it will have to be altered to meet the needs of the community or to attend a special activity or event. But for the most part, be diligent in staying with the established schedule.

When scheduling presentations or other events, the following factors should be considered:

- The relationship of the request to the organizational risk-reduction priorities or strategies
- Time required to prepare for the event or activity
- Time involved for delivery of the presentation or activity
- Time required to debrief the activity, clean up, or pack up
- Travel time to the event or travel time from one event to another
- If station personnel are involved, other commitments or scheduled activities (such as training, hydrant maintenance, and pre-incident planning)

Figure 3.5 A fire and life safety educator going over schedules with the officer in charge of a fire station.

Working around the schedules of operational personnel can help develop a good relationship between those performing the education function and those staffing the stations and engines.

Managing Your Time

As the risk-reduction activities of the fire department become visible and noticeable in the community, the demands for presentations and activities will increase to the point of overwhelming the capabilities of the individual educator. It is imperative that educators do not overload themselves or attempt to fill every request. View requests for service in light of the organization's risk-reduction initiatives and the educator's schedule. It is okay to say "no" to an event or activity that does not fit within the goals and initiatives of the organization. (**NOTE:** If you have to decline an event, refer the organization to available resources in its area.)

In larger communities especially, examining requests will allow the educator to concentrate time and effort on those activities where there will be the greatest impact in the community and on those that will impact the high-risk audiences who have been identified by the fire organization or risk-reduction managers.

What This Means to You

"Examine community requests in light of your department and city's missions and goals. This allows you to focus your time and energy on activities providing the greatest impact to your community and to those high-risk audiences identified by the fire organization or risk reduction managers," said Dena Schumacher, Champaign Fire Department, Champaign, IL.

A variety of resources are available to assist in the coordination of a standard work schedule. As previously mentioned, manual and electronic methods are available. Some educators may use a simple type of calendar binder, which is broken down by day, week, or month. Others may prefer a more sophisticated tool. There are electronic means of developing and maintaining a work schedule us-

ing electronic calendars and scheduling programs. Some agencies may require the use of a certain type of scheduling system, which allows for viewing by others in the office or department. Simply put, each individual must find a schedule system that works for his or her lifestyle, habits, and job requirements and stay with it. It goes without saying that an effective Level I educator will always use some type of calendar for scheduling purposes and will not depend on memory or recall for the scheduling of activities or events.

Summary of Time Management Tips

Many sources for information are available on time management, and many individuals have developed tips or practices that they believe will work. The following are just a few of those tips:

- Try to handle each piece of paper only once.
- Know your most productive time.
- Begin and complete the most important task first thing after arriving at work.
- Begin each day by establishing an agenda for the day.
- List all steps and tasks that need to be accomplished and number them in order of priority.
- Delegate as much as you can to others (returning phone calls, scheduling, and the like) while making sure that you take on your share of the work.
- Write out a "To Do" list every day, and keep to it. Mark off things when completed to give yourself a sense of accomplishment.
- Know your time limitations and be willing to say "no."
- Say "no" to the project, not the person. You cannot do everything everyone asks you to do.
- Schedule downtime for yourself — do not overcommit. Always plan time for balance: include family, fitness, recreation, social, and spiritual activities.

What This Means to You

We say "yes" to others because we want to please them. Recognize that a desire to please others often prevents us from saying "no." Stay with your plan. If you have a written set of goals and strategies, this gives you a reason to continue your course. Make sure that you understand exactly what is being asked of you before you respond. Perhaps the task is more time consuming than you thought. On the other hand, it may not take much effort at all.

Use the following guidelines when faced with these requests:

- Excel at just a few things, rather than being just average at many. Do not try to do everything.

- Remember that others may take you for granted and even lose respect for you if you do not ever turn down requests.

- Be polite but firm in saying no. You only build false hopes with wishy-washy responses. For instance, the phrase "I'll try to be there" in response to an invitation is giving yourself an excuse to avoid a commitment.

- Provide suggestions or alternatives to the person who is asking. (For example, "I cannot do that task today, but how about next week," or, "How about asking John instead?")

- When in doubt, it is easier to say no now, and then change your mind to a yes later, rather than the other way around.

Sometimes, saying "no" is simply unavoidable. Here are some techniques to use:

- Tell the person you can agree to their request this time, but ask how the two of you might plan better for the next time.

- Tell them yes, but remind them they owe you one. For example, they might cover you for a shift next time you need time off.

- Tell them yes, but take control by saying you will come back to them with a timetable. For instance, say, "I expect I will be able to do that for you by the end of the week."

- Put a tough condition on your agreement: "If it would only take an hour, I would be able to help, but I cannot give you more than that."

Source: Pace Productivity[1]

At times, the Level I educator may feel overwhelmed by the workload or the demands of the job. An open line of communication with his or her supervisor will benefit the Level I educator. Consulting one's supervisor concerning scheduling conflicts, involvement in projects, and the programs and events relating to the risk-reduction activities of the department will help to prioritize the work schedule. It will also help for the supervisor to understand the scope of the demands being made by the community on the risk-reduction division.

Responding to Community Needs

In many communities, the fire department is seen as a source of knowledge, information, supplies, equipment, manpower, and other forms of assistance for members of the community. Many times, requests for service come to the fire department simply because it is not known where else to send them.

Requests will come into the fire prevention office or risk-reduction division requesting information or assistance with problems or issues relating to fire and life safety and other societal issues or situations. In the course of any day, an educator out among the members of the community will field questions or receive requests for items or assistance that the fire department may be unable to provide. In many instances, the need is an important one, and saying "No, I cannot help" is simply not an appropriate response.

A variety of organizations and agencies in any community provide social services and assistance. Also available are national organizations, government organizations, private agencies, and organizations. Resources will vary from community to community. Those in the field of risk reduction need to become familiar with the agencies and organizations in their community in order to refer individuals to the proper source **(Figure 3.6)**.

Because fire and injury prevention is the focus of any risk-reduction division, the requests for equipment and service relating to those areas will be the most prevalent. Child safety seats, smoke alarms, and carbon monoxide alarms are frequent requests of a fire department, but there is often no source for funding or acquisition for these items. Bike helmets and personal floatation devices are also the subject of requests, many times from schools or childcare

Figure 3.6 Fire and life safety educators should be knowledgeable of specialized agencies and organizations within their communities.

organizations. New parents, individuals who are new to the community, or those who live in substandard housing may seek home safety devices. Senior residents or their caregivers often seek slip and fall prevention devices, such as grab bars, slip-proof rugs, and stairway lighting. There may be other, more innovative safety devices that come along about which the Level I educator must remain current.

Many times fire departments will receive requests for assistance that are outside the realm of fire and injury prevention and are not even within the scope of the organization's mission. Fire service organizations have the reputation of helping community members in many ways above and beyond emergencies. Citizens may request assistance with high utility bills during the cold winter months or extremely hot summers. Victims of residential fires may look to the fire department to assist with the replacement of necessary items lost in the fire. At holiday times, many requests may come to the fire department for assistance with food, gifts, and other items for those in the community who are less fortunate. The risk-reduction division may be the recipient of these requests, and it is important that all requests be handled or referred to the ap-

propriate agencies or organizations. The worst thing that could happen is for the fire department to seem uncaring or indifferent to the needs of the community.

Assisting community members with needs outside the realm of fire and life safety is not only good public relations. Actions such as these serve as door-openers for Level I educators to assist with fire and life safety issues that might exist. If the basic needs of the community members are not being met, then those individuals in need are less apt to be receptive to information concerning fire and injury prevention and may be the very ones who need it the most. In addition, any fire organization, at one time or another, will need the support of the community for budget issues, personnel issues, or simply a forum for risk-reduction programs. By taking care of the needs of the community, fire agencies are building equity that they can draw upon when needed.

To provide the proper referral, risk-reduction educators must be familiar with agencies and organizations in the community that can assist with a variety of needs. Standard to most communities are other emergency services organizations, such as private or government based EMS services and law enforcement agencies, including the county sheriff's offices and municipal police departments. These organizations may be able to provide assistance with bike helmets and child safety seats. Agencies providing protection and governance of public waterways, such as the Army Corps of Engineers and Department of Natural Resources, may be able to provide personal floatation devices as a part of a loaner program or through donations. Members of most communities have access to local chapters of the American Red Cross and the Salvation Army that can assist victims of fire with recovery efforts.

Local health departments and hospitals are good sources for child safety equipment, such as child passenger restraints, bike helmets, and carbon monoxide alarms. Social service agencies, such as Child Protective Services or family and children services, may have access to private donors who can assist families in a variety of ways. Local Safe Kids Worldwide organizations often have access to a variety of safety devices designed to keep children free from injury. There may be social service agencies that can assist older adults with special needs.

When seeking assistance, fire and life safety educators should not forget about local businesses that get involved in community service. Big-box stores and some national companies may be excellent partners in assisting community members with a variety of needs. Local organizations, such as personal aid groups and faith-based groups, are willing to assist in many ways. When looking for those agencies and organizations that might be able to assist, consider the target audience served by that agency. For example, those working with older adults may be a source for assistance with slip and fall prevention devices. Safe Kids organizations will seek to help individuals with safety concerns involving children.

Once fire and life safety educators have identified the organizations in the community that provide various types of assistance, the next step is to develop a relationship with these organizations. Government offices or the local Chamber of Commerce have lists of local nonprofit agencies, which should include the names of their directors or leaders. Often, because of the proper documentation of risk-reduction activities that have been conducted, a database of these agencies and representatives may already exist. It is only a matter of retrieving the information and developing a complete list of community resources.

Contact each agency and discuss what type of assistance the organization is able to provide and how individuals may avail themselves of the assistance and discuss what assistance the fire organization is able to provide for community members and the risk-reduction initiatives that are taking place or that are in the planning stages.

Coordination with these agencies can develop into partnerships for risk-reduction projects and programs in the community. A working relationship with other community service organizations can often aid the overburdened educator with events and activities that might otherwise be the responsibility of one individual. More information on the importance of networking and partnerships are provided in Chapter 4.

Chapter Summary

As with any career, administrative tasks have to be performed and cannot be overlooked. These tasks are vital to the success of a community risk-reduction program. The administrative task of properly completing documentation of activities and events can prove its worth.

Assisting Agencies or Organizations

In any community, a variety of organizations can assist with the needs of community members. Some of those organizations may be local, while some may be nationally based. Many times these organizations can be located through the local Chamber of Commerce, City Hall, county administration, or other government offices. The following are other programs that are available:

- Adult literacy programs
- Advocacy and ethnic organizations
- American Red Cross
- Burn and trauma centers
- Civic groups and organizations
- Faith-based organizations
- Family and children services
- Health departments and local hospitals
- Law enforcement agencies
- Local businesses and charities
- Local chapters of the American Academy of Pediatrics
- Local Cooperative Extension Services
- Local EMS organizations (non-fire based or private)
- Local philanthropists
- Local university and junior colleges
- PTA/PTO organizations
- Safe Kids organizations
- Salvation Army
- Scouting organizations
- Senior adult organizations (AARP)
- Shriner's Hospital for Children
- Welfare agencies

Level I educators are tasked with the awesome responsibility of delivering educational presentations. They must also be the ones to complete the documentation of these events and activities. This documentation should include basic information as well as anything special that occurred as a result of the presentation. Documentation reports provide a foundation for future educational efforts in the community and for continuing support from public officials and fire service employees.

Risk-reduction educators must be attentive to the details of documentation and stay current on the paperwork involved. Often, other tasks will need more attention or may seem more important than filling out forms and justifying dollars. However, it is in those tasks, such as paperwork, timekeeping, and activity reporting, that Level I educators will see the fruits of their work and the successes of their programs. Each program or presentation completed adds to the repertoire of success stories that can be presented to anyone who asks. Proper completion of documentation can certainly provide proof that fire and life safety education works, which is the goal of any risk-reduction program.

Review Questions

1. What is the benefit of documenting the fire and life safety education program activities?

2. What is appropriate information for a report documenting fire and life safety activities?

3. What are some methods for ensuring a fire and life safety educator's work schedule is free from conflicts?

4. What are common community organizations and resources to which citizens with needs may be referred by the fire and life safety educator?

5. What is the benefit of the fire and life safety educator finding an available resource to solve a citizen's need, even if it is not a fire department problem?

Key Terms

Curriculum — Broad term that refers to the sequence of presentation, the content of what is taught, and the structure of ideas and activities developed to meet the learning needs of students and achieve desired educational objectives; also the teaching and learning methods involved, how learner attainment of objectives is assessed, and the underlying theory and philosophy of education.

Lesson Plan — The road map providing general guidance for how a presentation is to be delivered. It contains information and instructions on what will be taught and the teaching procedures to be followed. It covers lessons that may vary in length from a few minutes to several hours.

Presentation — (1) Second of the four teaching steps in which the educator teaches a class or individual and transfers facts and ideas. (2) Lesson plan component at which point an instructor provides to, shares with, demonstrates to, and involves the followers in the lesson information. *See* Lesson Plan. (3) Single delivery of fire and life safety information. *Also known as* Lesson or Delivery.

Risk-Reduction Program — Comprehensive strategy that addresses fire and life safety issues via educational means.

Risk-Reduction Strategy — A series of integrated programs designed to impact a common goal.

Chapter 3 Notes

1. "Tips." Pace Productivity. Source: http://www.getmoredone.com/tips.html. Accessed 10-15-09.

FLSE Level I Educators: Planning and Development

Chapter Contents

Photo courtesy of Brett Noakes.

chapter 4

Key Terms

Job Performance Requirements

This chapter provides information that addresses the following job performance requirements of NFPA® 1035, *Standard for Professional Qualifications for Fire and Life Safety Educator, Public Information Officer, and Juvenile Firesetter Intervention Specialist*, 2010 edition.

NFPA® 1035 References

5.2.4

5.3.1

FESHE Learning Objectives

Fire and Emergency Services Higher Education (FESHE) Objectives: *Fire and Life Safety Education*

3. Identify stakeholders; develop partnerships and coalitions to work on fire and life safety education activities.

Learning Objectives

After reading this chapter, students will be able to:

1. Explain the purpose in partnering with community organizations. (NFPA® 1035, 5.3.1)

2. Explain the difference between networking, partnerships, and coalitions.

3. Identify the benefits of forming partnerships with community organizations. (NFPA® 1035, 5.2.4, 5.3.1)

4. Discuss how to develop partnerships and the qualities of successful coalitions.

Chapter 4
FLSE Level I Educators: Planning and Development

Case History

On Friday, December 26, 2008, seven people died in a residential fire in Philadelphia, PA. Three of the seven who died were children — ages 1, 7, and 8. Another resident was burned. Six of those who died were found huddled together in the basement, and the seventh was found near the basement's only exit to the outside. The interior basement stairs had been removed from the home. There were no smoke alarms in the house, although working alarms may not have made a difference. The fire started when gasoline was used to refill a kerosene heater.

On the following Sunday, the mother of the three children addressed a packed church in the neighborhood and pleaded with members to not let her children die in vain. She held up pictures of her three children and begged members to get smoke alarms for their homes. Members of the Philadelphia Fire Department were at the worship service and answered questions about the fire and provided fire safety information. This moving and heart-wrenching plea brought members from the community together to organize committees to educate the community about home safety and provide assistance.

The partnership between this grieving mother and the Philadelphia Fire Department gave a face to the problem and an urgency to the solution. The reality of the situation was apparent to the community members, and the neighbors saw that it really could happen to someone they knew. Without this victim's testament to fire's deadly force, the fire department's message had seemed empty and hollow.

Networking, partnerships, and coalitions bring life to a prevention program and make the work for the fire and life safety educator easier and more applicable. The following chapter provides valuable information on working with partnerships and coalitions and reinforces the value of those relationships.

Source: Dave Statter 911, WUSA News, Philadelphia, PA

Chapter 2 introduced a variety of topics and subjects that are considered important in the fire and life safety field. The information presented involved developing an understanding of fire and unintentional injuries, the behavior and science of fire, and other relevant topics in the field of fire and life safety. There is much more information for the Level I educator to learn, for example: how to properly install a child safety seat, how to fit a bike helmet, and how to prevent falls for older adults **(Figure 4.1, p. 96)**.

Figure 4.1 Fire and life safety educator preparing to give a presentation on the installation of child safety seats. *Courtesy of Lt. Beverley Walker, Hall County Fire Services, Gainesville, GA.*

In some agencies, the task of fire and life safety education is delegated to a single individual. In larger communities, there may be more than one person assigned this responsibility. In many fire departments, including volunteer departments, suppression personnel perform the education and prevention functions as a part of their regular duties. Whatever the arrangement, rarely are there enough trained individuals to meet the demands and needs of the community. In addition, money and other resources needed to provide educational programs are traditionally scarce or, more commonly, nonexistent.

The educator's job may seem insurmountable because there is so much to do and so few resources. The fire and life safety educator is presented with the unique challenge of meeting the demands and needs of the community with few or no resources while needing to maintain a working knowledge of all of the relevant community issues. In most instances, the Level I educator will be given a priority

risk issue and then will be expected to seek out community **partners** to assist with the risk issue. These partners assist in meeting the goals and objectives of risk-reduction initiatives.

This chapter introduces the concept of partnerships and defines the different levels of partnerships and relationships. Many of the benefits of partnering with other organizations are very obvious, while other benefits may not be as readily apparent. There can be a downside to working with partners, but for the majority of the time the benefits far outweigh the disadvantages. Partners have knowledge in their area of expertise and may have time, money, and other resources that the fire agencies do not have.

The previous chapter stressed that the Level I educator should be aware of community agencies or organizations to which individuals could be referred for assistance. In this chapter, that same knowledge of community agencies and organizations will be used for the purpose of developing partnerships to assist in the delivery of fire and life safety intervention programs.

Why Partnerships?

Many fire and life safety educators believe they can do everything. In fact, it may seem to a Level I educator that they ARE doing everything. Fire and life safety educators are trying to effectively serve each and every group within the community from the very young to the very old and everyone in between **(Figure 4.2)**.

Fire and life safety educators learn to work independently and often prefer it that way. It is their desire to develop programs and conduct presentations in the best and most effective way. They are often hesitant to share that responsibility with someone else, especially those outside the fire service. This hesitancy comes from the passion for the work and the commitment to perfection. However, by developing and maintaining partnerships, fire and life safety educators can more effectively meet the challenges of their communities.

The Level I educator must value the role that partnerships play in reducing fire and injury risk within a community. It is simply not feasible for an educator to be all-knowing in every area of fire and injury prevention. Teamwork and organizational

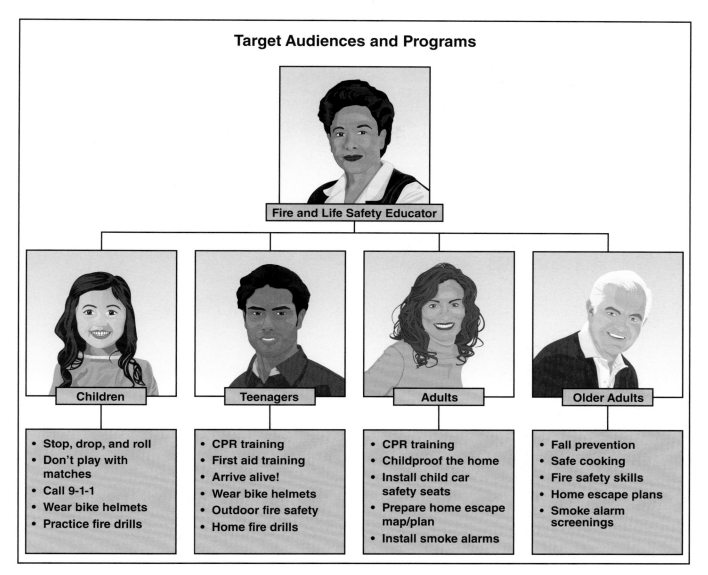

Target Audiences and Programs

Fire and Life Safety Educator

Children
- Stop, drop, and roll
- Don't play with matches
- Call 9-1-1
- Wear bike helmets
- Practice fire drills

Teenagers
- CPR training
- First aid training
- Arrive alive!
- Wear bike helmets
- Outdoor fire safety
- Home fire drills

Adults
- CPR training
- Childproof the home
- Install child car safety seats
- Prepare home escape map/plan
- Install smoke alarms

Older Adults
- Fall prevention
- Safe cooking
- Fire safety skills
- Home escape plans
- Smoke alarm screenings

Figure 4.2 Examples of the different age groups that fire and life safety educators must try to reach with their presentations.

support carry the efforts of the educator to a level of success in meeting the goals of community risk reduction that might not otherwise be achievable.

Community partnerships are essential to the goals of the Level I fire and life safety educator. Resources, human resources, recognition, new ideas, consistent messages, credibility, and outreach of programs are vital to the success of community partnerships.

- *Resources.* When looking for organizations or agencies to serve as potential partners, there are certain categories the Level I educator should explore. The first is learning and information. If an educator is tasked with delivering a program on burn prevention at the local senior center, it may be prudent to seek out professionals in the area of burn care and treatment to provide knowledge and insight into this topic. If participating in a bike rodeo at the local Boys and Girls club, the Level I educator will need to seek out those groups in the community, such as bike police units or local Safe Kids organizations, to provide assistance in the proper fitting of helmets.

- *Human resources.* Delivering fire and life safety education activities in the community takes a great deal of time, energy, and money. By **networking** and partnering with others, the Level I educator can build relationships with people and organizations that will allow more of the community to be reached and ultimately create a safer environment for everyone.

Figure 4.3 Recognition is important for the success of fire and life safety education programs.

- *Recognition.* Partnering with outside organizations can provide recognition for the fire and life safety educator. This may not seem like a resource, but recognition of the educator, the risk-reduction activities, and the fire department can pay off by preserving or increasing the education budget, or enabling more people to participate in fire and life safety activities. Recognition can inform people, both inside and outside the organization, about the risk-reduction activities and keep the efforts on track **(Figure 4.3)**.

- *New ideas.* Partnerships are a primary source of new information for Level I educators. Others in the community may have more experience or approach the problem from a different angle, and the Level I educator can take advantage of this inexpensive and invaluable resource experience.

- *Consistent messages.* Partnerships enable consistent messages to reach the community. If individuals receive conflicting messages from different organizations, they will not know what to do and will most likely do nothing. All the organizations in the community that address the current issues need to be on the same page, and the best way to accomplish this is through partnering **(Figure 4.4)**.

- *Credibility.* Partnering with community agencies and organizations enhances the credibility of the fire organization. When others see that organizations in the community are banding together for a cause, they are more likely to support that cause and adopt the messages being promoted.

- *Outreach of programs.* Partnering with other community organizations and agencies will increase the outreach of the programs being conducted by the fire organization. The ultimate goal of any fire and life safety education program is to reach as much of the community as possible in an effective manner with relevant and up-to-date advice on actions and behaviors. Community organizations, especially those serving high-risk groups, can provide an avenue for the Level I educator to get a foot in the door, an opening that might not otherwise exist.

> **Alone we can do so little; together we can do so much**. *Helen Keller*

Ultimately, the benefits of partnering with organizations and agencies that have similar goals far outweigh the benefits of working alone. Sharing the workload, using resources available from other groups, and drawing on the experience and

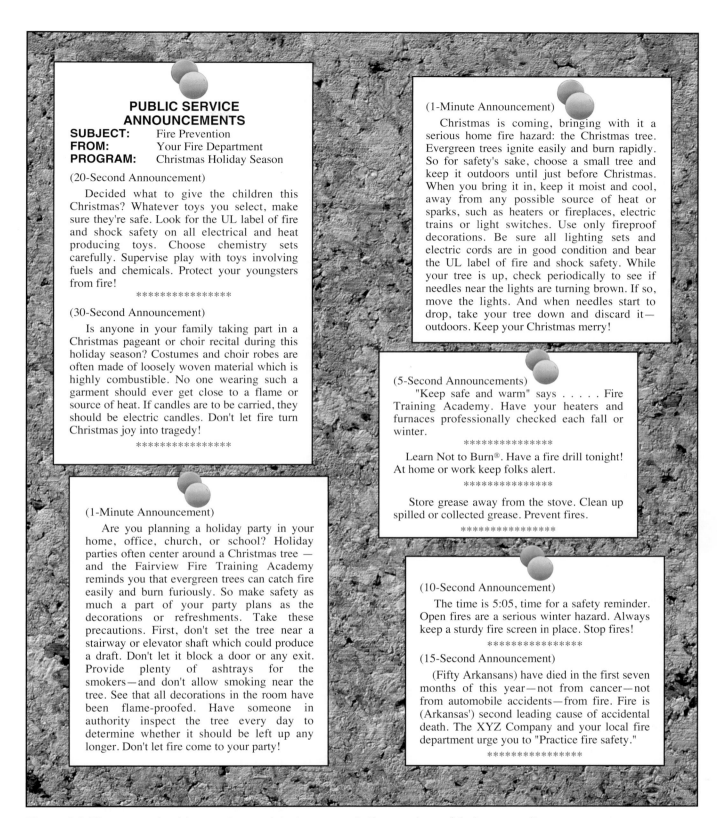

PUBLIC SERVICE ANNOUNCEMENTS

SUBJECT: Fire Prevention
FROM: Your Fire Department
PROGRAM: Christmas Holiday Season

(20-Second Announcement)

Decided what to give the children this Christmas? Whatever toys you select, make sure they're safe. Look for the UL label of fire and shock safety on all electrical and heat producing toys. Choose chemistry sets carefully. Supervise play with toys involving fuels and chemicals. Protect your youngsters from fire!

****

(30-Second Announcement)

Is anyone in your family taking part in a Christmas pageant or choir recital during this holiday season? Costumes and choir robes are often made of loosely woven material which is highly combustible. No one wearing such a garment should ever get close to a flame or source of heat. If candles are to be carried, they should be electric candles. Don't let fire turn Christmas joy into tragedy!

****

(1-Minute Announcement)

Are you planning a holiday party in your home, office, church, or school? Holiday parties often center around a Christmas tree — and the Fairview Fire Training Academy reminds you that evergreen trees can catch fire easily and burn furiously. So make safety as much a part of your party plans as the decorations or refreshments. Take these precautions. First, don't set the tree near a stairway or elevator shaft which could produce a draft. Don't let it block a door or any exit. Provide plenty of ashtrays for the smokers—and don't allow smoking near the tree. See that all decorations in the room have been flame-proofed. Have someone in authority inspect the tree every day to determine whether it should be left up any longer. Don't let fire come to your party!

(1-Minute Announcement)

Christmas is coming, bringing with it a serious home fire hazard: the Christmas tree. Evergreen trees ignite easily and burn rapidly. So for safety's sake, choose a small tree and keep it outdoors until just before Christmas. When you bring it in, keep it moist and cool, away from any possible source of heat or sparks, such as heaters or fireplaces, electric trains or light switches. Use only fireproof decorations. Be sure all lighting sets and electric cords are in good condition and bear the UL label of fire and shock safety. While your tree is up, check periodically to see if needles near the lights are turning brown. If so, move the lights. And when needles start to drop, take your tree down and discard it— outdoors. Keep your Christmas merry!

(5-Second Announcements)

"Keep safe and warm" says . . . . . Fire Training Academy. Have your heaters and furnaces professionally checked each fall or winter.

****

Learn Not to Burn®. Have a fire drill tonight! At home or work keep folks alert.

****

Store grease away from the stove. Clean up spilled or collected grease. Prevent fires.

****

(10-Second Announcement)

The time is 5:05, time for a safety reminder. Open fires are a serious winter hazard. Always keep a sturdy fire screen in place. Stop fires!

****

(15-Second Announcement)

(Fifty Arkansans) have died in the first seven months of this year—not from cancer—not from automobile accidents—from fire. Fire is (Arkansas') second leading cause of accidental death. The XYZ Company and your local fire department urge you to "Practice fire safety."

****

Figure 4.4 All partners should present a consistent message to the members of their community.

knowledge of other individuals and groups in the field contribute to an increase in the effectiveness of the risk-reduction programs and allow for better customer service for the community.

Types of Partnerships

Partnerships can differ, depending on the purpose and goals of the relationship. Some partnerships may be long-lasting, while others may exist only for the duration of a project. Each type of partnership serves its own specific purpose. Networking is often the starting point in forming a partnership. Through collaboration, "informal" partnerships are formed and through coalitions, "formal" partnerships may be formed.

Networking

Networking is the process of meeting others and determining who has resources that could assist the fire and life safety educator with the goals and objectives of the programs. Networking is often informal. Oftentimes, resources such as knowledge, information, financial support, or human resources can be determined from this process. The personal benefits of networking can often be greater than the FLSE I will expect.

Networking Opportunities

Many states have fire and life safety educator associations that are open to anyone interested in the field of fire safety and injury prevention. Organizations such as these are excellent networking opportunities. Particularly for the Level I educator, these groups can provide a wealth of information about the job, up-to-date methods and approaches to education, and which programs other communities are using for risk reduction. Educators who have been in the field for many years can serve as mentors for an up-and-coming educator. Many of these organizations conduct annual conferences dedicated to the field of injury prevention and life-safety issues. By participating in organizations and activities at the state level, the Level I educator can take valuable information back to the home community for use in developing partnerships and strategies to reduce risk and change behaviors. Offices of the state fire marshal or other fire and life safety educators should be able to provide information on local or state organizations.

Collaboration

Collaboration is another term for an informal partnership. Collaboration is the result of networking and involves working with one or more people on a specific project. Networking leads the educator to individuals who know about a subject or have a particular interest. Collaboration on a project or program draws together those individuals who share a common goal, and the project becomes a collaborative effort (partnership) characterized by decision making and the allocation of resources related to

Partnership for Safety Educational Activities for Adults

The Home Safety Council, Fire Protection Publications (FPP), and ProLiteracy Worldwide formed a partnership that led to successful safety educational activities for adults with a low reading level.

- The Home Safety Council is a national, nonprofit organization solely dedicated to preventing home-related injuries.[1]

- FPP is the world's leading publisher of training materials for the fire and emergency services, publishing and distributing the IFSTA-validated training manuals.

- ProLiteracy is the oldest and largest nonprofit adult literacy organization in the world.

These three organizations collaborated to provide effective, low-cost fire safety and disaster preparedness educational materials to be used by adults at all reading levels. Thus, the Home Safety Literacy Project was born. Low literacy rates have been a serious barrier to learning necessary home fire-safety skills and to understand and apply key fire protection and disaster preparedness measures in the home. This partnership has proved highly successful in providing materials to communities throughout the country to present safety information in a format that can be understood by adults at all reading levels so that all will have access to this vital information. The Home Safety Literacy Project has since partnered with various communities to implement the program and received impressive evaluation results. Since these three agencies partnered on this project, the results are farther reaching and more effective than if any of them had tried it on their own.

Source: Home Safety Council

the activities of the program or project. Once the program or project is completed, the collaboration may end temporarily.

Coalition

A **coalition** is a group of individuals and members from organizations who come together for a specific purpose. A coalition is more formal than a collaboration. It is an alliance of those who share common goals. Coalitions may involve a variety of people and may produce a product or service. The purpose of a coalition may be to increase communication and understanding or to disseminate information to the community.

When a coalition comes together, its members share a common goal. In fact, before a coalition begins its work, members should agree upon common goals and reach a consensus about those goals, both among the members of the coalition and the organizations represented by the members. For this reason, it is important to identify the common goals for community education issues in a community or neighborhood.

The Benefits of Partnering

While many of the benefits have already been mentioned, it is important to enumerate the benefits of partnering with organizations and agencies in the community for risk-reduction efforts.

Consider a fire department that provides or receives mutual aid from a neighboring department. Mutual aid occurs when the resources of a jurisdiction are overwhelmed or inadequate for an incident or situation. Is partnering for risk reduction any different? One department simply will not have all the necessary knowledge, resources, equipment, and time to tackle significant community risk issues or solutions. It is just too much work for one individual to be effective and to make a long-term, positive difference or change in the community. Change requires teamwork.

Community Attention

Involving community organizations may give more attention to the issue or problem being addressed. If only one organization is promoting a behavioral change, it might not get the attention that it would if several organizations are promoting the issue.

Wider Knowledge and Skill Base

By partnering with other agencies and organizations, a broader knowledge base is available to the educator. As indicated in the introduction to this chapter, there is much knowledge that one individual would need to have in order to address the risk issues in the community. Sharing expertise is an important benefit of partnering with other community groups.

Working with community partners can provide a creativity level that may otherwise be nonexistent. Working alone, the Level I educator is limited to his or her own ideas and level of expertise. Members of other organizations may have more creative or innovative ideas for approaching the identified risk issues. It is possible that the ideas and concepts for

Professional Development

There are personal benefits to any fire and life safety educator who is networking and participating in coalitions. Professional development is very important to an educator who is trying to stay on top of the latest innovations in technology, messages, and program development. Professional development is a must for those who want to develop community risk-reduction programs for a variety of existing risk issues. While involvement in state and local fire organizations is important, networking with others in the fire service whose role is fire and life safety education is imperative. Educators in the fire service are known to readily share and assist others in the field with program information, lesson plans, and simple tips for effectiveness. Educator associations exist in many states, but there are other networking opportunities as well. Participation in training classes at the national level, such as at the National Fire Academy in Emmitsburg, Maryland, is an excellent way to form partnerships and relationships that serve to assist all in design and delivery of programs. Many fire and life safety educator associations sponsor annual conferences that usually are offered at a minimal fee and can enrich any educator's skills as well as provide a source for lasting relationships. Educators must realize the value in these personal enrichment opportunities, or they will become "stale" and less effective in the work in their home community.

risk-reduction programs may have already been tried by other agencies or organizations in the community and have not been successful. By partnering, educators can save valuable time and money by reaping the benefit of this knowledge; that is, they do not have to "reinvent the wheel."

Wider Range of Resources

Other benefits of partnering include extra people, more time, additional financial resources, and better access to those affected by the risk or solutions. The concept of developing partnerships illustrates the old adage "divide and conquer." In this age of limited time, resources, and energy, sharing the workload is one of the major benefits of partnering with community organizations **(Figure 4.5)**.

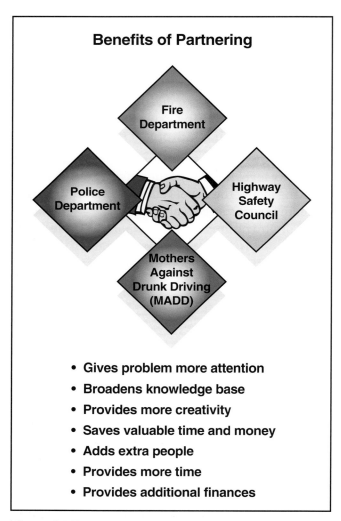

Benefits of Partnering

Fire Department

Police Department

Highway Safety Council

Mothers Against Drunk Driving (MADD)

- Gives problem more attention
- Broadens knowledge base
- Provides more creativity
- Saves valuable time and money
- Adds extra people
- Provides more time
- Provides additional finances

Figure 4.5 Partnering with other organizations brings many benefits to a fire and life safety education program.

Developing Community Partnerships

A community partner is a person, group, or organization that is willing to join forces with others to address a community-risk issue. These partners must have a stake in the success of the program or project being developed.

In seeking partnerships, fire and life safety educators need to look for those organizations and agencies that are a good fit with the goals and mission of the fire and life safety education programs. It is important for partnerships to bring something to the table that will benefit the entire community.

It is important to consider which part of the population is being targeted by the risk-reduction program and think about which groups or organizations are already providing services to that particular population. Also, think about those individuals or groups that care about the risk issues and the people who are affected. These may be the best individuals to deliver the message. The bottom line is this: Who in the community will be able to assist in getting the effort started and the job done? Look for individuals, groups, or agencies that can offer leadership, skills, credibility, contacts, influence, and resources.

Who are these groups or individuals? Some possibilities include:

- Groups already interested or addressing the same or a similar risk issue.

- Members of the population who are affected by the issue or who will benefit from the programs or project.

- Those who feel the financial impact of the problem (insurance companies, property owners, disaster services, other community aid services).

- Groups already providing services to the population.

- Advocacy groups.

- Groups that can help deliver the messages (media, clergy, schools, or marketing organizations).

It is important to discuss the intention of forming partnerships to address fire and or injury issues. Explain what your organization can provide, and determine if the organization will be a good partner in the project or program being planned.

An action plan should be developed for the partnership. This action plan should include the following:

Partnership Action Plan

	Verde Valley Community Fire and Life Safety Education Coalition Action Plan	
TASK:	ASSIGNED TO:	COMPLETION:
Assess community needs	Dena (Fire Department) Bruce (Fire Department)	05-30-2011
Develop objectives	Terry (Fire Department) Nancy (City Commission)	06-30-2011
Develop goals	Dayna (Children's Hospital) Beverly (Police Department)	07-31-2011
Design budget	Chris (Community Service) Angela (Fire Department)	08-31-2011
Evaluate results	Pat (City Hospital) Mike (Police Department) Jeff (City Hall)	11-30-2011

Figure 4.6 An example of a partnership action plan.

- Specific tasks to be accomplished
- Assignment of responsibilities
- Timetable with deadlines for each task

Depending on the formality of the partnerships, tasks may include:

- Assessing community needs
- Developing goals
- Developing objectives
- Designing a budget
- Evaluating the results

Successful coalitions or partnerships benefit from a written plan; the tasks and associated timelines can be included in the action plan for the group, for agreement by all parties involved **(Figure 4.6)**.

The Challenges of Partnerships

As previously discussed, the benefits of developing partnerships far outweigh the costs. However, it is important to be aware of some of the traps or pitfalls in working with a coalition. Some will be unavoidable, but recognition of the problem can help lead to the successful resolution of the issue.

Individuals can lose sight of the focus or direction of the coalition. Many individuals want to get involved in too many areas or perhaps try to involve unrelated issues. Those participating in coalitions must work to maintain the focus of the group by reviewing the statement of purpose or mission statement of the group and making sure that all projects and programs focus on the purpose of the organization. For example, National Safe Kids Campaign deals with unintentional injuries to children age 14 and under. Therefore, a local Safe Kids coalition would not be participating or working with a fall prevention program for older adults.

Another problem that can arise in coalitions is the question of rightful leadership. Some solutions to this problem could include a rotation in leadership and the use of committees. Leaders who are selected should be neutral and representative of the coalition. Leaders of coalitions must be encouraged to share the leadership and responsibility with the remaining coalition members.

In coalitions where the members represent different organizations, members must individually weigh what is best for the coalition and what is best for their organization. Sometimes the members try to put the goals of their organization ahead of the goals of the coalition. It is especially important that the group focuses on the common ground found between the organizations and the similarities in the goals and mission of the coalition and the organizations involved.

The Level I educator should be aware that often the higher the level of the agency and the greater the number of agencies involved, the greater the challenges to partnerships can become. Local agencies working with state agencies, or local and national nonprofits can sometimes create inner struggles for leadership or control. However, all of the challenges mentioned can be overcome, and they are far outweighed by the great benefit of the partnerships to the community as a whole.

Tips for Developing Successful Partnerships

In order to reduce the possibility of potential barriers to successful partnerships, certain activities can be performed. These include the following:

- Start small. Keep activities simple.

- Communicate regularly with everyone involved. Make clear communication a priority.

- Get to know the people in the partnership. This will assist in the team-building aspect of the partnership or collaboration.

- Encourage members to voice their needs. A win/win situation will make the relationship even stronger.

- Establish clear roles for members and leaders. Develop written statements to document the commitment expected of each participant.

- Ensure that the work and activities of the partnership are enjoyable.

- Celebrate accomplishments. Recognize the contributions of members, and reward them for their accomplishments.

Working With Others

The fire and life safety educator is responsible and accountable to his or her own organization. It is important to be familiar with the goals and objectives of the new collaborative organization being represented: its culture, values, and goals. Many organizations may not be supportive of collabora-

What This Means to You

The Internet and the widespread use of the World Wide Web have opened up endless possibilities for virtual networking and partnering. No longer do partners or colleagues have to meet face to face to collaborate, plan, or share information. Partnerships can exist across jurisdictional and even state boundaries. The use of e-mail, chat rooms, and virtual bulletin boards has greatly enhanced risk-reduction activities in individual communities and organizations. Virtual collaboration can help minimize a feeling of isolation.

You should have an electronic Rolodex or address book filled with sources for collaboration, networking, and information. In addition, you should always be ready to share information as well as request it. To gather this information, however, you must get out in the fire and injury prevention community to make the initial contacts and find the individuals needed to fill that address book!

One such group that presently exists is an e-mail group called National Fire and Life Safety Educators. This group can be accessed through Yahoo! Groups <groups.yahoo.com> and may be found by searching for NFLSE. This list is not moderated and only requires a click on the "Join this Group!" link. Questions and comments from educators across the country can be e-mailed to the group and discussion in the form of real-time or daily digested e-mail. Topics include issues, problems, questions, or current events affecting fire and life safety educators across the U.S. Using a search engine to search for other fire and life safety groups will most likely yield similar groups in which to participate.

tive work because they do not understand the nature or value of the work, the potential impact, and the results for the educator's organization.

Because of the educator's responsibility to his or her organization, promises to the partnership must be made carefully and thoughtfully. It is important for the educator to receive a supervisor's buy-in before making promises. This will ensure personal success and earn respect from the educator's organization and the partnership. Once promises are made, the educator should do everything possible to keep them. Sometimes situations or events take precedent, such as fires and other emergency responses, that are outside the control of the educator. If the availability of resources, including time and money, changes, the educator should inform the partnership immediately.

The fire and life safety educator must be careful not to overcommit money, personnel, or time. Fire and life safety educators must be careful not to overextend themselves to the point that duties and responsibilities to the organization are not being fulfilled. In the same way, commitment of money without prior approval can cause the Level I educator trouble from his or her supervisor, chief, or organization. Committing personnel, such as engine companies or station firefighters, may take the involvement of an operations chief or captain.

The Level I educator must remember that his or her organization comes first in the area of commitment. If internal support or involvement from the fire agency is lost, it will damage the work of the partnership or coalition, and it can be disastrous to the other efforts undertaken by the educator. The leadership of the agency and the department's personnel, especially the operations staff, must understand and support the commitment.

Teamwork requires that members of the group work cooperatively in order to accomplish the common goals. Some people may be leaders while some may be followers. The Level I educator may find a place in either role. Leaders in a coalition serve as communicators establishing the tasks necessary to achieve the goals of the partnership. Leaders seek the input of the group to assist in assigning the work of the group. The leader serves as a mentor for members and also resolves conflicts that might arise among the group's members.

On the other hand, followers play as important a role as the leader in achieving the objectives of the group. These individuals can follow directions yet think for themselves. Followers are critical to the work actually being done; they permit groups and organizations to achieve their goals. Even leaders must be good followers (**Table 4.1**).

Successful Coalitions

Many examples exist of coalitions that have been successful in their work. MADD (Mothers Against Drunk Driving) and SADD (Students Against Drunk Driving) have both made an impact on the

Table 4.1 Followership Skills

- Respect authority.
- Be safe.
- Keep your fellow followers and leaders safe.
- Accept that authority goes with responsibility.
- Know the limits of your own authority.
- Desire to make the leader succeed.
- Possess good communications skills.
- Develop and maintain a positive learning attitude.
- Keep ego in check.
- Demand clear assignments.
- Establish an assertiveness/authority balance.
- Accept direction and information as needed.
- Publicly acknowledge mistakes.
- Report status of work.
- Be flexible.

Source: International Association of Fire Chiefs Crew Resource Management

incidence of driving while under the influence of alcohol. Firewise Communities is a national collaboration of governmental agencies that works with communities to create local coalitions to help prevent wildfires.

The following are characteristics of successful coalitions:

- The focus is on a common problem or issue that is relevant to the community.

- Those participating in the coalition have a vested interest in the success of the risk-reduction programs of the coalition.

- Resources are available, including knowledge, in-kind support, political and community support, and financial support.

- Members share the workload. Everyone has a role in a coalition, and it is important that all followers carry their share of the workload.

- Participants must follow through on commitments. It is important to commit to only what is possible and to always do what is promised.

- Follow-through is an especially important element for success and should be taken very seriously.

- No single agency or individual takes all the credit. All representatives and their respective agencies are allowed to take some credit, with the coalition receiving most of the credit. The ultimate goal is the reduction of the risk issue, and any credit that is shared is secondary to this fact.

Safe Kids Worldwide

One of the most successful and well-known national coalitions is Safe Kids Worldwide,[2] formerly National SAFE KIDS Campaign. This coalition was born out of the desire of two individuals to work to prevent childhood injuries, the number one killer of children. Started in 1988 as the only nonprofit organization dedicated to preventing unintentional childhood injuries, the National SAFE KIDS Campaign partnered with many national organizations, such as the National Head Injury Foundation, the American Academy of Pediatrics, and the National Safety Council. National SAFE KIDS Campaign worked to start chapters of SAFE KIDS coalitions, which in turn worked to create local coalitions at the county or city level. In 2004, National SAFE KIDS Campaign merged its mission and goals with Safe Kids Worldwide, which turned this organization into an international forerunner in injury prevention for children.

Safe Kids coalitions are an integral part of many community safety programs. It brings together members of the public safety field, the medical arena, local education representatives, and other interested parties to work together for the common goal of preventing childhood injuries in the community. It is a grassroots effort, meaning each coalition is created at the local level and works with local representatives and local community risk issues. Local coalitions work together to advocate for legislation and enforcement at the state level. While each member of the coalition is employed by a related organization, Safe Kids members focus on the common goals and objectives to work collectively to resolve the issues.

Family Connection

Another example of a successful coalition is one that was formed in the state of Georgia, called Family Connection.[3] In 1991, Georgia was ranked 48th in the nation in child well-being, and Family Connection was formed in response to this startling statistic. This organization focuses on five areas:

1. Healthy children
2. Children ready for school
3. Children succeeding in school
4. Strong families
5. Self-sufficient families

There is a Family Connection collaborative in each of Georgia's 159 counties. Local partners include families, businesses, civic leaders, service providers, school-based and faith-based organizations, and other concerned citizens. This collaborative effort is successful because of the grassroots work and the involvement of individuals with a common goal or objective. This organization was started by individuals with a passion to address a problem in the state and has worked successfully to improve the state's national ranking of child well-being.

Chapter Summary

Effective risk reduction work does not occur in a vacuum. The Level I educator should take advantage of any and all help available in the community. Educators should ask for assistance from those agencies that are interested in the populations or audiences that are the target of the risk-reduction efforts.

The success of the fire service as a profession lies partly with teamwork. Station personnel rarely work completely independently; for example, emergency incidents are handled by a team of individuals who have the same goal and purpose. Fire and life safety education is no different. It takes a team of dedicated individuals (from a variety of backgrounds and organizations) to successfully resolve the risk issues in a community.

The benefits of partnering are numerous and widespread. Those listed in this chapter are just a few of the many. Educators must step outside their comfort zones and explore those resources that are available in the community to assist with risk-reduction efforts. It is then that the Level I educator will begin to really learn about his or her community and its members.

Review Questions

1. What is the purpose of partnering with other fire and life safety organizations and agencies?

2. What are the differences and similarities between networks, partnerships, and coalitions?

3. What are the benefits of forming partnerships with community organizations?

4. What process should a Level I educator follow to develop a partnership with one or more community organizations?

5. What are the characteristics of a successful coalition?

Key Terms

Coalition — An alliance that comes together for some specific purpose, particularly those who share common goals.

Collaboration — Partnering with one or more person to accomplish a specific project.

Networking — Process of meeting others and determining resources that others have that can assist with the accomplishment of the risk-reduction initiatives.

Partner — A person, group, or organization willing to join forces and address a community risk.

Chapter 4 Notes

National Fire Academy. **Presenting Effective Public Education Programs**. Student Manual. 2001.

1. Home Safety Council — www.homesafetycouncil. org

2. Safe Kids Worldwide — www.safekids.org

3. Georgia Family Connection Project — www.gafcp. org

FLSE Level I Educators:
Education and Implementation

Chapter Contents

Key Terms

Job Performance Requirements

This chapter provides information that addresses the following job performance requirements of NFPA® 1035, *Standard for Professional Qualifications for Fire and Life Safety Educator, Public Information Officer, and Juvenile Firesetter Intervention Specialist*, 2010 edition.

NFPA® 1035 References

5.4.1

5.4.2

5.4.3

5.4.4

5.4.5

5.4.6

FLSE Level I Educators: Education and Implementation

Learning Objectives

After reading this chapter, students will be able to:

1. Define the concept of learning, and apply the concepts of the learning process to fire and life safety education lessons and presentations. (NFPA® 1035, 5.4.3)

2. Incorporate the different theories on learning into fire and life safety education programs.

3. Apply the learning and developmental stages to the appropriate audiences in delivering fire and life safety education programs. (NFPA® 1035, 5.4.3)

4. Choose the appropriate lesson plan for use with a particular target audience. (NFPA® 1035, 5.4.3)

5. Adapt a lesson plan to meet the needs of the audience or presentation site. (NFPA® 1035, 5.4.4)

6. Use a lesson plan and other instructional techniques to effectively and appropriately deliver fire and life safety education programs. (NFPA® 1035, 5.4.4)

7. Select the appropriate educational materials for a particular audience or presentation. (NFPA® 1035, 5.4.2)

8. Create an environment that encourages learning for a variety of audiences.

9. Select the appropriate media for advertising a fire and life safety education program to the target audience.

Chapter 5
FLSE Level I Educators: Education and Implementation

Case History

Marion County (FL) Fire Service discovered that children were confused about when and where they should call 9-1-1 during a fire emergency. Test data revealed that children incorrectly thought they should call 9-1-1 from inside a burning building. To clear up the confusion, Marion County firefighters crafted their own fire prevention theme: *Get down. Get out. Get on the phone!*

Department members distributed grade-specific classroom curriculum and visited all 32 public elementary schools. The department also hosted a county-wide poster contest. Pretests and posttests were conducted to ensure that students not only knew the message, but understood how to apply it.

Source: 1st Responder Newspaper (SE), January, 2009

Education is a science as well as an art. To be most effective, formal education requires proper planning and delivery of information. Teaching is not a one-size-fits-all process! Methods, techniques, and even the information presented will vary from audience to audience and depend upon age, background, available tools, and materials.

While the Level I educator may be a firefighter, an inspector, a civilian employee, or a volunteer, more importantly this individual is an educator, a teacher, an instructor, and a trainer **(Figure 5.1, p. 112)**. The role of the fire and life safety educator revolves around the process of education. It does not matter what official title an individual holds as everyone is an educator when engaging in fire and life safety education activities.

This chapter gets to the root of the educational presentation — the use of appropriate instructional techniques, instructional methodologies, materials,

and instructional aids. For the Level I educator, it is essential to read, learn, and comprehend this chapter.

An educator may be afforded only a one-time opportunity to impress upon a participant the importance of fire and life safety behaviors and to change a behavior or action that will save a life. Fire and life safety educators do not have the luxury of seeing the same students regularly. Therefore, each presentation must be delivered as if it is the only time that the individual may hear the information, take it to heart, and make the necessary behavioral changes in their lives or lifestyle **(Figure 5.2, p. 112)**.

> "The mediocre teacher tells. The good teacher explains. The superior teacher demonstrates. The great teacher inspires."
>
> *William Arthur Ward (1921-1994), author, educator, and preacher*

Figure 5.1 Fire and life safety educators come from a variety of backgrounds. *Upper right photo courtesy of Dayna Hilton. Center photo courtesy of Lt. Beverley Walker, Hall County Fire Services, Gainesville, GA.*

Figure 5.2 Fire and life safety educators should modify presentations to their audiences.

Much of the information in this chapter is divided based upon age groupings. The use of age-appropriate materials, teaching methods, and instructional aids is imperative to the successful delivery of presentations and programs. Level I educators will encounter a wide range of ages in their audiences and must be well-versed on techniques and methods for appropriately impacting the different age-related ability levels with fire and life safety behaviors.

Education, Information, or Promotion

Often there is confusion between what is educational, informational, and promotional. While the three concepts are often interconnected, there are definite differences among them.

- *Education.* Public education is part of the community risk-reduction program, which includes information that increases knowledge and skills and encourages behavioral changes. Educational programs are measurable.

- *Information.* Public information is the sharing of facts. Public information may involve the use of the media to provide informational messages, news on emergency incidents, or upcoming activities in the community.

- *Promotion.* Promotional events are public relations events that sell or enhance the image of the fire department. Participation in community events, such as parades or carnivals, is considered a public relations activity.

Rarely are these three concepts mutually exclusive. While delivering information about an emergency or activity, it is possible to insert educational information. For instance, an excellent opportunity to deliver educational information about smoke alarms and their operation is to use an example from an actual incident, such as when a fire occurs at a residence and the occupants are alerted by the smoke alarm. During public relations events, educational information can be exchanged between those participating in the event and the emergency services present. Educational presentations provide information to the followers to change behaviors and can serve as public relations events for the fire agency involved.

While the focus of this manual is on fire and life safety education, it must be pointed out that education is just one component of community risk-reduction programs. Educational interventions are programs that are designed to change behavior, knowledge, and attitudes. Community risk reduction encompasses all of the Five Es that have been discussed in previous chapters.

The Concept of Learning

The goal of any fire and life safety presentation is to inform people in the community about fire and life safety measures that can be taken to avoid fires and serious injury. This process of education relies heavily on the learning abilities of the receiver of the information. In order to be as effective as possible, the fire and life safety educator must understand what constitutes learning, how learning occurs, and the steps involved in the learning process.

Basically, from the educator's perspective, the act of teaching involves helping people with the learning process, and the concept of teaching includes all the things that are done to make it happen. The goal of any educational presentation concerning community risk-reduction issues is for individuals to take the information and make changes in their daily lives.

Webster defines *learning* as knowledge or skill acquired by instruction or study; modification of a behavioral tendency by experience. Learning is often defined as an "enduring change in behavior or in the capacity to behave in a given fashion,"[1] where learning is demonstrated by people implementing knowledge, skills, or practices derived from education or other forms of experience.

Basic Learning Principles

In order for learning to take place, the Level I educator must comprehend the stages of the learning process and the different learning styles and theories. Several principles are basic to the learning process, and these have to be taken into account when planning and creating the learning experience.

- *Learning is an experience that occurs inside the learner and must be activated by the learner.* Learning is not visible, though the product of learning can be. Individuals must choose to learn and must have the drive or motivation to learn. It is often up to the Level I educator to provide that motivation or drive. Educators must supply the motivation for the learner to take the sometimes difficult step of proceeding through the doorway.

- *Learning is personal.* Learning is the process of discovering the personal meaning and relevance of the ideas being presented. The learner must see how the information being provided is relevant to his or her own needs and situation. If no relevance is seen, the learner will not retain the information.

- *Personal experience impacts the learning process.* The best resources that adult learners have are their experiences, ideas, thoughts, and opinions that can be drawn upon in the learning process. Conversely, these experiences, ideas, thoughts, and opinions can often be a barrier to learning. It is the role of the educator or presenter to recognize those experiences and ideas that need to be refocused or redirected.

- *Learning can be a difficult process.* Learning may require giving up what is comfortable in order to embrace new ideas or behaviors. Just as the experiences, ideas, thoughts, and opinions of the learner can serve as a resource, the pain or uneasiness involved in changing them can also be a barrier. Educators must be sensitive to this aspect of the learning process.

- *Behavioral change, or learning, is a consequence of experience.* In order for behavior to change, individuals must "try out" the new ideas or behaviors before they will buy in to them. Experience may provide the background for an incorrect behavior, and before it can be changed, individuals must be reassured that the new behavior is really better or more practical.

- *Learning is both emotional and intellectual.* Thinking and feeling must be in agreement, or learning will not occur. Sometimes ideas or concepts are acknowledged cognitively, but it takes longer for them to be adopted emotionally.

- *Learning methods differ, as do learning speeds.* People have different speeds of comprehension. Some may grasp a concept immediately, while for others it takes more time. All followers can benefit from repetition and varied presentations of the same information.

- *Learning occurs in sequence.* Information must be linked in a logical and sequential manner. Learning must make sense. The new information must be linked with information that is already known. Information that is outside of the context of a participant's experience and knowledge will be meaningless.

- *Learning should involve the senses.* By involving sight, hearing, smell, taste, and touch, learning is emphasized and retention of the information is increased **(Figure 5.3)**. A much smaller percentage of information is retained when it is only heard, but through seeing and doing, information is remembered and applied. Learning never stops and is a lifelong process, although the way individuals learn changes as they grow and develop.

The Learning Process

Many different theories have been developed and researched about the learning process. For years, researchers have evaluated learning and developed theories about the concept of learning and how people learn. Outlined below are a few of the more prominent theories.

- *Behaviorism.* Pavlov and others believed that a learner is passive and simply responds to an environmental stimulus. These behaviorists taught that behavior is shaped through negative or positive reinforcement. Under the behaviorism theory, *learning* is defined as a change in behavior, based upon the application or withholding of a stimulus.

- *Cognition theory.* Edward Tolman disregarded the theory of behaviorism. He believed that behavior was goal-oriented and had direction and purpose. He believed that learning could occur without

Figure 5.3 The audience at this demonstration could feel the heat of the fire, hear the crackling of the materials, and see how sprinklers can extinguisher a fire. *Courtesy of Fire Factor, Champaign (IL) Fire Department.*

reinforcement and that the motivation to learn was based upon the direction and purpose of the behavior. According to cognitivists, individuals must be motivated enough to turn the information and experiences into behaviors. Tolman believed that people require active participation in order to learn and that changes in behavior are a result of what is occurring in the learner's head.

- *Constructivism.* The constructivist approach to learning stated that learning is an active process of constructing knowledge rather than acquiring it. This construction process is based upon personal experiences and hypotheses about the environment, and the learner tests these hypotheses continuously. Constructivism assumes that all knowledge is constructed from the learner's previous knowledge. Swiss psychologist Jean Piaget was a major proponent of this approach to learning, especially with children. Piaget developed the widely accepted four stages of childhood development (sensorimotor, preoperational, concrete operational, and formal operational) that are discussed in later chapters.

- *Humanism.* This theory focuses on human freedom, dignity, and potential. Humanists believe that individuals are responsible for their life and actions and that they can creatively change their behavior through personal awareness and desire. A central assumption is that people act with intention. Learning should be student-centered and personalized according to the individual's values. Proponents of the humanism theory of learning were Carl Rogers and Abraham Maslow.

Domains of Learning

In the 1960s, a committee of college professors, chaired by Dr. Benjamin Bloom, identified three types or domains of learning: cognitive (knowledge), psychomotor (skills), and affective (attitude) **(Figure 5.4)**. This theory states that these domains are inter-

related areas in which learning occurs, rather than being independent areas of learning. When targeted by instructional methods, learning within the domains enables students to understand a concept, perform a task, or alter a behavior.

Having an understanding of these domains and how they interact will assist the instructor in presenting effective instruction. These three different domains of learning need to be considered when delivering fire and life safety education. How to address these domains is based upon each audience's needs.

- **Cognitive Domain** — involves what people know or what they understand. Usually has an emphasis on facts and figures.

- **Psychomotor Domain** — involves what people are able to do. This involves physically taking action, practice, or demonstration.

- **Affective Domain** — involves how people feel about a situation and is concerned with values and opinions.

These domains relate to specific areas of educational need and must be considered when developing **educational objectives** and planning for educational presentations. All three must be addressed in order to effectively meet the needs of all members of the audience.

These theories of learning provide a broad base of information and direction for any educator, including those who are seeking to change behavior in the area of fire and life safety. To effectively change behavior, learners must be presented with the information in a way that they can understand, learn, and retain the information, regardless of their age or stage of development.

Elements of the Learning Process

Researchers have identified the following critical elements in the learning process: motivation, reinforcement, relevance, and association. These

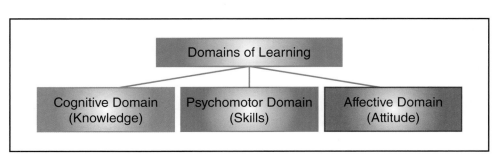

Figure 5.4 The Domains of Learning.

elements, or steps, should be examined and incorporated into any presentation or program dealing with risk-reduction issues to ensure the optimal result for the experience.

Motivation. Motivation is a critical element in the learning process. Unless the learner can see the need for the information, it is not very likely that learning will occur. It is incumbent upon the educator to provide the motivation for learning, which can be accomplished in a variety of ways:

- Demonstrating a friendly, open atmosphere and a level of concern for the learner

- Providing material that is not too easy or difficult or the learner will become bored or frustrated

- Providing the motivation when making a presentation on fire and life safety issues (often this is the hardest part)

Reinforcement. Another critical element of the learning process involves reinforcement. Reinforcement can be positive or negative, and it encourages the performance of the behavior being discussed. *Positive reinforcement* is the presentation of something pleasant or rewarding immediately following a behavior. It makes that behavior more likely to occur in the future. *Negative reinforcement* is the removal of something that when taken away, contingent on a response, tends to increase the probability or rate of that response. In other words, with negative reinforcement, individuals will perform the desired behavior so that the negative is removed, and with positive reinforcement, something positive is given to reward the behavior. Positive reinforcement is best used when teaching a new skill, while negative reinforcement is generally used when teaching a replacement skill. When young children see matches or lighters and tell an adult, they are likely to receive the positive reinforcement of praise from the adult. Alternatively, when children wear their seat belts or bike helmets, they eliminate the possibility of a ticket or citation in communities where such equipment is required by law.

Relevance. In order for learning to take place, the learner must remember the information. If students see a purpose in learning the information and are able to practice using it, it is more likely to be retained. Using the senses and a variety of teaching techniques in the learning process can also increase the probability of retention.

Association. Linkage or transfer of information is another critical element in learning. If a student can associate the new material with something he or she already knows, learning is more likely to occur. Students need to learn important material well initially in order to provide for transfer or linkage. For the learning process to be successful, the effective educator must assess the prior knowledge of the audience as it relates to the subject matter.

Ability to act. The learner must have the ability to act on the information. He or she must be able to take the measures being taught or discussed or have the ability and the means to make the changes. If a person does not feel capable. If a person does not feel capable of making the change (for whtever reason), the information will not be retained and the behavior will not be changed. The educator must enable the individual to make the change or adopt the new behavior by providing a means or the ability.

Learning for Life

As previously mentioned, learning is a lifelong process. How a person learns changes throughout his or her life. Developmental stages and age determine how people learn. This important characteristic of learning is one that the successful Level I educator must comprehend and master in order to have the best chance of success in changing behaviors relating to fire and life safety.

Life stages determine what is possible for individuals at a certain point in their lives. These stages involve motor skills and the different domains of learning. They are part of a sequence; that is, no one can skip around stages when progressing from one to another. Previous stages do not disappear but are incorporated into the new developmental stage.

While stages of development and age may correlate, they are not necessarily always the same. Age is more apparent and can be used as a guide to determine the most effective educational methods. From preschool to older adults, different age categories demand different instructional methodologies, materials, and programs to provide for an optimum learning experience leading to behavioral change.

Instructional methods and techniques that work effectively for one age group may be totally beyond the capabilities of another or too elementary for others. For learning to occur and behavior to be changed, messages and instructional activities

Summary of the Stages of Human Development

The following information is a compilation of the works of Erickson, Bloom, Hunter, Williams, Kohlberg, Havighurst, and Piaget in the area of human development as cited in the National Fire Academy curriculum on Fire and Life Safety.[2]

Developing an understanding of these stages of development will contribute to personal growth and knowledge and enable the educator to reach the target audience with a greater certainty of a positive outcome. Knowledge of these stages can be used to guide content, strategy development, and material selection for risk-reduction strategies. Knowledge of human development provides the Level I educator with the ability to provide educationally sound presentations meeting the needs of the various audiences.

Stage 0 – Blind Trust

- Limited to biological factors
- Individual is controlled by the environment
- No interaction between self and the environment

Stage 1 – Focused on Self

- Individual is capable of recognizing environment
- Realities include authority, obedience, and punishment
- Punishment is the basis of decisions between right and wrong
- Individual wants to avoid punishment and follows authority

Stage 2 – "Me and Thee"

- Recognizing that others have needs
- Satisfying the needs of others means maximizing the individual's personal gain
- Desiring personal gain: "What's in it for me?"
- Leaving if the situation demands more than it gives

Stage 3 – The Group Stage

- Needs to be a member of a group (family, friends, etc.); has a need for belonging
- Understands and conforms to the needs of the group
- Expects to be included, accepted, supported, and protected by the group
- Develops loyalty to serve the group
- Follows rules and remains loyal to group members

Stage 4 – Group Focus

- Believes in "the good of all"
- Desires social stability
- Has capacity to be loyal to groups that are more abstract
- Becomes loyal to ideas of institutions (loyal to the ideal of family)
- Follows rules of nation, church, etc.
- Believes that following rules and laws contributes to the order and the good of society

Stage 5 – Interactive and Independent

- Is truly independent, self-regulating, and aware of feelings
- Has the capability to make important decisions
- Has respect for tradition and institutions

must be tailored for the specific audience receiving the information. Planning for effective educational presentations must include knowledge of learning behaviors and styles.

Most audiences can be roughly grouped into the following categories:

- Preschool (3 to 5 years old)
- Elementary (Kindergarten to grade 5)
- Middle School (grades 6 to 8)
- High School (grades 9 to 12)
- Adult
- Older Adult

Preschool Children

Preschool children, specifically three to five year olds, are the youngest group to whom fire and life safety messages can effectively be taught and learned. Preschool children learn by seeing and doing, and learning fire and life safety messages is not any different. What they see will last longer than what they hear. What children do will last longer than what they see or hear. The fire and life safety educator should use the following methods when teaching preschool children:

- *Repetition.* Use repetition for behaviors to be learned. Children need to act out the behaviors in their center times, and they need to hear stories, draw pictures, and sing songs about the activities they are learning. Fire and life safety educators can provide resources to educators and childcare providers to enhance and provide this repetition, even when the FLSE is not on site.

- *Diversity.* Be aware that preschool children have a very limited attention span, approximately 10 to 15 minutes. To keep their attention, use new or different materials such as puppets, stories, songs, and activities; reduce outside distractions; and make sure that each child is an active participant in the learning process.

- *Performance.* Remember that preschool children learn through experience. Providing instructions verbally will not ensure that the child will follow the instructions. They need to perform the action. Demonstrate the behavior that the child is to learn or perform. Extinguishment of clothing fires is a popular activity for young children – Stop, Drop,

and Roll. It is an activity that is easily remembered because children can actually practice the behavior at the time of the presentation.

- *Language.* Keep messages short and simple. Preschool children are in the process of developing language skills and their vocabulary is limited. Use short, simple sentences while maintaining eye contact with the children. Using the proper language is extremely important, and consistency with language and word choice is important as well.

- *Friendly and trusting.* Get down to their level physically, not just intellectually. This may mean sitting on the floor with them or using a very small chair. The learning environment must be comfortable and friendly for children to learn and focus on the information being presented **(Figure 5.5)**. Also, present information to preschoolers in a nonthreatening way. Scare tactics and frightening a child are simply not appropriate tactics to use and will only inhibit the learning process.

Talking to Young Children — A Nonthreatening Approach

1. Be a good storyteller. Use the story-form method, involving the children whenever possible.
2. Use props instead of a chalkboard or overhead projector.
3. Be ready to ad-lib.
4. Be an actor. Use actions to keep the children interested.
5. Use lots and lots of demonstrations.
6. Use numerous hands-on activities.
7. Do not ask, "Are there any questions?" They do not know the difference between questions and stories.
8. Do not talk down to children.
9. Refuse to talk to large groups, if possible. Teachers insist on small classes for a reason and so should you.
10. Avoid sarcasm.
11. Exhibit a friendly attitude.

Figure 5.5 Children should be comfortable with the learning environment.

Implications for Risk-Reduction Presentations and Strategies

It has been shown that beginning fire and life safety at a young age is effective in changing behaviors, especially in the long term. Unlike many adolescents and adults, young children have not had the time to develop unsafe habits that need to be changed. Life safety education at the preschool level provides the opportunity to develop the safe habits that they will hopefully carry for a lifetime.

A necessary component for success in educating a preschool group on safety issues is the inclusion of parents or caregivers in this instruction. Parents and those caring for the children must understand

Timeless Study

In 1979, a landmark study was conducted by Peel & Schauble for Children's Television Workshop (CTW), the producers of *Sesame Street*, to identify how preschool children would react to televised fire-safety messages. The findings of this research have shaped the feelings of many professionals about teaching fire-safety behaviors to young children and provided guidelines that still hold true today.

Peel & Schauble identified several confusing messages for this age audience and some model messages as well. Controversial messages include those concerning evacuation; matches and lighters; the stop, drop, and roll maneuver; and crawling low under smoke. While it is appropriate to discuss the need for an evacuation plan, it must be emphasized that each family has its own plan. Younger children will not remember a long sequence of events for escape. Any discussion about matches and lighters must be positive. The audience may fail to connect the word "no" with an attractive visual of a lit match or lighter. While most educators taught the stop, drop, and roll maneuver for clothing fires, Peel & Schauble felt more information was needed to see if the child could transform this technique into action in a real-life emergency. The same idea held true for crawling low under smoke.

Model messages, according to Peel & Schauble, involved understanding fire, smoke alarms, firefighters as helpers, and scalds and burns. Young children can understand the concept of *hot* and that fire cooks our food and heats our homes. They can also comprehend that fire can also burn people and things. Children need to be introduced to the concept of a smoke alarm, its appearance, size, shape and sound, and its function in the house. Firefighters, who can often frighten young children during emergencies, need to be seen as community helpers and important individuals in the community. Children should begin to realize that the fire station is an important place. This study stressed the significance of modeling, or showing, only the correct or positive behaviors and to omit from the education process real fires, burning clothes, or individuals who have been burned.

While this study was conducted in 1978, its message for educators was heard and is still being applied today. The information developed from this study was the basis for the development of USFA's *Sesame Street Fire Safety Station* preschool fire safety curriculum that is still applicable and used today.

Messages included in the Sesame Street *Fire Safety Station* Curriculum:

1. Hot Things Burn.
2. Matches and Lighters are for Grown-Ups.
3. Put a Burn in Cool Water.
4. If Your Clothes Catch on Fire – Stop, Drop, and Roll!
5. Get Out and Stay Out.
6. A Smoke Detector Warns About Smoke or Fire.
7. Firefighters Rescue People and Put out Fires.
8. Plan and Practice Fire Drills.

the behaviors being taught and reinforce them at home. Because young children have no control over their environment, it is up the caregivers to create a safe environment for the children.

Examples of Appropriate Messages

In addition to the educational techniques used in the presentation, using the appropriate messages will help ensure that learning occurs and proper behaviors are adopted. Many times inappropriate messages are delivered to young children. This only causes confusion and disinterest in the program or presentation. The following appropriate messages should be delivered during the presentation:

- *Match and lighter safety*. This must be a positive message. If a child sees matches and lighters, he or she should tell an adult. Children must be told to never touch them.

- *When clothes are on fire, "Stop, Drop, and Roll"*: This is an activity that is often remembered and practiced. However, many children confuse this behavior with activities or behaviors to perform when their house is on fire. It is important to make the distinction between the two behaviors and to present the behaviors at different times.

- *Home escape*. Young children do not understand cause and effect, nor do they perform well when having to make choices. Teaching young children about "crawling low under smoke," "feeling the door," "if its hot, don't open it — use your second way out" present too many options, steps, and de-

cisions for the young child. However, it is possible to teach this process of home escape in small segments, with children mastering the first behavior, mastering the second, and putting them together. This instructional process will take time.

- *Firefighters as helpers*. This message is important to introduce at this young age. Children are often afraid of firefighters for a variety of reasons, but mainly due to the transformation that seems to occur in the eyes of young children when the turnout gear is donned. Firefighters should never enter a room of young children wearing full turnout gear. Each piece of equipment should be discussed and compared to something with which the child is familiar. The firefighter should dress slowly, allowing the children to see each piece as it is put on. Children should be encouraged to approach the firefighter, touch the gear, shake hands — but they should never be forced to approach if they do not want to **(Figure 5.6)**. Many children are afraid or become upset during this activity. When done correctly, it can lead to great success in introducing the firefighter into this child's world of community helpers.

- *Bike helmets*. By teaching preschool children about the importance of bike helmets, it creates a habit that they will retain for a lifetime. Because they are just learning to ride tricycles, scooters, or bicycles, it is important to teach not only about bike helmets, but about other safety rules of riding bikes, including rules of the road.

What This Means to You

Recent research has been conducted relating to the effectiveness of fire-safety messages for preschool children. It was found that some preschool children did not understand some of the messages as they were being presented, mainly relating to the wording that was being used. The following is a list of some of the modified messages for preschool children:

1. *Use a home escape map*. Children may not understand the word *plan*, but they do know the word *map*.

2. *Practice a home fire drill*. Again, children may not relate to the wording of practicing a home escape plan, but they do understand the term *fire drill*. An even better message is, "Practice a Home Fire Drill using your Escape Map."

3. *Know the sound and the purpose of the smoke alarm*. It is not enough to know the sound of the alarm, but young children need to understand what the alarm means when it sounds.

4. *Cool a burn with cold water*. Children may not understand how to cool a burn, so more explanation is needed.

5. *Tell a grown-up if you find matches or a lighter, and never touch*. Adding the words "never touch" provides emphasis. Some children may misunderstand telling an adult and will pick up these fire tools to give them to an adult.

Source: Center for Early Childhood Teaching and Learning, Fire Protection Publications, Oklahoma State University.

Figure 5.6 Children should learn that firefighters are there to help them, not to harm them.

- *Poison prevention.* Most poisonings occur among children around age five and under. The dangers of taking medications, vitamins, or other drugs without a parent present should be emphasized, as well as the look-alike products, drinks, and foods.

Elementary Age

This age group includes children ages 5 to 11, which is basically kindergarten through fifth grade. Many physical and cognitive growth changes occur during these years. These years are marked by steady growth in all areas, including physical, mental, and emotional. Because of the wide range of ability and comprehension between the different grade levels, any curricula used should be designed with a particular age range in mind.

Children at the younger end of this grouping are beginning a mastery of basic language and enjoy drama and poetry. They still like repetition and are good at modeling behaviors. As they grow older, children within the upper range of this grouping are starting to think logically and become good at directing others. They like to monitor others' behavior and take on responsibility for tasks **(Table 5.1, p. 122)**.

At this age, children are learning to get along with others and make friends. Children learn to distinguish between right and wrong, good and bad. As their independence grows, children begin to spend more time away from home by being with their peers. They also are developing important attitudes about themselves, their appearance, and their safety.

Elementary age children want to know how to do things correctly. They understand the concept of dangers and potential dangers. They are curious about all things and are very concrete in their thinking and reasoning.

Implications for Risk-Reduction Presentations and Strategies

Many curricula and school programs involve fire and life safety, and they offer a captive audience for fire departments and life safety educators to deliver their

Table 5.1
Characteristics of Elementary-Age Children

5-7 Years Old:	7-12 Years Old:
Self-centered	Becoming abstract thinkers
Able to understand some concepts	Able to use symbolism
Building new skills rapidly	Reading more fluently
Gaining independence	Influenced by peers
Inquisitive	Learning to value friendships
Imaginative	

Source: Home Safety Council, 2008

Table 5.2
School-Based Learning – Advantages vs. Obstacles

Advantages	Obstacles
Access to audience	Competing programs
Established, familiar learning environment	Requirements to meet standards
Extended opportunity for practice	Dependence on changing system
Professional staff is on the team	
Grouped by developmental ability	

Many of the obstacles can be overcome by showing mutual respect and understanding the local "system" of the school system. It is also helps to have someone on your side. Using appropriate materials and instructional methodologies will also be an asset.

Source: Home Safety Council, 2008

messages **(Table 5.2).** As children progress through the elementary years, older children can take on the responsibility of monitoring the behaviors of others and performing responsible tasks.

Fire and life safety programs should include the following criteria:

- Active participation in order for learning to be effective.

- Instructional methods that are more complex than for preschool and include components for making the right choices, increasing self-esteem, and developing positive values.

- Children at this age should be shown respect and not treated like "babies."

- Elementary age children are quite capable of taking the lead at home with safety issues, such as smoke alarm maintenance and fire-safety inspections.

Examples of Appropriate Messages

Fire and life safety messages for elementary children, while similar, are more complex than for preschool children. Some of the differences, and more appropriate messages, are as follows:

- *Home-escape planning.* This message is appropriate for elementary children, except for perhaps the very youngest ones. According to the National Fire Protection Association,[3] in 2004 only one-fifth to one-fourth of households (23%) in the United

States actually developed and practiced a home fire-escape plan to ensure they could escape quickly and safely. Elementary children are able to draw a floor plan of their home, designate two exits, and choose an outdoor meeting place (**Figure 5.7**). Coupled with an actual home fire drill, this creates a fun activity for children and one that can be of great benefit to the entire family.

- *Home fire drills.* Elementary age children are able to absorb the steps in the process of safely exiting a home and can certainly promote practice at home. Many times children at this age will role play a behavior that appears to be much more exciting or dramatic, such as breaking out a window, jumping to safety, holding their breath, or even extinguishing the fire. It is important to react to these expressions appropriately and dispel them as very dangerous.

- *Outdoor fire safety.* Older elementary children are beginning to take on more responsibilities involving fire safety. Campfires, outdoor cooking fires, and the use of flammable liquids all present special messages for the older elementary age child.

- *Home inspections.* Progression through the elementary years presents the opportunity for older children to take a lead at home in the area of safety and safety inspections. Checking the home for proper storage of flammable liquids, the security of matches and lighters, and maintenance of smoke alarms are tasks that elementary age children can perform, though some may need assistance from a parent or caregiver.

- *Vehicle occupant safety.* Older elementary-age children use a vehicle's safety belt as opposed to a child-restraint seat when riding in a car. Wearing the seat belt properly, sitting in the vehicle's seat appropriately, and always wearing a safety belt should be stressed.

- *Disaster preparedness plans.* Along with a home escape plan, elementary children should begin to think about the possibilities of natural and man-made disasters and the steps they can take to be prepared. Knowing what disasters are likely to occur in their area and preparation measures that can be implemented are important messages for these students.

- *Reinforce educational messages.* Educational activities for this group can include drama, storytelling, competition-type games, and activity sheets or word find puzzles. Children need to be active and perform the behaviors. For example, having them practice changing the battery in the smoke alarm or participating in a mock home fire drill are activities that reinforce educational messages.

Figure 5.7 Creating a home-escape plan can be a fun and useful project for children.

Summary for Educators Working with Elementary Children

- Work through the administration.
- Identify organizational affiliation and qualifications.
- Narrow focus and information.
- Ensure the presentation and material are appropriate for the group.
- Keep talking "to a minimum."
- Include hands-on activities and visuals.
- Be aware of special needs and include everyone.
- Talk with the teacher before arrival.
- Make presentations for no more than 2 classrooms at a time.
- Have follow-up materials for teacher or for take-home.

Source: Home Safety Council, 2008

Many fire and life safety programs and curricula have been developed and published targeting elementary-age children. These programs can serve as excellent resources for presentations with elementary-age children and can serve as a guide when developing a local curriculum.

Middle School

This age group contains children approximately ten to thirteen years old, which is sixth through eighth grade. Members of this age classification are bridging between being a child and an adult. Middle school children are entering puberty and experiencing fast physical and emotional growth. The physical growth can often be uneven, and there is awkwardness at this age until physical development evens out. For these children, their peer group is important — more important than their family. Middle school students are very concerned about their appearance and their pace of physical change. Fitting in with the group is of utmost importance.

Middle school children are beginning to develop abstract thinking and hypothesis testing. They can have a wide range of emotional swings about their appearance, achievement, or their own physical growth. They are extremely interested in themselves and make applications to personal situations.

Middle school students begin to move away from adult authority and often rebel against it. They require freedom, yet need to have a secure base during times of stress. While their attention span may tend to grow at this age, rapid physical development makes it difficult to remain sitting for long periods of time.

This age group has a growing interest in ethics and morality. They may begin to deviate from the acceptance of adult-formulated standards or values. They develop their own views, which may be in conflict with the previously held standards. During this age span, there is an increase in reliance on their own judgment and less on that of their parents. This shift may create uncertainties and anxieties for an individual.

Implications for Risk-Reduction Presentations and Strategies

Middle schools encourage their students to assume a greater responsibility for themselves in order to exercise their judgment appropriately. Middle schools also provide their students with the opportunity to explore interests through educational experiences, vocational choices, and social and recreational interests. The middle school experience is designed to provide a forum for these young people to develop value systems acceptable to themselves and society. With the right messages and teaching methodologies, fire and life safety education has a strong place in this type of educational setting. For teaching methodologies, the educator should be aware of the following characteristics of middle school students:

- Do not expect middle school students to sit still for long periods of time.

- Vary classroom activities and allow for movement. Role-plays with middle school students help them understand both sides of the decision-making process.

- Rely heavily on hands-on activities that require the student to reason about relationships.

- Provide activities in both formal and informal situations.

- Offer middle school students challenges. They can and do learn a lot, but not through lecture or busy work.

- Respect them as adults, but remember they still carry some of the traits of the elementary-age child.

Examples of Appropriate Messages

During the middle school years, students are encouraged to develop a sense of responsibility for someone or something during each day of their lives. It is this sense of responsibility that fire and life safety educators can draw upon as a motivating factor for making the right choices and following safe practices.

This is often a hard group for fire and life safety educators to reach. While this audience is not an adult audience, neither is it composed of children. Adolescents in this group may be taking on more responsibilities at home, such as caring for younger siblings or working with lawn equipment. This presents the need for new safety messages.

- *Burn care and prevention.* While this is a message for all audiences, it is of particular importance for middle school students. Adolescents feel invincible and will attempt activities that are very risky, including those involving fire and flammable liquids. Because they are very concerned with appearance, this is an appropriate age to discuss the idea of burn injuries, perhaps sharing the story of a burn survivor or having a burn survivor tell his or her story. Since flammable liquids may be involved, this is an appropriate time to discuss safety with flammable liquids and the proper use and storage of flammable liquids. Middle school children are impressed with flashy, exciting activities and need to be taught the risks involved.

- *Fire service careers.* Middle school is also a time to begin to discuss careers in the fire service. This can be combined with character education, proper choices, and personal development. Showing actual film footage of fire fighting activities, or fire recruit training, opens the door for questions about fire and fire safety measures. Educators should stress the importance of physical fitness and ability, remaining in school, and saying "no" to drugs when fire service careers are discussed.

- *Babysitting classes.* Many communities offer training classes for babysitting. While these classes may cover many topics, including a section on fire and life safety, this promotes fire safety both in the student's home and the homes of others. Many fire departments offer fire and life safety training through local middle school organizations. Basic

facts concerning safe cooking, burn prevention, candle safety, and general first aid are important items to cover during this training.

- *Firesetting and other risky activities.* Accompanying the risky behavior of adolescents is the intentional setting of fires. These fires might be set out of curiosity, on a dare from peers, out of boredom, for revenge, or as an expression of other underlying needs. Having discussions about arson as a crime and firesetting in general and emphasizing the consequences for such behavior will draw the interest of middle school adolescents. Level I educators must stress the negative consequences of firesetting behavior, especially the legal consequences. Many students are exposed to negative television and Internet influences that show activities or pranks involving fire or injury issues. Often students are challenged by their peers to participate in activities that can have very serious consequences. Fire and life safety educators must stress the importance of good choices and the importance of not participating in these types of activities or events. These influences must be addressed as risky behaviors and the consequences of such actions discussed openly in class **(Figure 5.8)**.

Figure 5.8 A fire and life safety educator discussing firesetting behaviors with young students.

Educational methodologies for middle school students should include the following:

- Encourage class participation.

- Incorporate the use of small group problem solving or research, and peer instruction.

- Encourage students to ask questions and make them comfortable doing so.

- Offer the opportunity to participate in role-plays or work with case studies. Students need real life examples.

- Demonstrate equipment and tools used by fire service and EMS providers to gain the attention of this audience.

Using Fire Science to Reach "Tweens" (11 to 13 years old)

The following concepts can be used for reaching middle school students:

- Explain the concept of *time* during a fire emergency.

- Discuss the *science* behind how fires work.

- Describe *lifesaving technologies*, such as fire sprinklers and interconnected smoke alarms.

The Home Fire Sprinkler Coalition has a curriculum targeting middle school students that uses the science of fire and the concept of time during a fire to promote fire safety and prevention interventions.

Source: Home Safety Council

High School

As children continue through middle school into high school, they begin to think more abstractly and develop responsibility for themselves and others. They are developing problem-solving skills and beginning to think in concepts. In general terms, the following traits can be found in high school adolescents:

- Preparing for the future, such as marriage, family life, and a career

- Developing strong feelings such as affection and anger

- Forming more mature relationships with others and acquiring a set of ethics that defines their behavior

- Beginning to develop civic-mindedness and community involvement

- Acquiring personal responsibility and responsibility for others

Teens like to work in the "real world" and need to uncover or discover information for themselves. It is best to do this from case studies, role plays, and hypothetical situations rather than from real-life experiences. Fire and life safety educators can work with teen groups to help develop a sense of caring about others and to see themselves in the future as productive, successful adults.

Summary for Working with High School Audiences

- Include teens in the design of the program.

- Structure the program to meet their developmental stages.

- Use programs to build self-esteem.

- Redirect risk taking through the program's message.

- Focus on life planning and caregiving.

- Use role-playing from real incidents.

- Use burn survivor groups.

- Work in organized small groups for best results.

Source: Pat Mieszala, RN, Burn Concerns, Inc.

Implications for Risk-Reduction Presentations and Strategies

High school students are looking to the future for a career, more advanced education, or even a family. For the most part, they are adults and should be treated as such. Educators should provide for an active learning experience and plan for hands-on classroom activities.

High school students should be allowed to participate in collaborative learning activities or cooperative educational activities. There should be less teacher-directed instruction and more discussion among the class members to provide for educational opportunities in real-life settings. Working with individuals who have experienced fires or serious injuries may reinforce the skills and behaviors that the fire and life safety educator is promoting. High school students can be tasked as mentors for younger students, teaching them the fire and life safety behaviors they have learned.

The fire and life safety educator must make a connection between real life and the behaviors and attitudes being discussed. It must be personally relevant and useful enough for the teenager to change his or her behavior.

Examples of Appropriate Messages

For the high school student, most fire and life safety messages are relevant. There are, however, some that are more prominent and relevant for students who are looking to a future that includes independence and decision-making.

- *Parenting skills.* Increasingly, high school students are themselves parents, which presents a unique opportunity for fire and life safety education. Teenage moms seek information to keep themselves and their children safe. This opens the door to provide relevant and applicable fire and life safety messages.

- *Candles.* A more recent risk for high school students is the use of candles. At the printing of this publication, residential fires caused by candles were on the increase. Many high school students use candles, and educators should encourage the use of flameless candles and identify the dangers involved with leaving lit candles unattended.

- *Fire service careers.* High school students will show interest in fire service careers, which again opens the door for fire and life safety education.

- *Independent living.* Another outlet for fire and life safety in the high school is for those students who are preparing to live on their own, either on a college campus or in a community. Expressing to high school students the importance of being a responsible roommate, tenant, or homeowner can increase their interest in fire and life safety matters.

- *Safe driving.* High school students are new drivers and more likely to be involved in traffic crashes than other, more experienced drivers. Fire and life safety educators should promote safe driving practices and can promote or be involved in crash reenactments or "ghost outs" at local high schools.

Crash Scene Reenactments

This type of event requires careful and thorough planning with all agencies involved. The focus must remain on the behavior and attitudinal change of the students, i.e. avoiding driving when drinking. It is easy for the message to get lost in the theatrics of the production. The use of a proven model or educational script from an existing program that has been proven effective is strongly recommended.

Crash scene reenactments and "ghost outs" are programs that are used with high school students to combat the incidence of driving while intoxicated and reckless driving. (The event is usually held at a track or ball field at the school.) Crash scene reenactments include students from the participating school who are " killed" in a mock crash that involves a student driving while drunk. It is very realistic, down to the hearse that carries away the "dead" student. Public safety personnel participate, with law enforcement "arresting" the student at fault, fire and EMS personnel extricating victims from the crashed vehicles, and even medical helicopters landing to transport the more seriously injured victims. The students participating as the victims provide narration about their thoughts and feelings. Some events go so far as to have the parents of the victims stage a funeral.

During a ghost out, the Grim Reaper visits the school and selects students (based upon the number of individuals who die daily in crashes involving DUI drivers) and takes them away. The students may or may not return to class; if they do, they are marked in some way as the deceased students, and no one is allowed to speak to them nor can they speak to others. The two events can be used together or separately and have proven to be very effective in preventing the incident of driving under the influence by high school students.

Some instructional approaches that motivate teen audiences include the following:

- *Experience-based discussions/case studies.* Teens like to talk about things and to hear how things are in reality. Taking experiences and learning from them is a good way to approach safety education for high school students.

- *Games/simulations.* High school students learn from simulated activities and age-appropriate games.

- *Role plays.* Allow students to role play various situations involving those that violate safety regulations and see how students interact to change the behaviors of their friends or colleagues.

- *Investigative reports.* Allow them to research fires, motor vehicle crashes, and other emergency situations (both present day or historical) to determine the prevention measures that could have prevented the incident from occurring and to show what happens to individuals who do not follow safety regulations.

- *Older students teaching younger students.* Many curricula propose that older students serve as mentors and educators to teach the younger students safety issues **(Figure 5.9)**.

- *Community outreach activities.* Many clubs or classes require **service learning** activities in the community. These can be related to fire and injury prevention or working with those who have been affected by fires, burns, and other injuries.

Adults

Most adults appreciate the need for training from a professional standpoint. They want practical programs that they can apply to their professional or personal experiences. These programs should revolve around solving problems, completing tasks, or handling the manner in which they live.

As adults grow and mature, creativity can reach its highest output, while social stresses can appear as well. Fears of aging may emerge, along with concerns about career aspirations and reality **(Table 5.3)**.

Implications for Risk-Reduction Presentations and Strategies

With adults of all ages, the key to effective fire and life safety presentations is the relevance of the message to their lives. This is the motivational piece that is often the hardest to discover. For some, the motivation results from their keen sense of family, for others it might be the safety of personal property and possessions, and for others it may be the events or occurrences faced by another community member. Factors to consider before setting up educational programs for adults include:

- The educator must earn the respect and the trust of the adult audience. Often this develops by creating a safe atmosphere for learning — one that is free from bias and where ideas and opinions are respected.

- Adults need participation in the learning process. It should be an active process and not a passive one. It is also important to provide constructive feedback to adult learners. This is feedback that is corrective, yet supportive.

- Adults must see where the information presented fits into their experiences and is applicable to their lives. It is the Level I educator's job to help adults along in that process.

Instructional methodologies can include role-play, debate, problem-solving discussion, demonstration, case studies, and skills practice. Many times **brainstorming** or group discussion exercises will work well with adult groups.

Figure 5.9 Older students can prove to be valuable mentors and instructors to younger children.

Table 5.3
Eleven Keys to Engaging the Adult Learner

Make it meaningful.	Answer the questions: How does this apply to me, and how will I benefit?
Ask them what they want.	Be prepared to modify the presentation to meet their expectations.
See, hear, do.	Let them hear and see through audiovisuals. Let them experience it by doing something with new information, such as application, problem solving, etc.
Discuss more, lecture less.	Discussion allows the participant to connect the new information with the information and experiences already stored in their memory.
Present, apply, and repeat as necessary.	Present one chunk of information and then apply it. Present the next chunk and then apply. This allows for a transference of information to long-term memory.
Connect with their experiences.	Connect the new information with their past experiences. In addition, make sure there is a relationship between the educator's past experiences and those of the participants.
Be a real person.	The only person to be is oneself.
Chunks, please.	Present six or seven pieces of information at a time and then ensure understanding.
More dos, less don'ts.	Express the message in a positive format. Tell the person what to do instead of what *not* to do.
Expect success.	Expect participants to be successful and to incorporate the training into their lives. Avoid negative attitudes or comments.
Say "thank you."	When done, thank the learners for their time and attention and for the opportunity to improve their skills and help them be safe.

Source: Ed Kirtley, IFSTA

Dale's Cone of Learning

We remember:

- 10% of what we read
- 20% of what we hear
- 30% of what we see
- 50% of what we hear and see
- 70% of what we say
- 90% of what we both say and do

Source: Edgar Dale, 1969

Examples of Appropriate Messages

All fire and life safety topics and messages are appropriate for adults, though the presentation of these messages will need to change **(Table 5.4, p. 130)**. Some messages may vary due to the characteristics of a particular audience or population. A sampling of the most common topics follows:

- *Smoke alarms.* Includes installation, maintenance, testing, and replacement.

- *Residential sprinklers for both new and existing construction.* Educators must be prepared to over-

Table 5.4
Nonformal Educational Methods

Role Play	Participants take turns acting out a prepared situation.
Case Study	A detailed story about a situation.
Brainstorming	Participants speak out with any sudden idea, no matter how impractical.
Sharing	Participants freely exchange knowledge, ideas, and opinions on a subject.
Problem Solving	Participants do a particular task that should lead to a desired result.
Small Group Discussion	Participants divide into smaller groups to discuss or perform a particular task. The group comes back together for a large group discussion.

come myths and answer questions concerning cost and performance.

- *Home escape planning and fire drills, particularly for parents of younger children.* Many families do not have an escape plan and have never even thought about having a fire drill. These are both lifesaving measures that families and other members of the household need to implement.

- *Disaster planning and preparedness for adults and families.* Developing a disaster plan, creating a disaster supplies kit, and establishing meeting places outside the neighborhood are important features that need to be planned.

- *Overall unintentional injury prevention.* Relating to children in the home and at play.

Older Adults

Older adults are one of the largest growing populations in the United States. Through improvements in health care and knowledge of exercise, many older adults are more active and involved in the community than perhaps used to be the case. Therefore, these adults can be wonderful advocates for community programs and organizations.

Older adults are more at risk for injuries due to fire and burn injuries, as well as injuries related to trips and falls. Because of their age and life experiences, they may be able to overcome many physical limitations in order to attain their goals in life. Some enjoy retirement, while others are frustrated by the inactivity that is forced on them. Physical limitations may be emerging, much to the dislike of the individual experiencing them.

Implications for Risk-Reduction Presentations and Strategies

Older adults are an important audience for fire and life safety education programs **(Figure 5.10)**. They are the fastest growing segment of the population, and these adults have an unusually high risk of fire injuries and burns (see the section on High-Risk Audiences).

While an important audience, older adults may be harder to reach both in a literal and educational sense. They bring with them a lifetime of experiences, many of which the educator has not had the chance to experience. It is important to spend time with older adults and learn about those experiences before addressing their fire-safety concerns. The Level I educator should demonstrate a great respect for this audience and draw those experiences from the group during any presentation.

Older adults may have concerns regarding home safety, their independence, health issues such as falls, and spending money on themselves or items that would increase their safety. Many scams attempt to scare older adults into buying products that claim

Figure 5.10 Fire and life safety educator giving a presentation to older adults.

to have protective properties. The educator must be very clear about what benefits their proposed solutions will afford and the limitations involved.

Instructional techniques for older adults include demonstrations and illustrations. Older adults enjoy props and to be able to touch and see any safety items being recommended by the educator. The experiences of older adults will often get in the way of learning a new or safer behavior, and the job of the educator is to overcome those experiences without discounting them.

Older adults must be treated with respect and shown appreciation for their wisdom. Discuss their fire and injury experiences. These discussions can assist others in the group in gaining understanding about the seriousness of the issues and the appropriate actions and behaviors.

Residential Fire Homebound Elderly Lifeline Project (Fire H.E.L.P.)

As was discussed in previous chapters, older adults are at a much higher risk for residential fire deaths. To reduce fire-related injuries and loss of life and property among homebound older adults, the Centers for Disease Control partnered with the Meals on Wheels Association of America (MOWAA) and the International Association of Fire Chiefs (IAFC) to develop and implement the Residential Fire Homebound Elderly Lifeline Project (Fire H.E.L.P.)

Fire H.E.L.P. consists of three major components:

- Home screening for smoke alarms
- Education on fire-risk factors and the importance of smoke alarms and escape planning
- Installation and periodic testing of free smoke alarms with long-life lithium batteries

Meals On Wheels (MOW) programs have regular contact with homebound elderly clients through the home delivery of meals. Fire H.E.L.P. uses this opportunity to distribute smoke alarms to the older adults who need them in their home. Local fire departments will install the alarms. The project also provides these men and women with the knowledge and skills needed to prevent a fire.

Fire H.E.L.P. was pilot-tested in 2007 in five Texas communities. Depending upon the success of the project, MOWAA will replicate it throughout Texas and ultimately across the U.S.

Source: Centers for Disease Control's National Center for Injury Prevention and Control.

Examples of Appropriate Messages

Smoking fires are the leading cause of fatalities among older adults, and cooking fires are the leading cause of injuries (USFA). Messages for older adults should focus on the following issues:

- *Safe cooking.* Many older adults experience fires or burns due to unattended cooking. Due to a diminishing sense of smell and touch, they may be less likely to detect dangers in the kitchen.

- *Careless smoking.* Drowsiness, overmedication, and the combination of prescription medications and alcohol all contribute to a greater risk for fires due to careless smoking by the older adult population.

- *Electrical appliances and equipment.* Older adults may not understand the dangers in using equipment or appliances that are old and may not be in good working order. They may be reluctant to replace items that appear to be insufficient even though there may be dangers from frayed or old wiring.

- *Falls.* For many older adults, falls are a common occurrence. Most falls take place inside the home. Falls may be caused by weakness, dizziness, diminishing vision, and medications. Preventative measures are necessary.

High-Risk Audiences

The following groups have been identified as being at a higher risk of fire and injury due to fire than that of the general population. These groups are often at a disproportionately higher risk than the general population to experience injuries and deaths due to fire. The risk for unintentional injury is greater among these populations than for the general population.[4] In any community, fire and life safety education professionals must take special measures to ensure that these populations are identified and that appropriate risk-reduction programs are designed to meet the needs of these target audiences.

- *Children under the age of five.* Infants and young children are at greater risk for many injuries. According to the Centers for Disease Control, this increased risk may be attributable to many factors. Children are curious and like to explore their environment. This characteristic may lead children to sample the pills in the medicine cabinet, play with matches, or venture into the family pool. Young children have limited physical coordination and cognitive abilities. This can lead to a greater risk for falls from bicycles and playground equipment and make it difficult for them to escape from a fire. Their small size and developing bones and muscles may make them more susceptible to injury in car crashes if they are not properly restrained. Younger children below the age of five are less likely to receive fire and life safety information than elementary school children. Fires set by other children unintentionally with match or lighter play affects many of this age group.

- *Adults over age 65.* Older adults are the fastest growing population among the other identified populations. As older adults age, their risk of experiencing a dangerous fire and injury increases according to the USFA. Smoking is the leading cause of fire deaths while cooking is more likely to cause injury. While some older adults may have diminished physical or mental capacities, others may be in good health and stay involved actively in the community. Older adults are more likely to suffer from reduced sensory abilities such as smell, touch, vision, and hearing and from diminished mental faculties such as dementia, Alzheimer's disease, and depression. Such impairments tend to reduce older adults' reaction times and place them at a higher risk of injury.

- *Individuals with a lower socioeconomic status and disabilities.* Economic and social concerns, living in poverty, failing health, and increasing disabilities are all factors that contribute to a greater risk of unintentional injuries and the incidence of fire **(Figure 5.11)**.

Working with High-Risk Groups

Fire and injury risk is a problem that affects all demographics of the country. Statistics show that the risk for fire and injury is greater for some groups than it is for others, and it is necessary for the risk-reduction specialists within a community to identify these populations and target these individuals.

Those interested in additional information about high-risk audiences and working with these target populations may wish to participate in training classes, including those at a state training agency, the National Fire Academy, public health agencies, or those conducted at a state or local college to receive further information and education on this issue.

Figure 5.11 Fire and life safety educators explaining the operation of a smoke alarm to a woman with hearing impairment.

In order to mitigate risk among young children, it might be necessary to target caregivers of these children, such as siblings, parents, grandparents, child care professionals, and babysitters. This would be in addition to and conjunction with programs for the children themselves. Young children only have limited control over their environment, and their mental and physical reactions may prevent them from saving their own lives.

In much the same way, reducing risk among older adults may require targeting additional audiences, other than the older adults themselves. Elder-care centers, working-age adults who may be caring for their parents, senior centers, home health professionals, or nursing homes are examples of a secondary target audience.

Regarding poverty as a fire risk, several studies have shown that poverty increases risk of fire involvement. Poverty crosses all demographic lines, including age, ethnicity, background, and location. When coupled with an additional risk factor, such as low education, the fire risk is increased. Fire risk seems to be greatest in large cities and small rural communities. This is due to the fact that these two types of areas have the largest percentage of their populations living in poverty.

Delivery of the Presentation

The Level I educator's primary focus is to provide effective and appropriate presentations on risk-reduction issues and strategies. Given a lesson plan or outline, the Level I educator presents the material to the appropriate audience, making adaptations as necessary to meet the needs of the audience. With the necessary research completed, it is time to use the lesson plan to make presentations that meet the needs of the audience.

A *lesson plan* is a guide for making a presentation. It is a road map: a simple format for presenting a lesson. It outlines the material to be taught and the teaching procedures to follow. By using the lesson plan, time is used efficiently and the subject is accurately presented. Using a lesson plan ensures that each presentation is uniform when used by more than one Level I educator **(Figure 5.12, p. 134)**.

Flexibility in a lesson plan is an indicator of a good lesson plan. It is not a document that has to be followed to the letter. The Level I educator may need additional time to explain a particular concept based upon the prior knowledge of the audience, or there may be a particular subject that lends itself to a lengthy discussion.

Lessons may be provided by a variety of people, and the use of a lesson plan ensures that all impor-

Figure 5.12 A Fire and Life Safety Educator I reviewing a lesson plan before giving a presentation.

Figure 5.13 A Fire and Life Safety Educator II creating a lesson plan.

tant topics and points are covered. Even something as simple as a station tour should have some form of a written lesson plan, so that each tour is handled in a consistent manner. As educators get promoted, move to other areas of the department, or retire, resources may change. If there is no formally-written lesson plan, information is lost **(Figure 5.13)**.

Educational Objectives

Lesson plans are developed around objectives. Educational objectives are often called the following:

- Instructional objectives
- Behavioral objectives
- Lesson objectives
- Learning objectives

Whatever they are called, objectives provide the goal or purpose for the lesson and ultimately indicate the desired performance of the participant. Objectives provide an answer to the question, "What will happen as a result of this presentation or program?"

Table 5.5 Types of Learning Objectives		
Cognitive	**Psychomotor**	**Affective**
What the participant is expected to **know**.	What the participant is expected to **do**.	What the participant is expected to **appreciate, value, or believe.**
Example: Participants will be able to identify how often batteries should be replaced in smoke alarms.	Example: Participants will be able to demonstrate stop, drop, and roll.	Example: Participants will recognize the value and importance of home fire-escape planning.

In most instances the Level I educator will be using a lesson plan that has already been prepared. However, an understanding of learning objectives is necessary so that the educator will know the purpose and goal of the presentation.

Objectives should focus on what people are expected to know, do, or believe upon completion of the presentation. As has already been discussed, the goal of any educational presentation is a change in behavior. For that reason, objectives are active, describing an action or behavior that the audience should perform as a result of the presentation **(Table 5.5)**.

Objectives are also measurable and specific. Measurable objectives allow the presenter and program developers to collect concrete evidence that the presentation has been effective. Specificity of the objectives also makes measuring the effectiveness of the presentation easier and more reliable.

Objectives answer three questions:

- *What must learners do to show they have learned?* (The performance component of the objective)

- *Under what conditions and with what resources should the learner be able to act?* (The condition component)

- *How well must it be done?* (The standard or criterion component of the objective)

The CBS Objective Format

C – Condition

B – Behavior

S – Standard

- **Condition**. The situation or environment under which the followers are expected to perform. *Example: Given a battery operated smoke alarm,.....*

- **Behavior**. The specific thing that the student is expected to know, do, or value. *Example: ...each student will remove the old battery and install the replacement battery.....*

- **Standard**. The expected level of student performance. *Example: .....so that the smoke alarm operates when tested.*

Source: IFSTA Fire and Emergency Services Instructor manual, 7th Edition

Educational objectives make lesson planning easier by stating a clear outcome. Objectives make learning easier because the student will know what skills will be taught.

Educational objectives for a lesson plan lay the foundation for the evaluation of the program or presentation. The evaluation instrument must directly relate to the program's objectives. Types of educational evaluation tools are discussed in the next chapter. Every lesson plan or presentation by the Level I educator needs to include some type of evaluation. This is not an evaluation of the educator or the presentation, but an evaluation of the followers to determine the level of knowledge gain or behavioral change.

Components of a Lesson Plan

Typically, the lesson plan includes the following components or subjects:

- *Topic.* A short, descriptive title should limit the content of the lesson and include enough information so that another fire and life safety educator would understand what is to be covered.

- *Time.* The estimated time needed to teach the lesson.

- *Prerequisites.* Any information or skill that the student should already have or have mastered. Using a pretest will help an educator determine some of this information.

- *Objectives.* The minimum acceptable behaviors that the student must be able to do after the presentation. Objectives should have been written before the writing of the lesson plan and should include behaviors for the affective, cognitive, and psychomotor domains.

- *Preclass preparation.* This section includes activities that the instructor needs to complete before entering the classroom. This would include "copy handouts" and "preview video."

- *References.* Specific reference materials that the fire and life safety educator should study prior to making the presentation. In some cases, this section may include the references for the material used to develop the lesson plan.

- *Preparation.* In this step, the educator prepares the student to learn. This is the motivational section where the educator must show why learning the information is relevant and important.

- *Presentation.* The lesson plan lists, in order, the information to be covered, how it will be covered, and what methods should be used to teach the information.

- *Application.* Activities, exercises, and tasks for the student to perform to apply the information.

- *Lesson summary.* The fire and life safety educator must restate and review the information that has been presented. This includes the important concepts and skills.

- *Evaluation.* During this final phase, the educator will test or otherwise evaluate the followers to determine whether the objectives were met and learning took place. Even though the followers are taking the evaluation, it is really the presentation and curriculum that are being evaluated.

A presentation may need to be adapted for use with special needs audiences, such as those with hearing, seeing, or mobility impairments. In adapting a lesson plan, it is important to make sure that the message is not lost. Some activities that are effective with small groups may not work with larger audiences.

Knowing the audience and its needs in advance of a presentation will enable the Level I educator to make the adaptations that may be needed prior to the delivery of the presentation. Visiting the site before the presentation, questioning the individual who schedules the presentation, and familiarity with the community will aid the Level I educator in providing the best possible presentation for the audience, based upon its needs and abilities.

> "I hear and I forget. I see and I remember. I do and I understand." *Confucius, Chinese philosopher and reformer (551 BC - 479 BC)*

Four-Step Method of Instruction

There are at least four parts to any effective educational presentation or program. These four steps are preparation, presentation and delivery, application, and evaluation. Using these four steps prepares the student for learning, involves them in the instruction, and provides a way to measure understanding. Lesson plans that are based on this method of instruction should be easy for the Level I educator to apply.

Preparation

Preparation refers to the preparation of the followers for learning. This step establishes the relevancy of the presentation for the participant. During this stage, the Level I educator will introduce the topic, gain the attention of the audience, and convey the objectives. This is the motivational part of the presentation. It is the educator's job to motivate followers by establishing why they need to know the information and relating the information being presented to their lifestyle and situation.

Presentation and Delivery

The actual teaching of the class or delivery of the presentation is the transfer of facts and ideas in a form and manner that the learner can comprehend and process. During the presentation, the educator follows the lesson plan using training aids and demonstrates methods and techniques. It is important that the educator makes the subject come alive for the audience — no matter what their age. Educators must use the most effective teaching methods and materials for the given audience.

Presentation Methods

Presentation methods, or instructional methods, are the vehicles by which fire and life safety information is delivered to a target audience. While there are several different instructional methods, it is the responsibility of the Level I educator to determine the appropriate method needed to effectively reach the target audience to meet the objectives of the presentation.

What This Means to You

In order to motivate followers to learn, you must:

1. Answer questions such as "How is this relevant to me?" and "What's in it for me?" How does the topic apply to the participant and how will each benefit from the presentation?

2. Gain credibility and rapport with the followers. Show genuine concern for their needs and concerns. Engage them in the instruction and actively listen to them.

3. Use effective instructional methods and techniques throughout the class. Be organized, present the content in a manner that connects with their previous experiences, and make the new experience fun and engaging.

4. Focus on motivation at the beginning of the presentation, during the middle or body of the presentation, and again at the end to be effective.

Source: Ed Kirtley, IFSTA

Some educators may feel more comfortable using one method over another and may be apprehensive to use a method that is not natural. However, the most important aspect of instructional methods is making sure that the level of development of the audience and the instructional method match. As indicated in the information at the beginning of the chapter, different age groups will respond better to a particular teaching method, and the effective Level I educator will employ that method for maximum results.

The following are several different types of instructional methods from which the Level I educator can choose:

Lecture. In a **lecture**, the educator talks, explains, and tells. While this can be an effective means of sending information to the audience, there is only one-way communication. That is, there is no real opportunity for feedback or a means for measuring understanding. There is virtually no audience participation. Lectures can be uninteresting and a barrier to effective communication. The use of audiovisual aids, such as multimedia presentations, can provide interest for the audience during lectures. Lectures are useful with large groups and can be effective for providing factual information. Of course, lecture is more appropriate for adults than children.

Discussion. Unlike the lecture method, **discussion** allows for the audience and the educator to interact. The educator is able to exchange views and opinions with the audience/students. The educator is able to ask and answer questions, provide examples, and measure understanding. The discussion method is ideal when the target audience already has some basic knowledge about the subject.

Discussion can take a variety of forms, including a case study where the group reviews real or hypothetical events, and **role playing** where the group acts out various scenarios. Brainstorming can be used during discussion, where many ideas and approaches are identified and recorded.

Illustration. The **illustration method** is useful either with the lecture method or the discussion method. The educator shows something to the audience — the parts of a smoke alarm or a frayed extension cord, for example. With illustration, the educator simply shows the item or a picture of an item; no behavior is performed or demonstrated. Teaching aids such as posters, pictures, videos, films, and diagrams are all useful tools when using the illustration method.

Demonstration. **Demonstration** is used when teaching the audience a skill. The educator actually performs the task step-by-step for the audience and then allows the audience to perform the task. Effective use of the demonstration method includes the following steps:

1. The educator explains the behavior that the demonstration will show the audience how to perform.
2. The educator demonstrates the behavior at normal speed and then repeats it more slowly, explaining each step as it is performed. The educator then demonstrates the behavior while a participant explains each step.
3. Next, a participant then demonstrates the skill, explaining each step. The educator supervises this step for accuracy.
4. Lastly, followers perform the behavior or skill under the supervision of the educator.

Team teaching. **Team teaching** is where a group of educators work together in a presentation for a single educational objective. Team teaching is appropriate where the material is perhaps too broad for one instructor or when more than one perspective is needed. Team teaching is also a way of building relationships with other organizations. By using educators from other organizations, agencies begin to work together on programs and projects.

Team teaching requires more advance planning than solo teaching. It also requires the acknowledgement of strengths and weaknesses of each educator. Team teaching helps keep the attention of the audience by capitalizing on the different styles, pace, and voice inflections of the different instructors.

These instructional methods are not mutually exclusive. It is possible to incorporate them at the same time, such as a lecture that uses illustrations. It is also prudent to integrate the different methods into one presentation. Because some people or age groups respond better to one method than another, using more than one method greatly increases the chances that learning has occurred and behaviors have been changed.

Web-based/interactive. No discussion of educational techniques would be complete without at least touching on the use of Web-based or computer-interactive instruction. This is certainly a viable form of instruction and one that is definitely on the increase in many different arenas.

Figure 5.14 A young child viewing a fire safety Web site. *Courtesy of Brett Noakes.*

Training programs have been created on DVD or CD for use with computer-based instruction. These programs provide safety information to a targeted audience. Some may be oriented toward young children, while others may be designed for use with middle-school or even high school students. Many times the educator can use these technology-aided forms of instruction in a classroom or small group with great success. However, all the same rules apply about the curriculum — age appropriateness, accuracy of messages, and ease of use.

Application

Application is when the audience uses or applies what is being taught. Students demonstrate that they can apply new ideas, information, techniques, and skills. When possible, each student should be given the opportunity to perform a task or solve a problem using the new information that has been presented **(Figure 5.15)**.

Evaluation

During this phase, the educator determines whether the educational objectives have been met. This portion of the presentation will show whether students can perform the task on their own or solve problems based upon the information presented.

The use of department or specialty Web sites can serve as a source or forum for teaching fire and life safety information. Many departments have developed "kid's pages" which contain a seemingly endless assortment of games, puzzles, activities, songs and the like, the main purpose of which is to provide safety information **(Figure 5.14)**. In addition, many adults use fire department Web sites to gather safety information on particular topics of interest.

Podcasts, Webinars, and Webcasts

A *podcast* is a Web feed of audio or video files placed on the Internet for download. The term also refers to the content of that feed. Files with video clips may be referred to as *vodcasts*. A subscription feed will automatically deliver new content to the device, and this feature is what distinguishes a podcast from a download or real-time streaming of audio or video. An iPod device is not required in order to enjoy podcasting. Podcasts can be played back on virtually all MP3-capable playback devices or home computers once the podcast stream has been downloaded in MP3 format. A retrieval program for the podcast must be used so that podcasts may be automatically downloaded. Podcasts are being used as virtual classrooms for lectures, lessons, and other instructional methods. The benefit of using podcasts is that they can be viewed at one's leisure and are automatically downloaded so that the user does not have to remember to do so.

A *webinar* is an abbreviation for a Web-based seminar. Individuals participate by watching the broadcast on their computer, and participate in the discussion via a discussion board. In some instances, followers can listen to the audio via telephone connection. Participants can attend the seminar from their own office, which cuts down on travel expenses. Often times, the webinar can be saved for a length of time and accessed later by participants.

A *webcast* is similar to a webinar, except that the participants watch and listen to the presentation via a computer connection. It is one-way communication, and there is no opportunity for interaction between the participants and the presenter.

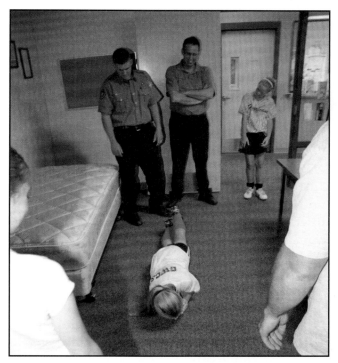
Figure 5.15 An older child applying what she learned from a presentation on Stop, Drop, and Roll.

From time to time, lesson plans need to be changed or updated. Information becomes outdated, or activities become obsolete. Each time the educator delivers a presentation, the educator should review and critique the lesson plan. This refreshes the educator on the content and the skills covered. It will also assist in preparing the Level I educator for the different audiences and determining what needs to be changed or altered to meet the needs of a specific group or audience.

It is imperative that Level I educators realize and understand that a lesson plan is usually developed around a particular audience. If the audience is different from the one targeted by a lesson plan, the Level I educator will have to make appropriate changes in the lesson plan to meet the learning style and developmental stages of the audience. This will include changes in the following:

- Preparation or motivation section
- Actual delivery or presentation methods
- Application process
- Method for evaluating the presentation

The information may not change, but all other aspects of the lesson plan will need to be adapted for a specific audience.

Informational Presentations

The educator, or other member of the department, may be required to deliver an informational or promotional presentation to an audience. While these are similar to an educational presentation, the topic may be more generic and the goal may not involve a behavior change as with an educational presentation. For example, fire departments are frequently asked to speak at civic organizations and clubs. Many times these groups simply want to know some background about the department, such as services offered, location of stations, and budget.

Another difference is that the information presentation does not require an educational lesson plan. Rather, a presentation outline with key speaking points is used. The speaking points must still be succinct, follow a logical sequence, and provide information that is appropriate for the target audience. Audiovisual materials should be used to enhance the presentation.

Planning for the Presentation

Once the informational topic has been chosen and the informational or promotional materials selected, there is still planning that needs to be done for the presentation. Simply put, planning illustrates a professional concern for the quality of the presentation and a respect for the audience.

Each informational presentation, while following the speaking points, should have three components: introduction, body, and conclusion. All three components have important roles in the effective presentation. The introduction must be motivational and sufficient to capture the attention of the audience. The body of the presentation, where the new information is relayed, cannot be underestimated. The conclusion wraps it all up and may be the final opportunity to have an impact on someone in the audience. The following explains each component.

Introduction

The introduction of a presentation contains information about the topic and why the audience should be interested. During the introduction, the educator should gain the attention of the audience and provide motivation for them to participate. The motivation may be to view the fire truck in the parking lot after the lesson. Or, the motivation may be for older adults to maintain the ability to remain independent and in their own home.

An introduction should focus the attention of the audience on the topic at hand. It sets the scene or climate for the presentation. The introduction should explain why the educator is there, the purpose of the presentation, what will take place, and a time frame involved. The introduction might include anecdotal stories, historical perspectives, topical information, or a review of information that the audience already knows.

Body of the Presentation

The body of the presentation follows the introduction, where new information is presented. The body includes clear directions, motivational practices, and reinforcement of the audience's interest and learning. It is during this time that the effective educator reminds the audience of what they know and presents the new information, knowledge, skill, and attitude. The body of the presentation should provide encouragement and guidance to the audience, as well as to reinforce and monitor audience interest and learning. The body should make use of appropriate instructional methodologies and appropriate materials.

Conclusion of the Presentation

The conclusion of the presentation is just as important as the introduction and the body. It allows for questions and an opportunity to generate additional interest in the topic.

During the conclusion, the educator consolidates the program content and assesses the level of comprehension. This may be from a posttest, survey, or simple question and answer period. The conclusion is the time when the educator needs to connect the information to real-life, review the major points, and list the resources available to the audience for assistance, including the fire agency involved.

Figure 5.16 Small children learn better in safe, familiar environments.

The Learning Environment

Everything about a presentation can be perfect, but if the learning environment is inappropriate, effectiveness will be minimized if not lost. The wrong learning environment — the physical facilities and room arrangement — can ruin even the best presentation effort.

Just as with subject matter and teaching methodologies, the most effective learning environment will depend on the makeup of the audience. For the most optimum environment conducive to learning, different age groups require different settings and room arrangements.

Preschool Children

For preschool children, the appropriate setting is the one to which they are accustomed. This should be one that encourages learning and allows the children to feel safe. Most of the time younger children will be more attentive sitting on the floor, on a rug, or in a circle **(Figure 5.16)**. Ensure that there is adequate space before gathering large groups of young children, otherwise the group size can create distractions. An educator addressing young children should sit on the floor or in a small chair to be near eye level with them. Distractions need to be kept to a minimum. Classes or presentations to young children should take place in a classroom or similar controlled area. Trying to deliver educational presentations outside and next to a fire apparatus simply will not work.

Elementary Children

When addressing elementary children in the classroom, allow the children to sit at their usual desks or tables. Once again, keeping the groups small will assist in maintaining attention and minimizing distractions. When using drama, games, or other activities, make sure that there is ample space for these activities. When addressing elementary children outside of a classroom setting, such as Boy Scouts or after-school groups, plan ahead to limit the distractions as much as possible. If using multimedia, make sure that all the children can see the entire screen clearly.

Older Adults

When working with older adults, the following guidelines can be used when planning these programs:

- Limit programs to 30 minutes or less. Like anyone else, older adults may get anxious during longer presentations.

- Include question and answer periods in discussions. Many older adults like to participate in classroom discussion.

- Dim or control the lights if PowerPoint or transparencies are being used. Sunlight or glare may present a problem for this audience.

- Keep the room at a steady, warm temperature.

- Make sure that all members can hear the speaker. Speak clearly and make sure that a microphone is available.

General Considerations

General considerations for an effective learning environment include the following:

- *Room size.* Is the room too big or too small for the audience?

- *Temperature.* Is it a comfortable temperature for the audience?

- *Lighting level.* Is it too bright or dark? This is an important consideration when using audiovisual materials.

- *Ventilation.* Can the vents be adjusted if they are creating uncomfortable situations?

- *Background noises.* Are there ways to minimize disruption from neighboring rooms, the hall, outside areas, or other parts of the building?

- *Acoustics.* Can the audience hear the presentation? Is a microphone needed?

- *Comfort.* Are the chairs and tables comfortable?

- *Physical arrangement of the room.* Can the room be rearranged? Can all audience members see every resource available?

Arriving early for a presentation is an important part of the educator's job. This allows for inspection of the room where the presentation is to take place and to perhaps observe the class for a few minutes. Arriving early will ensure that there is time to alter the physical environment or the presentation if possible.

The physical arrangement of the room is something that the educator often can control. Room arrangement may depend on the size of the group, the needs of the group, and whether or not tables are used. Proper room arrangement will ensure the following for a positive presentation:

- Everyone can see and hear the educator and the audiovisual materials.

- Everyone in the audience can see and hear each other.

- The maximum number of people can sit close to the educator.

A variety of seating arrangements are available to the educator. The optimal choice may depend on whether tables are used, the size of the group, and the length of the presentation **(Figure 5.17, p. 142)**. Each has its advantages and disadvantages.

- *Auditorium* seating works well with large groups and is effective for lecture presentations. It is also an efficient arrangement for showing projected media. There is limited opportunity for interaction with the audience, limited involvement among the followers, and few possibilities for audience participation in the presentation.

- The *chevron arrangement*, sometimes referred to as the *herringbone*, is also appropriate for lecture presentations and those where projected media is used. It does, however, allow for more interaction between the audience and the presenter and among the followers. This arrangement places the followers closer to the educator.

- The *traditional classroom* setting is designed for a moderate number of followers. This is the most restrictive of the classroom setups and limits class interaction. It is, however, effective for audience control and use with lectures and projected media.

- The *horseshoe/U-shaped* arrangement is popular.

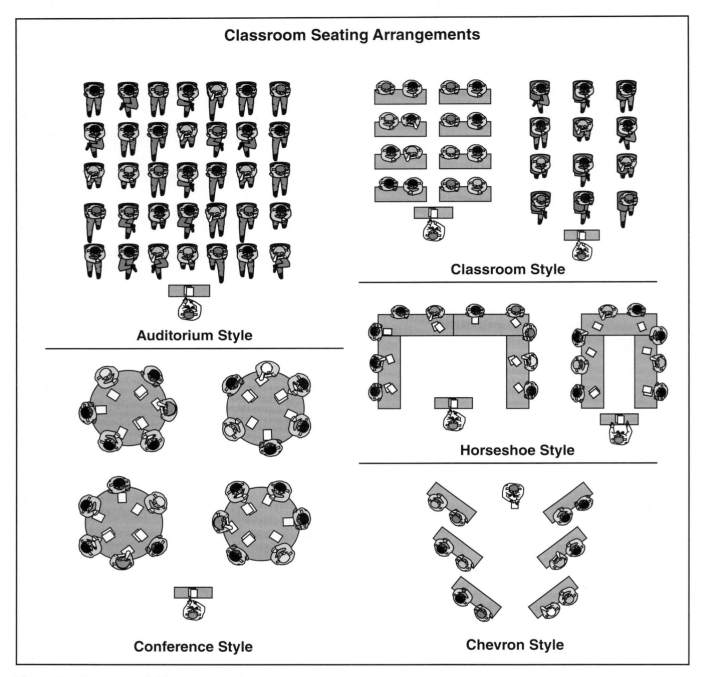

Classroom Seating Arrangements

Auditorium Style

Classroom Style

Horseshoe Style

Conference Style

Chevron Style

Figure 5.17 Examples of different types of seating arrangements.

This arrangements allows for all followers to see the educator and each other. It also allows for movement by the educator in the middle. It is good for demonstrations and skills training. It is, however, limiting in the number of followers that can be accommodated and can limit class control.

- The *small group arrangement* is excellent if the followers are going to be working in groups. This arrangement allows for good instructor movement and line of sight for followers. This permits greater participation among group members. This arrangement does need to be monitored to see how each group mixes. Moving around some of the class members may be necessary for the instructor.

The learning environment supports everything that the educator does in the classroom. For this reason, choosing the appropriate arrangement is as important as the selection of the appropriate instructional techniques.

Occasions may exist when the educator has no control over the environment. Rearrangement of the room may not be possible due to stationary tables and chairs. A smaller, less distracting environment may not be possible. In these situations, the effective Level I educator must be flexible and make adjustments as needed. As the Level I educator gains experience in delivering risk-reduction presentations in less than desirable environments, he or she will be able to overcome the problems and issues to provide productive, effective fire and life safety information to the followers.

Safety During Presentations

Any time people are gathered in a group, especially children, safety must be a consideration in all activities being conducted. Many presentations with children are active, as they should be. It is incumbent upon the Level I educator to make sure that all activities are age-appropriate and safe for each child's participation.

- When teaching the Stop, Drop, and Roll maneuver for clothing fires, many children will take the word "drop" quite literally! Make sure that this activity takes place on a cushioned surface or mat!

- Showing an apparatus to children or adults has the potential for danger and injury. Children will climb when given the opportunity, and even the most careful adults can trip and fall. Making sure that this activity takes place away from vehicle traffic is important as well. Adequate personnel for this demonstration will help to eliminate the possibility for injury.

- Fire safety trailers, or mobile safety houses, also have the potential for injury. Children may potentially become frightened or get in a hurry. If a window is being used as a practice escape route, fire department personnel must be on the inside to assist them out the window and personnel must be outside as well to assist the children down.

- Educators may be required to provide fire extinguisher training to various groups or businesses. While the use of live fire for this activity is up to the jurisdiction having authority, it must be done with an adequate number of fire department personnel in order for it to be safe. Many departments no longer approve live fire training for fire extinguisher training with the public, except in certain circumstances, due to liability and safety issues. Many departments are now using fire simulators for use with this type of training.

- Any time equipment is being used as a demonstration or prop, the educator should check the operation of the equipment before the presentation. This will not only ensure that it works, but will also verify that the Level I educator knows how to operate the equipment in a safe manner.

- Safety must also be a consideration in the classroom. Secure and use in a safe manner any extension cords or power cords, equipment that you have brought, and any props or illustration materials. Remember that every educator must set a positive example for both children and adults.

- When performing activities in the classroom or outdoors, it is necessary to provide the followers with safety rules and instructions for the activities. This may be as simple as having children form a single-file line or providing more intensive safety instructions when using fire extinguishers.

Some fire departments or school systems may require permission slips or waivers of liability when using fire safety houses, touring fire stations, or using other interactive resources. Level I educators should be aware of this requirement and be prepared to assist in obtaining the proper paperwork.

Educational Materials

The key to any effective presentation is the use of **educational materials**. Materials such as brochures, newsletters, and signs are an important part of fire and life safety education programs. By using these items appropriately and properly, followers are able to see the effects of fires, burns, and unsafe practices, as well as learn how to avoid them.

It is important to point out that materials alone do not constitute an educational program. It is not possible to determine if education has taken place without specific, measurable objectives; evaluation instruments; and valid instructional techniques. Materials used during the educational process can certainly supplement, reinforce, and clarify the issues and points made during the educational presentation.

Types of Materials

The Level I educator will use two basic types, or categories, of materials in the presentation processes: informational and educational. These categories are broad and are based on the intended use for the materials.

Informational materials. Informational or awareness materials (sometimes referred to as *promotional materials*) are used to make an audience more aware of a particular problem or issue. These materials make a statement and increase an individual's awareness that a problem exists. Some informational materials may also suggest an action or solution to the problem or issue being addressed. Informational materials may also include facts and figures supporting the issue or solution. The famous statement of Smokey Bear, "Only you can prevent forest fires," is a perfect example of an informational message **(Figure 5.18)**.

Educational materials. These are designed to educate a particular audience or group of people about a specific issue or problem. That is, educational materials are designed to elicit a change in behavior that is measurable. Educational materials that are used during the presentation process come in several forms. The three most common are print materials, audiovisual materials, and props.

- Print materials include posters, brochures, activity books, fact sheets, card or board games, and even the pretest and posttest student forms. These materials should be age-appropriate and relevant to the topic of the presentation. Print materials are usually cheaper to produce and use and can be provided to the audience as take-home materials. Print materials are sometimes referred to as *consumables* since they are usually a one-time use item.

- Audiovisual materials include a host of items including older formats such as videotapes, slides, transparencies, easel charts, chalkboards, dry erase boards, and stand-up displays **(Figure 5.19)**. Newer media include computerized simulations, presentations, and interactive programs. Again, these need to be age-appropriate and relevant to the presentation.

- Props are objects that the audience can see, touch, hear, and smell. These may include items such as a smoke alarm, a child safety seat, a fire extinguisher, or a bike helmet. Props may also include items that have been retrieved from fires or accidents,

Figure 5.18 A Smoky Bear sign in a national park. *Courtesy of Linda and Annie Miller.*

Figure 5.19 A fire prevention program stand-up display.

such as remnants of toys, melted smoke alarms, or a damaged bike helmet. Props are extremely effective tools for educational presentations because they bring the subject to life. The use of props during a presentation will involve several of the senses, which increases the retention and value of the information and behaviors. In making decisions about using props, the educator must keep several things in mind. The prop should help the audience learn how to perform a particular behavior or reinforce the need for the behavior. If a prop is more for "show and tell," it might be distracting to the audience and take away from the educational component. Another consideration is the tastefulness and nonthreatening aspect of the prop. Props that are used for their "shock value" may distract or upset the audience, and the educational message is once again lost. Props should also be age-appropriate.

Choosing the Appropriate Materials

The value of educational materials is not in their cost, but in their applicability to the audience and the message being delivered. Just because some materials cost a lot of money does not necessarily mean that they are appropriate for a particular audience or a community. Conversely, free materials are not always appropriate either. Some materials may be created in-house, while others can be purchased, borrowed, or adapted from another department or educator by securing the appropriate permission. The key for selecting the appropriate materials is to examine them for the appropriate messages for a particular target audience, based upon the characteristics of that audience.

The fire and life safety educator may want to establish a checklist for reviewing materials. Qualities to look for include the following:

- Suitability of the materials to the educational objectives of the program or presentation
- Technical accuracy
- Reputation of the producer or creator
- Clarity of message, that is, can the intended message or action be understood by the target audience
- Reading ease or readability
- Age appropriateness
- Bias-free and representative of the target audience

In other words, quality educational materials include those that are all encompassing; nondiscriminatory; and free of ethnic, racial, age, and gender stereotyping. For example, if educational materials represent firefighters as only Caucasian males, this will likely not have the appropriate impact on the target audience.

Use of characterization in instructional methods. Many fire departments are using characterization in their fire and life safety educational programs. The use of puppetry, clowning, robotics, and other characters greatly enhances educational programs, especially those for children **(Figure 5.20)**. The use of these instructional methods provides a medium for relaying important safety information and changing behaviors in a creative and fun way. Characterization programs make the material engaging so that young minds do not get bored.

The more adventurous a program, the more effective it will be in engaging the audience and providing an active learning experience. Some educators also use specially trained dogs in their education programs to illustrate important actions such as crawling low under smoke and stop, drop, and roll.[5]

Interactive electronic whiteboard. An interactive electronic whiteboard (also called a smart board) is a presentation device that interfaces with a computer so that images are displayed on the board by a projector **(Figure 5.21, p. 146)**[6]. It is essentially a live computer desktop. Items can be highlighted, emphasized, or added. Once the presentation is complete,

Figure 5.20 Examples of puppets used in fire and life safety education presentations.

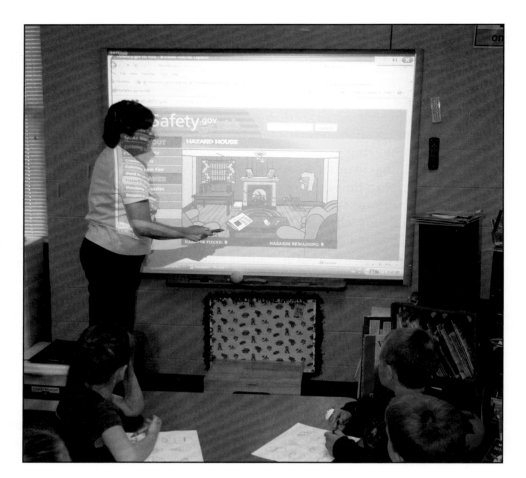

Figure 5.21 A teacher using a smart board during a fire safety lesson.

the information can be saved and e-mailed, made available to other users, or printed out. Computers may be connected to the whiteboard via USB cables or wireless technology.

There are many benefits of using an interactive whiteboard:

- *Presentations and projects* — Students can present projects without ever touching a computer keyboard.

- *Web streaming and video* — Viewing streamed or downloaded clips is made easier.

- *Printing and saving notes* — Since they will save anything that is written on them, notes can be easily shared and distributed.

- *Encouraging critical thinking* — Students' ideas can be written directly on the board and then the entire group can brainstorm together.

- *Special-needs students* — Use of large fonts, bright colors, and the touch feature of the board will assist students who may be visually impaired, have trouble staying on task, or are kinesthetic learners.

Legal Considerations

While the educator may not be a lawyer or a professional public information specialist, he or she must possess an understanding of the laws relating to freedom of speech and the use of the press. Probably the most important of these that the educator will need to know are copyright laws.

Educators must follow copyright laws. Any time educators use materials written by someone else, they must obtain permission from the copyright holder to use the material or logo and give appropriate credit in the document. The educator must include the copyright symbol ©, date of publication, and the owner of the copyright.

In addition to written materials, logos, and pictures, copyright laws apply to electronic photographs and materials downloaded from the Internet. The Digital Millennium Copyright Act of 1998 provides protection for those materials that are copyrighted and accessible on the Internet.

Digital Millennium Copyright Act

The Digital Millennium Copyright Act was signed into law in 1998. It is designed to govern copyright issues as they relate to the use of Internet and other electronic materials. In general, the Act:

- Makes it a crime to circumvent antipiracy measures built into most commercial software.

- Outlaws the manufacture, sale, or distribution of code-cracking devices used to illegally copy software.

- Permits the cracking of copyright protection devices but only to conduct encryption research, assess product interoperability, and test computer security systems.

- Provides exemptions from anti-circumvention provisions for nonprofit libraries, archives, and educational institutions under certain circumstances.

- Limits Internet service providers from copyright infringement liability for simply transmitting information over the Internet.

- Expects service providers, however, to remove material from users' Web sites that appears to constitute copyright infringement.

- Limits liability of nonprofit institutions of higher education – when they serve as online service providers and under certain circumstances – for copyright infringement by faculty members or graduate students.

- Requires that "webcasters" pay licensing fees to record companies.

- Requires that the Register of Copyrights, after consultation with relevant parties, submit to Congress recommendations regarding how to promote distance education through digital technologies while "maintaining an appropriate balance between the rights of copyright owners and the needs of users."

- States explicitly that "[n]othing in this section shall affect rights, remedies, limitations, or defenses to copyright infringement, including fair use..."

This is not to say that copyrighted materials cannot be used. The law provides clearly defined guidelines for how the materials can be used, and it is up to the educator to use the materials properly. Even when materials are not copyrighted, it is good practice to give credit to the individual who provided the artwork or material for a brochure or presentation.

Working with the Media

Working with the media is an important element of success in promoting fire and life safety educational and informational programs in any community. Media sources have access to an entire community of audiences. Understanding how the media fits into the education process, matching the media with the message, and understanding why fire and life safety educators must build communication ties with the representatives of local media will contribute to the success of the programs and presentations of the fire department. Educators need to view media representatives as partners in the risk-reduction process.

A channel or system that a person uses to communicate messages is called the *medium* (plural is media). *Media* is a term that commonly refers to "the mass media." Mass media are publications, broadcasts, and visuals designed to reach large numbers of individuals and usually carry advertising. These can include letters, posters, pamphlets, billboards, computers, radios, televisions, newspapers, and magazines.

Many departments may have a public information officer (PIO) who handles relationships with the media to convey information and news. In some departments, that individual may also serve as fire and life safety educator. An educator may be required to produce public service announcements (PSAs) for use by the local media, or he or she may be required to speak on radio or television broadcasts to promote an event or activity. Educators need to understand their role in working with their local media.

A *news release*, or press release, is used to provide the media with information in a ready-to-use news format. The news release can include stories of human interest, investigations, incident summaries, department policy issues, and educational stories. The news release is directed toward the public, but provided to the media (**Figure 5.22, p. 148**).

A *news advisory* is a means of communicating with the media to provide information about important events. It is basically a message to the media about an upcoming event or other issue. News advisories must stress the importance of the event, why it is newsworthy, and the location and time of the event (**Figure 5.23, p. 150**).

City of
CHAMPAIGN

Champaign Fire Department

MEDIA INFORMATION UPDATE

Address:	1531 Hedge Rd.	Incident #: 07-0002872

Day: Sunday	Date: June 24, 2009
Dispatch Time: 2:05 AM	Arrival Time: 2:10 AM

OCCUPANT(S):

Name	Age	Phone Number	Insurance
John Doe	18		

OWNER(S):

Name	Address	Phone Number	Insurance
Jane Doe			Yes

CONDITIONS FOUND:

Upon arrival, firefighters noted smoke in the area. As they moved to the back of the home, flames in the SW corner room could be seen.
An occupant was outside. He confirmed that everyone was out of the home.

ACTION TAKEN:

Fire personnel extinguished fire in the kitchen and dining areas of the single-story home. Kitchen cabinets were removed in the overhaul process.

Figure 5.22 An example of a news release. *Courtesy of Fire Factor, Champaign (IL) Fire Department.*

STRIKE TIME (Emergency Over): 2:16 AM	CLEAR TIME (Leave Scene): 3:32 AM

DOLLAR LOSS SUSTAINED:

Total Dollar Loss: $40,000	Structure Dollar Loss: $30,000	Contents Dollar Loss: $10,000

TYPES OF DAMAGE SUSTAINED:

Location: Kitchen	Amount of Room Damage: Heavy Fire, Heat, and Smoke
Location: Dining Room	Amount of Room Damage: Moderate Fire, Heat, and Smoke
Location: Remainder of the Home	Amount of Room Damage: Light Fire, Heat, and Smoke

CAUSE:
The occupant fell asleep forgetting the hamburger and french fries he'd begun to cook on the kitchen stove.

FIRE PREVENTION LESSON:
The number one cause of fires in AMERICA and in Champaign is food left on the stove.

Never leave cooking unattended.

NOTES:

For further information, contact:	PIO Dena Schumacher	217.XXX.XXXX
	DC Tim Wild	217.XXX.XXXX

Figure 5.22 Concluded

City of
CHAMPAIGN

Champaign Fire Department

NEWS ADVISORY   Editor: **Dena Schumacher**
                                                    217.XXX.XXXX

Date: March 8, 2009   Contact: **SAME**

Fire Chief for a Day 2009

The 2009 **Champaign Fire Chief for a Day** will assume his place of honor tomorrow,

Friday, March 16.

South Side School student James Doe will ride to Champaign Fire Station One, 307 S. Randolph in a fire engine. He will visit with DC John Smith, Acting Fire Chief, and learn the "ropes" from on-duty fire personnel.

Chief Smith will take James back to school to eat lunch with classmates from Chief Doe's and Ms. Applebee's classroom.

James was selected from a drawing conducted during Fire Prevention Week festivities at Market Place Mall and Fire Station Six Open House.

A tentative schedule follows:

9:30   James is picked up at school by fire personnel in an engine.

10:00   Chief Smith and Chief Doe will meet to determine and conduct the business of the day.

12:15 AM   City of Champaign Fire Chiefs will eat lunch together in the South Side lunch room/gym.

Champaign Fire Department 307 S. Randolph St. Champaign IL   61820

Figure 5.23 An example of a news advisory. *Courtesy of Fire Factor, Champaign (IL) Fire Department.*

News can be categorized into two categories:

- **Hard news** must be delivered immediately or it has no real value. It is news for today, but may not be news for tomorrow.
- **Soft news** can be broadcast today, tomorrow, or even next week. Most soft news contains a human-interest value.

Many times department public information officers have the ability to save the soft news stories for times when there is no hard news available.

Types of Media

In working with the media, matching the message with the appropriate media outlet must be accomplished before releasing information. Each type of media has its own audience and its own distinguishing features. Effective use of the media requires that the Level I educator have knowledge of the various types of outlets and specific knowledge about the ones available in their community. The various types of media include radio, television, print journalism, and electronic media such as an Internet site or online newspaper.

Deadlines

Deadlines are extremely critical in the business of broadcast and journalism. Determine deadlines for each outlet and consistently meet them. Being late is inexcusable due to the fast-paced, competitive, and content-driven markets.

Radio

Radio is a medium that is available in almost every city and town. According to Arbitron's "Radio Today" 2006 annual report, radio reaches 94 percent of the country's population 12 years of age and older. Even the newest technologies, such as Internet streaming, have not affected this number, which has remained steady for the past few years. Radio listening carries with it a definite strength, which is its lack of direct cost.

Fire and life safety educators can use radio to promote events, activities, and even to deliver fire and life safety messages. An event notification will provide information about events, open houses, presentations, and safety house times. Public service announcements provide information that can serve as a reminder about activities such as smoke alarm testing, home fire drills, and holiday safety issues.

For the fire and life safety educator, determining the appropriate station for the message is important. Different radio stations target different listening audiences. Talk or news radio is attractive to those listeners 65 years of age and older. Other categories of stations, such as country, religious, and urban to name a few, focus on a specified age or cultural group.

In order to build a relationship with the radio station, the fire and life safety educator needs to understand the organization of the station. Smaller

Summary of Radio Programming

- Radio programming is fast paced, sound-bite oriented, and broadcast in real time.
- Audiences include a variety of listeners in various locations; therefore, it is easy to target a specific group.
- Radio has hourly deadlines because it is always live.
- Programming may be interactive, such as talk shows, where there are on-air questions from listeners.
- Radio reaches large numbers of people quickly.

Example of a 30-Second Radio Public Service Announcement

Are space heaters in your home close to curtains, a stack of newspapers, or other flammable materials? Heating is the second leading cause of fire death for older adults. To make sure you will stay warm and safe this winter, follow these lifesaving tips:

- Know the location of the auto-off feature should the heater fall over.
- Keep space heaters at least three feet away from other objects.
- Ensure that your fireplace has a screen large enough to catch flying sparks and rolling logs.

This message is brought to you by the United States Fire Administration, your local fire department, and this radio station.

Source: United State Fire Administration

stations may have the owner serving as the station manager, who should be the primary point of contact. In larger stations, the point of contact will be the program director.

Television

Television is a commonplace item in most homes in the U.S. today. Many individuals have access to an enormous number of channels, whether it is by cable or satellite. The choices for viewers are quite vast.

Interestingly, at the time of this publication, television viewing, especially of the nightly news, had dropped significantly. In 1980, when CNN launched its news channel, 75 percent of all televisions were tuned to the nightly news during the "dinner hour," a common time for news broadcasts. In 2003, this number had dropped to 40 percent. During that time the number of broadcast options has increased, as well as other means of obtaining news, such as online media.

However, the Level I educator can still use local channels for promotion of events and safety messages. This is especially true with local cable channels, public access channels, or government-sponsored channels. Many departments are producing television shows for the local cable or government channel and providing fire and life safety information for children and adults alike.

The Level I educator may encounter television cameras and reporters at specific events or activities that are newsworthy in the community. Do not be afraid to ask these individuals to help support programs or activities. This might be the opportunity to promote a specific program, such as smoke alarm installations or juvenile firesetter intervention programs **(Figure 5.24)**. Make responses to questions short and to the point. Providing "action shots" or footage will prove to be beneficial to promote the airing of the news story or information.

Contacting the station's public affairs and public service directors is the first step in establishing a relationship with the television station. For smaller areas, the news director or the assignment editor may be the individual who should be approached. These individuals will be able to keep the educator up-to-date on the format and procedures for the station's programming.

Figure 5.24 A fire and life safety educator being interviewed for television. *Courtesy of Dayna Hilton.*

Summary of Television Programming

- Television is headline-oriented. The reporter needs to get the viewer's attention without sensationalizing.
- It can give segments in 60 seconds or less.
- It is fast-paced, action-oriented, and highly competitive.
- It may have aerial shots or provide more access for the viewer.
- The deadline for television is usually two hours before a broadcast.
- Programming themes will differ for the morning, noon, and evening news.

Print Media

Newspapers are a common type of print media that work well for communicating fire and life safety information. The educator should know the local outlets and what is expected in order for information to be published. A news release, which is nothing more than a written release of liability for the newspaper, is an important part of the communication process.

If not prepared properly, it is likely that the story or information will not be published.

Good basic journalism guidelines include the following:

- Use active voice.
- Make every word count.
- Limit sentence length to 20 words.
- Write clearly and concisely.
- Leave out technical terminology and jargon.
- Write no more than four or five lines per paragraph.
- Put the most important facts first, starting by summarizing the story in the first sentence.

Developing a working relationship with the representatives of local media is an essential part of the educator's role in the fire department and in the community. The media plays a powerful role in the community. Having a good working relationship with local media can increase the fire department's visibility, which can serve to provide an outlet for the educational messages. Fire departments must regularly provide the media with the information they are seeking in order for the department to get the assistance they need. Knowing the community's media services, identifying the key contacts for each, keeping promises for information, and meeting deadlines benefits the department and the community as a whole.

Summary for Developing Positive Relationships with the Media

- Treat the media as customers.
- Help them understand the design and function of the fire department.
- Create a one-on-one relationship with members of the media.
- Understand the media's needs such as deadlines, information, and openness in stories and details.
- Provide information before they ask and keep commitments. Be accurate, honest, and timely.

Using Other Forms of Media for Educational Messages

Television, radio, and print are not the only media sources that can assist with educational efforts in a community. Other forms of media, such as publicity and informational items, can serve to deliver educational messages to a particular audience. These alternative media outlets and educational strategies can have an impact on the success of risk-reduction activities. The educator must first decide the message, the audience, and the appropriate source for delivery. For example, alternative sources of message delivery can include everything from billboards, newsletters, Web sites, grocery bags, restaurant place mats, t-shirts, buttons, pens, rulers, trading cards, and other handout items.

Trading Cards

Trading cards are an inexpensive way to share fire safety messages and provide children and adults with items that will last. Stickers and other small giveaways may be discarded, but trading cards have a lasting power. Johnson County RFD #1 Public Fire and Life Safety Educator, Dayna Hilton, designs and uses trading cards to supplement her department's fire and life safety education program (**Figure 5.25**). Trading cards are limited only to imagination and can be designed to fit any program.

Figure 5.25 Examples of fire safety trading cards. *Courtesy of Dayna Hilton and Johnson County (AR) RFD #1.*

What This Means to You

Social marketing is a tool that has been used successfully in the public health field for many years. It uses the principles of commercial marketing and advertising and applies them to campaigns regarding social issues or problems. For example, attitudes and behaviors relating to fire safety, seat belt usage, healthy living, and the environment have been permanently changed.

Social marketing requires that you really know the target audience and place it at the center of your every decision about the program. Social marketing is also about knowing what motivates the target audience. Knowing what will motivate members of the audience will lead you to success in the marketing campaign. Social marketing borrows four basic principles, the Four Ps, from the marketing field.

- **Product** —Desired behavior from the audience and the associated benefits.
- **Price** — Monetary as well as emotional, psychological, or time-related costs.
- **Place** — Where the audience will access the program information or services and where followers will perform the desired behavior.
- **Promotion** — Materials, channels, and activities that will effectively reach the target audience.

Social marketing targets a specific audience — those who have a reason to care and are ready to change. Social marketing must be strategic and should involve members of the target audience. It must remove barriers that prevent behavioral change and, in order to do that, the barriers to change must be identified.

Social marketing has been used successfully by some fire departments in promotion of fire and life safety education. It is a long-term process and you must be committed to the process.

Source: Turning Point's Basics of Social Marketing www.turningpointprogram.org

---

Before ordering and using these items, the educator must first plan the message and the audience. Market research can be conducted by taking a poll, asking individuals within the target audience to complete a survey, or employing the services of a professional marketing group. Once the audience has been identified, the appropriate medium needs to be selected. An evaluation process must be developed to evaluate the effectiveness of the project.

Chapter Summary

The information that has been covered in this chapter goes to the heart and soul of the work of a fire and life safety educator. If programs are not age-appropriate, if messages are not based upon the abilities of the student, or if the appropriate instructional methods are not used, true learning will not take place. Learning that changes behaviors and attitudes comes from a focused and targeted presentation. If the work of the Level I educator is not based upon sound educational principles, such as those discussed in this chapter, that individual may be doing nothing more than "spinning wheels in the mud."

Preparation for presentations is imperative. At the time the presentation is scheduled, vital information is obtained that will assist any educator in providing a focused and targeted presentation. This basic information is imperative in the planning and delivery of the educational presentation. Understandably, sometimes the information is incorrect or the audience is not the expected demographic. Educators have to be flexible and willing to adjust their focus to provide for the most effective educational opportunity. Independent of any other factor, educators must remember that their prime focus is about saving a life and nothing short of a professional and instructionally sound presentation will do. The diligence, preparation, and research of the FLSE provides that opportunity for the members of each and every community.

Review Questions

1. What is learning?
2. How are learning theories used to ensure fire and life safety educational programs are effective?
3. What are the stages of learning and development?
4. What is the four-step method of instruction?
5. What is the purpose of a lesson plan?
6. What are the common components of a lesson plan?

7. What are the considerations for selecting educational materials appropriate for the topic and target audience?

8. What are the three components of an informational presentation?

9. What are the most common types of media?

Key Terms

Affective Domain of Learning — Affective learning is demonstrated by behaviors that indicate attitudes of awareness, belief, and responsibility. Affective learning appeals to attitude change and behavior modification.

Brainstorming — Identifying as many ideas as possible in a relatively short period of time.

Cognitive Domain of Learning — Core domain of learning that involves knowledge recall and use of intellectual skill. Examples of cognitive process include how a person comprehends information, organizes subject matter, applies knowledge, and chooses alternatives.

Demonstration — Instructional/teaching method in which the instructor/educator actually performs a task or skill, usually explaining the procedure step-by-step.

Discussion — Instructional method in which an instructor generates interaction with and among a group. There are several formats of discussion: guided, conference, case study, role-play, and brainstorming.

Educational Materials — Printed matter, audiovisual materials, and "props" that an educator uses to enhance delivery of a lesson.

Educational Objective — Teaching and learning goal that answers the question: "What will happen as a result of the education program?" Sometimes called instructional objective, behavioral objective, or learning objective.

Illustration Method — Instructional method that uses the sense of sight. The instructor or educator provides information coupled with visuals such as drawings, pictures, slides, transparencies, film, models, and other visual aids to illustrate a lecture and help clarify details or processes.

Lecture — Instructional method utilizing one-way communication in which an instructor or educator provides material verbally by telling, talking, and explaining but allows no exchange of ideas or verbal feedback.

Psychomotor Domain of Learning — The learner uses physical movement, coordination, and use of motor-skills to develop proficiency of a skill.

Role-Playing — Discussion in which a group acts out various scenarios.

Service Learning — Educational trend that tries to connect young people to the community in which they live through community service projects.

Team Teaching — Instructional method in which a group of two or more instructors work together — combining their individual content, techniques, and materials — in presenting information, demonstrating skills, and supervising practice of a class or several classes. A lead instructor organizes and coordinates the activities of all instructors. The instructor with the expertise in a particular topic teaches that particular topic; remaining instructors share the responsibilities of assisting with instructional details and of supervising practice of skills.

Chapter 5 Notes

Hall, John R. *Children Playing with Fire*. Quincy, MA: National Fire Protection Association, 2003.

National Fire Protection Association, Learn Not to Burn Preschool Program.

Romano, L. & Georgiady, N. (1994). Building an Effective Middle School. Brown and Benchmark: Madison, Wisconsin.

The State of the News Media. *Pew Project for Excellence in Journalism*. www.stateofthenewsmedia.org Confirmed 10-16-09.

Trench, Nancy. Oklahoma State University, Center for Early Childhood Teaching and Learning, Fire Protection Publications.

United States Fire Administration, Sesame Street Fire Safety Station.

1. Shuell, T.J. (1986). *Cognitive Conceptions of Learning.* <u>Review of Educational Research</u>, 56, 411-436.

2. National Fire Academy, *Developing Fire and Life Safety Strategies*, (1999).

3. National Fire Academy, Discovering the Road to High Risk Audiences.

4. Centers for Disease Control, National Center for Injury Prevention and Control.

5. Bonner, Jerry. *Developing A(n) Education Characterization Program.* Emmitsburg, MD, 2001. Identification No. 33553.

6. Brandzburg, Jeffrey. How to Use an Interactive Whiteboard. January 15, 2006. Found at http://www.techlearning.com/showArticle.php?articleID=175803144

FLSE Level I Educators: Evaluation

Chapter Contents

chapter 6

Key Terms

Job Performance Requirements

This chapter provides information that addresses the following job performance requirements of NFPA® 1035, *Standard for Professional Qualifications for Fire and Life Safety Educator, Public Information Officer, and Juvenile Firesetter Intervention Specialist*, 2010 edition.

NFPA® 1035 References

5.5.1

5.5.2

FESHE Objectives

Fire and Emergency Services Higher Education (FESHE) Objectives: *Fire and Life Safety Education*

7.   Develop an accountability system to measure program delivery.

FLSE Level I Educators: Evaluation

Learning Objectives

After reading this chapter, students will be able to:

1. Explain the purpose and importance of the evaluation process. (NFPA® 1035, 5.5.1)

2. Explain the benefits and limitations of presentation evaluations. (NFPA® 1035, 5.5.1)

3. Recognize the different stages of evaluation.

4. Identify the role of Level I educator in the evaluation process.

5. Identify and select appropriate evaluation methods based upon the lesson objectives, audience, and environment. (NFPA® 1035, 5.5.1)

6. Administer an evaluation instrument so outcomes of a particular presentation or lesson are measured. (NFPA® 1035, 5.5.1)

7. Score an evaluation instrument so that lesson outcomes are assessed. (NFPA® 1035, 5.5.1)

Chapter 6
FLSE Level I Educators: Evaluation

Case History

Wasilla (AK) nine-year-old Charlie woke to find his bed and curtains blazing. Smoke was filling his room. He did not panic because he remembered the lessons that he had learned two weeks before in the Denali Safety Council's fire and safety training. The following lessons that Charlie learned saved five lives:

- *Get out of the house.* He woke his parents and younger sister and told them they must leave the house immediately.

- *Call 9-1-1 from another location.* Charlie's mother called 9-1-1 from the house. Charlie told her to call 9-1-1 from the neighbor's house. The 9-1-1 operator told the mother to hang up and call from the neighbor's home. Charlie's mother grabbed the baby, and they all left the house.

- *Never go back inside a burning building.* Charlie's dad tried to fight the fire himself with a garden hose. Charlie told his dad to never go back inside a burning building.

This is an example of evaluation in its ultimate form — an anecdotal story. This chapter discusses the evaluation of programs and presentations and the importance of accurate and meaningful evaluation information.

Source: Denali (AK) Safety Council, 2007.

Evaluation should drive the risk-reduction process. Evaluation of community risk issues should provide information regarding who is at risk and the most common risk issues. Evaluation of implementation will provide information about the process used to implement and deliver the safety information. Evaluation of presentations will provide information about the effectiveness of those events, determining if there has been an impact on behaviors and attitudes **(Figure 6.1, p. 162)**. The most effective risk-reduction efforts are those led by people who are willing to modify the program strategies based upon the results of evaluation efforts.

Evaluation is the process of identifying existing conditions, determining performance levels, making comparisons, and reaching conclusions. For many departments or divisions, evaluation can be the weakest aspect of the risk-reduction process. Many educators, from the newest to the most seasoned, often see evaluation as unnecessary, cumbersome, or complicated. Evaluation may be a challenge due to a lack of time or resources. Some individuals may be unsure how to conduct evaluations or believe that evaluation involves complex mathematical formulas **(Figure 6.2, p. 162)**. All that evaluation requires is simple math, as will be explained later in this chapter.

Figure 6.1 Fire and life safety presentations such as this one should be evaluated to determine if the presentation was effective and brought about changes in behaviors and attitudes.

Figure 6.2 For many reasons, evaluation can be the weakest aspect of the risk-reduction process.

Some individuals fear that evaluation may identify shortcomings in the program's efforts, viewing such revelations as a bad thing. Truthfully, this is one of the purposes of evaluation and one of the benefits. By uncovering shortcomings, the program can be altered and updated to be more effective **(Figure 6.3)**. Without evaluation, shortcomings may never be discovered, and the program's effectiveness will be hampered.

Figure 6.3 Fire and life safety educators updating a program to be more effective.

The myth that prevention efforts cannot be measured has often restricted organizations from attempting to conduct quality evaluation efforts. Prevention efforts can be measured quite well as long as the organization makes a commitment to do so in an organized, effective manner.

Why Evaluate?

Evaluation may provide the following:

- Meaningful and quantifiable evidence of success in saving lives!
- Funding.
- Increase in budget.
- Justification of the time and expense involved
- Additional personnel.
- Professional development.
- Successful milestones for annual reports.
- Fulfillment of the department's mission statement.
- Showcase of successful programs at conferences, meetings, etc.
- Good public relations for supervisor, department chief, and agency.

Evaluation and Its Purpose

The valid purpose of evaluation is to determine whether the goals and objectives of the program or presentation have been achieved and if not, why.

Demonstration of program value is critically important, but it is secondary to determining whether the goals have been achieved.

Evaluation incorporates the following steps:

- Process of determining whether a program, curriculum, or community initiative is effective and appropriate
- Systematic collection and analysis of data needed to make decisions about the program and its design
- Planned process with a distinct series of steps, with each providing a specific type of information
- Planned assessment or analysis — it is not a judgment or opinion
- Hard evidence of the success of a presentation that can also uncover flaws in a presentation, lesson, or curriculum

The evaluation process starts in the planning stages of the risk-reduction program and continues through each aspect or level of program implementation and delivery.

The data received from program evaluations answer several important questions:

- Is the program working?
- Is the target audience being reached?
- Are the desired results being achieved?
- To what degree are they being achieved?
- Is there a way to improve the program's results?

- Are there unintended consequences of the program, either positive or negative?
- If results are being achieved, are they a direct result of the program or a result of something else?
- Is the content appropriate to achieve the desired results?
- Is the delivery method and presentation format on target?

Evaluation must be valid and objective. If it is valid, it measures exactly what it is supposed to measure. If it is objective, it will not be affected by bias. Bias occurs when the attitude or expectation of the educator influences the outcome of the data being collected.

Benefits of Evaluation

Evaluation of programs and presentations has many benefits. First and foremost, the primary benefit of evaluation is determining how well a program is working and what needs to be revised to make it work better. Out of this comes the ability to justify a position or program. Evaluation results justify the existence of educational presentations and events for community-risk reduction. Level I educators must be able to prove to organizational leaders that their activities are effective in changing behaviors and reducing loss.

Evaluations can serve to motivate the Level I educator. Evaluation determines whether the goals and objectives of the presentation or program have been achieved. The educator who works hard on a presentation that achieves its objectives and reaches the target audience will feel good about the hard work accomplished and be inspired to continue.

Evaluating a presentation can also help to determine its strengths and weaknesses. By identifying problems with a particular presentation, the content or presentation methods can be altered to provide for the most effective delivery the next time the presentation is given. Identification of the effective points or factors in a presentation can also help in the development of future presentations or delivery of other programs.

The process of choosing the evaluation method and the evaluation process requires careful thought and preparation. An evaluation is more than simply asking several questions before or after a presentation. For evaluations to be effective, the outcome objectives of the presentation or lesson must be examined, as well as the characteristics of the target audience and the nature of the behaviors being presented.

Additionally, evaluations may not provide the information that is wanted or needed. There are circumstances or situations that are outside the control of the Level I educator. For example, if surveys are not returned, objective information cannot be gathered.

Evaluations may be inaccurate due to the biases of the target audience. Many times the audience may give the correct information, although it does not reflect the truth. A participant may respond positively to questions about smoke alarms because the individual knows the desired answer. In reality, the participant may not have a smoke alarm or understand its importance. Some audiences may resent the authority of the fire department official or educator. Other audiences, such as immigrant or nonnative individuals, may give the correct response for fear of retribution or interference from the government. The educator administering the evaluation tool must work to overcome these limitations as best as possible.

Conducting risk-reduction educational programs is the right thing to do in serving a community and reducing the fire and injury occurrence. However, no longer is this sufficient justification. It is imperative that these programs and presentations be effectively evaluated to show that not only is it the right thing, risk-reduction education is an effective process that lowers risk and reduces death and injury due to fire and other disasters.

Stages of the Evaluation Process

The focus of the Level I educator is the evaluation of individual presentations or lessons. It is important to grasp how the evaluation of these single events fits into the overall evaluation process of a comprehensive risk-reduction initiative. A complete description of the program evaluation process will be covered in later chapters. The stages of evaluation are presented in this chapter: process evaluation, impact evaluation, and outcome evaluation **(Figure 6.4)**.

Process Evaluation

Process evaluation occurs during the development and delivery of the program. Through process evaluation, the following can be accomplished:

- Community outreach can be measured; that is, how many people have been reached and through what media.

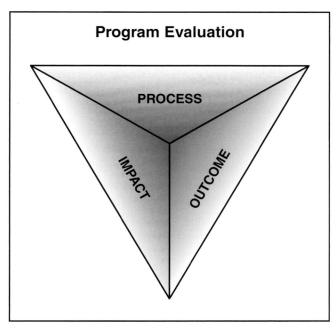

Program Evaluation

PROCESS

IMPACT

OUTCOME

Figure 6.4 Components of the program evaluation process.

- Program materials and activities can be described and assessed.

- The effectiveness of instructors in program delivery can be measured.

- The quantity and quality of programs delivered are evaluated to determine if changes are needed, additional funds are required, or remedial training for instructors should be provided.

- The program's implementation and progress is measured, not its effectiveness.

Process evaluation methods can include counting the number of presentations and the number of attendees, tracking budget details, and tracking the number of advertising pieces in newspapers or television.

Impact Evaluation

Impact evaluation identifies the effectiveness of the presentation on the audience, or the impact the program has made on the target population. Impact evaluation accomplishes the following:

- Measures changes in knowledge, skills, attitudes, behavior, and environmental modifications.

- Studies the immediate or direct effect of the presentation on the followers.

- Requires that baseline data be obtained before the beginning of the program or presentation and then that same data be compared to the informa-

tion obtained after delivery of the program or presentation. While process evaluation produces immediate results, impact evaluation may occur over a period of time.

- Measures knowledge or educational gains with pretests and posttests.

- Evaluates changes in behavior through observation or observational studies.

- Assesses **environmental changes** through mail or telephone surveys, home inspections, or by asking residents about their households.

In many ways, impact evaluation is the responsibility of the Level I educator. This individual must properly establish the baseline knowledge of an audience prior to the delivery of the presentation and then evaluate the change in that knowledge subsequent to the risk-reduction presentation. It must then be determined if the increase in knowledge created a change in behavior.

Outcome Evaluation

The most comprehensive level of evaluation is outcome evaluation. **Outcome evaluation** tracks statistical information and other evidence over a period of time and may take 5 to 10 years to complete. It is, however, the strongest evidence that a program is working, because it uses verifiable data to show a decrease in the occurrence of incidents, injuries, and loss of life. Outcome evaluation looks at all aspects of the risk-reduction program, from the presentations being made in the community, environmental changes being initiated, and any legislative actions being enforced. Outcome evaluation will determine if the objectives of the overall community risk-reduction initiative are being met: if lives are being saved, injuries and fires are prevented, and property is saved. Outcome evaluation methods include monitoring data to determine if there is a reduction in injuries or deaths and collecting anecdotal information or stories to provide evidence of program impact.

Impact Evaluation Methods

A variety of means are available to Level I educators to assess knowledge gain and behavioral change. It is important to keep in mind that the evaluation instrument should be a part of the lesson plan and most likely will be provided with the curriculum. Development of valid and objective evaluation instruments will be covered in later chapters of this text.

The most common evaluation methods include:

- Pretests/posttests
- Skills tests
- Surveys **(Figure 6.5)**
- Inspections
- Direct observations

Inspections and direct observations are mainly concerned with behavioral change, while pretests/posttests, skills tests, and inspections are used to determine knowledge gain.

Pretests/Posttests

The **pretest/posttest** is used to compare knowledge or skills of the audience before and after a presentation. By comparing the knowledge of the target audience before the presentation and then after, the educator will be able to determine the knowledge gained as a result of the presentation.

Pretest and posttest data is also useful in identifying the strengths and weaknesses of a presentation. If everyone misses the same question or questions, the information may not have been presented clearly and concisely for the audience or the lesson plan could need revision.

Pretests and posttests are simple in design and easily administered by the educator. In addition, they are usually well accepted by a target audience. However, members of the audience may experience anxiety any time an evaluation instrument is included as a part of the presentation. The most common types of test questions are multiple choice, fill in the blank, true/false, and picture identification.

- *Multiple choice* — asks a question and provides several choices from which to choose a correct answer. The participant selects the most appropriate answer.

- *Fill in the blank* — provides the participant with a statement that has a key word or phrase missing. The participant must fill in the key word or phrase to complete the statement.

- *True/false* — provides the participant with a statement, and the participant must choose whether the statement is true or false. Both fill-in-the-blank and true/false questions are very basic and do not provide in-depth information about the participant's level of understanding.

- *Picture identification* — used primarily with younger children or those with low literacy capabilities. Much like a true/false test, a picture identification test gives illustrations of behaviors, and the participant must choose the illustration of the proper behavior **(Figure 6.6)**.

Many pretests and posttests use a combination of the different types of questions. Using a variety of questions can provide basic information as well as meet the needs of the audience, members of which may do better on one style question than another. Some educators choose to use different formats for the pretest and the posttest questions to allow for a more accurate assessment of knowledge gain.

Pretests and posttests are generally most effective when used in a formal setting such as a classroom. The formal setting allows for control and management during the testing process. These types of evaluation tools are also best used with children and young adults. They are not as effective with adults and older adults.

Tips for Creating Written Tests

- Match test items to objectives of lesson or presentation. Questions should provide a measure of the intended objectives.

- Avoid giving clues to answers in other questions through the use of plural or singular words, and avoid using words such as *always* or *never*.

- Select a proper level of test item difficulty. This will depend upon the age level or ability of the audience.

- Determine the appropriate number of test items. It should be enough to measure the participant's understanding and ability, and to reflect the importance of the information presented.

- Ensure ease of testing and scoring. Use simple and direct instructions, provide sufficient time for administration, and ensure that it is cost-effective and easy to score.

Source: IFSTA's **Fire and Emergency Services Instructor,** *7th Edition*

Children's Safety Village – Fire Safety Program Evaluation

Please assist our program by evaluating the program presented to your students.

Evaluation Scale: 1 Needs Improvement   3 Good
                   2 Adequate   4 Excellent

Please circle your response.

1. Classroom rules were explained and a structured learning environment maintained throughout the day.

   1 2 3 4

2. All students participated in the safety tool activity.

   1 2 3 4

3. All students tested a smoke alarm.

   1 2 3 4

4. All students performed stop, drop and roll, get low and go, and practiced two ways of escape.

   1 2 3 4

5. All students were given the opportunity to practice calling 9-1-1.

   1 2 3 4

6. The tour of the burned house was conducted in an organized manner.

   1 2 3 4

Constructive feedback is important to our instructors and program. Objective comments and suggestions:

_____

_____

_____

Figure 6.5 A survey is a common evaluation method.

Figure 6.6 Students from a kindergarten class take a picture identification test.

Skills Tests

A **skills test** evaluates a person's ability to perform a specific physical behavior or task. Examples include installation of child passenger safety seats, demonstration of crawling low under smoke, or the steps in performing cardiopulmonary resuscitation (CPR) **(Figure 6.7)**. Many times assumptions are made that individuals know how to perform these behaviors when they are explained, and this is an erroneous assumption. The only way to know for sure that someone can properly perform a skill is to have the person go through the steps in front of an evaluator.

A skills test uses an evaluation sheet, which lists the proper steps of the behavior. The sheet is used as a guide to determine if the individual can properly perform each step of the behavior **(Figure 6.8)**.

Skills tests should be scenario-based to help individuals understand the context of the need for the skill. Individuals should be allowed the opportunity to practice the skill with instructor feedback prior to the actual administration of the test.

Figure 6.7 A fire and life safety educator teaching the steps in performing CPR.

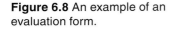

Figure 6.8 An example of an evaluation form.

Smithville Fire Department
Fire Prevention Division

Smoke Alarm Battery Change
Evaluation Checklist

Participant: _____ Date: _____

Objective: The participant should be able to change the battery in a smoke alarm.

The participant was able to:

Step	YES	NO
1. Open the smoke alarm cover.		
2. Remove the old battery.		
3. Install the new battery.		
4. Close the smoke alarm cover.		
5. Test smoke alarm.		

_____
Instructor/Evaluator

An example of a skills evaluation is the demonstration of the steps of home escape by a group of children using a fire safety trailer. The steps are introduced and explained to the group, and the educator demonstrates the procedure for the class. Class members are given the opportunity to observe the educator, discuss the skills being demonstrated, and ask questions. Children are given the opportunity to practice the steps, and finally each child demonstrates the skill on his or her own while the educator observes and assesses each participant's performance.

Surveys

A **survey** is an instrument used to identify an attitude or behavior of the target audience. Surveys are most generally used with adult audiences. A survey will ask a series of questions about a specific safety issue. Use of a survey instrument is an excellent way to determine if the audience has acted upon the information received as a result of the presentation. Surveys can also be used to determine the attitudes and behaviors of the audience prior to the presentation being delivered.

When designing a survey instrument, it is important that the questions be carefully worded. They must not be worded in such a way that they will elicit a particular response and should be directly related to the presentation. Surveys should be short and easy to complete. If a survey is lengthy or hard to understand, it is less likely to be completed accurately by the audience.

A variety of sources provide assistance with the creation, distribution, and results compilation of survey forms. Sources are available on the Internet that can assist in developing an appropriate survey form and can be delivered electronically to the audience (surveymonkey.com; zoomerang.com). Most of the programs are easy to use and will collect and calculate the information as it is returned. In addition, educators can seek out community members from local colleges or universities to assist in the preparation of a properly worded and distributed survey.

On any survey form, it is important to ask the respondent to provide any anecdotal information or testimonial stories that support the successes of the

What This Means to You

To have the most statistically valid survey results, it is always best to aim for the highest return rate possible. These evaluation results can be analyzed and used for future programs. The following ways increase return rates:

- **Evaluation planning**. Early on, communicate with participants about the importance of the evaluation process — and get their buy-in. Also, consider having an independent evaluation source, such as a local college, conduct the evaluation study, as some participants may be more willing to share their responses if they are sure they can do so anonymously.

- **Form design**. When designing evaluation forms, make sure that questions are clear, brief, and easy to answer. Always do a pilot test on the questions with several participants or a focus group. If they find flaws, it can save time, money, and aggravation by clarifying the questions before they go out to the entire group.

- **Delivery**. Allow participants to be able to provide the survey or evaluation data electronically through e-mail or posting on web sites. Collecting data electronically also saves time when processing the results.

- **Timing**. Participants who are given an evaluation and allowed time to complete it during a formal meeting session will likely do so. E-mailing a post-meeting questionnaire to participants within one or two weeks of the event may also produce high response rates, since it will still be fresh in the attendees' minds. Provide a deadline date for responding, and send out e-mail reminders a couple of days before the deadline to those who have not completed it. If a post-meeting evaluation is sent weeks or months after the event, participants may have forgotten some elements of the meeting.

- **Communications**. When sending out surveys, clearly communicate the why, when, what, and who to the reader. Share the reasons for the evaluation, when participants will be asked to complete the evaluations, what will be done with the results, and who will see and act on the results.

- **Incentives**. Participants can be encouraged to return their evaluations with an offer or chance of a gift for those who respond quickly. Alternatively, enclose a giveaway, such as a pen or a keychain, with the evaluation to encourage people to return it. Keep in mind that, in some circles, no response means the participants felt that they received no value or benefits from the event. Thus, the more responses the better!

Source: www.meetingsnet.com

presentation or program. Information such as lives saved as a result of working smoke alarms and the use of seat belts or bicycle helmets is invaluable to the evaluation process and to the credibility of the program. Real-life application of the behaviors and skills being taught is the ultimate in success of the risk-reduction initiative.

Inspections and Observations

These two evaluation methods are very closely related. They are also more accurate than other methods because the evaluation is actually completed by the Level I educator. **Inspection** programs have been used for many years to ensure compliance with fire codes.

Home inspections can be performed on a voluntary basis to determine the extent to which community members are implementing fire and life safety behaviors where they live **(Figure 6.9)**. Home inspections can provide information about the amount and kind of safety equipment in the home, such as smoke alarms, safety gates across stairs, and grab bars in bathrooms.

Home inspections must be treated as an educational opportunity and not an enforcement tool **(Figure 6.10)**. They are voluntary in nature, and residents should be informed about the purpose of the inspection. Furthermore, those conducting the inspections must be trained in proper inspection practices.

Observation as a form of evaluation is beneficial when the behaviors can be observed in a natural setting. A good example of this would be the rate of bike helmet or child safety seat usage. Observations of participants need to take place prior to the presentation or program, and again after. For example, an educator can observe children who are properly restrained in a

vehicle when arriving at school. After giving a presentation on the importance of child safety seats and seat belts, the educator would then return to make the same observation and compare the results of the before and after observation.

When Observation Is Useful

- *For direct information* — seeing is more reliable than simply asking.
- *When there is physical evidence, a product, or an outcome that can be readily seen* — drivers and passengers wearing seat belts, children wearing bike helmets.
- *When written or other data collection seems inappropriate* — use observation instead of a questionnaire: observations concerning changes in attitudes, nonverbal expressions.

Source: Ellen Taylor-Powell, Collecting Evaluation Data: Direct Observation

Administering the Evaluation

The approach used to administer the evaluation tool is as important as the tool itself. When using pretest/posttest and survey instruments, the manner in which the educator approaches the evaluation, the environment in which the evaluation is administered, and the instructions provided to the audience all have an impact on the outcome of the evaluation.

Figure 6.9 During this voluntary home inspection, a fire and life safety educator inspects the fire extinguisher.

Palm Beach Gardens Fire Rescue
Residential Fire Safety Survey

1 Are combustible materials kept on or near stove tops, fryers, or
   pilot lights?_____ Y N C

2 Are power cords worn, frayed, broken, taped, spliced, stapled,
   or under rugs?_____ Y N C

3 Do residents use space heaters? Three feet away from
   combustibles?_____ Y N C

4 Do space heaters have a tip-over "kill" feature?_____ Y N C

5 Are surge protectors in use? Properly matched wiring?
   Good condition? _____ Y N C

6 Are multi-plug adapters used to increase the number of outlets?_ Y N C

7 Do coffee maker, iron, chargers, and other heat-producing
   appliances have automatic "off" timer switches or **unplugged**
   when not in use? _____ Y N C

8 Are there two separate, accessible exits from the home?_____ Y N C

9 If not two doors, is there a secondary means of escape?_____ Y N C

10 Are exits or means of escape obstructed (furniture,
   storage, etc.)? _____ Y N C

11 Are all exit locks designed to allow egress without the use of
   a key? _____ Y N C

12 Working smoke detectors in proper location(s) i.e., in living
   areas and outside bedrooms? _____ Y N C

13 Working fire extinguisher mounted in proper location? _____ Y N C

14 Do residents know how/when to use the fire extinguisher?_____ Y N C

15 Do residents know how to safely use candles? (never while
   sleeping) _____ Y N C

16 Are flammable combustible liquids properly stored? Lids on,
   not in or under home, or porch or garage. _____ Y N C

17 Does the family have a fire/emergency exit plan? _____ Y N C

18 Does the family practice a fire exit plan? _____ Y N C

19 Is the area beneath the home properly secured to keep out
   kids/animals?_____ Y N C

20 Cigarette smoking in the home? Any evidence of unsafe
   practices?_____ Y N C

21 Are there handicapped/bedridden occupants? _____ Y N C

22 Are bedrooms doors kept closed while sleeping? _____ Y N C

Figure 6.10 An example of a residential fire safety survey form.

When administering an evaluation tool, such as a pretest or posttest, the Level I educator must demonstrate to the audience that the information derived from the evaluation is important and valued by the fire organization. The information can be used to improve future programs and presentations, and the audience must understand the significance of its role in this process.

The Level I educator can demonstrate the proper attitude during administration of the evaluation instrument in a variety of ways, which include the following tactics:

- Be positive about the presentation and the evaluation process. Express the importance of evaluation and that the information provided will be used to improve the presentation.

- Avoid influencing the participants. The evaluation should provide objective information, whether good or bad. If participants do not know the answer, or cannot perform the behavior, avoid providing them with the information they need.

- Provide clear instructions to the target audience before the evaluation. If a survey instrument is used, make sure the instructions are straightforward.

- Provide positive feedback to target audience members after the completion of the evaluation by stating how much their participation is appreciated.

- Follow the instructions provided with the evaluation instrument.

- Always maintain and respect the anonymity of those taking part in the evaluation. Seldom should identifiable results be shared with others.

- Thank the participants for their participation in the evaluation process.

The area where the evaluation tool is administered is considered the environment. In a school, the environment may be one over which there is control, such as a classroom. In other situations, there may be no choice about the environment. There may be situations where the environment is not ideal. However, the following actions may ensure that the proper environment exists for the evaluation:

- Keep the environment free from distractions. Allow the audience to concentrate upon the questions.

- Create a relaxed atmosphere for the audience. Many individuals, particularly adults, can become extremely nervous about evaluation tools.

- Ensure that the area is well lit and have tables or hard surfaces available, if possible.

- Keep the area free of hazards when performing skills tests.

Finally, the instructions given to the audience must be very explicit. The instructions should include not only how to take the evaluation but also its purpose. If a survey is being used, the instructions must be clear, as there may not be anyone available to explain the instructions.

When giving written tests and skills tests, the participants must be able to understand the instructions. The Level I educator must explain them in a way that reaches the audience. The instructions should be easy to read and should be written at the comprehension level of the target audience (**Figure 6.11**). Once again, the purpose of the evaluation should be explained when serving adult audiences.

Written evaluations and surveys must be administered in a fair and equitable fashion. The Level I educator must not do or say anything that will lead the participant to answer the questions in one way or to choose one answer over another. Doing so will lead to inaccurate evaluation results and will not allow for the most effective presentation possible.

Evaluation of the Results

Once the evaluations have been administered and properly scored, the data must be compiled, evaluated, and interpreted. The evaluation instruments themselves only provide data — it is up to the Level I educator to make sense out of the information.

The goal of evaluation is to determine if there has been a gain in knowledge, a positive change in behavior, or a positive change in the environment as a result of the presentation or lesson. This quantifiable amount of change is called educational gain and is determined by comparing the knowledge or behavior the presentation with the knowledge or behavior after the presentation. For example, an evaluation of a presentation may show the average posttest score was 30 points higher than the pretest. This indicates there was an educational gain as a result of the program.

Two basic type of calculations are used to assist in interpreting the data received from the evaluation: mean of scores and percentages. In mathematics, there are three principal ways of designating the average value of a list of numbers, or in this case, test scores (**Figure 6.12, p. 174**).

- The **mean** is found by adding the test scores and dividing the sum by the number of test scores on the list. This is what is most often meant by an average.

- The **median** is the middle value in a list ordered from smallest to largest.

- The **mode** is the most frequently occurring value on the list.

Adapting Evaluations to Meet Special Needs of the Audience

There may be times when the Level I educator may need to adapt or alter an evaluation or the evaluation process to meet special needs of the audience. These needs may be obvious, such as with physical impairments or disabilities. On other occasions, they may not be so apparent, such as with those for whom English is a second language and those who have a low literacy level or comprehension difficulties.

Having information about the audience prior to the presentation will assist in making these adjustments. However, some of these issues may not be known even to the individual scheduling the presentation. At first appearance, an educator will not be able to identify those individuals with literacy problems or cognitive issues.

To effectively administer a knowledge evaluation, such as a multiple-choice exam, the educator needs to be prepared to administer the test orally to the group or to any individual participant. In establishing the environment and the attitude for the evaluation, the Level I educator should provide for an open environment that allows for the expression of these limitations. In addition, the educator must be able to "read" the audience and identify the signs of low literacy or lack of comprehension by recognizing such indicators as the amount of time spent on questions or hesitation in getting started on the exam. A good educator will move through the classroom during the evaluation or assessment time to uncover these obstacles.

With skills testing, there may be physical limitations that keep participants from being able to effectively perform the skill as taught. Working with this participant, the educator may be able to establish alternative ways to complete the activity with the end result the same.

For those for whom English is a second language, the educator will hopefully be able to have this information prior to the presentation and have the evaluation instrument in the appropriate language or individuals present who can assist with translation. With written evaluations, it is okay to have picture identification exams for use by adults with lower literacy, comprehension, or language barriers.

Any educator should make every effort not to embarrass or alienate any participant by putting him or her "on the spot" or pointing out any of his or her limitations in the evaluation process. The end result is to establish that individuals at the presentation have actually gained knowledge and changed their behavior in a positive way.

Smithville Fire Department
Fire Prevention Division

Smoke Alarm Battery Change
Post-Presentation Quiz

Participant: _____ Date: _____

Instructions: Read each of the following questions carefully and select the best answer of those provided. Write the letter of the answer you have chosen on the line next to the question. Once you have completed this quiz, return it to the instructor to be graded.

_____ 1. Smoke alarm batteries should be changed once a year.

a. True
b. False

_____ 2. Which size battery does the average smoke alarm use?

a. AA
b. AAA
c. C
d. 9-volt

Figure 6.11 An example of instructions for completing a post-presentation quiz.

Confusing the Concepts of *Mean*, *Median*, and *Mode*

MEAN??? MEDIAN??? MODE???

Figure 6.12 The principal ways to designate test scores.

Mean of Scores

The mean of scores is nothing more than an average score. The average is determined by adding the scores from all the tests and then dividing by the number of scores. The formula is shown below:

> **Mean = Sum of the Participants' Test Scores**
> _____
> **Number of Participants**

While this may sound complicated, it really is an easy calculation. Consider the results from a presentation to a grade school class. Twenty children participated in the presentation. The scores from the students are listed below:

95	90	85	85	60
70	80	90	70	95
60	95	85	85	85
90	90	95	70	75

To calculate the mean score, or the average, first add all the scores together. In this case, the total sum of the scores is 1,650. Then divide by the number of scores, which in this case is 20.

> **Mean = 1 650/20**

In this case, the mean score is 82.5. This shows that the average test score for the children is 82.5.

Determining Percentages

The other calculation method for the evaluation process is determining percentages. A percentage is a part of a whole expressed in hundredths. To show the concept of a percentage, the following example is used:

A presentation was given to a group of homeowners on home escape planning. Twenty participants were in the group. A week after the presentation, a survey was sent to each of the participants to determine if he or she had completed a home escape plan. Fifteen of the participants returned the survey. Of the fifteen, ten had completed a home-escape plan as a result of the presentation.

In this example, the percentage of participants returning the survey must be calculated, as well as the percentage of participants that did a home-escape plan.

To determine the percentage of participants who returned the survey, divide the number of participants who returned the survey by the total number of participants who received the survey and then multiply by 100, which is called the *rate of return*. In this case, the calculation would look as follows:

$$\text{Percentage (\%)} = \frac{15\ (\#\ \text{who returned survey}) \times 100}{20\ (\#\ \text{of surveys sent})}$$

In this example, 75 percent of the participants completed the survey. Next, calculate the percentage of participants who completed a home-escape plan. Again, divide the number of participants who completed the plan by the number of participants who returned the survey and multiply by 100. In this case, the calculation would be:

$$\text{Percentage} = \frac{10\ (\#\ \text{home escape plans}) \times 100}{15\ (\#\ \text{completed surveys})}$$

Based upon the results of the survey, it can be determined that 66 percent of the participants who returned the survey completed a home-escape plan because of the presentation. This may not represent the actual number of participants who did a home-escape plan since you did not get all of the surveys back.

Percentages can also be used with skills tests results. A presentation is given to 35 adults on the proper installation of a child safety seat, and 27 of the adults completed the skills test successfully. To calculate the percentage of accuracy, simply divide the number of adults who successfully completed the skills exam by the number of adults who took the test and then multiply by 100. The calculation would look like this:

$$\text{Percentage} = 27\ (\#\ \text{successful})/35\ (\#\ \text{participants}) \times 100$$

Based on this, 77 percent of the adults were successful in the skills test.

Interpretation of Results

While the calculation of the mean of scores or percentages helps to clarify the data from the evaluation instruments, further evaluation is needed to give this information meaning. A conclusion must be drawn about the effectiveness of the presentation based upon the results of the data calculation. This conclusion must be based upon an objective interpretation of the results. In order to develop an accurate conclusion, consider one or all of the following factors:

- The difference between the average pretest and posttest scores
- Any patterns in the scores, such as specific questions that are missed, lack of improvement in any one area, confusion, and specific behaviors
- The differences in scores from one presentation to another or from one target audience to another
- The outcome objectives for the presentation

In determining whether the educational gain levels are acceptable, the Level I educator should compare the educational gain with the desired outcome identified in the learning objectives. This will determine whether further education is needed with this particular audience.

In looking at the example of the homeowner group and home-escape planning, it may be important to determine why some participants did not return the survey. Depending on the objectives of the program, the return rate as well as the completion rate may be acceptable. But if not, determining why some did not return the survey form or did not develop the home escape plan will help with future presentations and evaluations.

When looking at the results of evaluation compilation, it is certainly acceptable and advisable to seek the help of someone who may be more qualified or have more experience in interpreting evaluation results, such as a Level II manager or Level III administrator. If such a person is not readily available, feel free to look outside the fire organization, such as the local community college, health department, or even private marketing firms.

When interpreting the results of presentation evaluations, consider the following:

- Make sure that the evaluation method is appropriate for the presentation.
- Spend the necessary time to develop a good evaluation plan before the presentation.

- Request assistance (if needed) during the planning stage in developing an evaluation tool.

- Explain the purpose of the evaluation to the target audience, especially if they are adults.

- Consider each piece of information gained from the evaluation. Look for patterns, differences in scores, and the desired outcome objectives.

- If the evaluations indicate that the objectives were not received, ask why. Discuss changes that could be made to improve the presentation.

- Ask for help if the results are unclear or if it is difficult to develop a conclusion.

Selecting the Proper Evaluation Instrument

In most situations, the evaluation instrument will be provided to the Level I educator as a part of the lesson plan or curriculum. It is, however, important for the Level I educator to understand which evaluation tool works best for certain objectives. Any evaluation must be specifically designed for the characteristics of the target audience and must be designed to measure the objectives of the lesson plan or presentation.

The best method for evaluating knowledge change is through a written test such as a multiple-choice or picture identification quiz. Alternatively, oral questions can be used, especially with younger children.

The best methods for evaluating behavioral change include skills tests and surveys. These are effective when the educator wants the target audience to go beyond simply knowing more — the objective is to promote a behavioral or environmental change. Skills tests are valuable when teaching physical behaviors such as properly wearing a bicycle helmet or "stop, drop and roll." For behaviors or actions that might occur in the home or the workplace, a survey must be used. Activities such as preparing a home-escape plan or checking a smoke alarm are best measured by a survey.

In order to effectively evaluate environmental changes, surveys or inspections are the best way. A survey can be mailed to the audience after the completion of the presentation. It is, however, important that the target audience be given time to act. If inspections are to be performed, it must be recognized that this is a labor-intensive method of evaluation.

Evaluation of the Presentation vs. Evaluation of the Presenter

Evaluating the results of the presentation is different than evaluating the ability of the presenter. However, both are important when it comes to determining and ensuring the successful outcome of any presentation.

An evaluation of educator performance includes areas such as ability, knowledge, experience, presentation methods, and organization (**Figure 6.13**). Learner comments provide information to the educator, administration, and program developers that is important in making final assessments about the presentation. If there is a consistent lack of knowledge gain, it may be the result of inadequacy on the part of the educator or an ill-prepared lesson plan. Presenter evaluations assist the educator and the program administrators in making the adjustments as necessary.

It is important that the Level I educator not confuse the focus of the two evaluations. While both may be performed, the results are targeted at two different areas. The educator may receive excellent evaluation scores, while the target audience experiences very little educational gain. It is up to the educator and the program administrators to determine the problem with the presentation and make revisions to the lesson plan or curriculum. If the Level I educator receives less than acceptable scores, this information can be used as an educational tool for skills improvement or remediation for the educator (**Figure 6.14**).

Figure 6.13 A fire and life safety educator receiving an evaluation of his presentation performance.

Children's Safety Village – Fire Safety Instructor Evaluation

Please assist our program by evaluating the instructor who gave the presentation.

Evaluation Scale: 1 Needs Improvement 3 Good
2 Adequate 4 Excellent

Instructor's Name: ____________________ Date of Visit: ____________

Please circle your response.

1. The instructor was familiar with the curriculum and presented the material smoothly.

   1 2 3 4

2. Classroom rules were explained and a structured learning environment maintained throughout the day.

   1 2 3 4

3. Cooperative learning techniques such as think, pair, and share were utilized.

   1 2 3 4

4. The instructor utilized effective classroom management strategies.

   1 2 3 4

5. The instructor clearly explained what was to be seen, done, and learned at Children's Village during the fire safety program.

   1 2 3 4

6. The instructor presented information on how to prevent fires in a context that students could understand.

   1 2 3 4

Objective comments and suggestions:

____

____

____

Figure 6.14 An example of a fire safety instructor evaluation form.

Chapter Summary

Evaluation of a presentation or program is just as important as the presentation itself. It should be a planned process: a part of the lesson outline or curriculum. It does not have to be elaborate or complicated. It can be as simple as asking a few questions before the presentation and then again upon its completion, or it can take the form of a formal written pretest and posttest.

Evaluations determine whether the objectives of a presentation or program have been met. Evaluations must be carefully planned by course or curriculum developers and the Level I educator. Evaluations may be easy to administer or may require the assistance of other educators or fire department personnel.

Evaluation is a valuable tool that should be an integral part of every program. The evaluation process provides the Level I educator, and his or her supervisors, with feedback relating to the effectiveness of the presentation, the educational gain of the target audience, and the instructional methodologies used in the presentation.

It is not enough to conduct the evaluation. The information received, once processed and interpreted, must be acted upon to be of any value to the Level I educator and the fire organization. Evaluation must be used to continually improve the presentations and programs to increase their effectiveness.

Evaluation must be given the same importance as any tool or process used by the Level I educator. Evaluation is the only way to know if the presentation has been effective, if individuals have absorbed the information, and if behavioral or environmental changes have been made to provide for the safety of the target audience.

Review Questions

1. What is the purpose of the evaluation process?

2. What is the importance of the evaluation process to the educator? To department decision makers?

3. What are the benefits and limitations of evaluating fire and life safety education presentations?

4. What are the three different stages of evaluation?

5. What is the role of the Level I educator in the evaluation process?

6. What are the different evaluation methods that are typically used to evaluate fire and life safety education presentations? When is each method used?

7. What is the proper procedure for administering an evaluation instrument for a fire and life safety education presentation?

8. What is the proper procedure for scoring the results of an evaluation following a fire and life safety education presentation?

Key Terms

Environmental Change — Change in a learner's surroundings, particularly the home or workplace, following a fire and life safety outreach activity.

Impact Evaluation — Measuring knowledge gain, behavioral change, and modifications to living conditions or lifestyles.

Inspection — Formal examination of an occupancy and its associated uses or processes to determine its compliance with the fire and life safety codes and standards.

Mean — Term that refers to the "average" of a set of scores and is calculated by adding all of the set of scores (values) and dividing by the total number of scores.

Median — Middle score in a set of scores (values) that are arranged or ranked in size (order) from high to low.

Mode — Most frequent score (value) in a set of scores.

Outcome Evaluation — Measures changes in the occurrence of incidents over time. It also involves documenting anecdotal success stories of how prevention efforts impacted community risk.

Pretest/Posttest — A test administered prior to and after a lesson or program has been conducted.

Process Evaluation — Documenting the creation of prevention efforts, monitoring program activity and tracking outreach into the community.

Skills Test — Evaluation instrument used to assess the individual's ability to perform a specific physical behavior; also called a performance test.

Survey — Evaluation instrument used to identify the behavior and/or attitude of an individual or audience both before and after a presentation.

Chapter 6 Notes

Community Fire and Life Safety Education: A Fire Step Process, United States Fire Administration. Emmitsburg, MD. August, 2002.

Developing Fire and Life Safety Strategies, National Fire Academy Curriculum, August, 2006.

Fire Protection Handbook, Nineteenth Edition. National Fire Protection Association. Quincy, MA: 2003.

Presenting Effective Public Education Programs. National Fire Academy curriculum. November, 2001.

FLSE Level II Managers: Knowledge and Skills

Chapter Contents

chapter 7

Key Terms

Job Performance Requirements

This chapter provides information that addresses the following job performance requirements of NFPA® 1035, *Standard for Professional Qualifications for Fire and Life Safety Educator, Public Information Officer, and Juvenile Firesetter Intervention Specialist*, 2010 edition.

NFPA® 1035 References

6.1.1

6.1.2

FESHE Objectives

Fire and Emergency Services Higher Education (FESHE) Objectives: *Fire and Life Safety Education*

3. Identify stakeholders; develop partnerships and coalitions to work on fire and life safety education activities.

Learning Objectives

After reading this chapter, students will be able to:

1. Explain the political process of decision-making within organizations and communities. (NFPA® 1035, 6.3.2)

2. Identify how political determinants can impact risk reduction. (NFPA® 1035, 6.3.2)

3. Explain how knowledge effects behavioral change.

4. Articulate how to create a community risk reduction plan. (NFPA® 1035, 6.3.1)

5. Clarify the leadership role of an educator meeting Level II of NFPA® 1035.

Chapter 7
FLSE Level II Managers: Knowledge and Skills

Case History

In a suburban community somewhere in the U.S., 20 young adults (between the ages of 17-23) had been killed over a two-year period in automobile crashes on one specific roadway. Factors contributing to the incidents included speed, a winding two-lane roadway, and alcohol use.

The emergency services, health community, and parents were rightfully concerned. Parents and community agencies, led by the health department's risk-reduction officer, formed a task force to address the issue.

Members of the task force recognized that an educational program should serve as the foundation to address the problem, but they also knew that education alone would not produce a significant reduction in crashes. Led by the health department's risk-reduction officer, the team crafted an action plan that included combined preventive interventions. The following summarizes what was initiated:

- **Education:** The task-force initiated a media campaign targeting young adults. The campaign provided information about the local problem and how incidents could be prevented. It also included information on the cost of incidents and what enforcement measures would be initiated.

- **Engineering:** A study of the crashes revealed that over half occurred on a winding road that traversed the suburban area. Local government agreed to erect warning signage, reduce the speed limit, and install lane dividers on curves where many fatalities had occurred.

- **Enforcement:** Local police agencies increased patrols, sobriety checkpoints, and speed enforcement throughout the area. Warnings for infractions were eliminated. Tickets and arrests became the primary penalties for speed and alcohol violations. Undercover stings were held to revoke the liquor licenses of establishments caught selling alcohol to minors. All enforcement measures were announced in advance of implementation and the infractions were highly publicized.

- **Economic incentives:** At sobriety checkpoints, police awarded sober law-abiding motorists under age 25 with gift certificates for free dinners sponsored by local corporations. More alcohol-free events for young adults were sponsored by local entertainment venues.

- **Emergency response:** The local fire department placed a roving fire/EMS unit in service on weekends throughout the area where most fatalities had occurred.

NFPA® 1035, *Standard for Professional Qualifications for Fire and Life Safety Educator, Public Information Officer, and Juvenile Firesetter Intervention Specialist*, requires Level II fire and life safety managers to exhibit proficiency in creating and leading community risk-reduction programs. Quality leadership, the development and use of strategic planning, and use of combined **prevention interventions** (5 Es) are important components of this process.

> When referring to the three levels of fire and life safety educators, the following terms are used: Level I is *educator*; Level II is *manager*; and Level III is *administrator*.

Level II managers know that successful risk-reduction requires support from many facets of a community. These managers obtain support though clear communication, fact-based rationales, and collaboration with others. Successful outcomes are achieved by understanding how people learn new information and organizations make decisions.

Educators who meet the Level II standard do so through a combination of education and experience. This chapter assists the reader toward that goal through an overview of the general requirements for NFPA® 1035 Level II.

Political Process and Community-Risk Reduction

The U.S. political processes operate from the federal level and transcends to localities and organizations **(Figure 7.1)**. All fire and life safety educators should have a basic understanding of how organizations and communities are governed. Because politics pervades every facet of society, it is important for the educator to realize that he or she cannot circumvent the due process of an organization or community.

Understanding political process also helps the manager realize why a fact-based rationale for reducing community risk must be created. Since Level II managers create and lead risk-reduction programs, they must have a mastery level understanding of how people make decisions on priorities, programs, and resource allocation.

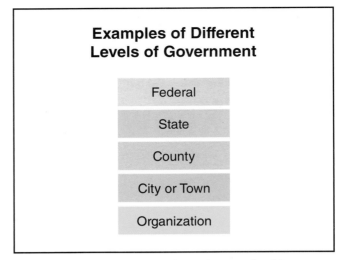

Examples of Different Levels of Government

Federal

State

County

City or Town

Organization

Figure 7.1 The fire and life safety educator should understand the levels of government and the basics of how each level works.

Organizational Political Process

Regardless of size, most organizations use chain of command to conduct business. Volunteer groups may use committees, boards, and line officers. Career departments often use bureaus, divisions, officers, and administrators. Regardless of the type of organization, a decision-making process exists for determining the priority and approach to issues at hand and resource allocation.

Organizational support is essential to successful community-risk reduction. Fire and life safety educators must understand that following a defined process for conducting business is extremely important. When requesting support for risk-reduction efforts, it is very important to follow the rules, budgetary timelines, and chain of command within an organization.

Community Political Process

Communities have a defined way of conducting business just as organizations do. As with organizational support, help from the community is essential to successful risk reduction. Most local communities are governed by councils, aldermen, commissions, or boards.

Political leaders represent constituents living within their jurisdiction. The opinion voiced by constituents often influences decisions made by political leaders. Political leaders are entrusted with ultimate power to approve and allocate resources for addressing community needs. These resources include people, time, money, and equipment. The level of attention devoted to an issue can also be classified as a resource.

Determinants that Affect Political Process

Political process drives organizations and communities. Political determinants influence the process and can impact the success of an idea, a project, or an initiative.

- Internal political determinants can drive decisions and actions taken by an organization. For example, a disagreement between labor and management can influence the level of support an organization is willing to allocate for a specific project. Or, a **stagnant organizational culture** that is opposed to performing risk reduction could impact the level of support granted to the effort.

- Political determinants within a community can also impact risk reduction. For example, if residents (constituents) are unhappy with their current tax rate, the local fire department may struggle in convincing decision-makers that a tax increase is necessary to fund a new position in the fire prevention bureau.

- Political decisions may not run parallel with the interests of risk-reduction goals. Examples include political undermining of laws that support manufacture of safer cigarettes or require fire sprinklers in new homes. In many states, **lobbyists** funded by corporate interests continue to negatively impact public safety by influencing decision-makers to reject legislation requiring use of safer products and materials.

Other determinants that influence the process and impact the success of an idea, a project, or an initiative include the following:

- Decision-makers, both organizationally and throughout the community, usually respond well to a fact-based rationale of why they should support a specific issue or program. If a person clearly understands the issue and why it should be addressed, he or she is more likely to join forces with others to support the cause.

- An organization that works cooperatively can realize important milestones such as **institutionalized behaviors** and growth of equity both within the organization and throughout a community. Institutionalized risk reduction is achieved through a process of clear communication, cooperation, collaboration, and compromise.

- Adversarial relationships produce negative results. Adversarial relationships can destroy productivity, organizational credibility, and community equity.

- Aggressive managers who fail to follow organizational protocol can interfere with the success of risk reduction. Many visionaries can clearly see an end goal, but they may forget the need to follow their organization's defined process of decision-making.

Level II managers must be able to develop a plan to address community risk. To do that well, it is helpful to have a strong understanding of how people receive and process information. It is also desirable to possess the ability to build fact-based, understandable justifications to support requests and proposals.

Understanding the Needs of the Community and Organization

Demanding support for risk reduction from the organization and community is a dangerous strategy that will likely result in failure. Fire and life safety educators must understand that risk reduction is not the only issue needing support by the organization and community. For example, an executive fire officer may be responsible for his or her organization's emergency response capabilities, staffing, equipment, maintenance, facilities, incident investigation, and community fire and injury prevention.

In addition to public safety, community decision-makers are responsible for utilities, roadways, planning, zoning, and parks and recreational opportunities for their constituents.

In any organization or community, there are usually a set amount of resources in the form of time, people, money, and equipment. Therefore, managers should recognize challenges faced by decision-makers and strive to integrate prevention into the larger mission of improving the constituents' quality of life.

How Knowledge Affects Change

Because **Level II fire and life safety educators** are expected to be leaders of risk-reduction programs, they will encounter situations where facilitating change becomes necessary. Level II managers want target populations to change behaviors or modify living environments in the name of safety. Leaders want followers to believe in their vision and carry out important tasks to reach set goals. Everyone wants decision-makers to allocate more resources for their specific cause. These concepts all involve some level of change.

Because change almost always requires support from others, it is relevant to examine how learning affects change. People often resist change because they fear the unknown, which can breed anger and resistance. Resistance to change may diminish when people are educated as to what changes are needed and why. Understanding how people learn can positively impact acceptance of new ideas and programs.

Applied learning is the concept of connecting real-life applications to information being presented. A person needs to see the relevance of learning or doing something new **(Figure 7.2)**.

Figure 7.2 A fire and life safety educator uses a real-life application in his presentation.

Learning occurs when a person connects what they already know about a subject to new information being presented. It is critical for the manager to know the learner's **baseline knowledge** about the topic being presented to be able to build upon it. If the presenter does not take time to learn about and understand his or her target audience, a presentation may be created that is either too basic or too advanced. Neither will precipitate a successful outcome.

Another concept important to planning presentations is that of employing diverse media. Most people learn best through a combination of listening (auditory), watching (visual), and doing (kinesthetic). Presentations must therefore address all three learning styles.

Presentations which appeal to both the head (factual, easy-to-understand material) and the heart (anecdotal evidence) are most effective. (More information about developing effective programs and presentations appears in Chapter 10.)

Creating a Plan to Address Community Risk

Managers must follow an organized process of identifying leading local risk issues, creating a logical plan of attack, implementing the effort, and evaluating its outcome. Level II requires fire and life safety educators to have a mastery level understanding of the nationally recognized *Five Step Planning Process to Reduce Community Risk*[1] **(Figure 7.3)**. The five-step planning process includes conducting a community analysis, developing community partnerships, creating an intervention strategy, implementing the strategy, and evaluating the results.

Community Analysis

Conducting a **community analysis** is arguably one of the most important tasks a fire and life safety educator will ever perform. If done well, it sets the stage for an effective risk-reduction outcome as leading problems and people being affected are identified.

Five distinct components of a community analysis should be followed sequentially:

1. *Identify data to be analyzed.* Such information includes leading causes of risks, where problems are occurring, and who is being affected. Information is obtained by conducting research, asking questions, and making comparisons using reliable data.

Five-Step Process for Community Risk

- Evaluate the Results
- Implement the Strategy
- Create an Intervention Strategy
- Develop Community Partnerships
- Conduct a Community Analysis

Figure 7.3 Level II managers must have a thorough understanding of the five-step process.

2. *Develop a community risk profile.* The profile outlines demographics of a community and high-risk populations and includes a brief description of priority risk issues. It also highlights public perception of a problem, examines political support for risk reduction, and identifies available resources.

3. *Prioritize risk issues.* Such triage of problems, determined after analysis of local need, may be based on frequency of occurrence, large dollar loss, mortality, and injuries.

4. *Write a problem statement.* The statement provides a fact-based overview of the highest priority problem and the population most affected. It also includes a vision of how the organization will address the problem.

5. *Identify target areas and populations.* High-risk areas/groups, sociocultural/economic status, and gender are all factors that require attention in development of the risk-reduction approach.

NOTE: Additional information specific to data, risk assessment, and prioritizing is covered in Chapter 9.

Community Partnerships

Effective community risk reduction requires cooperative effort from organizations, communities, target populations, and decision-makers. Attacking risk collaboratively makes sense in terms of resource availability (people, money, and equipment). Sharing tasks to address risk is more productive in terms of creativity, credibility, and effectiveness. The most successful risk-reduction efforts are those that involve the community in the planning and solution process.

Community partners are individuals, groups, or organizations willing to help a sponsoring organization address risk. A smart strategy is to identify and recruit partners who have a stake in the success of a risk-reduction program.

Logical partners in a risk-reduction program may include the following:

- Emergency service organizations
- Hospitals and health departments
- Human service groups such as Social Services, Commission on Aging, and Community Action Council
- Community service clubs and groups
- Insurance companies and local agents
- Local businesses and corporations patronized by older adults
- Communities that offer housing exclusively for older adults
- Local media
- Children of older adults
- Citizens at-large

Networking, partnerships, and coalitions are ways to enlist support for risk reduction.

- Networking provides an excellent opportunity to brainstorm about interests in risk reduction such as best approaches, challenges, strengths, weaknesses, technology, new ideas, different perspectives, and mentoring. Networking often leads to the formation of partnerships as people buy-in to the relevance of an initiative as it pertains to their personal interests.
- Partnerships are created by joining forces with other groups to address common interests. Partnerships can be formal or informal; short or long term. Many outstanding risk-reduction programs, projects, and initiatives have grown to fruition through partnerships of emergency services, corporations, government, and the community at large.

- Coalitions represent a more formal partnership of groups working toward a common goal. Coalitions may be small or large scale and have local, regional, or national interests. What often distinguishes a coalition from networking and partnerships is the presence of a formal organizational structure. Coalitions usually meet regularly, are led by officers, and are governed through bylaws. They may also have a budget, business plan, and paid staff. Coalitions often address long-term solutions for issues. The benefits of a coalition include broad-based organizational support, combined talents of members, and increased resources. Coalitions also offer increased credibility through multiagency membership. Challenges associated with coalitions include the agendas specific to member organizations, different styles and personalities of members, group dynamics, and personal time factors.

Whether it is a formal or informal effort, creating a planning team of knowledgeable people to develop and implement an overall risk-reduction plan is an effective way to address community risk.

Intervention Strategy

An *intervention strategy* is the action plan that describes how a risk-reduction program will be implemented and evaluated. It includes what will be done, where it will be implemented, how implementation will occur, and who will conduct the program. It also includes an evaluation component that measures the effectiveness of the process and program.

A comprehensive intervention strategy can help produce measurable reduction of community risk over a period of time. The community planning team reviews the problem statement and community profile. Using the following process guides development of the strategy and ensures a successful risk-reduction outcome.

- Identify and prioritize leading risks.
- Examine the sequence of events leading to priority risks.
- Identify places within the sequence of events where intervention may prove successful.
- Identify potential target populations and the physical locations for intervention opportunities.
- Agree on interventions to address the problem.

- Identify the resources required to implement and sustain the strategy.
- Develop an evaluation plan with measurable objectives so that the intervention strategy can be monitored and adjusted as needed.

What Interventions Will Be Used?

The next step in the intervention strategy is deciding what interventions will be used. While educating people about the causation and solutions to local risk is the foundation of prevention, managers must recognize the ultimate effectiveness of using a combination of interventions. Addressing a complex risk issue requires more than a single-dimension strategy.

As part of the strategy, well-planned interventions should include as a minimum both educational and engineering components. Integrating equipment and materials that provide built-in or automatic protection against risk is highly advisable. Incentives to employ use of enhanced products and materials are effective ways to encourage use. Standards and codes requiring such use are ways to ensure compliance. (Additional information on combined prevention interventions[1] will be provided in Chapter 14.)

What Resources Will Be Needed?

Once the intervention methodologies have been determined, the next step is to consider what resources will be needed to implement the overall strategy. Managers must remember that resources include more than only the instructional materials used to present a program. People, time, money, materials, and equipment are just a few of the resources that must be included in the budget to effectively address community risk.

How Can Resources Be Generated?

Understanding how resources that can support risk reduction are created is also important. Tax dollars, financial and in-kind donations, foundations, grants, partnerships, and matching government funds are examples of ways that resources can be generated to support risk reduction. Often overlooked are the people who devote a high level of attention to an issue and who are very important resources.

How Do You Prepare Budget Proposals?

Knowing how communities and organizations make decisions on budget proposals and resource allocation is another attribute that the Level II manager should possess. Managers must also have an understanding of organizational **budget cycles** and how to make funding proposals for inclusion into their specific organization's budget.

Why Should a Supporter Get Involved?

Managers must be able to articulate the need for support through a factual rationale that explains the following:

● Why there is a need for resources

● What resources are needed

● How resources will be used to address risk

People are more likely to support a cause for which they share a vested interest. Highlight why potential supporters should get involved and how their efforts will benefit the cause. (See Chapter 9 for additional information on resource acquisition.)

What Is an Evaluation Plan?

The final component of the implementation strategy is critically important. The evaluation plan includes the problem statement, goal, and a series of measurable objectives that support the goal. The objectives allow the evaluation of three levels of performance: final outcome, impact of initiative, and the process of implementation.

Developing a good evaluation plan is not difficult, but it does involve research and takes patience. Doing the research to find baseline information about citizen knowledge of risks, community living environments, and incident experience is the aspect of the job that takes the most time and effort. However, this is an essential part of the plan and there is no room for guesswork.

Implementation of Strategy

Now that a plan for reducing community risk has been developed, it is time to test each proposed intervention, modify accordingly, and eventually implement the full risk- reduction strategy. The following components represent logical steps to take during implementation:

● Decide how, where, and when the interventions will be conducted.

● Identify the roles and responsibilities of those who will be involved with implementing proposed interventions. Because fire and life safety educators should be using a team approach to prevention, it is important that everyone involved knows his or her specific responsibilities during the implementation process.

● Pilot-test and evaluate proposed interventions. Pilot testing is an *essential* component of the implementation process. **Pilot testing** of interventions allows the planning team to evaluate the effectiveness of components on a small scale. Much effort and expense can be saved by identifying problems with a proposed intervention before large-scale resources have been invested. Representatives of the target population for whom the intervention is directed should be part of the team that evaluates pilot efforts.

● Revise interventions as needed.

● Market the intervention strategy.

NOTE: The term *intervention* is listed in the previous listed steps. While the word *program* could easily be substituted, managers should consider broadening their view of prevention to include integrated interventions including resources such as education, technology, materials, codes, and standards **(Figure 7.4, p. 190)**.

Upon completion of pilot testing, evaluation, and modifications, the full intervention strategy can be initiated. Marketing the final intervention strategy is important too. Because the organization, target populations, and community have a stake in the effort, everyone should be kept apprised of progress.

Evaluation of the Results

Fear of working with statistics or a general lack of knowledge about evaluation are two reasons why many managers omit this component from the risk-reduction planning process. Evaluation is essential to an effective risk-reduction program, plan, or community-wide strategy.

Once managers have obtained baseline data on leading community risks, target population knowledge, and household environmental conditions, the evaluation effort becomes exponentially easier. It now becomes a process of measuring conditions before interventions were implemented to what they are at some defined point afterward. This is where

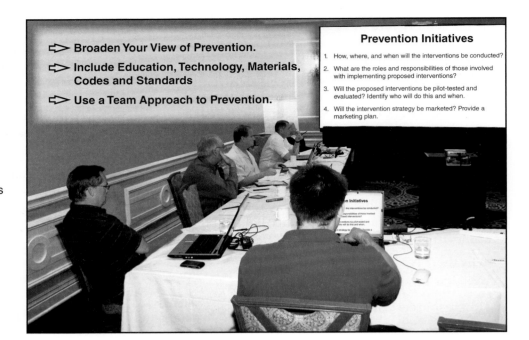

Figure 7.4 Managers should include integrated interventions when preparing prevention initiatives.

process, impact, and outcome evaluation come into play **(Figure 7.5)**.

- *Process evaluation* involves documenting the creation of prevention efforts, monitoring program activity, and tracking outreach into the community.

- *Impact evaluation* measures knowledge gain, behavioral change, and modifications to living conditions or lifestyles.

- *Outcome evaluation* measures changes in the occurrence of incidents over time. It also involves documenting anecdotal success stories of how prevention efforts have impacted community risk.

Most managers focus their efforts on conducting process evaluation. However, impact and outcome evaluation are essential components of planning that must also be performed. In fire and life safety educational programs, it is not prudent to invest resources into a prevention effort if progress is not being monitored.

In addition, educators have a moral responsibility to take action based on the results of evaluations. Educators should modify the program for improved outcome, expand the program's outreach efforts for greater impact, or cancel the program and develop a new strategy.

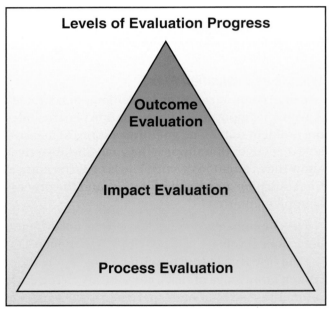

Figure 7.5 Progress must be monitored through evaluation in fire and life safety education programs.

Chapter Summary

This chapter has provided a general overview of the requisite knowledge required to function as a Level II fire and life safety educator as outlined in NFPA® 1035. Proficiency in creating and leading community risk-reduction programs requires quality leadership, the development and use of strategic planning, and the integration of combined prevention interventions (5 Es).

Leadership is a key component of risk reduction. Following specific performance standards and organizational policy allows leaders to evaluate others objectively and fairly, and leaders earn respect by demonstrating the use of fair practices. Competent leaders challenge team members to excel by providing measurable feedback that documents performance and encourages professional growth.

Review Questions

1. What is the political process of decision-making that occurs in the local community?

2. How do political determinants impact community risk reduction?

3. What is the role of knowledge in behavioral change?

4. What is the proper process for creating a community risk-reduction plan?

5. What are the steps in the five step planning process?

6. How is a Level II manager a department and community leader?

Key Terms

Applied Learning — Making information relevant so that the proposed learner understands why she or he should receive and process the material.

Baseline Knowledge — What a person knows about a topic before a presentation is conducted.

Budget Cycle — Specific timelines used by organizations and communities to receive and act on requests for resources to support general operations.

Community Analysis — Process of creating a risk profile that identifies leading risks, who is affected, and where problems are occurring.

Institutionalized Behaviors — Collective support shown for a project by an organization. This includes the investment of time, people, money, and equipment to support the project.

Level II Fire and Life Safety Educator — Manager who exhibits proficiency in creating and leading community risk-reduction programs.

Lobbyists — People compensated by an organization to influence decision-makers to favor the special interests of the sponsoring organization.

Pilot Testing — Testing a specific intervention for effectiveness.

Prevention Intervention — Using a component of education, technology, fire codes, standards, supporting incentives, or emergency response to reduce risk.

Stagnant Organizational Culture — A group of people satisfied with the status quo of an organization and not interested in engaging in progressive change.

Chapter 7 Notes

Public Fire Education Planning — A Five Step Process. Federal Emergency Management Agency. August, 2002.

1. *Integrated Prevention Interventions.* National Fire Academy Risk Reduction Curriculum.

FLSE Level II Managers: Administration

Chapter Contents

chapter **8**

Key Terms

Job Performance Requirements

This chapter provides information that addresses the following job performance requirements of NFPA® 1035, *Standard for Professional Qualifications for Fire and Life Safety Educator, Public Information Officer, and Juvenile Firesetter Intervention Specialist*, 2010 edition.

NFPA® 1035 References

6.2.1

6.2.2

6.2.3

6.2.4

FESHE Objectives

Fire and Emergency Services Higher Education (FESHE) Objectives: *Fire and Life Safety Education*

5. Identify budget needs for program delivery and the process for requesting funds.

Learning Objectives

After reading this chapter, students will be able to:

1. Develop and present a budget proposal that supports a specific risk-reduction effort. (NFPA® 1035, 6.2.1)

2. Explain how to draft and present to their organization's decision-makers a public policy proposal that supports a local risk-reduction initiative. (NFPA® 1035, 6.2.3)

3. Overview the process of evaluating team member performance. (NFPA® 1035, 6.2.4)

Chapter 8
FLSE Level II Managers: Administration

Case History

Last February, Jayne, the fire and life safety educator (FLSE) in Wellsville, set out on a mission. First, she identified her community's most frequently occurring preventable risk as falls among older adults. Next, she examined the sequence of events leading to most occurrences. Jayne quickly discovered that most falls were occurring in bathrooms that were lacking grab bars near showers and toilets.

Jayne developed a vision for a new program, "Bathroom Fall Prevention for Older Adults." By March 1 she had a commitment from local Rotary Club volunteers to help install grab rails. On March 15 she appeared at the town's annual senior fair to solicit interest from older adults. The response was overwhelming with many citizens wanting to know when they could expect their FREE grab rails.

Jayne was proud that she had analyzed her leading risk, identified a target population, and envisioned potential solutions. Now, all she needed was the chief's support and money to buy materials.

Upon meeting with the chief, Jayne was perplexed at his response. While he liked the program's concept, he expressed disappointment that she had not discussed her vision with him prior to sharing it publicly. Second, he was very concerned that she could only estimate that "about" $8,000.00 worth of materials would be needed.

The biggest disappointment came when Jayne learned she would have to wait nearly a year to be considered for funding. She was told the department's budget for the next fiscal year had already been approved on March 1. Jayne left the meeting feeling that her great idea had been defeated.

This chapter provides specific information on the basics of budgeting, public policy recommendations, and evaluation of a team member's performance. All three are important administrative components of a risk-reduction process.

The Level II fire and life safety educator is expected to prepare written budget proposals for specific programs and activities such as smoke-alarm programs, school-based activities, and fire station open houses **(Figure 8.1, p. 196)**. (**NOTE:** Level II fire and life safety educators are referred to as *managers*). The manager is then expected to monitor expenditures and evaluate if program costs have produced desired outcomes.

The following prerequisites are needed for managers to develop budget proposals:

- Resource development and appropriation
- Communication of leadership
- Importance of a cost/benefit analysis
- Making public policy recommendations to management

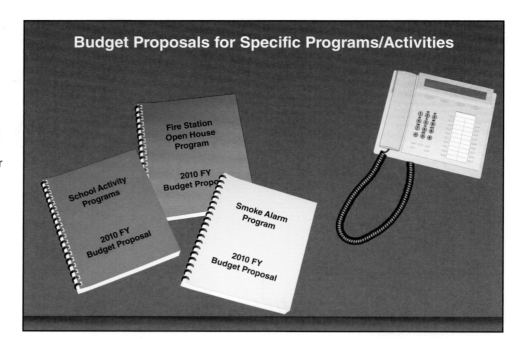

Budget Proposals for Specific Programs/Activities

Figure 8.1 The Level II fire and life safety educator is required to prepare budget proposals for specific programs.

School Activity Programs — 2010 FY Budget Proposal

Fire Station Open House Program — 2010 FY Budget Propo...

Smoke Alarm Program — 2010 FY Budget Proposal

Resource Development and Appropriation

Funds for risk-reduction projects can be generated in a variety of ways. Donations, in-kind services, and grants represent three sources often used by volunteer, career, and allied health organizations. In larger communities, the majority of funding for organizational budgets is allocated by the municipality. The municipality receives money through a combination of property taxes and charges for service.

Directors, commissions, boards, and councils are examples of the decision-making bodies that appropriate funding to the organizations under their supervision. The amount of funding dispersed is often related to staffing levels, types of services, and the overall action plan an organization has created to help guide its mission. Therefore, the Level II manager must be cognizant of the funding process and adhere to the guidelines that are applicable for each type of organization or department.

Many municipalities employ a July 1 to June 30 budget schedule. Other communities either follow a January 1 to December 31 timeline or October 1 to September 30 budget cycles.

It is important to maintain awareness of applicable budget cycles. Many potentially great programs have been delayed or cancelled because the educator failed to get his or her proposal to organizational decision-makers prior to budget submission deadlines. In most

organizations and communities, if the program or activity is not included in the budget, it is not going to get funding **(Figure 8.2)**.

Communication with Leadership

Open communication with departmental leadership is essential for managers who have budgetary responsibilities within their organization. While Level II managers may not be responsible for an entire risk-reduction budget, they do submit budget proposals for specific programs and activities. Therefore, it is prudent to have at least a baseline understanding of organizational priorities, activities, and budgets. This knowledge can only be obtained through an open channel of communication with superiors.

Evaluation Plan

The foundation of any risk-reduction budget proposal is the evaluation plan. The evaluation plan includes a problem statement, the program's goal, and a series of measurable objectives that outline how the plan will be carried out.

Level II managers must be proficient at applying the Five Es (see Chapter 7 for detailed information on the Five Es, also known as *integrated interventions*). This process includes the development of an evaluation plan. Connecting a funding proposal to your specific objective(s) allows decision-makers to see how the resources will impact overall outcome.

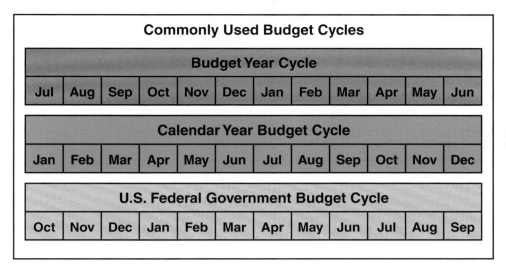

Commonly Used Budget Cycles

Budget Year Cycle

Jul	Aug	Sep	Oct	Nov	Dec	Jan	Feb	Mar	Apr	May	Jun

Calendar Year Budget Cycle

Jan	Feb	Mar	Apr	May	Jun	Jul	Aug	Sep	Oct	Nov	Dec

U.S. Federal Government Budget Cycle

Oct	Nov	Dec	Jan	Feb	Mar	Apr	May	Jun	Jul	Aug	Sep

Figure 8.2 An example of various budget cycles.

Budget Request Example

To: Fire Marshal Martha Delray

From: Fire Prevention Officer Brett Hilton

Re: Budget Request – Fire Department Smoke Alarm Program

The Anywhere Fire Department has offered a free smoke alarm program to residents of the community for 20 years. During this period, 5,000 nine-volt battery-powered smoke alarms have been installed by firefighters in nearly 2,000 homes. Nine lives have been saved as a direct result of the program.

While our work has demonstrated impressive results, I believe our program can be further enhanced. Here's why:

Six months after firefighters installed a free smoke alarm, we revisited the property to check the operability of the unit. Sadly, impact studies reveal that in 20% of homes revisited, smoke alarms were inoperable due to missing batteries or the alarm was taken down.

Some of the reasons given by residents for inoperable alarms have included:

- "I took out the battery when it chirped and forgot to get another one."
- "I took down the unit because it went off when we cook food."

A concerning fact is that the greatest number of nonworking alarms seems to be found in homes where highest-risk populations reside. To remedy this problem, I propose discontinuing use of nine-volt battery alarms in favor of lithium-powered units. Several manufacturers offer units with batteries warranted to last ten years. The units feature sealed battery compartments, a hush button to quiet nuisance alarms, and tamper resistive mounting brackets.

Our cost per smoke alarm would be approximately $15.00. While the cost is triple that of nine-volt units, I believe the benefits of this new technology are worthy of investment. Existing installation kits will continue to be used and firefighters will receive training on the new alarms while on-duty.

In addition to the cost of smoke alarms, I propose the use of a marketing campaign to inform the community of our enhanced services. Commercials on local TV and radio stations will cost $20.00 each per month. I would like to run commercials for one month.

Finally, an evaluation component is needed to monitor the impact of our enhanced program. I would like to compensate each firefighter at his or her current overtime rate to perform 30 hours of post-installation follow-up visitation.

Attached is an itemized summary of the proposal (**Table 8.1, p. 198**).

Thank you for considering this request.

Table 8.1
Budget Request

Item	Quantity	Unit Cost	Total Cost of Item
Lithium smoke alarms	200	$15.00	$3,000.00
Commercials to market program	100	$20.00	$2,000.00
Firefighter overtime impact evaluation	30 Hours	$25.00	$750.00
Total Request			$5,750.00

Budget Proposal

Creating a budget proposal for a specific program or activity is very similar to developing an evaluation plan for addressing a risk issue — a familiar task for a Level II manager. Components of a proposal usually include the following:

- Rationale of why the program should be funded
- Scope of the proposed program
- Estimate of project costs to include:
  — Staffing and training

  — Supplies, equipment, transportation, and fuel
  — Implementation and marketing
  — Evaluation

Scope of the Proposed Program

When seeking specific services (even from organizational staff), thoroughly outline the scope of work to be performed. This action helps clarify expectations and makes it easier to evaluate performance as work is being performed.

Scope of Work – Impact Evaluation of Smoke Alarm Program

The Anywhere Fire Department is accepting applications from departmental personnel to conduct impact evaluation of the department's smoke alarm program. Participants will be paid their current overtime rate as specified by contractual agreement.

Duties shall include:

1. Random follow-up visitation to households that have received a free smoke alarm from the fire department within the past six months.

2. A post-installation interview with the recipient to obtain the following information:
   - Condition and operability of the alarms that were installed. Staff shall physically inspect and test the alarm(s).
   - Determine how often the recipient tests the alarm(s).
   - If an alarm is nonoperational, determine actions that led to the condition. Rectify the situation by installing new alarm(s).
   - Inquire if there has been a fire in the household since the alarms were installed.
   - Determine if the alarms alerted the recipient/family to a fire in progress.
   - Obtain feedback from a recipient about his or her knowledge/practice of home fire-safety measures.
   - Obtain feedback that may enhance the smoke alarm/fire safety program.

Overtime will be awarded based upon seniority, education, experience, and previous involvement with departmental life-safety initiatives.

Please make application to the department's fire prevention officer by (date).

Staffing and Training

Drafting a budget proposal involves more than guesswork about how much money will be needed. If paid staff is involved, projected work time must be estimated and salaries calculated. Staff training time should be considered as well.

Supplies, Equipment, Transportation, and Fuel

Always check current (and projected) pricing prior to developing a proposal. Costs can be projected with reasonable accuracy because of current technology, including access to the Internet. Transportation and fuel are costs often absorbed by the educator's organization but warrant mention in case other arrangements are needed. If travel is anticipated, check current per diem rates. Rates specific to geographic areas can be located by conducting an Internet search.

Implementation and Marketing

Program implementation and marketing costs are items often overlooked when preparing a budget proposal. Very few programs can be implemented without some level of start-up costs. If the program is addressing a specific risk issue, the public needs to be aware of the risk and understand how it occurs. They must also believe that they are at risk and know what preventative actions need to be taken. Marketing campaigns should convey the risk issue.

Marketing is best accomplished through saturation of print and broadcast media. Print media consists of newspaper reporting and signage placement in target areas. Broadcast media consists of radio, television, and the Internet.

Evaluation

An evaluation component to monitor the program/ activity must be included in the budget proposal. The educator, decision-makers, and target populations need to know if the program or activity is working. Future monetary allocation is often contingent on program success. The manager must therefore be able to accurately and factually document program impact and outcome.

Evaluation costs do not have to be expensive. Many simply involve budgeting time for staff to document community outreach and assess if impact is being made. Review of program deliveries, pretesting and posttesting, and observational surveys are examples

of process and impact evaluation. Most professionals recommend adding 15% to the total projected budget to cover the expenses of evaluation.

When developing a budget, always consider contingencies. While creating a line item labeled "contingencies" is not recommended due to its broad interpretation, consider requesting the maximum amount allowed in each category as budgets are often "adjusted" (or reduced) by decision-makers. Do not be outrageous with the request, but be sure to ask for what is reasonably needed.

The Importance of a Cost/Benefit Analysis

A **cost/benefit analysis** involves examining the proposed expense of an effort and deciding if the overall benefit is worth the investment of money and time. A well-written evaluation plan becomes invaluable in order to compare the cost of the proposed program to the anticipated level of impact and outcome as listed in the evaluation plan. Decision-makers are more likely to support a proposal that makes good sense and may ultimately save lives.

Example of Cost/Benefit Analysis

The Anywhere Fire Department had been installing free nine-volt battery-operated smoke alarms in homes within their community for 20 years. Unfortunately, follow-up visitations (impact evaluation) identified that 20% of FD supplied smoke alarms were inoperable due to missing batteries or the alarm had been taken down.

The fire prevention officer conducted the following cost/benefit analysis, which led him to recommend discontinuing use of nine-volt powered alarms in favor of lithium operated units **(Table 8.2, p. 200)**.

Presenting a Budget Proposal to Decision-Makers

The importance of a well-prepared community presentation cannot be understated. Fact-based rationales, a good plan, clear visuals, and quality printed materials are components that comprise an effective presentation. The time allotted for

Table 8.2
Cost-Benefit Analysis

Unit Cost of 9-Volt Battery-Operated Smoke Alarm	Quantity Purchased Annually	Total Cost of Smoke Alarms	Current Rate of Inoperability on Impact Visit
$5.00	200	$1,000.00	20%
Unit Cost of Lithium Battery-Operated Smoke Alarm	**Quantity Purchased Annually**	**Total Cost of Smoke Alarms**	**Projected Rate of Inoperability on Impact Visit**
$15.00	200	$3,000.00	Less than 5%

your budget presentation may be rigidly defined. Therefore, it is important to keep budget proposals concise, clear, and easy to follow.

Regardless of the educator's level of comfort with technical writing, there is no excuse for unprofessional work in today's society. Managers should take advantage of all that computer programs offer in spelling and grammatical help. Multimedia programs can also enhance the educator's ability to help decision-makers visualize what they are being asked to fund.

Program Budget Management

Regardless of size, most organizations have specific guidelines on how budgeted funds can be spent. If the organization is part of a larger municipality, the community has even more requirements that must be followed.

Laws often govern how the municipality spends money. These checks and balances systems are in place as a safeguard for public funds. Accountability and accurate record-keeping are often the responsibility of the Level II manager.

Requests for Purchase

Most organizations have a purchase requisition system used when dispersing funds for a budgeted item. The system usually requires a competitive bid process for items exceeding a specific amount set by the organization.

Busy managers investing time into obtaining bids or proposals for programs and activities must remember that this is time well spent. This work allows the educator to carefully examine each product

or service to ensure financial value and also the professional integrity of the vendor.

When considering the purchase of equipment, it is a good idea to draft a **request for proposal** (RFP) document. A well-written RFP clearly specifies exactly what the purchaser wants the product to do and provides the design specifications of the *type* (not brand) of equipment that the department or organization is interested in acquiring **(Figure 8.3)**.

Purchase Orders

Once a bid is awarded for a product or service, the organization generates a **purchase order** (PO). A PO allows vendors to invoice for monies owed. This action serves as an official record that the organization and vendor or contractor have conducted financial business according to the specifications set forth by the purchaser's organization and authority having jurisdiction (AHJ).

A wide variety of software programs are available to track activity and financial expenditures. Although the initial learning curve is steep, the data output is eventually clearer and more professional in appearance and content.

Tax Exemptions

Local government and nonprofit organizations are eligible for tax-exempt status. Having tax-exempt status allows the purchaser to buy equipment and materials without having to pay sales tax. This is an excellent privilege that should be used when applicable. To receive tax-exempt status, an organization must apply to the federal government. Once this status is granted, vendors must verify and document that

RFP for Lithium Smoke Alarms

The Anywhere Fire Department is accepting bids for 200 lithium battery-powered smoke alarms. The smoke alarms must meet the following specifications:

1. Lithium battery power with sealed battery compartment so consumers cannot remove batteries.

2. Lithium batteries and alarm must be warranted to operate without maintenance for ten years.

3. Test button located on the face of the alarm.

4. Hush feature that silences alarm in the event of a nuisance alert.

5. Tamper-resistive hardware to deter customers from removing the alarm from mounting bracket.

Please address sealed bids to the following address by (noted date):

Anywhere Fire Department
2800 Safety Drive
Anywhere, USA
Attn: Fire Prevention Officer

Figure 8.3 A document that provides an example of an RFP.

a purchaser is indeed exempt. Presenting vendors with proof of exemption (tax-exemption ID card) is all that is required **(Table 8.3, p. 202)**.

Making Public Policy Recommendations to Management

Education is recognized as the root of prevention. However, used as a sole intervention, education may produce only moderate progress in the war against preventable fires and injury. A **public policy** can mandate injury prevention instruction and require the use of technology, safer products, and built-in risk protection. A well-developed public policy is a system of laws, regulatory measures, courses of action, and funding priorities by a government entity or its representatives. It can also dictate penalties for acts of negligence and failure to use or maintain required prevention equipment.

Public Policy

Public policy adopted at the national level could help reduce the overall occurrence of fatal smoking-related fires. Consider the sequence of events leading to a typical smoking-related fire. Example 1 projects a potential outcome without use of preventative intervention. Example 2 projects a potential outcome with the use of preventative measures.

Example 1 — Potential Outcome Without Prevention Intervention

1. A consumer, lounging on non-flame- resistive upholstered furnishings, smokes a cigarette after consuming alcohol or taking prescribed medications.

2. The consumer becomes drowsy and falls asleep. The cigarette falls from his or her fingers and makes contact with the upholstered furnishings.

3. The lit cigarette ignites the upholstered furnishings, which creates a smoldering fire. After a period of time, the fire enters flame stage and quickly envelops the area of origin.

4. A nearby smoke alarm fails to operate because its battery had been removed by the consumer.

5. Furnishings ignite and envelop the consumer in flames. He or she suffers debilitating burn injuries and is permanently disabled.

Example 2 — Potential Outcome With Preventive Intervention

1. A consumer, lounging on flame-resistive upholstered furnishings, smokes a cigarette after consuming alcohol or taking prescribed medications.

2. The consumer falls asleep and the cigarette makes contact with upholstered furnishings.

3. The furniture smolders but does not ignite for two reasons:

   a. The safer cigarette self-extinguished because it had not been inhaled upon for a period of time.

   b. The flame-resistive materials present in the furnishings helped prohibit ignition.

4. A nearby smoke alarm sounds, alerting the drowsy consumer to the incident. The alarm was in operable condition because it had electric/battery power and was permanently affixed to the ceiling nearby.

5. No significant fire or injury occurs.

Table 8.3
Steps for Obtaining Tax-Exempt Status

Step 1	Determine whether the organization qualifies for tax exemption under the 501(a) or 501(c)(3) rules. Included under 501(c)(3) are religious organizations, charities, scientific organizations, groups that test for public safety, groups that promote literary or educational purposes, or groups that advocate against cruelty to children or animals. Organizations that can be exempt under 501(a) include universities with special government-approved programs.
Step 2	Obtain an Employer Identification Number (EIN) (even if the organization has only one employee or volunteer.). The IRS form number is SS-4.
Step 3	Fill out the appropriate form based on the organization's 501(a) or 501(c) (3) status. 501(a) status requires IRS Form 1024. 503(c)(3) status requires Form 1023. The organization may want to have a corporate or tax attorney look over the application.
Step 4	Gather the supporting documents that must be submitted along with Form 1023 or 1024. Be sure to include copies of the organization's articles of incorporation (or other organizing documents), as well as evidence of incorporation. Bylaws may also be included, although bylaws can't replace the articles of incorporation.
Step 5	Attach the relevant financial data. Include a current balance sheet and four years' worth of financial data (the current year and three prior years). The prior data needs to include all receipts and expenditures, with explanatory statements. For more information on how to document this, read IRS publication 557.
Step 6	Every included document must list the organization's name, address, Employer Identification Number, and the line item number of the form associated with that document.
Step 7	Submit *copies only* of any document. The IRS will keep the copies and they will not be returned. However, *all copies must contain original signatures from the same people who signed the original document.*
Step 8	Wait for the IRS judgment on the tax-exempt request. It should be made within 270 days. The IRS may be contacted periodically and requested to provide updates. The IRS is also permitted to contact the requesting organization to ask questions or request additional supporting documentation.

Source: United States Department of Treasury

Experienced managers and epidemiologists agree that requiring a safer environment that protects the population from exhibiting risky behavior will overcome the fire death rate plateau that has plagued the U.S. for nearly two decades.

NOTE: Epidemiologists study the frequency and distribution of diseases within human populations and environments. Specifically, they measure the incidence of disease occurrence and relate it to different characteristics of populations and environments. Epidemiologists perform research, education, and public health practice in universities, government agencies, international organizations, and private corporations.

Public policy can impact community risk at the national, state, and local levels. National examples of effective public policies include standards on child-resistant lighters, flame-resistive sleep garments, and the former 55 mph national speed limit. Local examples include smoke alarm ordinances, sprinkler mandates, and required seat belt usage.

Although government groups and, in some cases, communities at-large make the final decisions about adopting required preventative initiatives, emergency services and advocacy groups are often responsible for suggesting legislation that puts the process in motion.

Executive officers or Level III administrators have the ultimate responsibility for drafting public policy recommendations to community leaders. Because Level II program managers are important team members in risk evaluation, they are in an excellent position to make recommendations on public policy to their *organizational* leadership.

The following section explains how a Level II manager can propose public policy recommendations to their leadership:

1. Provide an overview of the risk and scope of the problem.

2. Present a profile that explains how the risks are affecting constituents, local economy, the organization, and the overall quality of life in the community.

3. Present a fact-based rationale of why the risk should be addressed.

4. Explain current public perception of the risk.

5. Summarize what actions have been initiated to date to address the risk(s) such as creation of programs, initiatives, and use of partnerships.

6. Explain what impact to mitigate the risk(s) has been realized to date.

7. Project what will happen if nothing is done or current efforts are simply maintained.

8. Identify a strategy of proposed solution(s) to the risk issue(s). Be sure the strategy includes all levels of prevention interventions.

9. Propose public policy(s) that may help reduce the risk(s) through use of integrated prevention interventions.

10. Present a cost/benefit analysis of the proposed policy.

11. Submit a budget, implementation schedule, and evaluation mechanism for the proposed policy.

12. Identify economic incentives that could help support the proposed policy.

13. Offer to assist with developing and presenting the proposal to community leaders.

Level II managers are in excellent positions to help formulate a public policy that their leadership can propose at a local level. They must be subject-matter experts on their community's leading fire risks before crafting any proposals. Managers must have in-depth understanding of the sequence of events leading to the top several fire risks occurring in their jurisdictions; specifically, places within the sequence of risks where prevention interventions may be employed. Having insight into how the top several risks occur may lead to proposing policy that can address factors common to several risks. For example, a public policy that requires landlords to discuss the importance of supervising heat-producing products may prove effective in reducing the occurrence of fires started in rental occupancies from cooking, candles, or smoking. The policy could be further strengthened by suggesting lease-penalty agreements between property owners and tenants that require responsible behaviors from those who rent. It could be made even stronger by mandating fire-resistive building construction and the installation of sprinkler systems in new residential occupancies.

An important point to all educators: When considering public policy, always examine how preventative interventions such as technology, safer products, and codes requiring usage could be proposed. Public policy requiring the use of life-safety initiatives is one of the most powerful and effective tools that educators can employ in the war against the American Paradigm of Fire.

Public Policy at the Local Level

Public policy does not always have to occur at the national level. Consider the following example: A community has experienced a documented trend in the number of residential fires started by the misuse of fireworks. The fire department documents the trend and prepares a presentation for local legislators (city council or county commissioners) that proposes outlawing fireworks in the community. The presentation includes an explanation of the problem, proposed solution, and benefits to the community. Legislative decision-makers (with fire department support) draft a proposed ordinance that prohibits the sale and use of fireworks in the community.

Evaluating Performance

Whether being paid for a job or volunteering service, people want objective feedback on their performance. If critique or suggestions for improvement are provided, individuals also want open and direct feedback by subject-matter experts in risk reduction. This is why Level II managers need to be proficient and current in their field of expertise.

Performance evaluation can be very subjective, depending on the knowledge and experience of the evaluator. Although evaluation is defined as the appraisal of something in relation to stated criteria or standards, the interpretation of the criteria or standards is subject to personal bias or experience.

An effective way to reduce subjective evaluation is to plan ahead for an objective experience. This is accomplished when leaders and team members understand in advance what performance criteria will be measured during a personnel evaluation.

Organizational policies are the standard operating and governing rules by which a department or agency operates. They include the guidelines of personal conduct, ethics, and core values expected of all organizational members. These components are dictated by the overall mission of the organization.

Fire and life safety educators may be formally evaluated as part of an annual performance review or for promotional or disciplinary purposes. A performance evaluation typically measures the following:

- Job performance
- Responsibility
- Professional appearance and demeanor
- Technical ability and knowledge of subject matter
- Adherence to organizational policies
- Ability to function within the organization

When such an evaluation is administered, it is important that organizational policy is followed. It is critical that managers inform team members of their expectations and explain how they will be evaluated by the organization.

When functioning in a career or combination organization, it is prudent to be aware of contractual agreements between labor and management that may include obligations regarding the following:

- Vacation, holiday, sick time, **Family Medical Leave**, and worker's compensation issues
- Overtime, **compensatory time**, and **Fair Labor Standards Act** requirements
- Required representation from union officials in cases where disciplinary actions to an employee may occur

Performance evaluation may become a more significant responsibility for the career Level II manager as risk reduction becomes an institutionalized value in more organizations. Currently, most U.S. fire departments already have a small group of firefighters with significant interest in risk-reduction development and activity.

While there are exceptions to any rule, nearly *every* educator serves as a leader to line staff and community volunteers. CERT and Fire Corps units are examples of such volunteer groups.

For the benefit of the reader, this section on performance evaluation includes two sections:

1. Evaluating the performance of a team
2. Evaluating the performance of individuals

Evaluating Team Performance

Leading teams of people who are attempting to mitigate risk is a task performed by many program managers. Regardless whether the team is comprised of career staff, volunteers, or a combination of both, team members need and deserve objective feedback on their activities **(Figure 8.4)**.

Evaluating team performance actually starts during the planning phase of risk reduction. Arguably one of the most important components of an evaluation process is involving team members in planning risk-reduction strategies so that everyone has a stake in the overall mission and knows what is being expected of them.

An evaluation plan for a risk-reduction strategy can serve as the criteria for measuring group performance. Completion of specific tasks and measurement of a program's outreach, impact, and outcome are all measurable benchmarks of a team's performance.

Once a plan has been formulated, group performance benchmarks can be established and timelines set for objectives to be accomplished. Upon identifying benchmarks and creating completion timelines, performance evaluation schedules can be formulated.

Evaluating the performance of a team is an endeavor that must be done in a fair, nonbiased, and objective manner. It is critical that a group of people know what is being expected of them and how performance will be evaluated *before* they begin a task.

Figure 8.4 Program managers meet to discuss their risk-reduction strategies.

Communication

Ongoing communication is also an essential component of evaluation. This task is accomplished by meeting regularly with the team to share accomplishments, review challenges, and plan for success.

Should a challenge or problem arise between formal evaluation intervals, the issue must be addressed immediately. Allowing problems or deficiencies to continue will result in decreased morale of the team, and the goal of reducing risk may not be achieved.

Corrective Actions

It is important to remember that leaders earn respect and build equity among team members by being part of the solution to any problem. They also do so by knowing when to address an individual instead of a team. When evaluating a team's performance, do it fairly, provide constructive feedback, and modify expectations according to group consensus. If a team needs to make improvement in an area, try to outline the barriers to expected job performance and offer assistance in making improvement.

Evaluating Individual Performance

Fire and emergency services organizations should have an established personnel evaluation program. This program establishes the requirements for all evaluations and guidelines for implementing them.

A well-organized personnel evaluation process includes the following benefits:

- Strengths and challenges of each educator become part of a permanent record. This record is typically used for awards, promotions, transfers, discipline, or termination.

- Objective evaluation can provide positive feedback that recognizes job performance. It can also help motivate an individual to strive for professional excellence.

- Performance evaluations help identify the specific talents of individuals that can be applied in other areas of the organization.

- An effective evaluation process helps to improve the efficiency of both instructors and the training organization as a whole.

Following Specific Guidelines

Performance evaluations have specific guidelines and when these standards are applied properly to the process, performance evaluations can then be effective tools in the management of educators. These guidelines include the following:

- *Apply in a timely manner.* Conduct evaluations regularly and at appropriate intervals if needed.

- *State criteria clearly.* State goals and objectives clearly and concisely. Maintain written job-performance criteria for review at each successive evaluation.

- *Ensure standards are not discriminatory.* Apply job-performance standards regardless of gender, race, ethnicity, age, or other classifications.

- *Maintain consistency.* Apply job-performance standards equally based on the duties and responsibilities assigned to the position.

- *Maintain thorough records.* Maintain thorough and complete records of each evaluation in the employee's personnel file. Although these records are confidential and may not be made public, give a copy of the evaluation to the educator being evaluated.

- *Train supervisors properly.* Supervisors performing evaluations must be trained in the process used by the jurisdiction.

- *Ensure objectivity.* Overcome personal bias, and base the evaluation on established criteria. Objectivity is essential in all of the organization's personnel evaluations.

Managers striving to meet the NFPA® 1035 Level II standard may consider creating a custom evaluation for educators or prevention teams under their command.

Informal and Formal Evaluations

Evaluating team members occurs both informally and through a formal process.

- Informal evaluations occur daily. They are based upon personal observations of the staff member at work.

- Informal evaluations provide immediate feedback to the staff member. When observation shows a team member performing effectively, the person can be praised privately or in front of peers by the leader.

- Formal evaluations may occur annually or as needed for a specific event such as a promotional examination or to help rectify substandard performance.

- Formal evaluations use the results of both observations and information obtained from process level evaluation instruments such as student evaluations. Formal evaluations are always held in private.

- Critique of personal performance is *always* done privately. The evaluator first provides positive comments on the individual's performance and then addresses areas that need improvement. Constructive suggestions that guide or direct the team member on how to improve are essential. Comments should refer to specific behaviors.

Steps for Individual Evaluation

Before the evaluation:

1. Communicate the date, time, and location of the evaluation to the educator being evaluated. The location should provide privacy and limited potential for distraction.

2. Review the evaluation materials, including process evaluation information.

3. Review organizational polices and the evaluation criteria specific to the individual being evaluated.

4. Discuss the evaluation process with the individual being evaluated.

   During the evaluation:

1. Have organizational polices and evaluation criteria available to review.

2. Take notes during the evaluation and provide feedback to the educator being evaluated.

3. Use the evaluation form provided by the organization to reduce the potential for subjectivity and ensure consistency between evaluations.

4. Evaluate based on the team member's level of responsibility and designated criteria.

5. Remain fair and nonbiased in order to provide honest, constructive feedback.

6. Compliment the educator on positive performance and provide tangible examples.

7. Work collaboratively to identify and reach solutions that will resolve areas where improvements are needed.

8. Maintain an open line of communication and accept feedback from the team member being evaluated.

9. Document the evaluation with the appropriate date and signatures.

After discussing the evaluation results with the educator, the leader must continue regularly monitoring the individual's performance and provide feedback as appropriate.

Responsibility as a Leader/Evaluator

Level II managers may have the responsibility of supervising Level I fire and life safety educators. To fulfill this responsibility, the leader must be trained in the following elements:

- Evaluation techniques
- Administration of the organization's personnel evaluation program
- Development of evaluation forms and surveys
- Use of information gained from evaluation of Level I educators by those who have received training from or interacted with the individual

The leader may choose to create the requisite evaluation form. The skills required must be fully understood and practiced to produce accurate and applicable information that can be used to improve risk-reduction efforts. Quality leaders challenge people to be their best. The most effective leaders act as a chief, communicator, team builder, coach, mentor, and peer. Team members usually support the suggestions of a person they admire and respect.

Leading educators and teams promoting risk reduction is an important task of a Level II fire and life safety manager. It is essential for leaders to help set team goals, evaluate progress, and make sure that educators have the basic tools and resources to accomplish what is expected of them.

Managers are often self-motivated people who set high standards for themselves. While motivation is an essential component of success, it can also drive a person to accept too much responsibility. Too much work can become counterproductive, resulting in stress, depression, and anger. An objective evaluation may be an excellent tool to evaluate workload and ensure that it is optimal and healthy for the team member.

Another attribute of many managers is that they are visionaries. They should be encouraged to explore their vision of risk solutions and provide their ideas of how the organization could grow to reach the vision. Collaboration is critical to successful prevention initiatives.

Flexibility is essential to effective risk reduction. Managers are expected to be responsible and function with limited supervision. They should allow their staff reasonable flexibility and autonomy. In return, the manager should be kept aware of the educator's progress. Clear direction, open communication, and established performance benchmarks will make this type of collaborative relationship possible. The

evaluation process represents an excellent way to promote the value of this culture by establishing benchmarks to measure such behaviors. It also can open dialogue to discuss the importance of understanding organizational, community, and political determinants that affect risk reduction.

Communication and cooperation are two essential components needed to reach most goals. As a leader, the Level II manager must be able to articulate this need to team members. One way to accomplish this task is through example, as team members often adopt the behavior of their leader.

The manager can use the evaluation process to promote the professional development of the educator. Through experience, higher education, evaluation, and mentoring, team members will develop into subject-matter experts in the field of reducing community risk.

Chapter Summary

This chapter has provided specific information pertinent to administrative duties that Level II managers are expected to perform. Proposing program budgets, helping leadership develop public policy recommendations, and evaluating team members are all components of this process.

Proficiency in administering community risk-reduction efforts requires subject-matter expertise, experience, and a commitment to achieving intended outcomes. To ensure an effective and legal process is followed, managers should collaborate with their respective organization's leadership and finance officers prior to initiating this important position of responsibility.

Review Questions

1. What is the process for developing a fire or life safety education budget for a specific project?

2. What information should be contained in a budget proposal?

3. What is the process for approving a budget proposal in most departments and communities?

4. Why are performance evaluations important?

5. What is the procedure for evaluating the performance of a subordinate?

Key Terms

Compensatory Time — Often referred to as "comp time." Work time earned by an individual that is space-banked by the employer. This time off may be used by the employee in place of vacation, holiday, or sick leave.

Cost/Benefit Analysis — Examination of the proposed expense of an effort and deciding if the overall benefit is worth the investment of money and/or time.

Fair Labor Standards Act — A federal law requiring employers to compensate employees at a pay/comp rate of time and a half for services performed off-duty in the local community on behalf of the agency where the individual is employed.

Family Medical Leave Act — A federal law requiring employers to allow employees specific use of personal sick leave to care for an ill spouse or other immediate family member.

Public Policy — A system of laws, regulatory measures, courses of action, and funding priorities by a government entity or its representatives. Public policy is often created through a legislative process at either the federal, state, or local level.

Purchase Order (PO) — A written document generated by the purchaser that allows vendors to invoice for monies owed. This action serves as an official record that the organization and vendor/contractor have conducted financial business.

Request for Proposal (RFP) — A document sent to a vendor that specifies exactly what the purchaser wants a product or service to do. The proposed vendor is expected to meet the specification and provide an itemized bid for the product or service.

Chapter 8 Notes

Cost/Benefit Analysis. National Fire Academy Risk Reduction Curriculum.

Evaluating Subordinate Performance. International Fire Service Training Association.

IFSTA **Fire and Emergency Services Instructor**; Seventh Edition.

FLSE Level II Managers: Planning and Development

Chapter Contents

chapter 9

Key Terms

Job Performance Requirements

This chapter provides information that addresses the following job performance requirements of NFPA®
1035, *Standard for Professional Qualifications for Fire and Life Safety Educator, Public Information
Officer, and Juvenile Firesetter Intervention Specialist*, 2010 edition.

NFPA® 1035 References

6.3.1

6.3.2

6.3.3

FESHE Objectives

Fire and Emergency Services Higher Education (FESHE) Objectives: *Fire and Life Safety
Education*

4. Identify and use local, regional and national sources of data for fire and injury prevention programs.

Learning Objectives

After reading this chapter, students will be able to:

1. Define how to identify and prioritize local risks using nationally recognized practices. (NFPA® 1035, 6.3.1)

2. Explain how to facilitate a collaborative partnership in support of a risk-reduction initiative. (NFPA® 1035, 6.3.2)

3. Summarize strategies to request support for risk reduction from an external organization. (NFPA® 1035, 6.3.3)

Chapter 9
FLSE Level II Managers: Planning and Development

Case History

Blue Hill is a city of 27,000 in the southeastern United States. Its emergency services division provides both fire and paramedic level response. There is no official position dedicated to overseeing community risk reduction.

Blue Hill's emergency services team wants to prevent loss in the community. Each year all stations host open houses during both fire prevention and EMS weeks. Fire drills are held at all schools and emergency equipment is displayed to students.

Over the past five years, a multitude of severe residential fires have occurred in Blue Hill. Several people have been killed and property loss has been extensive. One fire threatened the business district by destroying a half dozen row homes near the city square.

Throughout the same period, car crashes have killed multiple Blue Hill high school students. These events have been highly publicized. In addition, backyard pools and the river that runs through town has been the scene of several drownings. As well, EMS crews often talk about the high occurrence of fall incidents in the homes of older adults.

The chief of Blue Hill Emergency Services wants her organization to take a more active role in the prevention of fire and injury. She believes an important first step is an objective analysis of Blue Hill's problems.

This chapter expands on the components of administration by examining how to prioritize local risks, facilitate risk-reduction partnerships, and secure supportive resources from external organizations.

Chapter 7 discussed the application of the Five Step Planning Process to Reduce Community Risk. Analyzing incident occurrences, developing a risk profile, prioritizing problems, and selecting target populations are logical first steps in that process.

The ability to locate and use reliable data creates the foundation to complete these tasks.

The Importance of a Community Analysis

Community risk analysis is a process that identifies fire and life safety problems and the demographic characteristics of those at risk in a community. It is the first and most important step toward deciding which risk issue and target population to address. The analysis includes an objective and systematic examination of problem and people-related information. Omitting this step could result in overlooking the leading, most lethal, or costly risks.

Selecting Reliable Sources of Problem-Related Data

Reliable data is essential to a risk-reduction planning process. The term *reliable* means that the statistics must come from an organization with proven expertise in collecting and disseminating data.

When starting a risk-reduction planning process, it is prudent to review nationwide **problem-related data**. This national profile suggests where to start looking in state and local data for trends of special interest. National fire and injury databases are potentially useful to identify the overall risk profile of the United States. Because of the Internet, this task can be accomplished both quickly and efficiently.

National Fire Databases

The following agencies provide reliable sources of information about fires in the United States:

- National Fire Data Center operated by the USFA. This data originates from the National Fire Incident Reporting System (NFIRS).
- Annual NFPA® survey of fire departments and Fire Incident Data Organization (FIDO).

Each of these databases takes a slightly different look at U.S. fire experience.[1]

National Fire Data Center

The United States Fire Administration (USFA) oversees the National Fire Data Center (NFDC) which collects, analyzes, and publishes information related to the U.S. fire problem. USFA began the **National Fire Incident Reporting System** (NFIRS) in 1975. Under NFIRS, local fire departments forward fire incident data to a state coordinator. The coordinator collates statewide fire-incident data and reports information to the USFA.

NFIRS has two objectives:

1. Help state and local governments develop fire reporting and analysis capability for their own use.

2. Obtain data that can be used to more accurately assess and subsequently combat the fire problem at a national level.

NFIRS uses a standard format that is based on NFPA® 901, *Standard Classifications for Incident Reporting and Fire Protection Data.*[2] NFIRS data provide detailed information about hundreds of property-use types and fire causes. Information about a building's construction, flame spread, smoke travel, and sprinkler and smoke alarm performance is also included in NFIRS. The current NFIRS package includes incident and casualty forms, a coding structure for data processing purposes, manuals, computer software, and a National Fire Academy training course for using the system.

NFIRS data began to be widely distributed in 1982. The USFA publication, *Fire in the United States* is a publication of fire data, based largely on data submitted by fire departments to the National Fire Incident Reporting System.

NOTE: *Fire in the United States* is an excellent resource for fire and life safety educators who want to compare the details of fire in their region or state to those nearby. For example, this publication uses charts and text to explain the causes of residential fire death on a state-by-state basis. To obtain a current copy of the report or for additional information about NFIRS, contact the Office of Fire Data and Analysis, U.S. Fire Administration, 16825 South Seton Avenue, Emmitsburg, Maryland, 21727. Or visit on the web at www.usfa.dhs.gov.

Membership in NFIRS is largely voluntary although some states require participation. Each year, localities from 50 states and the District of Columbia gather and deliver information on more than 11 million incidents. This equates to approximately one-half of all reported fires that occur annually in the U.S.

Because fire departments and states take part in NFIRS voluntarily, NFIRS conclusions may not completely reflect the entire nation's fire experience. This factor reinforces why examination of local data is a key component of a risk-reduction process **(Figure 9.1)**.

Figure 9.1 Local fire data is a key component of a risk-reduction process.

National Fire Protection Association (NFPA®) Data

Each year, the NFPA® surveys a sample of roughly 3,000 U.S. fire departments to make national projections of the fire problem. The participating departments are a stratified random sample of the nearly 30,000 fire departments listed in the NFPA® Fire Service Inventory (FSI) file.

The sample is stratified by the size of the community protected. Because they constitute a small number of departments serving a large share of the total population, all U.S. fire departments that protect communities with populations of 100,000 or more are included in the sample.

For all other departments, a sample is selected based on the size of the community protected. Consequently, communities of one size are not overrepresented or underrepresented by the sample.

The survey allows NFPA® to make national projections by weighing sample results according to the proportion of the total U.S. population accounted for by communities of each size. For each estimate, NFPA® calculates a sampling (or standard) error, which is a measure of the error created because estimates are based on a sampling of fire losses rather than on a complete census of the fire problem.

The annual survey collects the follow types of data:

- Number of fire incidents, civilian deaths and injuries, and estimated property loss for the nine major property-use groups listed in NFPA® 901.

- Incendiary and suspicious fires categorized to include structure and vehicle incidents.

- Number of on-duty firefighter injuries and deaths.
- Type and size of community protected. Type of community refers to county, township, city, etc.
- Media coverage or other reports on multiple-death fires, large-loss fires, and firefighter fatalities. The fires are researched by NFPA® and may be included in the Fire Information Data Organization (FIDO).

NOTE: NFPA® has conducted its annual survey since 1977. Results of the annual survey are published as "Fire Loss in the United States" in the September/October *NFPA Journal®*. "U.S. Fire Fighter Injuries" appear in the November/December *NFPA Journal®*, and as special studies.

The Fire Incident Data Organization (FIDO) System

Operated by NFPA®, the FIDO system provides an in-depth look at a specific profile of fires. FIDO captures almost all reported fires involving five or more civilian deaths, one or more firefighter death, or large dollar loss.

FIDO reports include the following information:

- Performance of built-in fire protection systems
- Analysis of factors that contributed to flame and smoke spread
- Timeline of events that occurred during the fire
- Analysis of factors that influenced the fire's outcome
- Direct and indirect losses from the incident
- Escapes and rescues
- Building height

FIDO is the source of background information for several annual NFPA® reports including "U.S. Fire Fighter Deaths" and "Catastrophic Multiple-Death Fires" in the United States. Both reports are published in the July/August *NFPA Journal®*. Reports on "U.S. Fire Fighter Injuries" and "Large-Loss Fires in the United States" follow in the November/December issue.

NOTE: For more information about the NFPA® annual survey or FIDO, contact Fire Analysis and Research, National Fire Protection Association or visit the Web at www.nfpa.org.

National data can serve as a reference benchmark to compare the extent of risks that affect many communities around the country to those occurring at the local level. USFA and NFPA® data are considered both objective and reliable for the following reasons:

- Data is being collected and examined by a non-biased group of data analysis professionals.
- Enough data has been collected so statistically valid conclusions can be made.

National Injury Data Sources

As previously mentioned in the Level I chapter on unintentional injuries, there are several data sources for information. The Level II manager has a wider scope of interest in determining which kinds of injuries are occurring, although several of the following can be used for both scopes of research.

Centers for Disease Control and Prevention (CDC)

The CDC is one of 13 major operating components of the Department of Health and Human Services (HHS). HHS is the principal U.S. government agency charged with protecting the health and safety of citizens. It also has a major interest in protecting high-risk populations. As part of its mission, CDC operates several areas of interest to managers. Among them include the following:

- The National Center for Injury Prevention and Control (NCIPC)
- Web-based Injury Statistics Query and Reporting System (WISQARS)
- National Center for Health Statistics (NCHS)

The NCIPC, WISQARS, and NCHS can assist managers in locating information to profile morbidity, mortality, and obtain injury prevention recommendations. Both national and state information are available through the CDC and can be found on the Web at www.cdc.gov.

U.S. Consumer Product Safety Commission (CPSC)

The CPSC has operated the National Electronic Injury Surveillance System (NEISS) since 1972. NEISS is based on a sample of hospital emergency rooms, focusing on the role of consumer products. Fire and burn incidents that involve a consumer product are included.

National Transportation Safety Board (NTSB) and National Highway Traffic Safety Administration (NHTSA)

These two agencies within the U.S. Department of Transportation collect fire-related data. NTSB investigates aircraft and railway incidents as well as highway crashes involving hazardous materials. Published reports are available by visiting www.ntsb.gov and www.nhtsa.dot.gov.

American Association of Poison Control Centers (AAPCC)

AAPCC is a nationwide organization of poison centers and interested individuals. It provides a forum for poison centers and interested individuals to promote the reduction of morbidity and mortality from poisonings through public and professional education and scientific research. AAPCC also sets voluntary standards for poison center operations.

International Association of Fire Fighters (IAFF)

The IAFF gathers data about on-duty firefighter deaths and injuries. For more information, contact the IAFF at www.iaff.org.

Statewide Data Sources

After gaining perspective from national data, it is important to gather local information to see the specific factors that will affect people in the community.

Fire Data

Statewide fire data can be particularly useful when comparing fire loss in the educator's home community with other communities of similar size across the state or nation. Most states collect standardized fire data through participation in the NFIRS. Information about statewide NFIRS participation is usually available from the state fire marshal's office.

In instances where states have a statewide fire reporting system but do not participate in NFIRS, the state fire marshal's office still represents a logical point of contact. In addition, state departments of insurance or health, state data centers, and state medical examiners are potential data sources.

Burn Data

While some states have mandated burn injury reporting, it is far less common than that of fire data. Burn data is often collected at hospitals and routed to the state fire marshal or a related agency. However, despite enormous effort by the burn prevention and treatment communities, not all states require that burn injuries be reported. A state fire marshal's office is a good source of information about how individual states report burn injuries.

Injury Data

Many states have reporting systems for EMS delivery. Examination of the data collected by a state EMS reporting system may be a helpful resource for an educator attempting to profile leading injury risks. State EMS organizations represent a possible point of contact for this information.

The Importance of Collecting and Using Local Data

Local data is the most important source of risk information. Through local data, specific risks in your community are identified. It is critical to collect and analyze local data because risk issues may be different from those at the state or national level.

Having data from all three levels (national, state, and local) is important so that comparisons can be made and potential local trends examined. This level of knowledge can also build credibility for managers and their organizations.

Local Fire Data

Most fire departments contribute information on the origin and cause of incidents to a recognized data collection agency. If this is the case, the agency should be used as a resource when seeking information on local fire risks. The fire marshal's office for a state, city, or county is a potential starting point when seeking information.

While creating an organized data collection and tracking system can have an initial learning curve, it is well worth the effort. Having a reliable system in place makes it easier to track incident frequency and growth rates, deaths, injuries, and property loss.

If an organization does not have a data collection and tracking system in place, it is never too late to begin developing one. It is also beneficial to include past response information, thereby chronicling incident experience.

Many local departments have created their own independent data systems to track and profile incidents. A variety of commercial software programs exist or are being developed to help organizations track fire incidents and occurrences of preventable injury. Many programs are compatible with data fields utilized by NFIRS.

Local Injury Data
Since many organizations provide both fire and EMS services, it is also important to examine local data on preventable injury. Possible sources of local injury data include the health department and medical examiner as well as local or regional hospitals. Hospital data can include information on admissions and emergency room treatment (which may or may not result in a hospital admission). Municipal EMS or commercial ambulance services are other sources for local injury data.

Risk Data
Collection, analysis, and reporting of risk data is not only critical to the success of risk-mitigation initiatives. Policy makers depend on a fact-based rationale when considering adoption of codes and related standards that support preventive measures.

National and state data can provide reliable information about leading risk issues occurring nationally or regionally. This type of data can serve as a benchmark to track trends in risk and compare issues occurring in communities of similar size and demographic profile.

Finally, there is no substitute for reliable and objective *local* data on risks and the people who are affected by such. The educator has an obligation to his or her constituents to provide an accurate and objective profile of community risks.

The Need for Objective Reporting
Because local risk data ultimately drives prevention strategies, it is critical to collect data objectively and without bias. Objective reporting means using data to formulate conclusions based upon facts and not perceptions. Failure to determine risk causation and its associated factors objectively can lead to data that inaccurately profiles risk.

Risk-reduction data can become distorted when people interpret root causation factors differently. A way to avoid distorted data is to ensure that people who report on risk causation and other factors do so in the same manner. Since the objective collection, analysis, and reporting of data is essential to an effective risk-reduction process, an organization may wish to establish the position of data control officer.

Using Objective Data to Prioritize Risk
One of the greatest challenges to a risk-reduction planning process is ensuring objective data is being used to prioritize risk. Reporting that does not identify the real causation of an incident may lead to data that fails to identify leading risks and contributing factors.

Consider the typical kitchen fire involving food burning on a stove. If multiple fire officers are involved in the reporting process and have many reporting choices on root causation, the real culprits such as inattentive human behavior, use of grease, and high heat settings may be underreported due to the variety of subjective selections available.

One possible way to increase objective reporting is to identify categories where subjectivity often occurs and agree upon standard reporting entries. Consider creating a data dictionary that clarifies how specific incidents such as unattended cooking will be documented. Once decisions on reporting guidelines have been made, all staff members who have responsibility for incident reporting or data entry must be trained on and adhere to the protocol.

Using Fire and Injury Data to Prioritize Risks
Making an objective decision on what local risk(s) deserve priority attention takes time, effort, and patience. To conduct an objective risk analysis, the following types of data are needed:

- Types of incidents (fires, falls, motor vehicle crashes, etc.)

- Root factors leading to the incident (Why did the incident occur?)

- Incident frequency (How often does it occur?)
- Geographical distribution of incident occurrence and populations being affected (Where are incidents occurring and who are they affecting?)
- When incidents occur (time, day, month)
- Physical threats from risk (injury, loss of life to civilians and emergency services staff)
- Monetary cost of incidents (expense to community and emergency services)

When examining risk, it is important to study at least three (preferably more) years of incident data. This strategy provides enough information so that baseline statistics can be studied and possible trends identified.

Use of a database is helpful (if not essential) to a risk-analysis process. Large departments need databases because of their call volume. Small organizations also benefit from using a database. This is because the occurrence of fewer incidents demands examination of a longer history sample to achieve statistical significance. An electronic database program can help the evaluator create graphs and charts to visually create a risk profile.

Once an adequate amount of data has been collected and analyzed, decisions about what leading risk(s) to prioritize can be made. Factors to consider include:

- Frequency of incident occurrence
- Morbidity/mortality
- Rates of rise
- Economic impact

Selecting Reliable Sources of People and Community-Related Data

As explained in previous chapters, creating a community-risk profile is an important part of risk analysis. Two important components of the profile include the demographics of the local community and identification of high-risk populations residing there.

Examining root causation of fire and injury will often reveal human-related factors that lead to risk occurrences. Risk is sometimes closely correlated with social and physical factors that affect people. It can also be influenced by the demographics of a community.

Creating an Important Baseline of Information to Study

Determining what risks are occurring and how often they happen create an important baseline of information to study. These steps can help in that process:

- Maintain good data on the root factors leading to the occurrence of an incident. This helps identify human behavioral errors, failed equipment, and potentially unsafe products.
- Show the geographic distribution of risk occurrence per census tract. This makes it easier to compare problem-related data with demographical information.
- Track the time, day, and month of occurrences which can identify profiles of when incidents occur.
- Assess the physical threats from risks, not only in terms of injuries and deaths to civilians, but to emergency responders who handled the incidents as well.
- Examine the monetary costs associated with community risks.
- Examine the damages to property and possessions along with how much it costs the community to handle incidents.

Once the risks have been prioritized, the next step is to examine who is at risk and why (Table 9.1, p. 220).

Demographic data is useful to managers because it produces information about those who live in, work in, or visit the community. Information of interest to managers includes:

- Population size of the community
- How the population is distributed throughout the community
- Housing profiles: rental vs. owner occupied and condition of homes
- Gender profiles and age distribution
- Family size and structure
- Income and educational levels
- Employment and school system demographics
- Risk factors such as poverty, population transience, and disabilities

Table 9.1
The Typical Six Leading Causes of Fire

Typical Leading Causes of Fire	Annual Number of Occurrences	Injuries	Deaths	Property Loss	Rate of Incident Rise Compared with Previous Years	Geographical Distribution of Risk by Census Tract
Unattended Cooking	220	19	0	$300,000.00	Up 5% over previous year	Occurs most frequently in census tracts 2, 5 and 9
Arson	59	3	3	1.3 million dollars	Up 2% over previous year	Occurs most frequently in census tracts 2 and 5
Electricity	97	1	0	2.7 million dollars	Down 5% over previous year	Even distribution among census tracts
Heating Appliances	35	1	2	$900,000.00	Down 5% over previous year	Occurs most frequently in census tracts 2, 3 and 7
Candles	56	4	2	$770,000.00	Up 2% over previous year	Occurs most frequently in census tracts 2, 6 and 7
Smoking	23	4	4	$600,000.00	Up 10% over previous year	Occurs most frequently in census tracts 2, 5 and 7

NOTE: Demographic information can be obtained for nearly all communities in America by visiting the U.S Census Bureau at www.census.gov. Once on the site, locate the *American Fact Finder* database and navigate to obtain the desired information.

The Bureau collects **census data** every ten years. The data is recorded and profiled by **census tracts**. Census tracts are defined geographical areas within a city, town, county, or village. Each tract carries a numerical identification. An educator can access the Bureau's Web site, launch a query on his or her community, and obtain current demographical information.

Analyzing data by census tract represents one of the easiest and most accurate ways to build a community profile. Managers can locate demographic information about people residing in very specific geographical regions. In cities, the area may encompass less than a square mile. In rural areas, the distribution area may be larger.

When seeking census information, a manager may conduct a query using a city's name or by zip code. Caution should be employed when querying by zip code as it may equate to a relatively large distribution area. Examination by city or community name may prove to be a more effective strategy.

While the most formal source of demographic information is the Census Bureau, managers should remember that census data is only compiled every ten years. Since demographics can change quickly in growing or challenged communities, examination of current local data sources is essential. Sources of valid demographic information on the local community may include:

● City and county planning departments

● Office of community development

● Economic development director

● Chamber of Commerce

● Community Action Council

- Local schools, hospitals, and health departments
- Head start programs and child care organizations
- Department of Social Services
- Commission on Aging
- Neighborhood Associations

Not only can these agencies provide valuable data on local demographics, they can help identify the location and profiles of high-risk populations. Such local collaboration may serve as a gateway to reaching populations that historically have been the hardest to impact.

When researching local demographics, it is also important to examine where confirmed high-risk populations reside. National research has identified five populations that are at the greatest risk from fire and other preventable injury. They include:

- Older adults (age 65+).
- People with disabilities.
- People affected by poverty.
- Young children (birth to age two) represent a dependent population.
- Young children (birth to age five). Toddlers and children three to five years old are active, exploratory, and often not capable of understanding the consequence of unsafe actions.

People with low literacy levels may be considered a high-risk subgroup. There are 93 million adults with low literacy skills who live in America.

Americans are living longer and the older adult population is growing exponentially. While many older adults enjoy an active lifestyle, others suffer from chronic illness or debilitating conditions. Millions of Americans are affected by some form of physical, mental, or cognitive disability. Poverty and disability can affect any age group and represent huge factors to consider when planning a risk-reduction strategy.

When more than one risk factor is present, the potential for fire or injury increases dramatically. Add factors such as challenging living conditions, limited support services, or social isolation and situations become even more tenuous.

While examination of census data and local demographic information is useful for building a community profile, there is no substitute for personal observation. Getting to know who lives, works, and visits the community provides a reality-based perspective of community demographics and verifies the risk-reduction process. It also helps managers understand the root factors that lead to the creation of risk.

Combining Risk and People-Related Data to Form a Problem Statement

Comparing problem-related information with community demographics helps build the foundation for a mitigation strategy by providing the following information:

- Objective data on leading risk issues
- Identification of where problems are occurring
- Identification of factors that are placing people at risk
- Profile of populations at greatest risk

Armed with this information, a Level II manager can create a problem statement that overviews community risk in his or her home community (**Figure 9.2, p. 222**). The statement provides a fact-based overview of the highest priority problems and the populations most affected. It also includes a vision of how the organization will address the problem.

Facilitation of a Collaborative Partnership

Knowing and understanding leading local risks establishes a powerful foundation on which to build community risk-reduction strategies. Because the root causes of fire and injuries often lie in social issues such as poverty, risky behaviors, and the American Paradigm of Fire, it is prudent to develop broad-based intervention strategies.

While it is tempting to create intervention strategies as an independent organization, the most effective plans are those crafted and implemented by a partnership of agencies working to reduce risks of common interest. The Level II manager must exhibit proficiency in facilitating a fire and life safety **collaborative partnership**.

Facilitating a collaborative partnership to address local risk is an important component of risk reduction.[3] A prerequisite to success includes the

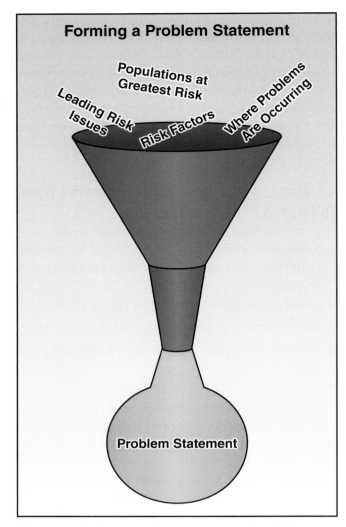

Forming a Problem Statement

Leading Risk Issues

Populations at Greatest Risk

Risk Factors

Where Problems Are Occurring

Problem Statement

Figure 9.2 To form a problem statement, a Level II manager combines risk- and people-related data.

fire and life safety educator's knowledge of leading local risks, causation factors, geographic distribution, populations affected, and a vision of combined intervention strategies.

Effective risk reduction requires cooperative effort from organizations, the community, target populations, and decision-makers. Attacking risk collaboratively makes sense in terms of gaining resources such as people, money, and equipment. Sharing tasks to address risk is more productive in terms of creativity, credibility, and effectiveness.

Collaborative partnerships exhibit great potential for successfully reducing risk through use of the following:

- Subject matter experts (SMEs) who share interest in local risks may be recruited from organizations within the home community.

- SMEs can help coordinate the efforts of their organizations to help achieve shared goals of the partnership.

- The use of integrated prevention interventions is made easier through a collaborative partnership of several respected organizations.

Members of a Collaborative Risk-Reduction Partnership

Logical members of a collaborative risk-reduction partnership should include representation from each domain of the integrated prevention intervention network (all Five Es represented) and target populations affected by priority risks **(Figure 9.3)**. Members should include those who represent the following:

1. Support groups for education interventions such as the emergency services, school systems, community outreach networks, and employers of people who live in the targeted area.

2. Entities that support integration of prevention technology, safer building materials, and products.

3. Organizations that can influence development of codes, standards, and ordinances that require use of prevention technology, safer products, and responsible human behavior.

4. Groups that can influence support for incentives that will encourage or require use of integrated prevention interventions.

5. Agencies such as fire, EMS, and hospitals that provide response when primary prevention efforts fail **(Figure 9.4)**. It is important to include this component as many incidents involve nonrevenue generating clients and cost the agencies money and place response staff at risk.

6. Populations most affected by priority risks.

When considering the creation of a risk-reduction partnership, the fire and life safety educator should first investigate local partnerships or coalitions that already exist. This is an important step because other local organizations may already be addressing problems that have similar root factors. A logical option may be to consider joining such an effort in lieu of creating a new partnership.

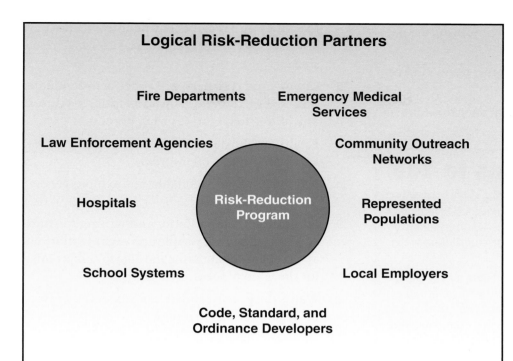

Logical Risk-Reduction Partners

Fire Departments

Emergency Medical Services

Law Enforcement Agencies

Community Outreach Networks

Hospitals

Risk-Reduction Program

Represented Populations

School Systems

Local Employers

Code, Standard, and Ordinance Developers

Figure 9.3 Members of potential collaborative risk-reduction partnerships.

Figure 9.4 Firefighters during an emergency response that might have been preventable.

If research shows that no such conditions exist, a manager may decide to initiate a partnership to address specific risk issues. While forming a partnership may sound simple, many fail due to a variety of factors. Some common factors include:

- The partnership's failure to understand and pursue underlying causation factors that lead to the occurrence of the risks being addressed

- Lack of goals, development of measurable objectives, and benchmarks of success

- Lack of structure, leadership, and synergy among the group

- Personal and organizational agendas that interfere with group progress

- Interpersonal conflicts among group members

- Not enough members or omission of key stakeholders and decision-makers

- Too many people involved

- Valuable time wasted because of lack of direction

- Wasted time leading to frustration among members, poor attendance, and a lack of commitment to the partnership

Strategies for Success

To contrast the previous, an effective collaborative leader understands the steps that must be taken to make positive things happen. The individual can engage partners in a productive and efficient planning process. He or she can also help others see and share a vision of what can be accomplished through group synergy.

Carefully selecting a core group of primary stakeholders to include in a partnership is a way to avoid potentially unpleasant challenges. **Primary stakeholders** are representatives from organizations that will perform the following functions:

- Directly benefit their mission by joining the partnership

- Help facilitate resources for prevention interventions (Five Es)

- Have influence with potential decision-makers

The following strategies have been successfully used by fire and life safety educators in facilitating collaborative risk-reduction partnerships. A successful Level II manager uses the following strategies:

1. Understands the process of comprehensive community risk reduction.

2. Has approval and support from his or her organization to facilitate a partnership.

3. Has developed a fact-based rationale of why potential partners should join the partnership. Can communicate a vision of how everyone can benefit from the collaborative effort.

4. Identifies and recruits key stakeholders who have a professional or personal stake in the partnership. (NOTE: Nothing shapes the culture, process, or outcomes of a collaborative partnership as its membership does.)

5. Identifies and recruits key people who are empowered by their organizations to make decisions.

6. Understands the personal styles of individuals, possesses excellent communication abilities, and is able to facilitate group processes.

7. Facilitates the development of goals, objectives, and benchmarks of progress.

8. Has integrity, is dependable, and exhibits general "can-do" optimism.

9. Is unselfish, empathetic, and willing to share success with other people and organizations. Is an excellent collaborator and able to compromise for the good of the overall goals.

10. Wants the partnership to help meet the goals of all organizations involved.

11. Understands when to consider inviting additional representatives to join the partnership.

12. Identifies and uses individual talents of group members, facilitates team building, and helps create strong work groups.

13. Identifies challenges to progress and helps facilitate solutions.

14. Leads efforts to praise the team for accomplishments and helps maintain positive group synergy.

15. Has patience and understands the need for members of the partnership to have an equal voice in the process.

As mentioned in previous chapters, educators at all levels are often people with drive and vision. This is particularly true of those involved with planning and leading the process of community-risk reduction. Many visionaries can clearly see an end goal but may forget the need to follow a defined process of decision-making (**Figure 9.5**).

An aggressive manager who circumvents group process interferes with a successful partnership. Facilitating an effective collaborative partnership is achieved through a process of clear communication, cooperation, collaboration, and compromise.

Facilitating Group Process and Conducting Meetings

Once stakeholders have agreed to serve, the first step is to begin identifying issues that need to be addressed. This can be accomplished through a group

Figure 9.5 A group of decision makers participating in a collaborative partnership.

facilitation process. The following section provides suggestions on how to facilitate group process, brainstorm, and build consensus.

A Level II manager facilitating a collaborative partnership is leading the effort to bring a group of organizations together to address common interests. Facilitating a collaborative partnership is not the same as facilitating a comprehensive brainstorming and consensus-building session. While members of a collaborative partnership may take turns running a meeting or facilitating routine brainstorming sessions, those who facilitate comprehensive sessions should come from a nonbiased independent organization with experience in facilitating group process.

Facilitating Group Process

Whether working within a collaborative partnership, building a coalition, or running a task-group meeting, a manager may be asked to facilitate the meeting. A facilitator's job is to stimulate others to participate in group discussion. The goal is to lead the group to consensus.

Facilitating is an important job. A good facilitator keeps group discussions on track and moving toward an established goal. He or she makes sure that all viewpoints are heard by encouraging participation from everyone and not allowing a few vocal people to dominate the discussion.

A good facilitator also helps document the group's discussions for later reference. The facilitator does not dominate the group discussion or argue for his or her own position.

General Techniques for Facilitation

The guidelines discussed in the following sections can help make the facilitator's job more enjoyable — and the facilitator more effective.

1. Begin by reviewing the goals to be accomplished during the session.

2. Keep facilitator comments brief and consistent with the goal to be accomplished.

3. Explain that the session will have two parts:
   - A brainstorming section to generate a wide variety of ideas
   - A **consensus** section for group members to find areas of agreement

4. Advise group members how much time they will designate to brainstorming and to building consensus. Most facilitators usually assign an equal amount of time for both brainstorming and consensus building.

5. Explain that all ideas are acceptable and encouraged during the brainstorming time period. Clarify that ideas will not be evaluated until the consensus stage of the discussion.

6. Encourage participation from everyone in the group once the session is underway. Strategies for accomplishing this task appear in the next section.

7. Maintain eye contact with the group. Be alert to nonverbal cues that someone wants to speak (head nodding or sitting up more straightly).

8. Coordinate a respectful session by doing the following:
   - Ensure that only one person at a time is speaking.

- Discourage side conversations that involve only a few people.
- Acknowledge all contributions made by group members.
- Do not allow negative or nonproductive comments.
- Be a good timekeeper. Periodically let group members know how much time is left in the session.

9. Assign someone to record notes from the session and disseminate to group members. Be sure action steps and individual/group responsibilities are noted.

Brainstorming Techniques

The purpose of brainstorming is to identify as many ideas as possible in a relatively short period of time. Pioneered by advertising executive Alex Osborn, brainstorming encourages new ideas, builds on the ideas of others, seeks quantity, and is marked by a lack of initial evaluation. Brainstorming takes three basic forms: freewheeling, round-robin, and the slip method **(Table 9.2)**.

Because freewheeling is the most common form of brainstorming, the techniques for brainstorming and consensus that follow are based on the freewheeling format. However, the following could be modified to use with round-robin or slip brainstorming.

1. Record each contribution as soon as it is stated, and number each idea.

2. Acknowledge the contributor, and encourage response from others.

3. Encourage different people to offer ideas. Try saying things like, "That sounds like an issue with codes. What ideas do the authorities having jurisdiction (AHJs) have?" Avoid calling on one individual by name.

4. Let participants offer their ideas randomly. Do not go around the table from one person to the next. (**NOTE:** This applies to the freewheeling format.)

5. If group members start debating during brainstorming, remind them that the intent of brainstorming is to collect as many ideas as possible and that debate and agreement will occur during the consensus part of the discussion.

Consensus Techniques

The objective of consensus is to get as much agreement as possible and not to get unanimous agreement on details.

**Table 9.2
Types of Brainstorming**

Type	Process	Remarks
Freewheeling	Members speak ideas spontaneously. Ideas are recorded immediately.	Most spontaneous form of brainstorming.
Round-Robin	Group members offer ideas in turn. Participants may pass. Session continues until all have passed. Ideas are documented when stated.	Difficult for one or two people to dominate the group. Discourages spontaneity and building one idea upon another.
Slip Method	Each person writes ideas on a slip of paper. Slips are collected and organized.	May be used for large groups. Helpful for shy people or dealing with sensitive topics. Offers no spontaneity and "hitchhiking" of ideas. People cannot explain ideas.

1. Open the consensus activity by allowing the group to decide which ideas duplicate each other or may be combined without losing the original idea.

2. Ask the group to prioritize the most significant ideas. Assign a designation such as numbering or stars.

3. Frequently ask the group questions such as, "Do you agree?" or, "How do you feel about that?" This is most important if a few people try to dominate the group.

4. Obtain a sense of group agreement on broad issues, rather than trying for unanimous choices on small points. Do not ask participants to vote because voting may create a division within the group.

5. Use a fresh easel pad sheet to write the group's consensus.

When the session concludes, gather all easel pad sheets in order, putting the consensus sheet on top.

Strategies for Effective Meetings

Once a general strategy of intervention has been identified, the partnership (and subgroups) will obviously need to have meetings. Before initiating any meetings, it is important to remember that while meetings are an important component of group process, they are often overused and misdirected. According to national surveys, up to 50 percent of meeting time is wasted.

Unproductive meetings result in frustrated members and poor efficiency. More meetings are then needed to accomplish intended objectives. Ineffective meetings also result in members of the partnership failing to get work done for their organization. This downward spiral can quickly lead to members dropping out of the partnership.

The following steps outline how to run a meeting, stay on track, and ensure progress is made:

- Set goals and be clear about the purpose of the meeting. Explain what needs to be accomplished. This strategy creates the agenda for the meeting.

- Invite a neutral facilitator to guide sensitive meetings.

- Have an agenda that includes discussion topics and decide who will lead the discussions and how much time is allotted for each.

- Provide for everyone a copy of the objectives, agenda, background information, and items needed for review in advance of the meeting.

- Stay on track. Use the agenda to stay on time and on the right topic. When side issues come up, help the group get back on track. Allow the group at large to decide when to end a discussion that is going on too long. Know when and how to use a subgroup.

- Insist that participants are on time, prepared, speak concisely, and participate in a constructive manner

- Focus on important topics. Set a certain amount of time for each item of the agenda, based on the importance of the item. Small details can be worked out by individuals or committees — meetings are for the decisions that need to involve the entire group.

- Encourage participation. Everyone should have a chance to speak their ideas. Ask people what they think, but also be prepared to gently remind people when they are talking too much. Document group decisions, action items, and who is responsible for getting tasks done.

- Record, save, and distribute meeting notes to members.

- Evaluate meeting effectiveness, seek improvement suggestions, and act accordingly.

Requesting Resources from External Organizations

Level II managers must exhibit proficiency in preparing a request for resources from an **external organization**. The following section provides background information specific to making a request for support.

Why Ask for Help?

Having adequate resources to address risk is an essential component of risk mitigation. Far too often, a manager's intervention strategy falls short of intended outcomes due to a lack of resources.

Even in today's fast-paced world, many potential partners stand willing to help an organization that can clearly demonstrate why its request for assistance should be granted. The effort can result in a partnership that provides vital resources and leads to a successful outcome. Before learning how to ask for assistance, it is important to examine the types of external resources that may be available.

Grants and In-Kind Contributions

Grants are gifts of money to a nonprofit, tax-exempt organization or to a government organization. Examples of nonprofit organizations include associations, foundations, privately funded schools or hospitals, charities, museums or other cultural institutions, and religious groups. There are four common types of grants: capital, general support (unrestricted), matching, and project **(Table 9.3)**.

In-Kind Contributions

As opposed to grants which involve money, **in-kind contributions** are gifts of services, time, staff, or products. Free printing of educational materials by a local print shop or a corporation with its own print shop is an example of an in-kind contribution. Another example may be the donation of batteries from a local retail outlet to a fire department's smoke alarm program.

In-kind contributions are as valuable as gifts of money because these contributions provide for free

Nonprofit Organizations

The term *nonprofit* is especially important. A lack of profit or even a charitable or public interest intent does not make an organization nonprofit.

Nonprofit is a legal status that the U.S. Internal Revenue Service (IRS) may give to an organization after the IRS has reviewed a written application. Nonprofit, tax-exempt organizations are sometimes called "501 (c) 3" organizations, after the section of the Internal Revenue Code that describes them.

Do not call an organization nonprofit or tax-exempt unless the Internal Revenue Service has granted that status to the organization. Many funders ask for proof of tax-exempt status. Other funders may check nonprofit status with the state attorney general or secretary of state, which may require nonprofit organizations to register with them. (**NOTE:** Government organizations do not need tax-exempt status.)

what would normally need to be purchased. These contributions can also increase a sense of community involvement.

Table 9.3
Types of Grants

Type	Use	Examples
Capital	Large-scale fund-raising activity Used most often to build something	Raising money to construct a safety village
General Support (Unrestricted)	Can be applied to any legitimate operating expenses	Salaries
Matching	Supporters give an amount equal to (or a specific ratio of) the amount another supporter provides Very popular with public television and radio	Employer offers to match employee dontation
Project	Money is given for a specific activity or expense Organization must ensure funds are applied to the specific activity identified in the request	Resources for free smoke alarm programs

In-kind contributions are also attractive because they may be easier to obtain than cash grants. Local businesses that are reluctant to write a check for a grant may be much more willing to give an in-kind contribution.

NOTE: Be cautious of accepting in-kind contributions from companies that may also provide competitive bids for other projects being conducted by your organization. This could create serious ethical considerations.

Locating Resources for Risk Reduction

At development time of this manual, Assistance to Firefighters Grants sponsored by the federal government was among the most popular sources of funding for risk-reduction initiatives. As part of the program, a special noncompetitive fire prevention section had provided billions of dollars in support of initiatives.

Government. The government has also sponsored community block grants through the Department of Housing and Urban Development (HUD). Many communities use HUD monies to support projects such as home inspections and smoke alarm installation programs in high-risk neighborhoods.

Corporate. Corporate support of community-risk reduction is another way to orchestrate resources. Not only do many corporations (national and local) provide monetary grants, many are willing to donate in-kind resources such as products, materials, and employee time. Other potential donor sources include

Summary of Tips for Preparing Grant or In-Kind Resource Requests

1. Find out what interests your prospects already have. Link your request to one of these interests.

2. Consider visiting the prospective donor before preparing a proposal. Tell the prospect about your idea, and ask whether it is something the person/organization would consider supporting.

3. Remember that the potential donor may not know much about your organization (or may misunderstand what you do and how your organization pays for its functions). In the proposal, introduce your organization to the perspective donor.

4. Create a factual profile of the community, risk(s), and proposed target populations. Describe the problem that your organization, with the prospective donor's help, is trying to solve. Include a series of measurable objectives that outline how the plan will be carried out.

5. Provide specifics about how the prospective donor's generosity will help solve the problem. Show how the funding will benefit not only the recipient but the target audience and the community as a whole.

6. Create a specific and clear budget worksheet. Have someone who is unfamiliar with your work to review the budget for clarity.

7. Write a one-page cover letter to go with the proposal. Include the following:
   - Provide an introduction of yourself
   - Identify the problem to be solved
   - Provide the amount of money that is being requested
   - Describe how the funding will help solve the problem
   - Explain why the proposal is important to the prospective donor and how the request is compatible with their organization's mission
   - Include a note thanking the prospect for considering the proposal

8. Write a concise executive summary for the beginning of your proposal. The **executive summary** is a condensed version of the narrative. In 50 to 100 words, it states concisely the proposed activity and what will be accomplished.

9 Follow any rules that the potential donor has established about the format of your proposal. Include *all* requested information and meet submission deadlines.

10. Follow up with a telephone call about a week after submitting your proposal to make sure that it arrived. Offer to provide additional information.

local service organizations such as Kiwanis, Lions, Optimist Clubs, and Shriners.

Foundations. Foundations represent yet another avenue of potential support. Many communities have local foundations that have been established by a person, family, or organization. A foundation serves as a medium for the donor to channel monies into cause-specific projects or programs.

National Versus Local Sources for Grants

Many types of national-level grants exist to support risk reduction. The trick is locating the source and successfully competing with other organizations. As a general rule, resource requests have a better chance of being granted to local organizations than requests to more remote agencies. It may also be easier to find a local donor with an interest in fire and life safety education than to locate a national source. Many managers fund their initiatives by obtaining combined support from several local sources.

Researching Potential Supporters

Managers often use the Internet to investigate potential sources of support at the national, state, and local levels. Many corporations, organizations, and governmental agencies have posting guidelines for resource allocation and the application process.

Many companies (especially larger ones) have their own charitable foundations that handle giving. A time-saving way to research company foundations is to consult the *Taft Corporate Giving Directory*.[4]

Whether the prospective donor is a large foundation or a local business, it is important to learn about the organization's philanthropic culture prior to asking for help:

- Investigate compatibility between your mission and that of the prospective donor. The closer the compatibility, the greater the chances are for success.

- Find out what requirements the potential recipient must meet in order to qualify as an eligible candidate. Requirements may include factors such as being a nonprofit organization and having an established system to manage donations.

- Determine when applications are accepted. Some funding organizations have specific deadlines

The Taft Corporate Giving Directory

The Taft Corporate Giving Directory contains detailed information on thousands of corporate-giving programs. Entries for each company include the following information:

- Name, title, address, phone, and e-mail of the primary contact
- Total dollar amounts given away in recent years
- Type of grants given (such as capital, general support, matching, and project)
- Giving priorities (examples include: social services, arts and humanities, education, civic and public affairs, health, safety, etc.)
- Typical recipients for each giving priority (For the health area, the following could be listed: emergency/ambulance services, health funds, health organizations, hospitals, medical rehabilitation, medical research, mental health, nursing services, nutrition and health maintenance, and single disease health associations.)
- Where they give ("Communities where ABC Company maintains operating facilities" is an example of a typical entry.)
  - Where they operate, by city and state
  - Who runs the company?
  - Who runs the foundation?
- How to approach them (initial contact, what information to include, and when to submit funding requests)
- Recent giving (total dollar amount of grants, number of grants, amount of average grant, amount of highest and lowest grants, type range, and total foundation assets)

Larger public libraries may have a copy of the *Taft Corporate Giving Directory*. A copy may also be available from the development office of a local college or university.

for receiving grant proposals. These deadlines may be tied to the fiscal year or a regularly scheduled meeting of the board of directors. Even the most comprehensive applications will not be considered if it is submitted past the deadline.

- Research the giving history of the prospective donor. Find out who they have supported, what has been given, and why the donor supported the request. Most potential donors will be happy to share this information as it shows the potential recipient is performing important background work.

Strategies for a Successful Outcome

Developing a written proposal for resources is often stereotyped as a mysterious and difficult chore best accomplished by a professional grant writer. Advice from experienced grant writers is always helpful but developing an effective proposal is *not* beyond the reach of the manager.

The importance of effective planning and evaluation were previously overviewed in Chapter 7, and it included the *Five Step Planning Process to Reduce Community Risk*. Completing several components of that process is essential before making a request for resources from an external source. These include:

- Developing a community demographic profile
- Analyzing and prioritizing leading risks
- Developing a problem statement
- Creating an evaluation plan that specifies what is wrong, who is at risk, proposed interventions, and measurable benchmarks of outreach, impact, and outcome.

Performing these tasks will demonstrate a fact-based rationale explaining why an organization needs help and how resources will be used to facilitate a successful outcome.

Developing a Proposal

A *proposal* is a document that describes what accomplishments the applicant proposes to achieve in return for the investment of the sponsor's resources. Whether seeking a grant or an in-kind contribution, a proposal will be needed. Proposals can be formal or informal in nature. A formal proposal should include the following:

1. A cover letter that introduces the applicant's organization and why it is requesting assistance.

2. A written narrative that overviews the applicant's organization, community, specific problem, proposed interventions, and resources being requested. The narrative should start with an executive summary.

An informal proposal may be an in-person request for help that occurs over a cup of coffee. The same kind of information is needed for *both* the written and verbal request. However, even if a request is informal, the educator should provide a written proposal for other decision-makers within the potential donor's organization to review.

Describing Your Organization

Describing your organization and its mission helps potential donors understand who you are and why you may be compatible with their philanthropic goals. The following information is helpful to include:

- Is your agency a municipal, district, or county organization?
- How many people and square miles does it protect?
- Is it fully paid, paid on call, or volunteer?
- How many members does the organization have?
- What is the organization's budget?
- What past risk-reduction initiatives have been completed?

Describing the Community

Because potential donors want to know where their resources will be invested, a profile of the community needs to be created. Components of the profile should include:

- The community's population size and how it is distributed
- Housing demographics including the total number of occupancies, owner versus renter profile, population transience, and housing vacancy issues
- Social and family characteristics such as education levels, income ranges, poverty issues, gender, ethnic, and cultural diversity
- Distribution of high-risk groups such as the very young, older adults, people suffering from disability, and poverty issues

Describing the Problem and Who Is at Risk

It is critical to define a specific problem, explain why it was prioritized, and describe what populations are at greatest risk. Being able to articulate this information personalizes risk to the local community and should include:

- Explanation of why and how the selected risk was chosen. (NOTE: It is very important to be able to offer a rationale explaining why the risk was selected. Even if data is not available, the potential funding source must understand why the risk was chosen.)

- Description of why and how the risk occurs.

- Identification of who is most affected by the risk and why.

- Identification of the proposed target population(s) and rationale for selection.

- Explanation of how the risk not only affects the community, but your organization as well.

Once the community, its leading risks, and target populations have been profiled, the next step is to describe the intervention strategy that has been developed.

The most effective proposals are those that identify use of combined prevention interventions (the 5 Es). It is also important to explain how the interventions will be implemented and evaluated. Summarize the intended outreach, how impact will be measured, and the desired outcome of the strategy.

NOTE: Even when requesting items, such as a piece of equipment for a specific program or materials for a project, the manager should explain how the resource supports the overall risk-reduction strategy.

Explaining How Support Will Impact the Problem

The next step includes being able to explain how a successful risk-reduction effort will benefit the target audience, community, and prospective donor. Doing this helps the donors understand how they become part of the solution to the problem being addressed. This information should be presented in the written narrative and summarized in the cover letter as well.

Be specific when asking for resources. Prospective donors need to know exactly what is being requested from them and how the support will be used.

If the requested resource is money, suggest a specific dollar amount. Link the dollar figure to the positive things (outreach, impact, and outcome) that the risk reduction effort is intended accomplish (Figure 9.6).

Requests for larger amounts of money (for example, anything over $1,000) need to have an accompanying budget. Although the idea of creating a budget for a grant proposal may sound intimidating, a budget is really just a breakdown of the requested material and its cost. Typical budget categories for a grant are the same as for any other budget (Table 9.4, p. 234).

Thanking Donors for Their Support

If a request for support is successful, send prompt correspondence thanking the donor. Consider public recognition of the support as well. A very important point to remember: use the contribution the way your proposal said it would. Do *not* use the gift for *any* other purpose. Keep the donor apprised of activities through reports, e-mails, letters, or phone calls.

Chapter Summary

Prioritizing risk, understanding its causation, and knowing who it is affecting are some of the most important tasks a Level II manager will undertake. Done well, the effort will produce accurate information that helps create a foundation for successful community-risk reduction.

Reducing risk is best accomplished through use of a broad-based team approach. Fire and life safety educators most successful at this strategy actively use collaborative partnerships.

People will often support a cause in which they share a vested interest. Grants and in-kind contributions from sources external to an educator's organization can provide significant support to a prevention effort. Managers most successful at generating resources are those who articulate the need for support through a well-developed proposal. The most effective proposals motivate donors by identifying a need and suggesting potential solutions through broad-based collaborative support.

Review Questions

1. What is the proper process for identifying and prioritizing local risks?

2. What is the proper method for facilitating a collaborate risk-reduction partnership?

3. What are some common strategies for requesting support for risk-reduction initiatives?

Monetary Request Letter

Smithville Fire and Life Safety Consortium
123 South Blair
Smithville, OR 97037

November 30, 2010

Cynthia Brakhage
2702 Winter Park Lane
Smithville, OR 97038

Dear Ms. Brakhage,

Your gift of $500 will provide one copy of the NFPA® Risk Watch® Curriculum for each teacher at the Smithville Elementary School. The lessons taught by teachers will enable over 1,000 students to educate family members about injury prevention. Follow-up surveys are projected to reveal that a positive life safety behavioral change will occur in 80% of local homes who have a child that receives the training. A long-term goal of the program is to reduce unintentional injuries in the community of Smithville by 30 percent.

The Smithville Fire and Life Safety Consortium thanks you for your continued support!

Sincerely,

JD Appleton

J.D. Appleton
President
Smithville Fire and Life Safety Consortium

Figure 9.6 Be specific when asking for resources from prospective donors.

Key Terms

Census Data — Demographical information about people and communities that is collected by the U.S. Census Bureau every ten years.

Census Tracts — Defined geographical areas within a city, town, county, or village. Each tract carries a numerical identification.

Collaborative Partnership — Plans implemented by a partnership of agencies working to reduce risks of common interest.

Consensus — Group agreement on a topic.

Executive Summary — A condensed single page synopsis of the written narrative.

External Organizations — Groups from outside the organization with which the educator is associated.

Grants — Gifts of money to a nonprofit, tax-exempt organization or to a government organization.

In-Kind Contributions — Donations of services, time, or products.

National Fire Incident Reporting System (NFIRS) — National fire incident data collection system managed by the United States Fire Administration. Local fire departments forward incident data to a state coordinator. The coordinator collates statewide fire incident data and reports information to the USFA.

Primary Stakeholder — People, groups, or organizations that have a vested interest in a specific issue.

Table 9.4
Budget Categories

Categories	Descriptions
Materials and equipment	Some organizations are more receptive to requests for donation of materials and equipment. For example, retail and supply corporations may be interested in providing a quantity of materials like smoke alarms or installation equipment. A printing firm may agree to sponsor printed materials that carry its name as a co-sponsor of the program.
People costs	In today's busy world, things are seldom free, including a person's time. When requesting resources, it may be necessary to budget for people to perform risk-reduction efforts. This could include overtime costs for staff or services provided by independent contractors. Whether your organization is financially compensating staff or using volunteers, be sure to note it as an in-kind service. Donors often support collaborative partnerships where the organization requesting help can show that it is contributing resources to the overall effort.
Marketing costs	A component often missing from a risk-reduction initiative is marketing. Gone are the days when radio, television stations, and newspapers were required to donate marketing resources for public safety organizations. If the community, target populations, and potential supporters don't know about a risk-reduction effort, a successful outcome may be difficult. Consider including marketing expenses as part of a request for resources. The media (or private sources) may be interested in sponsoring advertising in return for acknowledgment as a supporter.
Transportation	Having safe and reliable transportation is a basic tool that should be accessible to the educator. Unfortunately, due to resource constraints, many educators do not have a reliable vehicle dedicated for their use. This circumstance can often be resolved through external help. If asking for a vehicle, you must justify why it is needed and how it will impact the outcome of reducing risk.
Travel and tuition expenses	Travel and tuition expenses to attend a life safety conference are sometimes sponsored by organizations outside the emergency services. Sponsors will often underwrite the expense for educators to visit another community to learn about a successful prevention initiative.
Evaluation costs	When requesting support for a program or initiative, include the cost of performing evaluation of the proposed activity. Program evaluation costs can be estimated by adding approximately 10 to 20% to the estimated expense of an activity.

Problem-Related Data — Statistics that can be used to analyze incident occurrences, develop a risk profile, prioritize problems, and identify at-risk populations.

Reliable Data — Statistics that come from an organization with proven expertise in collecting and disseminating data.

Chapter 9 Notes

1. The "National Fire Databases" section is largely based on John R. Hall, Jr., "Use of Fire Loss Information," *Fire Protection Handbook*. Reprinted with permission from *Fire Protection Handbook*, 17th edition, Copyright ©1991, National Fire Protection Association, Quincy, MA 02269.

2. NFPA® 901, *Standard Classifications for Incident Reporting and Fire Protection Data*, National Fire Protection Association, Quincy, MA.

3. *Process of Effective Risk Reduction*. National Fire Academy Risk Reduction Curriculum.

4. Taft Corporate Giving Directory: Comprehensive Profiles of America's Major Corporate Foundations and Corporate Charitable Giving Programs, 10th ed., Taft Corporate Information Service, The Taft Group, Washington, DC.

FLSE Level II Managers: Education and Implementation

Chapter Contents

Key Terms

Job Performance Requirements

This chapter provides information that addresses the following job performance requirements of NFPA® 1035, *Standard for Professional Qualifications for Fire and Life Safety Educator, Public Information Officer, and Juvenile Firesetter Intervention Specialist*, 2010 edition.

NFPA® 1035 References

6.4.1

6.4.2

6.4.3

FESHE Objectives

Fire and Emergency Services Higher Education (FESHE) Objectives: *Fire and Life Safety Education*

6.   Select, design, implement, and evaluate fire and life safety education programs that address specific community risk issues.

FLSE Level II Managers: Education and Implementation

Learning Objectives

After reading this chapter, students will be able to:

1. Explain the process of learning.

2. Describe challenges to the learning process.

3. Outline strategies for designing a positive learning outcome.

4. Describe how to develop informational materials that support an educational program. (NFPA® 1035, 6.4.1)

5. Discuss how to develop a lesson plan for a fire and life safety presentation. (NFPA® 1035, 6.4.2)

6. Describe how to develop educational materials that support an educational program. (NFPA® 1035, 6.4.3)

7. Explain how to design educational programs that support an existing risk-reduction strategy. (NFPA® 1035, 6.4.3)

8. Assess the effectiveness of an educational program and explain how to make revisions that support an existing risk-reduction strategy.

Chapter 10
FLSE Level II Managers: Education and Implementation

Case History

Fire departments in many U.S. communities have been using fire-damaged homes as interactive neighborhood classrooms since the mid-1980s. (NOTE: The structure must be inspected before use to make sure it is safe to use.) Allowing residents to tour a burned home under the guidance of firefighters is a very powerful window of opportunity that draws attention to the importance of fire prevention. For example, in Hagerstown, Maryland, the fire department moved a fire-damaged home from a city neighborhood to the community's Children's Safety Village. The prefabricated home was moved in two sections by firefighters with assistance from local construction companies. Each year, 10,000 people visit the reality-based instructional prop.

Using burned homes for educational purposes is a strategy that gives attendees an "up close and personal" look at the destructive power of fire. Done well, the program can show the relationship between all components of prevention (5 Es). Attendees of the program learn about fire department operations and see first-hand what was lost and saved. Most importantly, they learn the sequence of events that led to the incident's occurrence and how it could have been prevented.

This type of program requires extensive planning when developing the initial program and thereafter when conducting each specific event. However, return on investment is huge with most communities seeing an average of 100 attendees at each event.

A successful learning experience requires learners to actively construct meaning from the information they are receiving. A learner's prior understanding and opinion of a topic before instruction have a major influence over what they will learn during instruction or exchange of information.

How Learning Occurs

An educator cannot force a person to learn. Instead, the effective educator facilitates a change in the learner's way of organizing his or her world. A prospective learner uses his or her senses (seeing, hearing, smelling, or touching) to receive information. The

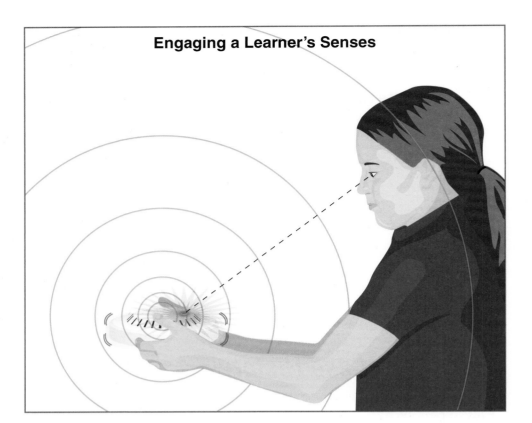

Figure 10.1 The more senses a learner uses at one time, the more likely that learning will occur.

Engaging a Learner's Senses

more senses that are involved in the information gathering process, the greater the likelihood that learning will occur **(Figure 10.1)**.

After information has been received, it is stored in the learner's short-term memory. A person's **short-term memory** is similar in concept to random access memory (RAM) on a computer — there is a finite amount of space available to store information. Once the information is planted in a learner's short-term memory, he or she places a level of value on the information and immediately begins searching for a connection between the new and the known information.

Once a connection is made and a level of value assigned, the learner may (or may not) transfer the new information to long-term memory. **Long-term memory** is like the hard drive on a computer — it has much more capacity to process, apply, and store information. The ability of a learner to transfer information is based upon cognitive ability, intellectual development, life experience, and the quality of educational experience. Since Level II managers develop educational materials and experiences, it is important to examine how learning can be measured.

Measuring Learning

The domains of learning were categorized by Dr. Benjamin Bloom in the 1950s. Dr. Bloom contended that most teaching was focused on fact-transfer and information recall (the lowest level of comprehension) rather than true personal development. The measurement of knowledge, attitude, and skill development are divided into three domains:

- Cognitive
- Affective
- Psychomotor

Dr. Bloom's work is relevant to Level II managers because it creates a foundation for developing educational performance outcomes that apply to a student's attitude and skill development.

Cognitive Learning

Cognitive learning is demonstrated by knowledge recall and use of intellectual skill. Examples of the cognitive process include how a person comprehends information, organizes subject matter, applies knowledge, and chooses alternatives. The cognitive domain is the core domain of learning; both other domains (affective and psychomotor) require some form of integrated cognitive process.

The following words describe cognitive processing ability, from basic to advanced **(Figure 10.2)**:

- *Knowledge.* The learner can recall information and facts.

- *Comprehension.* The learner exhibits understanding of the information.

- *Application.* The learner is able to use the information in response to real circumstances.

- *Analysis.* The learner can interpret, organize, and structure information. Quality and reliability of the information is processed.

- *Synthesis.* Through creative thinking, the learner can build upon the information to develop new ideas, approaches, and systems.

- *Evaluation.* The learner is able to assess the effectiveness of whole concepts and make judgments based upon facts.

Affective Learning

Once a person has learned new information, he or she forms opinions, attitudes, and values about the topic. Affective learning is demonstrated by behaviors that indicate attitudes of awareness, belief, and responsibility. When developing educational materials, Level II managers should consider applying affective learning techniques so that strategies are integrated that motivate target populations to act on a desired outcome.

The following words describe, in ascending order, the structure and sequence of attitude and beliefs development **(Figure 10.3)**:

- *Receive.* The learner is open to experience and willing to listen.

- *Respond.* The learner reacts and participates actively.

- *Value.* The learner attaches value to the information and expresses personal opinions.

- *Organize or conceptualize values.* The learner can reconcile internal conflicts about the information and develops a value system toward the topic.

- *Internalize or characterize values.* The learner adopts a belief system and philosophy about the topic.

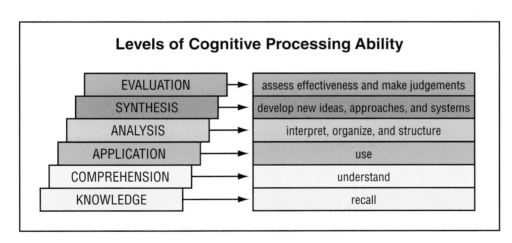

Figure 10.2 Cognitive processing ability is developed in a predictable sequence.

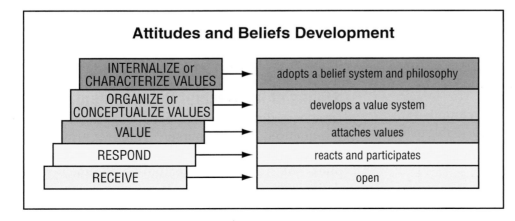

Figure 10.3 Attitudes and beliefs are developed in a predictable sequence.

Psychomotor Learning

Physical movement, coordination, and use of motor skills are processed through psychomotor learning. Development of psychomotor skills requires hands-on practice from the learner **(Figure 10.4)**.

While the psychomotor domain was originally established to assess skill development relating to manual tasks and physical movement, it should also incorporate modern skills such as use of technology and public speaking.

The following terms describe in order of the structure and sequence of psychomotor skill development:

- *Imitation.* The learner can observe and duplicate the actions of the teacher.

- *Manipulation.* The learner can reproduce the activity from instruction or memory.

- *Precision.* The learner can execute the skill reliably and independently.

- *Articulation.* The learner can adapt and integrate expertise to satisfy a nonstandard objective.

- *Naturalization.* The learner exhibits automated mastery skill at a strategic level.

Summary of Effective Learning Experiences

The most effective learning experiences are those that involve all physical senses and combine the domains of learning.

- Empower a person with knowledge (cognitive domain) and open the door to his or her attitude.

- Influence a person's attitude (affective domain) and open the door to a change in behavior.

- Teach a person how to perform a skill (psychomotor domain) and change his or her ability to serve his or her own needs.

Intellectual Development and Learning

A person's stage of intellectual development influences how and to what level he or she is able to learn. Unlike aging, intellectual development does not happen automatically.

Intellectual development occurs when the person is cognitively ready and when the environment is

Figure 10.4 A student is able to act on the information she has learned.

right. Social, cultural, and environmental factors such as family, friends, school, and work may restrict or encourage intellectual growth.

People may remain frozen in a particular developmental stage even though they continue to age. They may also regress to an earlier developmental stage due to cognitive disability resulting from medical or psychiatric conditions.

As designers of educational products and experiences, Level II managers need to possess an understanding of the **stages of intellectual development** in order to design age-appropriate information, lessons, and programs.

Stages of Intellectual Development

Intellectual development occurs in stages and in a sequential order. A person's intellect grows and develops in stages that build upon the previous ones. The stages of intellectual development were defined by cognition expert Jean Piaget, as discussed in Chapter 5.

Sensorimotor Stage

The **sensorimotor stage** is the first stage of intellectual development. It generally takes place from birth to age two. In this stage, infants construct an understanding of the world by coordinating sensory experiences (seeing and hearing) with motor actions (doing). An infant perceiving a ball as a round object that can be held, thrown, or bounced is an example of sensorimotor-stage intellect.

Very young children are a dependent population. They cannot care for themselves and must depend upon others to ensure that their basic needs are being met. This age group is at high risk from fire injury and death.

Safety education information and programs should be directed at caregivers of this group. Appeal to the affective learning domain of adults by integrating a rationale of why they are responsible for the safety of this population. Some of the most effective ways to protect very young children include higher order interventions such as rapid smoke detection, suppression systems, and flame-resistive building construction.

Preoperational Stage

The **preoperational stage** is the second stage of intellectual development. It typically occurs from age two to seven. During this stage, children begin to represent the world with words, images, and drawings and acquire the ability to think about objects. During this stage, children acquire the ability to think about objects that are not present in the immediate environment. They can also depict objects in mental pictures, sound, images, and words.

At this stage, children can imitate behavior and will vigorously explore their living environment. They often exhibit egocentric behaviors and intentionally violate rules to test the response of caregivers. Symbolic play also takes place during this stage.

The following are examples of preoperational intellect:

- A young child knows a smoke alarm makes a beeping sound.
- A young child can ignite a cigarette lighter after observing an adult perform the behavior.
- A young child learns where adults keep lighters within the home.

For a normally developing child, a time of rapid intellectual growth occurs between the ages of two and six. Experience shows that fire safety education can play a critical role in keeping this group safe.

One of the greatest challenges for Level I educators is being able to effectively teach fire-safety lessons in a manner that this group can comprehend. Level II managers must carefully design lessons to reflect the intellectual abilities and limitations of this age group.

Children aged three to five years learn fire and burn safety the same way they learn everything else — by seeing, hearing, and doing **(Figure 10.5)**.

Figure 10.5 Practicing safety behaviors can be fun when they are made into an activity.

What young children do has a more lasting effect than what they see. Young children love repetition. Unlike older children or adults, they are content to do one thing or hear one story over and over.

Preschoolers must have positive modeling. Design lessons that direct presenters to tell and show young children what to do instead of what not to do.

A six-year old can usually process more information than a three-year old. Still, each population has a limited vocabulary and attention span. Materials, lessons, and programs must use age-appropriate and time-sensitive educational strategies. Spending time with childcare providers, teachers, and their students is an excellent way to refine your ability as a developer of safety-education programs.

Concrete Operational Stage

The **concrete operational stage** is the third stage of intellectual development. It normally spans the age group of 7 to 11 years. Children at this stage can perform operations, a basic cognitive structure that is used to transform information or "operate" on information. Simply stated, the learner can do something with the information that he or she has received.

In the concrete stage of development, the learner is capable of logical reasoning as long as it can be applied to specific or concrete examples. The learner can reason about things physically present but has difficulties with abstractions or complex hypothetical propositions. An example of concrete reasoning is as follows: Children can understand the relationship between the presence of smoke, the sound of a smoke alarm, and the need to escape a burning building rapidly.

Learners operating in the concrete stage have a longer attention span than their younger cohorts. However, just like adolescent and adult learners, elementary age students must remain actively engaged in the learning process, and they expect interactivity as an instructional norm. Designing cooperative age-appropriate learning strategies and guided skill practice yields positive results with this group.

Concrete thinkers should be guided into connecting relevance of new information or skill development. The instructor can educate this population through the use of simple case studies, risk-sequencing activities, and problem-solving lessons.

Formal Operational Stage

The **formal operational stage** is the fourth stage of intellectual development. It usually occurs between the ages of 11 and 15. Individuals in this stage move beyond actual, concrete experiences and are able to think abstractly and in more logical terms. Individuals operating at the formal operational stage can:

- Develop mental images of ideal circumstances.
- Think systematically to develop hypotheses about why something is happening the way it is.
- Test the hypotheses with deductive reasoning.

NOTE: Portions of the at-large population may not function to their fullest potential in the formal operational stage of intellectual development. Genetic factors may stunt intellectual growth. Environmental and social experiences can also exhibit major influence over intellectual development.

Adolescent and Adult Learning

Adolescents and adults operating at the stage of formal operations should be capable of abstract thought, value system formation, and skill development. Maturity combined with the learner's intellect, social influences, and life experiences impact how a person processes information. The following section provides considerations for Level II managers to enhance the design of learning strategies to impact adolescent and adult target populations.

Adolescents

Many adolescents experiment with life — with relationships, sex, drinking, smoking, drugs, and driving — in ways that involve risk. Knowing how adolescents develop and learn helps makes designing educational experiences easier.

The largest marker of adolescence is change. Teens experience all sorts of exciting, confusing, and sometimes terrifying change. Physical changes in their appearance, influence from peers, and views of themselves all impact an adolescent's world.

Adolescence is the bridge between childhood and adulthood. Becoming an adult involves much more than enduring physiological changes, inheriting social responsibilities, and facing decisions that will affect long-term planning.

Adolescents are faced with several developmental tasks, as identified by H.D. Thornburg in his book *Development in Adolescence*. Thornburg suggests that most adolescents:

- Develop conceptual thinking and problem-solving skills.
- Form more mature relationships with peers of both sexes.
- Achieve a masculine or feminine social role.
- Prepare for marriage and family life.
- Prepare for a career.
- Acquire a set of ethics to guide behavior.
- Develop civic competence and responsible community behavior.

A major challenge for Level II managers is designing strategies that integrate risk mitigation into the big picture of adolescent development. This is often best accomplished by integrating risk mitigation into components of a school curriculum such as "Life Skills." The following are examples of this:

- A discussion about knowing who is pulling false alarms in school and deciding whether to report them can be positioned as ethics.
- The role of smoking and alcohol in residential fire deaths can be taught in terms of responsibility toward others.

When developing a program targeting adolescents, understanding how adolescents learn becomes important. Many of the following strategies are effective with adult learners as well.

Reality-based experiences. Reality-based experiences are very effective at influencing the cognitive and affective learning domains of the student. Allowing people to tour a fire-damaged home under the guidance of firefighters is an example of a reality-based learning experience.

Distributive learning. As with younger cohorts, adolescent learners expect interactive learning experiences that compare with fast-paced, high-tech video and computer programs. Distributive learning uses technology to enhance and expand the learning environment through Web-based programming such as Podcasts, Webinars, video conferences, and distance education.

Hypothetical projection. Thinking ahead about what might happen allows adolescents to make realistic life choices. Consider structuring a learning activity so that it requires use of critical thinking to describe what consequences could occur as the result of irresponsible behavior. It is essential to be current because both adolescents and adults demand knowledge of how their new knowledge or skill applies to and can be used during real-world situations.

Role model emulation. This strategy involves seeing (and judging) how someone else handles a situation. An activity requiring the learner to analyze how someone they respect behaves during a given situation is an example of this technique. This strategy often works well because peer approval is enormously important to an adolescent.

Instruction and demonstration. This learning technique has been familiar to adolescents since their preschool days. It can be used to teach many fire and life safety skills, such as changing a battery in a smoke alarm or performing CPR.

Guided practice with feedback on performance. The learner is instructed how to perform a skill, observes it being done, and then practices under direct supervision. Performance feedback is provided.

Teaching best practices to others. Teaching someone else a skill is a good test of how well the teacher can perform. Allowing a person to teach his or her peers gives the learner a sense of competence.

Service learning. Service learning is an educational trend that connects young people to the community in which they live. The basic idea is to offer community service projects through schools and other venues, such as churches. Classes of high school students sandbagging during floods and student groups working with Habitat for Humanity to build homes are experiencing service learning. Colleges often use service learning as a capstone class to provide a culminating experience for students seeking a specific type of degree.

The fire service can benefit from the service learning trend. For instance, high school or college students could be recruited to join Fire Corps teams. Students could be trained in fire and burn safety and then they could teach younger children, their peers, adults, or older adults.

Adults

While effective adult-learning strategies often mirror those used for adolescents, additional principles of adult education should be considered:

Adult learners need to be self-directing. Adults like to be in control of their lives. They place great value on being able to decide where they will live, work, and spend their money. In much the same way, adults like to control what they learn, how they will learn it, and when the learning will take place.

Adults need to know why they must learn something. As with adolescents, one of the biggest questions from the adult learner is, "What's in it for me?" Establishing a rationale of why the learner needs to know a piece of information, perform a skill, or change a behavior is the cornerstone of teaching adults. While this population demands practical, nuts-and-bolts-type information, they also respond well to strategies that stimulate affective learning. While a person may know the facts, his or her attitude, opinions, and value system ultimately guide changes in his or her behavior.

The need to know "why" and "what's in it for me" are aspects of the affective domain of learning. While past generations often responded without question to directives from authority figures, current and future populations will expect a clear rationale for why they should act and for what benefit.

Adults bring their own experiences into learning. Adult learners bring life experiences with them. Such experiences positively and negatively impact the fire and life safety educator's efforts.

On the positive side, adult learners are rich resources for each other and the educator. Instructional strategies that encourage active participation take advantage of the learner's life experiences and knowledge. Hearing testimony from peers also helps learners form opinions, attitudes, and values about a topic **(Figure 10.6)**.

Conversely, adults may have already made up their minds about how fire safe they are — or want to be. Incorporating instructional strategies that appeal to the learner's cognitive and affective domains of learning can help overcome challenges such as predisposing attitudes.

Adults are task-centered learners. Adults tend to focus their learning around completing tasks, solving problems, or handling the way they live. Conversely, children are subject-centered learners; that is, they study subjects such as grammar or arithmetic and take tests to show whether or not they have mastered the subject. Designing active methods that encourage participation such as problem-solving activities, case study analysis, and skills-practice exercises helps keep adult learners involved.

Older Adults – A Growing High-Risk Population

Older adults, senior citizens, seniors, the *elderly, elders* — perhaps no other group has so many names. Regardless of what they are called, older adults are an important audience for fire and life safety education for several reasons including:

- Older adults are the fastest growing segment of the population.

- Older adults have an unusually high risk of fire injuries and death.

While Americans are living longer, healthier, and happier lives, advancing age increases the probability of a person acquiring a chronic illness or disability.

Figure 10.6 Encourage active participation in an adult learning environment.

This includes challenges with sight, hearing, speech, mobility, and cognitive processing. Level II managers must be sensitive about this reality when designing educational materials, lessons, and programs. Level II managers should consider strategies that will assist older adults in the learning process.

Care must be used to develop printed and broadcast media that is sensitive to the needs of older adults. If a person cannot see, hear, or process information, learning and behavioral change will not occur.

Print Media

- Use appropriate font size and spacing—at minimum size 12 font, sans serif or other simple type.

- Utilize black print on white paper; red is the first color to be obscured as vision deteriorates.

- Use uncoated paper with matte finish (buff instead of shiny); this helps reduce glare.

Broadcast Media

- Choose a narrator with a clear voice.

- Limit background noise and distracting music.

- Select a spokesperson credible to the target population.

- Avoid overstimulating visuals that present too much information.

- Portray older adults in positive, active roles in the community.

Applying the Health Belief Model

The Health Belief Model[1] was developed by the public health profession over the course of many years experience with health promotion initiatives. Risk-reduction curriculum developed by the National Fire Academy includes this model because of its applicability to safety education initiatives.

The model is a set of conditions that must occur for a person to make a life safety behavior change. Accommodating these conditions will reasonably produce positive results:

- The person is aware that a problem exists as a result of his or her own behavior.

- The person understands the problem and the factors contributing to it.

- The person believes that he or she may be personally at risk from the problem. The person also believes that someone under his or her care may also be at risk.

- The person believes the benefits to change outweigh any barriers to do so.

- The person believes he or she is capable of successfully making the behavioral change.

- A clear understanding exists of what the person must do to reduce the risk.

- There is an understanding and personal commitment to the reasons for changing the behavior.

- The person has the resources and ability to successfully make the change in behavior.

- Positive feedback is provided when the change is made.

Fire and life safety educators should apply the principles of the Health Belief Model when designing informational material, writing lessons, or creating programs.

Applying the Principles of the Health Belief Model – A National Example

Problem: Over half of the smoke alarms in homes may be inoperable.

Root Factors: Dead or missing batteries, age of alarms, or lack of personal responsibility by individuals.

Action 1: A nationwide campaign is launched to educate consumers about the problem of nonworking smoke alarms. National statistics profile the problem to show the relationship between nonworking alarms and fire deaths. Fire departments across the country educate their constituencies through use of local statistics and reality-based strategies.

Action 2: Nationwide initiatives are created whereby local fire departments begin intensive door-to-door campaigns offering free home inspections and education about smoke alarms and installation programs.

Action 3: As evaluation begins to show fire death rates declining, media campaigns are used to show positive impact and encourage continued responsible behavior by residents.

Challenges to Learning

Several factors affect a person's ability to hear, see, and understand a message. After accounting for age-related development, an educator must understand other considerations that may be influencing the audience's capacity and willingness to change specific behaviors.

Social-Related Challenges

Winning the competition for a prospective learner's attention can be a challenge. Advancing technology also influences how consumers prefer to receive information. Instant messaging, high-definition media, and interactive gaming continue to command consumer attention. Conversely, many consumers are intimidated by or do not desire to embrace new technology. This can create a challenge for Level II managers as they work to design strategies that will effectively reach all facets of the target population with safety information.

Family structure and dynamics remain strong influences over childhood development. The percentage of children living with two parents continues to decline among all major racial and ethnic groups. The amount, type, and quality of parental support can have a direct influence on the psychosocial development of both children and adolescents. Social forces such as poverty and low education levels also remain contributing factors that often challenge learning.

Cognitive-Related Challenges

Cognitive-related challenges are seldom simple to identify or diagnose, but a basic understanding of the symptoms is useful for any educator. Awareness of the variety and severity of symptoms of these challenges will allow an educator to bring appropriate solutions to individuals.

Learning Disabilities

A **learning disability** is a disorder that diminishes a person's capacity to interpret what they see and hear or to link information from different parts of the brain. Up to 20 percent of the U.S. population exhibits some form of learning disability. If a person is unable to process information being presented, learning and behavior change will not occur.

Fire and life safety educators may work with a person who has one of the following types of learning disabilities:

- Attention Deficit Disorder (ADD)
- Attention Deficit Hyperactivity Disorder (ADHD)

- Autism
- Pervasive Development Disorder (PDD)

Learning disabilities may be familial. Although a lifelong condition, many individuals with learning disabilities can compensate for their difficulties with appropriate intervention, support, and accommodations.

Attention Deficit Disorder (ADD) and Attention Deficit Hyperactivity Disorder (ADHD)

Attention Deficit Disorder (ADD) is the inability to maintain attention to a specific stimulus for an extended time period. ADD is the result of a combination of neurological, biochemical, social, and cognitive factors. Family stability and environmental stimuli can affect the disorder either positively or negatively.

ADD can be associated with hyperactivity. Attention Deficit Hyperactivity Disorder (ADHD) is nonpurposeful excessive movement combined with the inability to sustain meaningful attention. ADHD sometimes co-exists with learning disabilities. The symptoms of learning disabilities may vary from person to person.

ADD and ADHD may be easier to diagnose in males than in females. Males often exhibit very noticeable behaviors such as disruptive actions and talking out of turn. Females may manifest more subtle behaviors, such as quietly daydreaming. With either gender, the most effective way to engage the ADD or ADHD student is though active learning techniques.

Autism

Autism is a brain development disorder characterized by impairments in social interaction and communication. Restricted and repetitive behaviors are often exhibited by an autistic person. A child affected by autism will display the behaviors associated with the condition prior to age three.

The number of people known to have autism has increased dramatically since the 1980s. This is partly due to changes in diagnostic practice. Autism is the most common condition in a group of developmental disorders known as the autism spectrum disorders (ASDs).

The following text describes distinctive behaviors that characterize autism. These behaviors can range from mild to disabling.

Difficulties with social interaction. The hallmark feature of autism is impaired social interaction. Parents are usually the first to notice symptoms of autism in their child. As early as infancy, a baby with autism may be unresponsive to people or focus intently on one item to the exclusion of others for long periods of time. A child with autism may appear to develop normally and then withdraw and become indifferent to social engagement.

Problems with verbal and nonverbal communication. Children with autism may fail to respond to their name and often avoid eye contact with other people. They have difficulty interpreting what others are thinking or feeling because they cannot understand social cues, such as tone of voice or facial expressions, and do not watch other people's faces for clues about appropriate behavior. They often lack empathy.

Repetitive behaviors. Many children with autism engage in repetitive movements such as rocking and twirling or in self-abusive behavior such as biting or head-banging. They also tend to start speaking later than other children and may refer to themselves by name instead of "I" or "me." Children with autism do not know how to play interactively with other children. Some speak in a sing-song voice about a narrow range of favorite topics, with little regard for the interests of the person to whom they are speaking.

Autism varies widely in its severity and symptoms and may go unrecognized, especially in mildly affected children or when it is masked by more debilitating handicaps. Doctors rely on a core group of behaviors to alert them to the possibility of a diagnosis of autism.

Pervasive Development Disorder (PDD)

Children with some symptoms of autism, but not enough to be diagnosed with classical autism, are often diagnosed with pervasive development disorder (PDD). PDD includes a broad range of disabilities within its definition to include ADHD, Asperger's syndrome, and autism. Children with autistic behaviors but with well-developed language skills are often diagnosed with Asperger's syndrome. Children who develop normally and then suddenly deteriorate between the ages of 3 to 10 years and show marked autistic behaviors may be diagnosed with childhood disintegrative disorder. Girls with autistic symptoms may be suffering from Rett syndrome, a sex-linked genetic disorder characterized by social withdrawal, regressed language skills, and hand wringing.

Rationale for Taking Action

A significant proportion of the American population suffers from some level of learning disability. Because it is often difficult to identify a person who suffers from a learning disability, the educator must incorporate strategies that enhance communication with diverse audiences.

Before developing informational materials or creating lesson plans, Level II managers must consider the potential learning challenges afflicting the target audience. Effective learning experiences can be created for all populations. It simply requires education, planning, empathy, and patience from educators. Information on how to design a structured learning environment follows later in this chapter under the section on developing lesson plans.

Successful learning experiences do not just happen. Learning experiences are designed by someone who is knowledgeable in subject matter, learning theory, and program development. A Level II manager is responsible for designing educational components that will be used by Level I educators. This includes informational material, lesson plans, and educational programs that effectively guide and support the learning process.

Strategies for Successful Learning Outcomes

While it is true that society is always changing, the basic strategies for facilitating a successful learning outcome remain the same. The following general strategies should be followed for designing informational materials, writing lessons, and developing programs:

- A learner must receive and understand the information being presented. The use of appropriate time management strategies is essential. Obviously, a six-year old cannot be expected to remain engaged throughout a 45-minute lecture.

- Learners best succeed when they see, hear, read, and record new information. Consider using multiple message media and active learning strategies.

- New information must be presented in a logical sequence that is easy to comprehend and relevant to the learner. It must make sense or it may well be rejected!

- The developer should learn as much as possible about his or her intended target population before designing educational strategies. One style does not fit all needs!

- Learners must connect the new information to existing knowledge about a subject. Consider presenting new information incrementally, thereby incorporating new information in a step-wise fashion.

- Limiting distractions helps facilitate a successful learning outcome.

- Attitudes and values are best influenced once a learner has successfully processed information. People need to find relevance in what they are being asked to learn.

- Incorporate strategies that appeal to the affective domain of learning.

- Information must be accurate, fact based, and age appropriate.

Regardless of the domain of learning being targeted, engage learners through active participation. Skills are best learned through demonstration and guided practice.

Developing Informational Material

Level II managers must exhibit proficiency in developing informational materials that support risk reduction. The information they collect and share is expected to be accurate, relevant to a given objective, and specific to the needs of an identified target audience.

Informational materials refer to the broad spectrum of media available for educators to disseminate information. Examples of print media include brochures, fliers, handout materials, newspaper ads, and billboards. Broadcast media are television, radio, and the Internet.

Informational materials are designed to raise public awareness about an issue. Many also suggest actions toward a solution to a problem. Level II managers often use informational materials to supplement a safety lesson or prevention campaign. Used appropriately, informational materials can be excellent enhancements to educational efforts.

The Need for Accuracy

Accuracy is an essential ingredient of credible informational material. Chapter 9 highlighted the benefits of accurate risk analysis and also explained how to accomplish this task. Part of that process involved identifying and prioritizing target populations.

Given current technological resources and information banks, there is no excuse for failing to identify target populations or publishing inaccurate information about local risks. Prevention information must be fact-based, locally centered, solution-oriented, and population specific.

The Need for Relevancy

Learners need to see relevance in the information they are being asked to receive and process. When target populations realize the impact of their behavior upon a specific problem, they understand the relevance of the information and are apt to participate in formulating solutions.

Appeal to Specific Populations

Not only does risk-reduction informational material need to be accurate and relevant, it must also appeal to the prospective learner. Strategies that will grab and hold the learner's attention long enough for information to be shared are continually being researched by marketers and can be effectively used by the fire service. Several of these tactics are explored in the next section.

The prospective learner must be able to receive and process the intended information in order for it to be actionable. Print media must be readable, and broadcast messages must be clear. It is important to remember that if a person cannot process the information, learning or behavior change will not occur.

When designing a strategy intended to impact diverse target groups, a prevention campaign often requires several formats of informational material. Each format features its own characteristics that will appeal to a specific target population.

Design Age-Appropriate Materials

Informational material that grabs the attention of young children may not be effective with an adolescent or older adult population and vice versa. The message medium should appeal to the specific group being targeted. A strategy of one product can fit all needs is not recommended. Target populations often respond well to prevention information endorsed by a source that is recognizable and credible to its respective group.

Consider the intellectual profile of target populations. As explained in the introductory section of this chapter, people pass through several distinct stages of intellectual development. Complex informational materials that are well received by a group of college graduates may not prove successful when used among a younger population.

Gender, age, race, and cultural considerations. Developing informational materials that appeal to specific target populations is essential to effective risk reduction. Corporations invest billions of dollars in the research and marketing of their products. Though the products may be diverse, the marketing campaigns have three major similarities:

- Specific target populations have been identified.

- Gender, age, race, and cultural considerations have been carefully analyzed and integrated into the marketing strategy.

- Target groups are always portrayed in a positive manner.

While the fire prevention service does not have the financial resources of the corporate world, strategies for designing informational materials should follow the same general direction. This requires research and planning.

Educationally and behaviorally sound. Informational material for prevention programs must be educationally and behaviorally sound. When developing prevention messages, promote "what to do" rather than what "actions not to take." The same strategy is true for showing behaviors: promote positive instead of negative actions.

Use focus groups and conduct pilot testing. The goal of a focus group is to help design a product that will be effective when used among the specific population being targeted. A focus group is comprised of members from a risk-reduction planning team, marketing professionals and, most importantly, representatives from the target group for whom the informational material will be used. A planning team uses the results of a pilot test to evaluate how the materials impacted the sample target population.

Use multiple message media. Marketing analysts indicate that a consumer may need to see and hear

What This Means to You

Your community is experiencing a rise in the number of portable heater fires. The risk-reduction officer researches the problem and discovers that most fires are occurring in a specific census tract and involve heaters placed too close to furniture.

Further investigation reveals most fire hosts to be single females of the same ethnicity, cultural background, and age group. The risk-reduction officer responds by consulting a local professional who specializes in developing marketing campaigns designed to target this specific population.

You work cooperatively with the marketing professional to design an intervention strategy that includes informational material specific for the at-risk population.

In this case, the informational materials featured female members of the targeted ethnic group demonstrating the safe use of portable heaters. The spokesperson for the strategy included a recognized female community leader from the specific target population. Informational materials were developed into a bilingual, age, and intellectually appropriate format. Print and broadcast message media were used.

a message up to seven times before it is fully assimilated. This is why professional marketing campaigns use multiple delivery media to reach consumers. The strategy is called *message medium saturation*.

Building relationships with the local business, communication, and media communities can strengthen the ability to disseminate risk information and solutions in an affordable manner.

Standard Risk-Reduction Terminology

Curriculum – A series of lessons designed to reach an educational goal.

Lesson Plan – A guide for making an educational presentation on a specific topic.

Presentation – A single delivery of fire and life safety information. A presentation can also be called a *lesson*.

Program – A series of presentations and activities designed to impact a common risk-reduction goal.

Risk-Reduction Strategy – A series of integrated programs designed to impact a common goal.

NOTE: Detailed information on the development and presentation of educational material is covered in Chapter 12.

Developing Lesson Plans

A lesson plan is the road map that provides general guidance for how a presentation is to be delivered. Because Level II managers develop presentations that may be delivered by others, proficiency in developing a lesson plan for a risk-reduction presentation is a required skill. This includes creating objectives that guide presenters to facilitate a successful learning outcome in a specified audience.

Research Before Writing

Conducting research is an essential first component of lesson plan development **(Figure 10.7)**. As presented in Chapter 7, the Five-Step Planning Process provides the framework for pertinent data collection and analysis. The following information is important to consider before developing a lesson plan:

- What is the problem or topic that needs to be addressed?

- Why does the lesson need to be presented?

- Who is the target audience?

- What is the profile of the audience (age, highest academic achievement, social/cultural background, and special needs)?

- What do members of the audience already know about the topic?

- What level of outcome is being sought through the lesson?

- What prerequisite knowledge and skills are needed by the audience to process the lesson?

- What informational or educational materials will be used?

- How will student performance be evaluated?

While some of the previously listed information is not always available to the developer, it is important to learn as much as possible about community risks and perspective target populations before writing. Discussion with teachers, examination of school-based curricula, and evaluation of testing results are ways to learn about school age students. Interviews, written surveys, and direct observation can produce information on community-based audiences.

Even if a developer does not have baseline information available on a prospective target audience, an introductory activity could be designed into a lesson plan to help the presenter obtain some level of background information from the group. Having baseline information about target audiences allows

Figure 10.7 An instructor conducts research to target key information relevant to a specific audience.

the developer to create a lesson that will help learners connect new information to knowledge they already hold. Additionally, since obtaining baseline information is the starting point of an evaluation process, having this information will make it easier to develop measurable learning outcomes. A lesson plan that includes background information on prospective learners can help enhance presenter performance as it provides the instructor with a profile of who he or she will be teaching.

The Lecture Method of Instruction

Because up to 70% of learning is dependent on students having the appropriate prerequisites, lecture (or a modified form of it) will always have a place in educational methodology. Lecture can provide important prerequisite information about a topic to prospective learners. Prerequisite knowledge is what the learner needs to know or be able to do to succeed and accomplish the lesson objective.

The lecture method of instruction was created many decades ago. It typically called for a teacher to read important passages from a book and explain what the content meant. Students were expected to listen, take notes, memorize, and ultimately repeat the material.

Although technology has influenced teaching in a positive way, current learning environments often remain strikingly similar to days gone by: The presenter stands in front of a room and reads or explains text that is projected digitally onto a screen (Figure 10.8). Students sit in their seats, take notes, ask questions, and learn the material sufficiently well to answer examination questions.

Because learning is a process of active construction by the learner, the teacher cannot do the work of learning for the student. He or she can, however, help facilitate a successful outcome for the learner. To effectively impart knowledge, public educators must use multiple instructional strategies.

Active Learning

Active learning techniques are effective at facilitating successful learning outcomes. Active learning works because it gets everyone in the group involved in the learning process. Examples of interactions include two-way communication, question and answer sessions, group/team events, demonstrations, case studies, problem-solving activities, games, and student presentations.

While active learning focuses on activity-based instruction, it does not entirely eliminate the need for lecture. The presenter still lectures to introduce new material and introduce the foundation of prerequisite knowledge among learners. However, the presenter spends the majority of his or her time guiding learners through the activity component of the process. A general rule for a one-hour lesson is: 15 minutes lecture and 45 minutes of activities.

Figure 10.8 Learning environments have become more interactive with time but they still often include lecture sessions.

Active learning is one of the most useful skills a Level II manager can share with a Level I educator. If a presenter's instructional experience has been solely based on delivering lectures, he or may be apprehensive about trying another technique.

Through mentoring, the Level II manager has a unique opportunity to help Level I presenters grow exponentially in their ability to facilitate a meaningful learning experience. Level II managers will need to research active learning strategies and learn and practice them prior to suggesting their use.

Another reason for integrating active learning into lesson plans is its proven effectiveness. To learn more, research **cooperative learning**.[2]

Peer Assistance

Lecturing is a passive, one-way method of instruction that often lacks any real two-way discussion or interaction from students. Students may ask a few questions, but there is often no immediate use of the material being presented. Information may briefly remain in the learners' short-term memory; however, it is soon lost because they did not have to do anything meaningful with it.

Learning is more powerful when students use new information while having meaningful interaction with peers and presenters. When students interact with each other, they are forced (in a positive way) to use the information that they are learning. This increases the probability that the information will be transferred into the learner's long-term memory and be available for future use.

The activity component of a lesson is designed to create the "ah-ha" experience for students. Instead of lecturing the entire time, the presenter guides the process of discovery among students and shares subject matter expert advice as needed. The presenter also ensures that the activity is progressing as designed and interjects pertinent information when appropriate.

Everyone benefits because they are involved in the learning process. Presenters enjoy active learning because they spend less time talking and more time facilitating. A focused room of interacting learners is a more powerful teaching device than a one-way lecture. For example, it can be found that most consumers know that smoke alarms are important. However, many have never had an open discussion with peers about smoke alarms, let alone the tactile opportunity to practice changing a battery or replacing an entire alarm.

Developing a Lesson

Before developing a lesson or planning the specifics of a learning activity, it is important to remember how people learn most effectively. People learn best when they:

- Know what is in it for them.
- Deem a lesson or activity relevant.
- Have mastered the prerequisites.
- Understand what is expected.
- Connect with other people.
- Are challenged to make choices.
- Feel safe about showing what they do and do not know.
- Control the pace, navigation, and delivery.
- Use a process that matches their preferred learning styles.
- Receive information in small segments.
- Receive frequent progress reports.
- Learn things close to the time when they will need them.
- Integrate new knowledge and skills into everyday life.
- Use new knowledge to solve problems.
- Receive encouragement from coaches or mentors.
- Use multisensory domains (see, hear, write, talk, and do it).
- Learn from a variety of styles (discussion followed by stimulation).
- Teach others.
- Receive positive reinforcement for small victories.
- Mess up, but try and try again.
- Just do it.

Source: Internettime.com – Unknown Author

Writing a Lesson Plan

Fire training academies often use lesson plans that are slightly different from those used within school-based learning environments. While the terminology may differ, the goal of any lesson plan remains the same: to provide a logical roadmap so that the instructor can facilitate a postive learning outcome for the student.

Because Level II managers are often responsible for developing lessons that coordinate with programs external to the fire service, the following section focuses on creating school and community-based lesson plans.

School and community-based lesson plans often include the following core components:

- *Lesson title.* Identify the topic on which the lesson will focus.

- *Level of students.* Include a profile of the prospective target audience. This profile includes age, education level, special needs, and baseline knowledge held by students on the subject matter.

- *Background information.* Identify student prerequisite knowledge and skills. This is a statement of what the learner needs to know or be able to do to succeed and accomplish the lesson objective. Up to 70% of learning is dependent on students having the appropriate prerequisites.

- *Lesson goal.* A single sentence stating the intended end result of the lesson.

- *Rationale for lesson.* A short fact-based summary of why the lesson is being presented. The statement should include relevance as to how the lesson content can be applied by the learner in real-world situations.

- *Objectives (also called outcomes).* Succinct statements of what the learner will be able to do as a result of the lesson. Objectives must be measurable and include an appropriate action verb. A balanced lesson includes enough objectives so that all domains of learning are used. (**NOTE:** Each objective should help facilitate a relevent connection between what the student already knows, is currently learning, and will be learning through future lesson objectives. More information on writing objectives follows in the next section.)

- *Time frame.* How long the lesson will take.

- *Materials.* The informational and educational materials that will be needed to process the lesson.

- *Assessment and evaluation.* How the learning objectives will be measured. Examples include observation, questioning, testing, presentation, and performance.

- *Steps to complete the lesson.* A step-by-step guide explaining how to present the lesson, and includes clear and easy-to-follow instructions on how to deliver the lecture and learning activities.

- *Extension activities.* A description of activities that are to be performed after the lesson is completed to extend and refine student knowledge/performance. Examples include student-led home safety inspections, Web-based exploration and reporting, and case study creation/submission.

- *Special instructions to presenter.* Any special information or instructions the developer wishes a presenter to have prior to teaching the lesson.

While a lesson plan guides how a presentation will be delivered, it is not a script that dictates minute by minute actions that are to occur. A good lesson plan is flexible and allows the presenter to incorporate strategies such as active learning.

However, a lesson plan should include enough detail so that another presenter, knowledgable in risk-reduction subject matter, could deliver the lesson without needing to contact the developer for further clarifications.

NOTE: When developing a lesson plan, be sure to include "white space" between sections. Having space between sections allows the user to better visualize the material.

> Conduct internet research on how to develop a lesson plan. As part of your research, examine the Madeline Hunter Lesson Design Model. Her work has stood the test of time and provides a benchmark for comparison with other strategies.

When developing a lesson plan, find a style that best suits the presenters and target audiences. Do not become overwhelmed with the academic terminologies used by many institutions. As long as the basic components (such as those listed in this chapter) are utilized, it does not matter what format is used.

Developing Learning Objectives and Outcomes

A **learning objective** is the learner's knowledge, attitude, and behavior that is expected after the lesson has been completed. Because learning objectives are one of the most important components of lesson development, it is prudent to devote special attention to their design.

As with lesson plans, the internet will provide a wealth of information on how to write learning objectives. In fact, information is so vast that it is easy to become overwhelmed with all the various suggestions available. The broad use of terminology used in the educational world can further intensify one's anxiety.

The following represent general suggestions for writing learning objectives:

1. Be succinct, relevent, specific, and remain consistent with the overall intended outcome of the lesson. A learning objective should be limited to a *single* sentence if possible.

2. State the prerequiste conditions that the learner must have to successfully achieve the objective. If the objective is to have students master a skill, begin the objective with a description of what materials and instruction will be included as a baseline. Example: Given a smoke alarm and provided with guided instruction, the student will be able to demonstrate with 100% accuracy how to replace the alarm's battery.

3. Make sure that the objective is measurable. An objective must include an action verb to make it measurable. Selection of the verb is contingent upon the domain of learning being used. (**NOTE:** In the previous example, the term *demonstrate* highlights the use of the psychomotor domain of learning.)

4. The objective should be achievable by students. Develop objectives that are appropriate for the target audience's abilities. Upon receipt of instruction and (if applicable) skill practice, the learner should be able to achieve the objective.

Developing Learning Activities

A **learning activity** is any component of a lesson requiring students to do something designed to enhance knowledge, attitude, or skill development. Activities are used to facilitate achievement of learning objectives. Their development, placement, and use are important factors related to student performance outcome.

Learning activities are at least as important as the lecture component of a lesson. Active learning represents the most powerful means of assimilating knowledge, modifying attitudes, teaching skills, and ultimately changing behaviors.

A learning activity could be as simple as children testing a smoke alarm or practicing stop, drop, and roll with guided assistance from an educator (**Figure 10.9**). A more complex activity may have an adult group case study a dysfunctional risk-reduction effort that is occurring in a ficticious community.

Learning activities can be designed for individual and small and large group formats. Guided text exploration, case study review, problem solving, interactive discussion, and guided skill practice are examples of learning activities. Because it is desirable for a lesson to incorporate all domains of learning, most will include several activities.

The following represent general suggestions for writing good learning activities:

1. Focus on facilitating achievement of the learning objectives.

2. Extend learning through skill development.

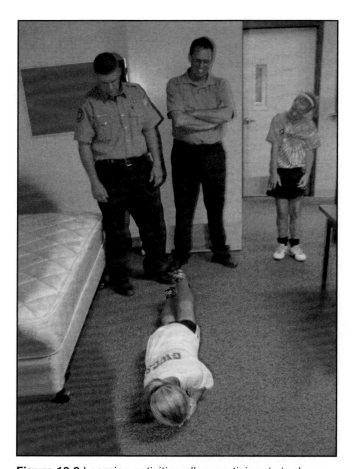

Figure 10.9 Learning activities allow participants to do an action and gain experience with the behaviors needed in specific instances.

3. Be well-structured and organized; actively involve students.

4. Include structured student-to-student interaction.

5. Allow multiple opportunities to process major ideas. The most important points are presented in several different formats so that learners see, hear, and practice the key content of the lesson. This strategy results in increased learning and longer retention.

6. Provide stimulating, relevant, and meaningful interaction.

7. Allocate sufficient time for learning to occur. Learners process information at different rates and levels. Build time into activities so everyone benefits.

Developing Educational Materials

Educational materials can be used to enhance a learner's knowledge on a specific topic. Educational materials include printed matter, audiovisual materials, and props that an educator uses to enhance delivery of a lesson. When considering integration of educational materials into a lesson, the most important factor to examine is how the materials will support the objectives and ultimate outcome of the learning experience.

Although the standard calls for proficiency in developing materials, it is prudent to include information on selection and evaluation of such products. This, in part, is because Level II managers often help select the materials that Level I educators use while delivering lessons.

Selecting Educational Materials

Edgar Dale is often cited as the father of modern media in education. Based on his experience in teaching and observing learners, Dale developed the "Cone of Experience" **(Figure 10.10)**.

The cone's utility in selecting instructional resources and activities is as practical as when Dale created it. According to Dale's research, people generally remember:

- 10% of what they read
- 20% of what they hear
- 30% of what they see
- 50% of what they see and hear (for example, through video)
- 70% of what they say or write
- 90% of what they say and do

The cone is based on the relationships of various educational experiences to real life. The bottom level of the cone, "direct purposeful experiences," represents reality or the closest things to real, everyday

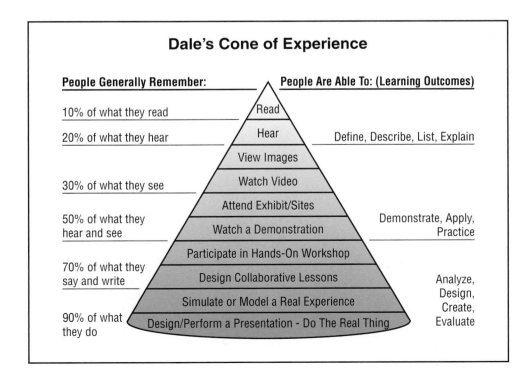

Dale's Cone of Experience

People Generally Remember:

10% of what they read
20% of what they hear
30% of what they see
50% of what they hear and see
70% of what they say and write
90% of what they do

People Are Able To: (Learning Outcomes)

Read
Hear
View Images
Watch Video
Attend Exhibit/Sites
Watch a Demonstration
Participate in Hands-On Workshop
Design Collaborative Lessons
Simulate or Model a Real Experience
Design/Perform a Presentation - Do The Real Thing

Define, Describe, List, Explain

Demonstrate, Apply, Practice

Analyze, Design, Create, Evaluate

Figure 10.10 Dale's Cone of Experience presents a visual representation of how people remember new information.

life. The opportunity for a learner to use a variety of senses such as sight, smell, hearing, touching, and movement is considered in the cone.

Direct experience allows all senses to be used. The more sensory channels that are used, the better the chance that students will learn from the experience. Moving up the cone, fewer senses are involved at each level and it moves the learner a step further away from real-life situations.

Because people are sensory learners, fire and life safety educators need to teach to the senses — especially to the sense of sight. Comprehension increases threefold over simply hearing when a picture replaces words and six-fold when pictures and words are used together.

Materials selected should be consistent with students' level of comprehension, ability, and responsibility. This is why it is important to learn as much as possible about the intended target population before developing a lesson.

Educational materials should be age appropriate, educationally and behaviorally sound, and culturally sensitive. Materials should also be considerate of potential disabilities (cognitive and/or physical) among the proposed target population.

Educational materials do not have to be expensive. Current technology allows educators to develop printed materials in-house. Computers, software,

and visual presentation equipment have become affordable to nearly everyone. Instructional props such as smoke alarms, bike helmets, and life jackets are often provided as in-kind resources from the retail community.

Technology has forever changed how people receive information. As quickly as a new medium is created, another is being developed.

While educational media such as textbooks, fact sheets, and easel pads continue to stand the test of time, use of computer-driven technology has become expected by many audiences. Advanced technology often provides the ability to create reality-based learning experiences. Instead of just talking about how risk occurs, technology can now be employed to create interactive media-based experiences such as cause/effect risk scenarios **(Figure 10.11)**.

Educators should keep aware of emerging technologies for information exchange. While this industry does not command the resources to purchase all the latest presentation gizmos used in the corporate world, message media trends should be watched carefully and budgeted for accordingly.

Evaluating Educational Materials

There are vast differences in the quality of fire and life safety education materials. Whether purchased commercially, adapted from another educator's

Figure 10.11 Computer programs enhance learning by adding interactive sensory experiences.

inventory, or created in-house, all educational materials should be evaluated. There are two types of evaluation techniques for educational materials: qualitative and quantitative.

Qualitative Analysis

A **qualitative analysis** of educational materials can be as simple as reviewing the material against a standard checklist. Several questions should be asked during the qualitative review:

- How well does the material match the specific educational objectives and intended outcome of the lesson?

- Does the material provide the information that is needed to bring about educational change? Does the material explain the action that the learners must take?

- Is the material educationally, technically, and behaviorally accurate?

- Has the material been produced by a reputable organization?

- Can the information be clearly understood by members of the audience?

- Is the material culturally sensitive with respect to the target audience?

While qualitative evaluation is less complex than quantitative analysis, it relies on the educator's experience, judgment, and interpretation of the material. Because this type of evaluation is not statistically based, results are subjective in nature.

Quantitative Analysis

A **quantitative analysis** uses statistical analysis to assess educational materials. The process is more sophisticated than qualitative methods and involves formal testing of the materials. The following section examines the components of quantitative analysis.

Readability is a major consideration in selecting written fire and life safety education materials. A seventh- to eighth-grade reading level is typical for adults in the United States. Daily newspapers are often written at a middle-school reading level. When evaluating readability levels of print materials, pay attention to the following:

- Look for sentences written in the active voice. Active sentences are shorter and easier to read than passive sentences.

  — *Active:* Steve taught the audience how to test smoke alarms.

  — *Passive:* The audience was taught how to test smoke detectors by Steve.

- Look for short sentences with straightforward subject and verb construction. Short sentences are easier to read than long sentences. Dependent clauses or phrases make reading more difficult.

  — *Easy:* The local smoke alarm ordinance requires interconnected units. The ordinance took effect on January 1.

  — *More difficult:* The local smoke alarm ordinance, which requires individual devices to be interconnected, became effective on January 1.

- Look for a majority of one- or two-syllable words. Generally, words of one or two syllables are easier to read (and comprehend) than words of three or more syllables.

Before selecting or developing text-based educational materials, the Level II manager should conduct an Internet search and examine evaluation tools on readability. The following are two trusted evaluation tools: Flesch Reading Ease and Flesch-Kincaid Grade Level Index[3] and the Gunning Index[4].

The Flesch Index is based on a 100-word passage of the written material. This index counts the average number of words per sentence and the average number of syllables in the passage. Grade level and reading ease are matched to each other. In contrast, the Gunning FOG Index combines the overall sentence length with the number of words containing more than one syllable per sentence.

Considerations Before Developing Educational Materials

Level II managers are able to develop their own customized educational materials using the technology available in most office settings, instead of purchasing materials from a commercial source. While the interest in developing materials is often related to saving money or giving materials a local flavor, a potential developer should consider the following:

1. **How much will it really cost to develop materials?** Production costs may be lower than a purchase price. However, the developer's time has value, and production costs do not include the time spent creating the material and coordinating production.

Figure 10.12 Good educational materials may require a collaborative effort within a department, thereby increasing the production costs.

Production costs also do not include the cost of mistakes. Mistakes happen all too easily and range from factual errors and typos to picking an unreadable combination of paper and ink. Mistakes cost both time and money to fix **(Figure 10.12)**.

2. **How important is local flavor?** Local flavor, while desirable, may be a luxury that fire and life safety educators simply cannot afford. Options for adding a local feeling to materials include stamping the name of the fire department or other local sponsor on printed material.

3. **What is the motivation to create the materials?** If the developer deems it necessary to publish current information on a risk issue specific to his or her home community, consider in-house development. In-house materials allow the developer to effectively focus on specific problems and proposed solutions. In contrast, consider a commercially produced or non-copyrighted web-based source if it can accomplish the same purpose at less cost.

4. **Does the fire and life safety educator have the technical knowledge, experience, and equipment to create materials?** This important point must be considered carefully. First, poorly designed education materials may not enhance student knowledge. Second, a substandard product will reflect poorly upon the developer's organization. Third, using a product that is not educationally and behaviorally sound could create a liability issue for the organization.

While purchasing educational materials from a trusted professional source may be expensive, these organizations and companies employ trained staff to help ensure that their products are appropriate for the intended use. In addition, reputable commercial sources will also outline suggested parameters for use, such as age and developmental levels.

Last, but not least, the equipment needed to create materials is not a small investment. While computers, software, printers, cameras, and presentation equipment have become more affordable, it might not be fiscally wise to invest in these components if they are not going to be used very often because they will become outdated quickly.

5. **How will the educator assess his or her ability to create materials? Who will provide backup for technical questions, review, and proofing?**

These two questions are presented in tandem because their answers are similar: Ask for review, feedback, and guidance from an experienced, reliable, and educated source. Local professional educators, colleges, and technical writers are excellent resources for nonbiased reviews of draft work.

Preparing Educational Materials

Experienced educators know the importance of using combined message media. Because technology has made it easier for educators to develop custom educational materials, it is wise to review basic guidelines for creating both print and audiovisual products.

Print Materials

Five basic elements make up the design of print material: text, illustrations, white space, paper, and ink **(Figure 10.13)**. The goal of print materials is to deliver information that an audience will read and remember. As a result, the product's design must appeal to the busy reader.

Today's readers share several characteristics:

- Scan written material, rather than read word for word.

- Expect short written pieces.

- Prefer visual to print materials. They rely on illustrations, headlines, captions, charts, graphs, and subheads for quick access to print information.

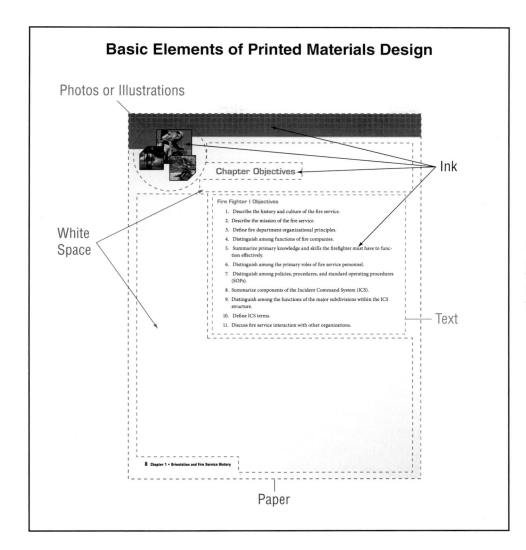

Basic Elements of Printed Materials Design

Photos or Illustrations

Chapter Objectives

Fire Fighter I Objectives

1. Describe the history and culture of the fire service.
2. Describe the mission of the fire service.
3. Define fire department organizational principles.
4. Distinguish among functions of fire companies.
5. Summarize primary knowledge and skills the firefighter must have to function effectively.
6. Distinguish among the primary roles of fire service personnel.
7. Distinguish among policies, procedures, and standard operating procedures (SOPs).
8. Summarize components of the Incident Command System (ICS).
9. Distinguish among the functions of the major subdivisions within the ICS structure.
10. Define ICS terms.
11. Discuss fire service interaction with other organizations.

White Space

Ink

Text

Paper

8 Chapter 1 • Orientation and Fire Service History

Figure 10.13 The five elements of printed materials design work together to present information in an attractive and functional format.

- Use subheads and captions to gain an overview of the information. In order to effectively communicate with this audience, the text should:

  — Be concise and provide specific examples.

  — Use shortened sentences and paragraphs for those who would rather read several short messages than one long one.

  — Use appropriate color and illustrative design to reach visually oriented readers.

Text

Follow these simple guidelines for the text of print materials:

- In general, follow the KISS acronym: **K**eep **I**t **S**hort and **S**imple.

- Use small words, short sentences, short paragraphs, and active voice.

- Assume that the reader will only read part of the written material. Put the most important information first.

- Use headlines, subheads, and captions.

- Supplement the text with illustrations.

Explaining complex subjects, such as fire safety, in simple language can be difficult. Start by getting complex information on paper and then editing the draft for simplicity. Several drafts may be needed to achieve the goal.

Developers also must decide how to present words so that they will be read. These decisions involve the type of font, type size, line length, and type alignment:

- *Type font.* Readability is the prime consideration in picking a font. Familiar fonts are generally more readable than unfamiliar ones. Many popular fonts are used in printing materials. The font should not only be readable but it should also reflect the purpose and complement the design of the printed piece.

- *Type size.* Type size also influences readability. Type is measured in points. A higher point represents a larger type size **(Figure 10.14)**. Twelve-point type is commonly used when writing a letter. When selecting type size, always consider the needs of the prospective learners. If the audience includes visually impaired members, consider increasing the point size.

- *Line length.* The ideal length of a line of type is related to how much material the eye can see without moving. The ideal length is 40 to 50 characters per line. Lines between 35 and 55 characters are within the acceptable range. Many publications designers choose to err on the narrow side.

- *Type alignment.* Type can be aligned in four ways: left justified (also called *ragged right*), centered, right justified (also called *ragged left*), or justified. Although headlines, subheads, and captions may be aligned in any of these ways, body text is usually left justified (ragged right) or justified **(Figure 10.15)**.

Special Needs Among Target Populations

Developers should always consider the potential for special needs among target populations. Print media that is overstimulating may distract a challenged reader away from the intended message. Target populations with visual deficiencies may not be able to read small print or focus on colorful text placed on glossy paper. When considering special needs, the basic strategy of appropriate-sized black Arial font on white buff paper is a very reader-friendly combination.

Illustrations

Illustrations serve four important purposes when used within print message media:

- Link the intended message to the target audience.
- State (or reinforce) the message.
- Persuade, reassure, or potentially alarm the reader.
- Move the reader's eye.

Many kinds of illustrations, but especially photographs, are strongly directional. A well-placed illustration can help guide the reader into the page.

Photographs are powerful, but they may increase the production costs of printed material. Check with a professional for typical production costs. Line drawings, diagrams, cartoons, icons, tables, charts, and graphs are acceptable alternatives to photographs. Type can also serve as an illustration. A boxed checklist, subhead, or quotation is still type but serves as an illustration by creating variation in the layout of a page.

Illustrations need to be strategically placed for maximum effect. Advertising studies have shown that a reader pays more attention to certain parts of the page than others. The upper left-hand corner of the page receives the most attention. Therefore, in most instances, the most important visual should be placed in the upper left-hand corner.

White Space

White space on printed material is not necessarily wasted space. Used wisely, white space makes a page appear light, open, and accessible. Roughly 40 percent of a page should be illustrations and white space while no more than 60 percent of a page should be text.

Publication designers use a "grid" to structure the parts of the page that will be devoted to white space. Desktop publishing programs usually provide several grids from which to choose. Typical grids are one-, two-, or three-column formats, with uniform margins and space between columns **(Figure 10.16)**. The three-column format is the most flexible because type and illustrations can be arranged across one, two, or all three columns.

Paper Selection

Choosing the paper on which to print is both a design and financial decision. From the design standpoint, the most important consideration is that paper and ink work together. The design goal of paper and ink is to have the highest possible contrast — for the simple reason that contrast helps readability. A bright white paper offers the greatest contrast with most inks. Light-colored paper with contrasting ink is especially important for materials that will be copied or faxed.

Additionally, the developer should check on any applicable department policies that may require use of recycled or recyclable paper. After selecting the

Examples of Font Type and Size

Font Type	12 point	16 point	24 point
Arial	Sample	Sample	Sample
Courier New	Sample	Sample	Sample
Times New Roman	Sample	Sample	Sample

Figure 10.14 Examples of how the size of a font affects its appearance and readability.

Examples of Four Types of Alignments

Flush Left Ragged Right

Text can be aligned
in several different ways.
This text has flush left,
ragged right alignment.

Flush Right Ragged Left

Text can be aligned
in several different ways.
This text has flush right,
ragged left alignment.

Centered

Text can be aligned
in several different ways.
This text has
centered alignment.

J u s t i f i e d

Text can be aligned
in several different ways.
This text has
justified alignment.

Figure 10.15 Text alignment can affect the readability of blocks of text.

Typical One-, Two-, and Three-Column Formats

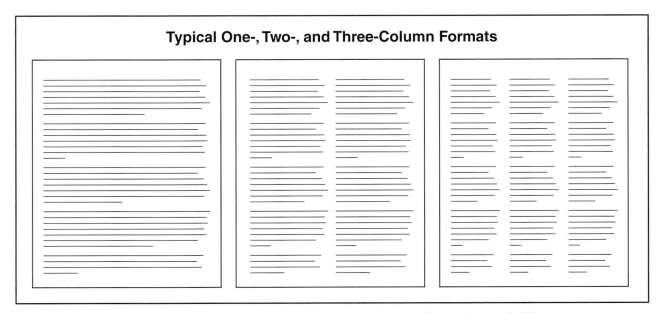

Figure 10.16 The grid structure allows designers flexibility in arranging text, illustrations, and white space.

paper color and weight — or narrowing the selection to a few different types — ask for a paper sample and get a written cost estimate before making a final selection.

Ink Selection

Red is a popular color with the fire service and is an effective attention-getter. However, red is the first color to become obscured as a person's vision deteriorates.

Educational materials can be one-color, two-color, or four-color (sometimes called full-color) printing **(Figure 10.17)**. The numbers refer to the number of colors of inks used on the page.

Audiovisual Materials

While technology-driven media have not yet completely dominated the learning environment, they certainly have influenced how billions of people receive information. As developers of educational material, Level II managers must be literate in current and emerging strategies to effectively convey information to potential learners.

Because what most people learn comes to them through a combination of visual and audio media, integrating audiovisual experience is an especially useful educational tool. At development time of this manual, Microsoft PowerPoint® was the lead-

ing product of choice used by Level II managers for creating custom audiovisual presentations. Product versions featured options such as text display, along with photo and video integration capabilities. These functions are used to enhance lessons for all audiences from children through older adults.

While easel pads are still found in use in adult continuing education, emerging technology introduced computer-driven SMART boards featuring wall-size projection capabilities. Undoubtedly, each passing year will bring more advancing technology.

Many developers insist on cramming as much information as possible on a single slide or video frame. The intended message often becomes lost in the sea of words, diagrams, or pictures **(Figure 10.18)**. (**NOTE:** It may be beneficial for Level II managers to attend a class for creating custom audiovisual presentations in PowerPoint®. Most colleges as well as many private training sources offer training programs on PowerPoint®.)

Use of Visuals

As previously mentioned, the appropriate use of visual aids will greatly enhance a presentation. These resources may be developed from a variety of sources and used in a range of media.

One-, Two-, and Four-Color Print Process

 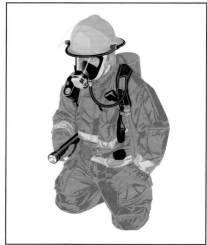 

Figure 10.17 Adding color to illustrations and text is an effective technique to gain attention, but more color is more expensive.

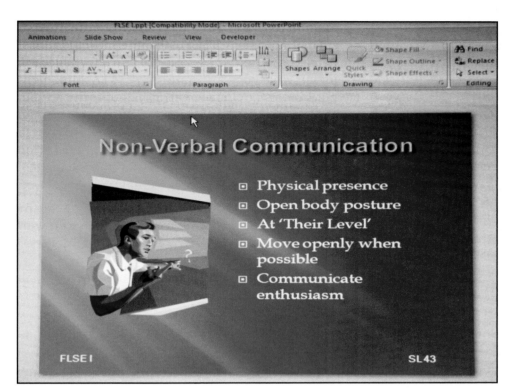

Figure 10.18 PowerPoint® must be used carefully in order to be effective.

Photos

Digital technology and laser printing capabilities have nearly replaced conventionally produced photographs. Digital pictures can be viewed instantly, enhanced as needed, and printed within minutes.

Because digital cameras and printers have become affordable to most educators, developers of educational materials should become familiar with how to capture, enhance, and produce photographs. This skill is important because digital technology makes many options available for using photos. Examples include:

- Printing custom photographs for use on display boards

- Enlarging photos for use during a lesson

- Integrating digital images into PowerPoint® or other media

Before setting out on a photography excursion, take time to consider what photos will best suit the needs of the presentation. The answers will likely come after asking how the images will support the objectives and ultimate outcome of the learning experience.

Since photographs can dramatically enhance an educational lesson, they are used often and with good reason. While it is tempting to search the Web for photographs, it can be very time consuming. Further, the images may be copyright protected.

Appropriately equipped, many educators are choosing to produce their own photographs **(Figure 10.19)**. While Photography 101 is beyond the scope of this manual, the following are several suggestions for obtaining quality photographs.

- *Get close-up shots.* Zero in on the person or object you want to capture.

Figure 10.19 With some practice, an educator can produce high quality photographs that are exactly on target for the department's objectives.

- *Do not pose the subjects.* Let them act naturally and catch the shot.

- *Use outside lighting when possible.* If outdoors, make sure that the sun is behind the photographer when taking the picture.

- *Be cognizant of available lighting sources during indoor photography.* Take a few moments to rearrange lighting so that the object of the photo is clearly illuminated.

- *When taking images of an overall scene, include a foreground subject.* This helps the viewer get a better sense of the distance or size of the object.

- *Avoid a cluttered background.* Background staging is a very important component in getting a good photo.

- *Hold the camera steady.* This is an important part of getting a quality shot. A tripod may help. Alternatively, prop your elbows on a stationary object to help steady the camera.

- *Try to shoot things that seem out of the ordinary.* Creativity is a key to taking good pictures.

- *Think about what type of picture would best convey your message.* Do this if you are taking shots for a particular purpose.

- *Experiment!* Where you hold the camera can create unique, unexpected, and exciting results.

NOTE: With digital cameras, the cost of film and developing is minimal because only the desired photos are taken to this step. Take advantage of the digital camera's large storage capacity and get several shots of each setup using different angles and camera settings. This does not cost more and generates a variety of options to choose from when selecting images to be used in educational materials.

Finally, before taking photographs, always be conscious of privacy. Most schools prohibit taking photos of students unless legal guardians have given advance permission in writing. In addition, privacy laws influence what is appropriate in the realm of emergency scene photography.

Video and Audio Production

Reality-based learning experiences are increasingly popular. Technology has led to production resources that are within an organization's financial reach. A wide range of affordable high-resolution devices exist for developers to capture, edit, and integrate video footage into educational presentations.

Because many reality-based TV shows use footage shot by handheld devices, society is more tolerant of "nonsterile" production efforts. The term *nonsterile* means that footage was not obtained using a high-end camera on a tripod within a production studio. This is *not* to say that the footage is unprofessional. It is just more casual and reality-based. Follow the general suggestions provided for photography when considering use of custom-created video production. If audio is to be used, additional pre-production planning is needed.

Many devices that record video also do well capturing audio. While the quality of microphones integrated within devices is always improving, it may be worthwhile considering purchase of a system to professionally capture sound. It is possible to connect a remote microphone that can help limit background noise should narration be desired.

Consider asking for advice or assistance from the local media production specialists. Assistance can also be sought from commercial broadcasting companies or private sources. Many communities have universities that offer higher education opportunities in media development or broadcast engineering.

Another option is the ability for developers to record narrative and integrate pictures or video to produce a custom media presentation. This strategy is often preferred by developers because it can lead to a very professional outcome. Powerful learning can occur when a person can see how something happens or is done.

When creating a custom-made audiovisual presentation, the following should be done:

1. Consider how the proposed presentation will impact the objectives and intended outcome of the lesson.

2. Write an outline script before shooting video. The outline script covers the main subject matter proposed for the presentation.

3. Design the pattern of the presentation so that it will proceed in a logical sequence or "flow."

4. Always begin with a dynamic introduction that explains what the student will see and learn as a result of the presentation.

5. Construct several short video segments (less than 5 minutes each) that build a body of information leading the audience to the ultimate goal of the presentation. Include only the most important and useful information in each segment.

6. Break information into segments; this helps maintain viewer interest. This strategy also permits the learner to construct meaning from the information and allows for inclusion of points within the presentation where student/instructor interaction can take place or learning activities can be introduced.

7. Develop a review/conclusion segment where the presentation's objectives are summarized.

8. Select a narrator or host who is compatible to the profile of potential target audiences. Be cognizant of the age, gender, and culture of the audience. Be sure that the narrator speaks clearly and reads at an appropriate rate based upon the characteristics of the audience.

Use Focus Groups and Pilot Test Materials

Developing educational materials often requires a substantial investment of time and, in some cases, money. To help ensure the investment will perform as designed, it is always wise to consider use of a focus group and pilot test a draft version of materials before final production. To review the concept of focus groups and pilot testing in this chapter, see the earlier section titled Design Age-Appropriate Materials.

Instructional Props

Instructional props include any type of physical object designed to enhance the outcome of a lesson through its demonstration or use. An educational prop could be as simple as using a smoke alarm for demonstration purposes. Props could be as comprehensive as allowing learners to tour a fire-damaged home under controlled conditions.

Used appropriately, instructional props can offer dynamic enhancement to an educator's presentation **(Figure 10.20)**. Props offer the learner visual and often "hands on" interaction with the topic being studied. When using an instructional prop, it is important to preface its use by explaining to the audience what knowledge is to be gained from the prop's use. The learner must connect relevance between the lesson and the instructional prop. This is most important when using props in a primary school environment

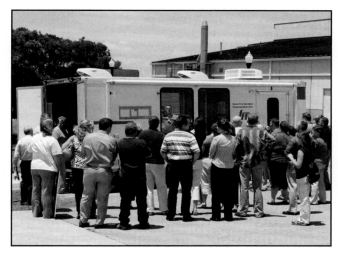

Figure 10.20 Instructional props like FPP's Home Fire Sprinkler Demonstration Unit can add value to abstract information.

or with high-risk audiences. The educator does not want the prop to overshadow the intended message and learning outcome.

If the educator chooses to use an instructional prop that relies upon mechanized equipment, he or she must be familiar with how to operate it. Knowing when and how to use an instructional prop can build credibility for the instructor. It can also prevent an embarrassing situation. It is also important to perform preventive maintenance so that equipment is always ready to be used.

In addition, be sure the prop is appropriate for the audience. Showing a group of Rotarians a puppet show may not be as effective as allowing hands-on examination of a variety of smoke alarms. In contrast, showing pre-school students a carbon monoxide alarm may not effectively convey the intended message.

When considering use of instructional props, be aware of space and storage requirements. If conducting mobile instruction, remember that each prop needs transportation and storage space. Be sure to have enough props so everyone is permitted a "hands on" experience when possible.

Designing a Fire and Life Safety Education Program

A fire and life safety **education program** is a series of lessons and activities designed to impact a specific risk-reduction outcome. School and community-based life safety programs are often used in tandem to support broad-based risk-reduction strategies.

This section will provide readers with information on how to enhance the design of school and community-based educational programs. School and community-based programs are defined as the following:

- A school-based program is a series of lessons that support specific outcome objectives of a curriculum.

- A community-based program is a series of lessons and activities that support an overall risk-reduction strategy.

School-Based Curriculum

Designing a school-based curriculum involves selecting and organizing content that will ultimately be presented to students. Curriculum objectives are the intended outcomes of programs that support the educational goals of a curriculum, and the content is positioned to support curriculum objectives.

Fire and injury prevention is often included in a health or life-skills curriculum. Collaboration with school officials may afford the Level II manager the opportunity to simply enhance and expand upon what is already in place. In addition, Level II managers can help create a win-win situation when they use the following strategy:

- Examine the essential curriculum.

- Help build programs that impact health and well-being of students and families.

- Offer assistance with the design and delivery of lessons.

- Provide resources as available.

Working With School Officials

The following represents general suggestions for working with school officials to enhance fire and life safety education curricula at the local level.

1. **Conduct research first.** Network with other educators to determine the level of fire and injury prevention being taught in their schools. Find out where risk reduction is positioned in their school's essential curriculum.

2. **Meet with local school officials.** Determine what fire safety and injury prevention material is already in place within the essential curriculum. The content would likely be part of a health or life-skills curriculum.

3. **Provide a rationale of why fire and injury prevention should be included as part of the essential curriculum.** Show baseline statistics of current local risk(s) and potential outcomes that could be realized through enhanced educational efforts.

   NOTE: Level II managers should possess mastery level subject matter knowledge about how to effectively analyze and reduce community risks. When approached in a professional manner, most school officials will consider collaborative efforts with the emergency services.

4. **Examine the objectives, content, and intended outcomes of all lessons if fire and injury prevention is already included in the essential curriculum.** Work with school officials to help enhance the design of existing curricula. Provide resources such as subject-matter knowledge, educational support materials, and assistance with delivering lessons.

5. **Work collaboratively with school officials.** In the rare case that fire and injury prevention is not part of the essential curriculum, find ways that risk reduction can be integrated into core subject content.

6. **Consider developing or purchasing a program that is taught by professional teachers.** This may be necessary if a fire and rescue agency does not have a safety educator. Firefighters and EMS staff can supplement lesson content by visiting schools to demonstrate equipment and provide case study discussions **(Figure 10.21)**.

7. **Examine how the program will be evaluated.** Ensure that evaluation mechanisms such as pretests and posttests, skill observations, and home extension activities are being conducted. Evaluation is essential to program monitoring, future enhancements, and overall outcome.

Figure 10.21 There are many benefits to working within an existing school structure.

Student Performance Requirements

The essential curriculum outlines the core content and learning objectives for all subject matter presented within a school system. It is divided into sections such as language arts, mathematics, science, and health.

The scope of a school system's essential curriculum can be likened to a fire department's standard operating procedure. It provides a precise overview of what topics will be taught, when, and how.

Performance-Based Outcome

Performance-based outcome is an essential component of schools in the United States. The federal "No Child Left Behind"[5] legislation dramatically influ-

Options to Consider When Designing School-Based Fire and Injury Prevention Programs

Collaboration with school officials and review of existing primary-age health curriculums led one community to custom-develop a program called the *Seven Lessons on Fire Safety*. The seven specific lessons provide support to the outcome of a health curriculum.

The lessons are taught by classroom teachers. Support materials are supplied by the county's volunteer firefighters' association. Firefighters visit schools after the lessons have been taught to reinforce the program's core outcomes.

Upon completion of prerequisite lessons, students will be able to identify, explain, and demonstrate the components of a comprehensive home fire-safety strategy.

The seven lessons support the following health curriculum objective:

Seven Lessons on Fire Safety

Lesson 1: Staying away from things that become hot.

Lesson 2: There are good and bad fires.
Fire is a tool and not a toy.

Lesson 3: If on fire — stop, drop, and roll.

Lesson 4: Smoke alarms — Important safety tools.

Lesson 5: Crawl low under smoke.

Lesson 6: Making a plan in case of fire.

Lesson 7: Dial 9-1-1 for help in an emergency.

Section 8: Evaluation component.

enced how schools evaluate student performance. This includes the health and well-being of students.

Performance standards require that students meet grade-specific academic benchmarks set by state and federal agencies. Meeting student performance standards is a determinant that affects an entire school system.

Facilitating student achievement of performance standards often places teachers under great stress. This, in part, is due to the multitude of demanding outcomes and the wide intellectual profiles of students.

Commercially Developed Products

NFPA's® *Learn Not to Burn*[6] and *Risk Watch*[7] are commercial alternatives to developing in-house curriculum materials. NFPA® is a trusted source of educationally sound and behaviorally correct media.

Conduct a cost/benefit analysis when considering development versus purchasing curriculums and materials. If qualified staff is not available to develop products, consider options such as commercial products or materials adapted from other school systems.

Understanding the determinants that influence a school's operation is insight that Level II managers must possess.

Determinants Affecting Schools and Curriculum

Determinants are factors that influence how an organization develops and operates. The following represent determinants that often have great influence over nearly every local school:

- Federal and state academic performance standards

- Interpersonal relations and cooperation among administrators, principals, and teachers

- Relationships between the emergency services and schools

- Political influences from various elected bodies and special interest groups

- Various academic and performance levels of students attending the school

- Exceptional students: learning challenged, talented and gifted, and physically challenged

Community-Based Programs

A community-based program is a series of integrated actions that support an overall risk-reduction strategy. A single program may have several components such as safety lessons, outreach activities, and media saturation. Activities that support risk reduction, such as smoke alarm installations, are often included in community-based programs **(Figure 10.22)**.

Figure 10.22 The installation of smoke alarms is a simple and cost-effective strategy that yields positive results.

Designing A Community-Based Smoke Alarm Program

In one community, a review of statistics showed that forty people perished in fires during the period studied. Smoke alarms were absent or nonworking in all cases. Residential property loss from fire was nearly five million dollars. Estimates from previous community surveys suggest that at least 30 percent of city homes had nonfunctional smoke alarms.

Led by a Level III administrator and planning team, a fire department in this community created a risk-reduction strategy that called for a 90 percent reduction in fatal fires and a 50 percent drop in significant fires (greater than $1,000.00 damage) over a ten-year period.

Development of a comprehensive smoke alarm program was selected as one of the interventions to be included in the strategy. A Level II manager was given the task of designing the smoke alarm program so that outreach, impact, and outcome could be demonstrated.

Problem Statement
Residents are dying from fires in homes that lack working smoke alarms.

Proposed Program
A neighborhood visitation and smoke alarm program. Firefighters will canvass confirmed high-risk neighborhoods to personally discuss leading fire causes and solutions with residents. Smoke alarm evaluation will be offered and free installation provided as needed.

Proposed Outreach
The community includes 10,000 homes. Firefighters will visit 2,000 homes annually. Resident contact rate is expected to be 40 percent. Rotation will ensure that all homes are visited at least once every five years.

Proposed Impact
Firefighters expect to install smoke alarms in approximately 750 homes annually. Six months after the alarms were installed, two firefighters will conduct an in-person, follow-up impact survey in 50 of the homes in which alarms were installed. It is projected that 90 percent of alarms will be found to be operational.

Proposed Outcome
Firefighters envision a 90 percent reduction in fatal fires and a 50 percent drop in significant fires (greater than $1,000.00 damage) over a ten-year period. The benchmark coordinates with the department's overall risk-reduction strategy.

Resources
Firefighters will educate residents on leading fire risks, install lithium-battery smoke alarms, and provide instruction on testing and replacement. Alarms will be purchased through combined support from service organizations and a federally funded block grant. Installation equipment will be provided at no cost from local retail outlets.

Marketing Strategy
Residents need to know that the program exists. In addition to neighborhood canvassing, the fire department will publicize the program through combined media saturation.

Just as in school programs, community-based efforts must be well organized and follow a structured delivery process. This process involves planning.

Level III administrators are responsible for designing the broad-based strategies aimed at lowering community risk. As a component of that process, Level II managers design programs to support risk-reduction strategies. Good planning and organizing skills are key ingredients to successful community-based risk-reduction programs.

Revising an Educational Program

The goal of educational programs is to facilitate achievement of risk-reduction objectives. Level II managers often develop the educational programs that are delivered by presenters. They also determine where programs fit within broad-based risk-reduction strategies. Because educational programs are used to impart knowledge, they must remain accurate, current, and effective.

Revision of an existing program is sometimes necessary to accomplish program goals, especially if the program is designed for ongoing delivery over time. The need to revise an educational program is driven by several factors:

- Objective risk analysis identifies the need to modify programs because of a change in the occurrence of specific risk issues.

- Program content, materials, and delivery methodolgies need to be updated to remain current for use.

- A credible stakeholder or special interest group has valid suggestions for updating or modifying a program.

Evaluation identifies when the program's intended outcomes are not being achieved. **Program revision** occurs as part of the evaluation process. Because evaluation should be an ongoing process, the previously listed determinants may influence the need to modify a program at any time throughout its life cycle.

The ultimate goal of school and community-based educational programs is to attain higher-order outcomes such as safer people and communities. However, these higher-order goals cannot be achieved until lesson and program objectives have been successfully reached. If evaluation identifies that lesson or program objectives are not being met, the next step must be to determine why. The following section presents factors that should be considered if evaluation identifies that a school-based program is not reaching its intended outcome.

Revising School-Based Programs

Six components should be examined if evaluation identifies that outcomes are not being met within school-based programs:

- Presenters
- Students
- Program content
- Instructional materials
- Evaluation instruments
- School system determinants

Summary of Evaluating Performance

The following highlights how the evaluation of performance is measured:

- **Knowledge Gain.** Pretests and posttests are the gold standard of measuring knowledge gain. Pretests are used to determine baseline student knowledge before instruction or information exchange is presented. Posttests, administered after the topic presentation, are compared with pretest results to evaluate knowledge gain.

- **Skill Performance.** Best measured by direct observation of student performance.

- **Behavioral Change and Environmental Modifications.** Both can be measured through telephone, paper-based, or e-mail surveys. The most effective medium is direct observation.

Examining Determinants Before Revising a Program

The first step to revising a school-based program is determining if revision is necessary. Developers should examine test data, instructor evaluations, comments from schools, and student feedback to identify whether deficiencies are present.

Finding the root cause of a deficiency is the next step of a revision process. The following are factors to look at when examining deficiencies that are occurring in a school-based educational program.

Presenters

If the problem is instructor-specific, retraining should be targeted instead of program overhaul. Level II managers should provide presenters with clear direction of how lessons are to be processed. Level II managers should look for the following factors when determining deficiencies in educational programs:

- Is the issue instructor-specific or does it involve multiple presenters?

- Examine the subject-matter knowledge level and presentation abilities of the instructor.

- Examine the instructor's understanding and interpretation of material.

- Is the instructor presenting the material as designed?

- What is the attitude of the presenter toward the subject matter?

Problems identified among multiple presenters deserve special consideration. In addition to speaking with these presenters, the Level II manager should carefully examine how the lesson or program is organized. If multiple presenters are having difficulty, consider enhancing the lesson plan's instructions. The ultimate goal of lessons and programs are to support higher-order curriculum objectives.

Students

If the root factors are found to be student-driven, strategies targeting the affected groups may resolve the problem. Discussion with presenters and teachers combined with modified lesson plans may prove successful at improving outcomes.

If the deficiencies are occurring among an entire school or system, maybe students do not possess prerequisite information needed to process a learning activity or demonstrate a skill. Perhaps students are not receiving information due to a chaotic learning environment in the classroom or they do not have a support system at home. Whatever the determinant, the issue demands immediate collaboration with school officials.

Program Content

Failure to use age-appropriate content can result in a program that is either too difficult or not challenging enough for learners. All learners demand information that is both current and relevant to their needs.

Managers should monitor local risks to ensure that program content remains consistent with their communities' needs. Finally, the content of all facets of the program must be accurate. Any of the previously mentioned deficiencies warrant close examination and strong consideration for program revisions.

Instructional Materials

Instructional materials include books, printed handouts, media products, skill training aids, and props. As with program content, it is important to remain aware of factors that drive the need to revise, update, or replace instructional materials.

Materials must not only be educationally and behaviorally sound, they should be safe for use among intended target populations. Learners should also find the materials appealing to their preferred style of learning. The manager should determine the following factors:

- Is the issue specific to one item or a group of materials?

- Are the materials age-appropriate?

- Do students find the materials relevant to their needs?

- Are the materials applicable to local need?

Evaluation Instruments

If test results are identifying deficiencies within a lesson or program, examine the test first. Identify which test questions are not being answered correctly by students. In the case of written tests, it could simply be a poorly written question.

If components of skill training are not being performed correctly by students, examine the prerequisite knowledge and sequence of instruction that leads the learner to perform the skill. Perhaps the students are lacking the prerequisite knowledge or skill demonstration required for a successful outcome. These types of issues can be resolved by correcting this deficiency.

Close examination of the evaluation instrument and program are in order when results indicate that the majority of students are not performing well. The first step is to make sure the instrument is objectively evaluating the program content it is designed to monitor.

Asking for help from an experienced evaluator may be a prudent strategy to employ. If the testing mechanism proves valid, the manager must search for other determinants that are affecting learner performance, and some form of program revision should be considered.

School System Determinants

School system determinants have direct influence over educational programs. In the case of the outcome-sensitive school environment, professional educators are required to prove knowledge gain among students in nearly all subject areas. This creates an excellent opportunity for the outcome of life safety programs to be monitored. Program content can then be modified according to need.

The pressure on schools to meet federally mandated outcome standards can create a challenging situation. Educational priorities often shift as standards for academic performance increase. This determinant can affect specific teachers, groups of educators, schools, and entire school systems.

If school-based determinants are negatively impacting the outcome of safety lessons or programs, managers should not resort to a confrontational or threatening approach. This reaction will only create an adversarial relationship with the school system.

Regardless of what issue a school-based determinant has created, it should be addressed in a professional manner. Collaborate with school officials to modify, reposition, or even revise injury prevention curriculums so that integration with the system's essential curriculum is accomplished. The following questions can be used as a guide for revising or modifying curriculum:

● Is the issue related to a specific teacher?
● Is the issue related to a group of teachers?
● Does the deficiency involve one school or a group of schools?
● Is the deficiency occurring system-wide?

Revising Community-Based Programs

A community-based program is a series of integrated actions that support an overall risk-reduction strategy. A single program may have several components such as safety lessons, outreach activities, and media saturation.

Community-based programs should be designed so that outreach, impact, and measurable outcomes can be demonstrated. Gathering baseline information before a program starts is the only way that success can be accurately measured after it has begun.

Measuring, evaluating, and revising community-based programs can sometimes be more challenging than school-based efforts for the following reasons:

● Community-based programs often target a wider profile of prospective learners.
● School-based learning environments are easier to control.
● Competition for capturing consumer attention is fierce.

Three levels of performance should be examined when evaluating a community-based program: outreach, impact, and outcome **(Table 10.1)**.

● *Program outreach* is evaluated by studying how well the program's content is saturating the intended target populations. It is measured by counting the number of lessons or messages delivered, people reached, and materials disseminated.
● *Program impact* is determined by use of evaluation tools such as written tests and surveys to measure knowledge gain, behavioral change, and environmental modifications among target populations.

Table 10.1
Three Levels of Performance

Type:	Evaluated By:	Measured By:
Outreach	Studying how well the program's content is saturating the intended target populations	Counting the number of lessons or messages delivered, people reached, and materials disseminated
Impact	Written tests and surveys	Knowledge gains, behavioral changes, and environmental modifications among target populations
Outcome	Monitoring changes in risk-specific data	Reductions in the number of incidents, injuries, and deaths caused by the risk the program is addressing

- *Program outcome* is evaluated by monitoring changes in risk-specific data. A long-term reduction in the number of incidents, injuries, and deaths caused by the risk the program is addressing is an example of measurable outcome.

Evaluating program outreach, impact, and outcome provides a profile of an educational program's effectiveness. This information creates a rationale for Level II managers to consider program revision if performance benchmarks are not being met.

Ways to measure the effectiveness of an educational program include the following:

- Pretesting and posttesting learners
- Presenter evaluations
- Post-lesson surveys
- Direct observation
- In-person discussion with target populations
- Data analysis

Several of the components identified as potentially problematic with school-based curriculums may also present a challenge with community-based programs. These components include the following:

- Presenters
- Target population
- Program content
- Evaluation instruments

The root cause analysis and solutions are similar and may be reviewed in the previous section. The following section overviews additional hurdles specific to community-based programs:

- Delivery media
- Community-based determinants

Delivery Media

Message media saturation is a recommended way to inform target populations about the existence of educational programs. It is also used to suggest changes in behavior that support risk reduction.

Delivery media includes print, electronic, and broadcast formats. The effectiveness of delivery media can be evaluated when the manager will:

- Determine if the message reached the intended target populations and if the target populations understood the messages and directions.

- Examine the initiative's media components if target populations are not responding to the directives of an educational program. Lack of response may indicate that they are unaware of the program.

- Use informal surveys among target groups to help identify whether an educational program's content has been received and understood. When consumers seek the services of a program, ask how they learned about the initiative and what prompted them to make contact with your agency.

- Present media in formats that are appealing and understandable. Media should be age and culturally sensitive. This becomes especially important when considering an audience's special needs or language variations.

- Consider timing and placement of information. Information directed at older adults may not reach the population if only aired on a radio station with a rock music format. In contrast, a campaign focusing on Hispanic females that includes language-appropriate radio announcements on a Latino station with bi-lingual signage placed throughout an ethnic neighborhood may work well.

Fire and life safety educators must make use of the changing world of media. Advancing technology and consumer preferences drive continuing change among print, electronic, and broadcast services. While many locally owned corporations remain sensitive to community needs, they are no longer required to provide free public services. Prime broadcast time or conspicuous print visibility will require careful budgeting.

Community-Based Determinants

Many determinants can influence consideration to modify or revise a community-based education program. Three of the most common factors include: political or special interest group influences, resource availability, and community demographical change. Political influence can originate from several sources. Elected officials, neighborhood groups, and other constituencies representing special interests can voice concern over the methodologies or content of a risk-reduction program.

While it may be tempting to resist outside influences, fire and life safety educators always give suggestions from constituents the respect of consideration. Many excellent enhancements to risk-reduction programs originate through input from community leaders, residents, and advisory panels.

Resource availability can affect program activity. Procuring grant funding or increases to a prevention budget may enable program expansion. Consequently, a reduction in resources may call for actions to be scaled back. Either way, some form of program modification or revision takes place.

Educators must monitor community demographics on a continuing basis. Changes in risk occurrence, population profiles, and housing demographics are examples of determinants that may influence the need to revise a program.

Chapter Summary

Empowering Level I educators with the tools to facilitate learning among target populations is a mastery level skill needed by Level II managers. Because informational materials are used extensively in risk-reduction lessons, programs and campaigns, Level II managers are expected to maintain proficiency in their design. While today's information-rich, technology-driven society creates competition for consumer attention, it also permits access to a wide range of helpful information.

Lesson plans are the heart and soul of educational programs. A well-designed plan can set up successful learning outcomes by clearly guiding the presenter through the steps of how to process the lesson. Level II managers should be proficient in designing a product that can be delivered independently by Level I educators. The Level II manager analyzes local risks, examines school curriculums, and is willing to offer resources to supplement the instructional process.

Earning professional credibility is a first step toward becoming a valued partner in the local educational community. School and community-based programs are a significant part of most reduction strategies. Level II managers recognize this reality and strive to obtain a skill set that includes planning, organizing, and designing a program that can be evaluated for outreach, impact, and outcome.

Review Questions

1. What is learning?

2. What are common challenges to the learning process?

3. What strategies can be used to design a positive learning outcome?

4. What is the proper procedure for developing informational materials which support a fire or life safety educational program?

5. What is the proper procedure for developing a lesson plan for a fire and life safety presentation?

6. What is the proper procedure for developing educational materials which support a fire or life safety education program?

7. What is the procedure for designing an educational program as part of a risk-reduction strategy?

8. What is the process for assessing the effectiveness of an educational program?

Key Terms

Concrete Operational Stage of Intellectual Development — Third stage of intellectual development; spans ages 7 to 11 years. Learner can perform operations logically with information as long as it can be applied to specific or concrete examples.

Cooperative Learning — Activity-based instruction that seeks to involve all students in the learning process.

Determinants — Internal and external factors that influence how an organization develops and operates.

Education Program — A series of lessons and activities designed to impact a specific risk-reduction outcome. Several programs are often used in tandem to support a broader-based risk-reduction strategy.

Formal Operational Stage of Intellectual Development — Fourth and highest stage of intellect; usually occurs between ages 11 and 15. Learners can think systematically to develop hypotheses about why something is happening the way it is. They can then test the hypotheses with deductive reasoning.

Learning Activity — Any component of a lesson designed to enhance knowledge, attitude, or skill development. Activities are used to facilitate achievement of learning objectives.

Learning Disability — Cognitive disorder that diminishes a person's capacity to interpret what they see and hear, and/or to link information from different parts of the brain.

Learning Objective — The learner's knowledge, attitude, and behavior that is expected after the lesson has been completed.

Long-Term Memory — A large cognitive storage area where information can be processed and applied.

Preoperational Stage of Intellectual Development — Second stage of intellectual development; occurs from age two to seven. Learners represent the world with words, images, and drawings.

Program Revision — Enhancement of a program so it is accurate, current, and effective in helping to achieve intended outcome.

Qualitative Analysis — Nonstatistical subjective analysis of educational materials that relies on a developer's experience, judgment, and interpretation of the material.

Quantitative Analysis — Statistical analysis of educational materials that includes formal testing of the products for ease of readability.

Sensorimotor Stage of Intellectual Development — First stage of intellectual development; occurs from birth to age two. Learner constructs understanding of the world by coordinating sensory experiences (seeing/hearing) with motor actions (doing).

Short-Term Memory — Information storage area with a finite amount of space. Information not acted upon or used by the learner within a relatively brief time period will be replaced.

Stages of Intellectual Development — Stages of intellect that build upon one another in sequential order.

Chapter 10 Notes

Dale's Cone of Experience (1960) – Bloomsburg University and San Jose University 2004.

Public Fire Education Planning – A Five Step Process. Federal Emergency Management Agency. August, 2002.

Using Instructional Props (2007) – Dayna Hilton

1. *Health Belief Model* – National Fire Academy Risk Reduction Curriculum.

2. Kagan, Dr. Spencer. *Kagan Cooperative Learning,* 1994.

3. Flesch, Rudolph. Flesch Reading Ease and Flesch-Kincaid Grade Level Index, 1951.

4. Gunning, Robert. Gunning FOG Index, 1952.

5. No Child Left Behind – United States Department of Education. 2007

6. *Learn Not to Burn®* is a registered trademark of the National Fire Protection Association, Inc., Quincy, MA 02269

7. *Risk Watch®* is a registered trademark of the National Fire Protection Association, Inc., Quincy, MA 02269

FLSE Level II Managers: Evaluation

Chapter Contents

chapter 11

Key Terms

Job Performance Requirements

This chapter provides information that addresses the following job performance requirements of NFPA® 1035, *Standard for Professional Qualifications for Fire and Life Safety Educator, Public Information Officer, and Juvenile Firesetter Intervention Specialist*, 2010 edition.

NFPA® 1035 References

6.5.1

6.5.2

6.5.3

FESHE Objectives

Fire and Emergency Services Higher Education (FESHE) Objectives: *Fire and Life Safety Education*

7. Develop an accountability system to measure program delivery.

Learning Objectives

After reading this chapter, students will be able to:

1. Develop an evaluation strategy that measures risk reduction program outcomes. (NFPA® 1035, 6.5.1)

2. Design an evaluation instrument that measures risk reduction program outcome. (NFPA® 1035, 6.5.2)

3. Explain how to implement an evaluation strategy so risk reduction program outcomes are measured in a reliable and valid manner. (NFPA® 1035, 6.5.3)

Chapter 11
FLSE Level II Managers: Evaluation

Case History

Breezewood Fire Department offers a wide range of prevention services to its community. Fire department personnel teach life safety at schools, provide home safety inspections, install smoke alarms, and offer child safety seat checks.

Breezewood wants to expand its level of preventive services but, like many communities, it lacks funding to permit significant expansion. The department's risk-reduction officer has applied for several grants from both public and private sources. Unfortunately, none of the requests have been approved.

The risk-reduction officer contacted several of the grant sources to inquire how the application for funding could be improved. Each source said that while Breezewood's programs were impressive, the grant application failed to identify measurable impact created by the prevention programs.

Decision-makers are more likely to support funding for risk-reduction budgets when they understand how progress can be measured. Level II managers and Level III administrators should educate decision-makers that the reduction of community risk can be tangibly measured through use of an evaluation strategy.

Process, impact, and outcome evaluation, when used in tandem with one another, can provide ascending levels of proof that prevention initiatives are working.

- Process evaluation (program monitoring) tracks a program's creation, implementation, and outreach. This method of evaluation provides the most immediate proof of program activity and performance.

- Impact studies, such as testing, surveys, and observations, provide a higher level of proof that a

program is working because knowledge gain and changes in behavior are measured.

- Outcome evaluation uses statistical measurement of incident rates and the citing of anecdotal evidence (personal testimony) that a program is creating impact.

Documenting statistically that programs are working takes time. It may take several years to notice a significant reduction in the occurrence of a specific risk.

Being able to show outreach and statistically prove impact represents the most effective way of justifying why a program should continue to be supported. Ask any fire and life safety educator who has been successful in maintaining or enhancing their budget and they will likely say, "I was able to get this (example) because I was able to prove this (example)."

Creating an Evaluation Strategy for an Educational Program

Evaluation should begin in the design stages of a program and continue throughout its life cycle. Program development, implementation, delivery, and outreach are measured through process evaluation. The effect of a program upon its target population is measured through impact studies. Outcome evaluation demonstrates long-term change. Each level of evaluation provides the evaluator with tangible evidence as to whether or not a program is delivering its intended results.

Educational programs should have the following goals:

- *Provide community outreach.* Outreach activities are the public presentations, lessons, and media saturation used by fire and life safety educators to raise awareness and impart knowledge.

- *Impart knowledge.* Changes in knowledge, attitudes, and behaviors are contingent upon a target population's receipt and comprehension of information.

- *Change attitudes and behaviors.* Behavioral change may follow changes in knowledge and attitude. Changes to one's living environment may also occur. This progression should remind educators of the powerful cognitive, social, and cultural influences through which a learner filters new information.

- *Produce positive impact.* Positive impact and end outcome are the desired goals of outreach, knowledge gain, attitude modification, and behavioral

change **(Figure 11.1)**. *Positive impact* is shown through measurable proof that knowledge gain and behavior change have occurred among a target group. *End outcome* is demonstrated by a reduction in the occurrence of incidents being targeted by the program.

Process Evaluation

Process evaluation is program monitoring **(Figure 11.2)**. It is used to track the evolution and outcome of a program. Accurate recordkeeping is required to track what is being done, who is being reached, and to what degree. Process evaluation provides no

Positive Impact and End Outcome

	Outreach
	Knowledge Gain
	Behavioral Change
+	Attitude Modification
=	Positive Impact and End Outcome

Figure 11.1 By adding together the components of an educational program, the appropriate end result will inevitably follow.

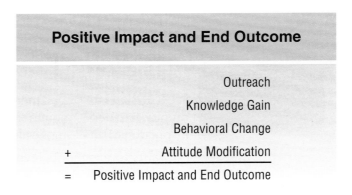

Process Evaluation

Measures:

Community outreach/saturation (# people reached/medium used)

Instructor effectiveness in program delivery

Measured by Documenting Program:

Creation
Outreach
Feedback

Tracks Quality/Quantity of Programs to Determine Need for:

Changes
Additional programs
Additional funding
Remedial instructor training

What It Doesn't Do:

Determine if audience has assimilated knowledge or adopted behavioral changes

Figure 11.2 Another term for process evaluation is *outreach evaluation*.

statistical proof that a program is educating learners or changing behaviors among target populations, simply that programs are being presented and people are attending them. While this seems like basic information, process evaluation also accomplishes the following:

- Measures strengths and weaknesses of a program.
- Determines the effectiveness of program materials and media for target populations.
- Examines program delivery.
- Evaluates presenters for their presentation skills, content coverage, and compatibility with target populations.
- Identifies challenges to a program early in its life cycle.
- Monitors a program's progress and not the impact or outcome being produced.

Process evaluation is, for the most part, nonstrategic, with the exception being pilot-testing of a program. During pilot testing, pretesting/posttesting and surveys are often used as evaluation instruments to determine if selected target populations are receiving and processing information as intended.

While proving impact and outcome are without doubt important, process evaluation should not be overlooked or shortcut. The information collected in process evaluation becomes critical if a program is failing to produce adequate impact. Without good data collected though process evaluation, it may be impossible to diagnose why a program or initiative is failing.

Impact Evaluation

The only way that accurate and objective impact can be proven is to obtain baseline information on target populations before conducting a program. Comparing **baseline data** with post-program results identifies the impact the program has made on the target population. Impact is demonstrated through knowledge gain, behavioral change, and modification to one's environment.

If impact evaluation identifies that knowledge gain or behavioral or environmental changes are not occurring, components of a program can be modified. These actions can take place relatively early in a program's life cycle. Impact studies provide stronger proof over process evaluation because they

Baseline Data — A Starting Point

Programs cannot be measured without existing data on risk issues and target populations. Reliable data on problems and people-related issues creates a baseline so that comparisons can be made before and after programs are delivered. Data to examine may include the following:

- Profile of leading risks and causation
- Profile of target populations (including skill levels and knowledge of risks)
- Current smoke alarm compliance rates
- Profile of existing codes and standards
- Morbidity and mortality profiles

Baseline data must be gathered before designing a risk-reduction program. The goal of evaluation is being able to compare conditions before a program began to after it has been operating for a set amount of time.

measure knowledge gain, behavioral change, and modifications to lifestyle.

Impact evaluation is the second highest level of evaluation **(Figure 11.3, p. 284)**. Unfortunately, Level II managers may omit impact evaluation because they perceive that it involves a lot more time and effort than program monitoring. Omitting impact evaluation can be a mistake.

Knowledge gain can be measured through pretesting/posttesting, surveys, and inquiries about services being offered. Tracking behavior change and modifications to a person's living environment or lifestyle involves greater effort, but produces an even higher level of proof that a program is working. Changes can also be measured through observational surveys and home inspections.

The three most visible forms of impact are manifest through a change in legislation, adoption of a local ordinance, and changes in the number of written citations for a specific type of incident. As mentioned in the Case History, grant reviewers consider impact evaluation a critical part of the application. Proposals must not only be well-written but must also demonstrate need by contrasting current baseline statistics to proposed future impact.

Documenting behaviors leads to institutionalized risk reduction as a core value at both the organizational and community level. A fire department that

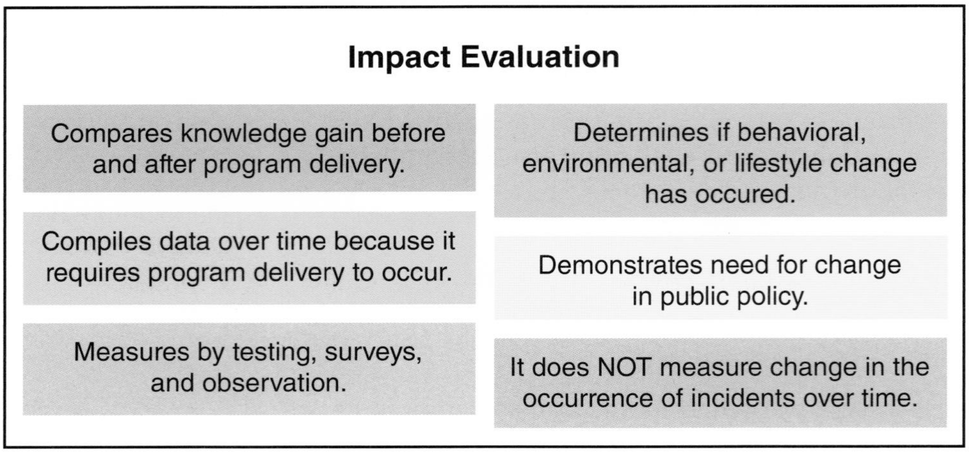

Figure 11.3 The results of impact evaluation have many immediate uses.

Impact Evaluation

Compares knowledge gain before and after program delivery.	Determines if behavioral, environmental, or lifestyle change has occured.
Compiles data over time because it requires program delivery to occur.	Demonstrates need for change in public policy.
Measures by testing, surveys, and observation.	It does NOT measure change in the occurrence of incidents over time.

makes risk reduction a priority by allocating resources in the form of staff, money, equipment, and time is demonstrating a measurable form of impact.

While process evaluation results are immediate, impact takes longer to evolve, often taking at least several months and usually over a year. However, the extra time spent can produce more measurable results.

Outcome Evaluation

Outcome evaluation is the highest stage of program evaluation. It tracks statistical and anecdotal evidence collected over a period of time – usually 5 to 10 years **(Figure 11.4)**. Outcome evaluation is usually performed by Level III administrators. However, it is included in this manual whenever evaluation is discussed because it examines the ultimate aim of risk-reduction strategies — a reduction in the occurrence of incidents.

The strongest evidence that a program is working is a reduction in the occurrence of incidents, injuries, and loss of life. As with measuring impact, baseline risk statistics must be available so comparisons can be made. A statistically significant drop in a community's fire or injury rate is usually related to a broad-based strategy that includes several risk-reduction programs **(Figure 11.5)**.

NOTE: *Demonstrating Your Program's Worth – A Primer on Evaluation for Programs to Prevent Unintentional Injury*[1] is a publication offered by the Centers for Disease Control and Prevention. This user friendly document provides suggestions on how fire and life safety educators can better evaluate programs at three levels. The United States Fire Administration's *Public Fire Education Planning – A Five Step Process*[2]

is another resource that offers guidance on how to perform evaluation of a program or initiative.

Developing an Evaluation Plan

Level III administrators develop an evaluation plan to track risk-reduction strategies. Developing and following an evaluation plan represents the best way to demonstrate that risk-reduction programs are producing tangible results. An **evaluation plan** outlines the methodologies that will be used in a risk-reduction program or strategy. A broad-based risk-reduction strategy will likely include several programs that are developed and supervised by Level II managers. Community outreach activities are often delivered by Level I educators.

Level II managers are responsible for the overall long-term outcome of risk-reduction strategies used within a community. Level II managers develop, supervise, and evaluate programs that support broader-based strategies. While all fire and life safety educators should understand the concept of an evaluation plan, Level II managers and Level III administrators should possess expertise in its design and use.

Development and use of an evaluation plan will help keep an intervention strategy (and supporting programs) on track by clearly outlining measurable and time-sensitive delivery methodologies. It also serves as a means to direct when and how changes in knowledge and behavior will be examined. A good evaluation plan includes the components shown in **Figure 11.6**.

Developing an evaluation plan is not difficult, but it requires research and takes patience. Developing objectives for an evaluation plan is similar to creating a lesson plan. Objectives must be succinct, measur-

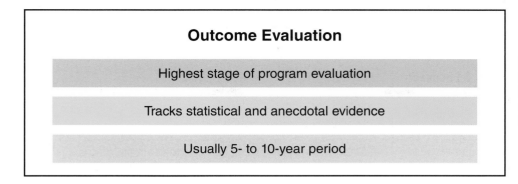

Outcome Evaluation

Highest stage of program evaluation

Tracks statistical and anecdotal evidence

Usually 5- to 10-year period

Figure 11.4 Outcome evaluation takes time to establish results, but the information gathered is essential for long-term proof of change.

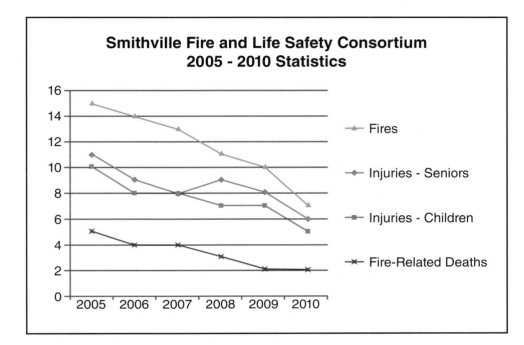

Smithville Fire and Life Safety Consortium
2005 - 2010 Statistics

Fires
Injuries - Seniors
Injuries - Children
Fire-Related Deaths

Figure 11.5 A consortium provides resources to enable broad-based strategies.

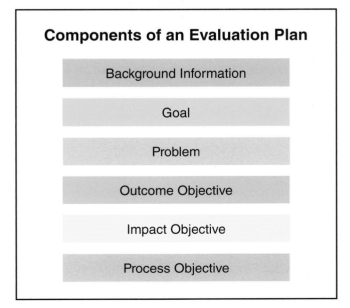

Components of an Evaluation Plan

Background Information

Goal

Problem

Outcome Objective

Impact Objective

Process Objective

Figure 11.6 Each of the six components generates more information that contributes to the success of the overall program.

able, achievable, and consistent with the goals of the program. The program should also support an overall risk-reduction strategy.

Each objective of an evaluation plan must also include a method of evaluation. **Figure 11.7, p. 286**, presents an evaluation plan for a smoke alarm program developed for implementation in the fictitious community of Liberty. Background information on the community precedes the plan.

Potential Challenges Associated with Evaluation

Program evaluation is often neglected because people dread working with statistics. In contrast, most fire and life safety educators find that the most challenging component of evaluation is the time required to collect data. A thorough evaluation of a program can be accomplished by collecting data and employing basic mathematics.

Figure 11.7 caption (left margin)

Figure 11.7 By establishing a reasonable timeline and a concrete benchmark for evaluation, the program evaluation will be likely to stay on track.

Liberty Smoke Alarm Program Evaluation Plan

Component	Description
Background Information	Liberty, a community of 29,000, is experiencing an increase in fire deaths in low-income housing.
Problem	40% of low-income housing lacks working smoke alarms.
Goal	Increase working smoke alarm protection in low-income housing within the community.
Outcome Objective	By January 2015: Reduce number of fire fatalities in low-income housing by 90%. *Method of evaluation: statistical analysis*
Impact Objectives	By October 2012: Firefighters will have visited and installed smoke alarms in 500 low-income rental properties. *Method of evaluation: record of visit and installation* By January 2013: Increase the number of low-income housing units with smoke alarms by 80%.
Process Objectives	By January 2011: Have secured approval from the fire chief and city administration to proceed with a smoke alarm program. *Method of evaluation: written agreement from city* By July 2011: Have secured all materials needed to begin the smoke alarm program. *Method of evaluation: possession of materials* By October 2011: Have implemented a community-wide smoke alarm program. *Method of evaluation: implementation of program* By January 2012: All community service organizations/media outlets will disseminate information about the smoke alarm program. *Method of evaluation: records from participating organizations*

A possible solution to statistical anxiety is to consider enlisting help from someone who enjoys data collection and evaluation. Also, most organizations have someone who would prefer to not interact directly with the public and would be willing to focus on evaluation. A word of caution, however: involving too many people in the collection and analysis of data can lead to subjective interpretation and skewed results.

Occasionally, decision-makers worry that a thorough evaluation may identify shortcomings in program efforts. In reality, this is exactly what evaluation is designed to do! An objective evaluation process can save incredible amounts of time, effort, and money through early identification of challenges.

Another potential challenge occurs when staff does not understand the role of evaluation in program delivery. Level II managers should educate everyone who assists with a program about the reason why they are collecting information or documenting services. Staff members who understand how a program's objectives can be measured develop a vested interest in determining if actions are working.

Finally, managers should not assume that evaluation should only occur after a program has been initiated. Evaluation must begin in the planning stages and continue throughout the life cycle of a program.

Designing Evaluation Instruments for Educational Programs

A combination of school and community-based educational programs comprise most risk-reduction strategies. Their performance is measured through process and impact evaluation.

The term **evaluation instrument** prompts most people to think "test." While designing and administering tests are components of evaluation, a much wider strategy is used to track the performance of a risk-reduction program. The type and design of a performance measuring instrument is driven by the level of evaluation that will be conducted. This section overviews instruments to document, monitor, and measure a risk-reduction program's performance as these tasks are related to process and impact evaluation.

Nonstrategic Evaluation

Process evaluation is primarily nonstrategic and examines the progress of a program's development, its implementation, delivery methodologies, and outreach.

Good tracking skills are essential for organizing and recording process evaluation data because each component of a program is monitored for activity and outreach. Components to document in process evaluation include:

- Tasks required to create the program
- Tasks required to implement the program
- Performance of staff as they deliver programs
- Documentation of program outreach into the community (number and location of programs delivered)
- Effectiveness of media saturation
- Overall public opinion of a program
- Documentation of resource acquisition required for risk-reduction program activities

The evaluation instruments for process evaluation are primarily comprised of tracking documents. Current computer software offers a variety of affordable user-friendly options to document program development, implementation, delivery, and outreach.

Strategic Evaluation

The goal of impact evaluation is to produce evidence that a risk-reduction program is creating change among target populations. Evaluating the impact of a risk-reduction program is considered strategic because it involves statistical analysis of conditions before and after the program is delivered.

It is important to remember that process evaluation measures the physical performance of a program and its associated outreach. Impact evaluation provides a higher level of evaluation because it provides answers to the following questions:

- Has learning occurred within the target audience?
- Has the program caused behavioral change among the target group?
- Have target audiences made lifestyle or living environment modifications due to the program?
- Has the program helped to change public policy?
- Have cultural changes occurred in the organization or community in support of risk reduction?

Several types of evaluation instruments can be used to measure impact. The effectiveness of measurement is often correlated to the design and delivery of the evaluation.

Level I educators use evaluation instruments created by Level II managers. Instruments must be designed so that they are reliable and reproducible when administered by multiple evaluators.

A component of impact evaluation is measuring if learning has occurred within a target population. The two media most frequently used to measure knowledge gain are the pretest/posttest and surveys.

The gold standard of measuring knowledge gain is through pretesting/posttesting. While tests are used most often in school-based environments, they may also be used in community-based settings when applicable.

Developing a written test that effectively measures knowledge gain requires careful planning. A good test uses several formats of questions so that ascending levels of cognitive process can be evaluated (**Figure 11.8**). Types of questions may include the following:

- Multiple choice
- Completion
- Matching
- True/False
- Short answer and essay (where applicable)

Developing a Written Test

Using a written test to evaluate learner performance provides feedback to the instructor on the effectiveness of instructional delivery and learning activities. It also monitors the student's mastery of course-specific learning objectives.

Steps in Developing a Written Test

Test developers generally follow a three-step process in the development of tests and measurement devices (**Figure 11.9, p. 291**). Test writers face the dilemma of coordinating measurement of learning objectives with an acceptable test format. The following are important points to consider when deciding what format will be used:

- Response-limited items such as true/false and multiple choice questions are easily graded but may limit the ability to assess higher-order learning.
- Open-ended items, such as essay and fill-in-the-blank questions, promote higher-order thinking. The short essay format can also be used to measure changes in opinions and attitudes among target groups. The Level II manager should remember that open-ended items are time-consuming to evaluate.
- A variety of question types allows developers to implement structured assessments that reflect true learning goals. The key to effective application of the various question types is the design of the questions.

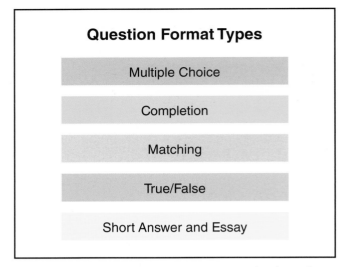

Figure 11.8 Some test formats are more complex than others.

Evaluating Skill Development

Directly viewing the skill implementation of learners is a form of observational survey. The evaluator monitors the proficiency level of the learner by watching him or her demonstrate a newly learned skill.

Direct observation is often used by public educators to monitor learner abilities in the following areas:

- Stop, drop, and roll (**Figure 11.10, p. 292**)
- Smoke alarm testing
- Get low and go under smoke
- Changing batteries in smoke alarms
- Calling 9-1-1 and reporting an emergency
- How to size and wear a bicycle helmet
- Proper use of seat belts and car safety seats
- How to size and wear a personal floatation device

Direct observation is well suited for an organized learning environment. A Level II manager can monitor learner performance and provide immediate feedback on progress. He or she may use a checklist to keep track of learner progress.

Measuring Behavioral, Lifestyle, and Living Environment Modifications

Once a person has learned new information, he or she forms opinions, attitudes, and values about the topic. Proof of affective learning is demonstrated by behaviors that indicate attitudes of awareness, belief, and responsibility.

Summary of How to Improve the Overall Quality of a Written Test

Content

- Identify what the test is going to measure.
- Use simple wording and proper grammar.
- Focus on important ideas and major concepts, not trivia.
- Within each group of test items, order questions from the least to most difficult.
- Write each test item so that it does not provide help in answering other items in the test.
- Write each test item so that the answer is one that would be agreed upon by experts.
- Match the requirements of the test items to the designated learning objectives.
- Write test items at a level of difficulty that matches the learning objectives and student population's abilities.
- Refrain from making test items intentionally difficult or tricky.
- Create items that are worded at the average reading level of the target student population. Consider use of Flesch Reading Ease, Flesch-Kincaid Grade Level Index, or Gunning FOG Index to help determine the most appropriate level.
- Ensure that each test item has one and only one undisputedly correct answer.
- Strive to measure higher-order thinking instead of shallow memorization of facts or details. Be aware of age and developmentally appropriate questions.
- Have an unbiased reader review test items to identify points of confusion or grammatical errors.

Format

- Determine the type and number of questions that will be used.
- Include a variety of test item formats (multiple choice, completion, matching, true/false, short answer, and essay where applicable).
- Use a format that most effectively measures the desired knowledge.
- Group items of the same format together.
- Refrain from including more test items than can be answered by the average student in the designated amount of time.
- Ensure that the number of questions targeting each objective matches the importance of that objective.
- Be aware of font selection and print size. Include enough white space so that the instrument does not appear cluttered.

Suggestions for Writing Matching Items

- Write clear and specific directions for matching items in Column I with items in Column II.
- Specify in the directions the basis for matching. Indicate if each response may be used once, more than once, or not at all.
- Keep the lists of items short. Put the brief responses on the right.
- Keep like items on one side and their match on the other.
- Include three or four extra choices as distracters. However, there should be only one correct match for each statement.
- Use parallel language in all items (same format and tense).

Suggestions for Writing True/False Items

- Include only one central significant idea in each statement.
- Make sure that the item is definitely true or false.
- Word the statement so precisely that it can be judged unequivocally true or false.
- Avoid verbal clues that indicate the answer.
- Keep statements short (less than 20 words). Use simple language structure.

continued on page 290

Summary of How to Improve the Overall Quality of a Written Test *(concluded)*

- Do not present the answers in an easily learned pattern.
- Use equal numbers of true and false statements of similar length.
- Do not copy sentences directly from textbooks and other written materials.
- Test important ideas rather than trivia.
- Use negative statements sparingly. Avoid double negatives (no, never) in the same statement.
- Do not use qualifiers such as always, never, only, none, and entirely.
- Attribute statements of opinion to an authoritative source.
- Use true/false questions sparingly. There is always a 50/50 chance of a guess being correct.

Suggestions for Writing Multiple-Choice Items
- Design each item to measure an important learning outcome.
- Present a single clearly formulated statement in the stem of the item.

  (**NOTE:** The *stem* is the main component of the question and the *response* is the answer being sought from the student.)
- Place the alternatives at the end of the question and not in the middle.
- Put as much of the wording as possible in the stem. The stem should be presented in simple, clear language.
- Construct items as a direct question or an incomplete answer.
- Eliminate unnecessary wordiness.
- Avoid negatively worded stems: "Which of the following is not…" Avoid textbook wording.
- Do not provide overt clues to answers in the stem.
- All distractors should be plausible, that is, almost but not completely correct. Make the distracters believable and attractive to the uninformed:
  — Use the common misconceptions or common errors of students as distracters.
  — State the alternatives in the language of the student.
  — Use words that are accurate, important, and technical in the distracters as well as in the correct answers.
  — Make the distracters similar to the correct answer in both length and complexity of wording.
- Write alternatives that are correctly punctuated, grammatically correct, and consistent with the stem.
- Do not repeat words in the options – rather, put them in the stem.
- List options vertically.
- Refrain from using "all" or "none of the above."
- Vary the relative length of the correct answers to eliminate length as a clue.
- Vary the position of the correct answer in a random manner.
- Promote higher-order thinking by using the terms why and how rather than who, where, and when.
- Ensure that each item is independent of the other items in the test.
- Make certain that the intended answer is correct or clearly best.

Suggestions for Writing Completion/Short-Answer Items
- State the question so that only a single, brief answer is possible.
- Leave only one blank. The answer should relate to the main point of the statement.
- Place the blanks at the end of the statement.
- Avoid statements in excess of 20 words.

Information adapted from Park University Faculty Resource Quick Tips. Questions concerning the Park University Faculty Development: Quick Tips Web site should be directed to Dr. Jean Mandernach at jean.mandernach@park.edu.

Test and Measurement Development
Three-Step Process

Step One: Research

Review learning objectives to be assessed by the test.	Learning objectives drive the content and design of evaluation instruments. Select and study the learning objectives that will be measured.
Review the activities that support the learning objectives.	Study the activities that support the learning objectives that will be measured.
Examine delivery methodologies of the lesson/program.	Examine how the lesson/program is being delivered.
Determine the material to be covered by the test.	Select content that must be mastered by a learner to prove that learning has occurred.
Determine the test length and format.	Consider the intellectual level of the learner.

Step Two: Development

Develop the test items.	Consider the cognitive processing ability of the target populations.
Format the test based on the types of questions used.	Recommended order of format: Matching True/False Multiple Choice Short Answer/Essay
Write directions for each group of items.	Consider the cognitive processing ability of the target populations. Use care to develop specific and clear directions for each section of the test.

Step Three: Testing/Evaluation

Pilot-test the exam among prospective target population(s).	Identify problems with specific test items.
Evaluate.	Revise, edit, or delete test items, as necessary.

Figure 11.9 Follow a process to develop evaluation devices to ensure that the intended goals are being met.

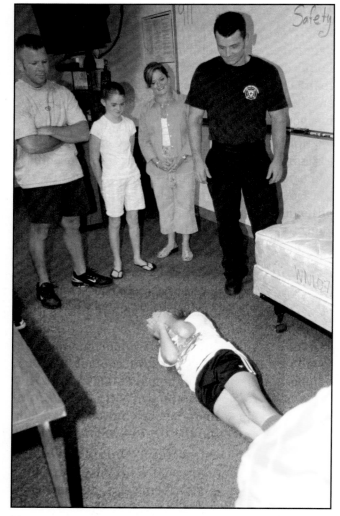

Figure 11.10 Even simple techniques can benefit from observation to ensure the steps are carried out correctly and completely.

- Behavior, environmental, and lifestyle changes within populations
- Skill development

The type of survey used to identify change is driven by what the evaluator wants to examine. The most popular types include questionnaires and physical and observational surveys. The following describes several types of survey questionnaires:

- *Post program.* A written survey completed by a person immediately after attending a program. The survey is collected on-site.
- *Mail-in.* A written survey distributed manually or by mail to a person. Recipient is asked to complete the survey and return it by mail.
- *In-person (face to face).* The evaluator asks questions and completes the survey in the presence of the interviewee.
- *Telephone.* The interviewee is asked questions by an evaluator through a telephone interview.
- *Online.* A person completes a survey in electronic format and emails it to the entity requesting information.

The following describes the types of physical and observational surveys (**Figure 11.11**):

- *Direct physical inspection.* The evaluator physically examines an environment in search of proof that behavioral change has occurred.
- *Observational.* An evaluator observes actions of a target population and records the information.

Designing a Survey Questionnaire

Developing good questions is one of the keys to securing valid and reliable data from a written survey. As previously discussed, an instrument that tests what it is supposed to is considered valid. It is considered reliable when it works as designed across a population of learners. The following section provides suggestions for designing a survey questionnaire.

- *Develop goals and objectives of the survey.* A Level II manager must know what he or she wants to study before developing the assessment instrument. Identify the goal of the survey before writing any questions. Develop a set of objectives that outline the information to be captured from the survey. The objectives build a foundation upon which to develop questions.

Motivating target populations to act on a desired outcome is a challenging goal. Even when a person is empowered with knowledge, there is no guarantee that he or she will behave in a certain manner. While it is paramount to evaluate whether a population has learned information, it is equally important to examine how they have acted over a period of time.

Surveying target populations helps fire and life safety educators develop baseline information of knowledge, attitudes, behaviors, and lifestyles. Comparing baseline information to data collected after a program is presented can provide evidence that it is producing desired changes in behavior.

Surveys can be used to assess the following areas:

- Knowledge gain among populations
- Personal values of constituents

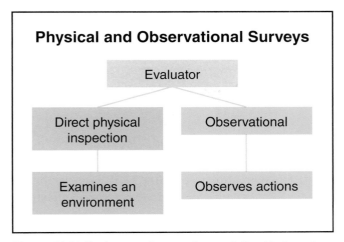

Physical and Observational Surveys

Figure 11.11 Each type of survey is specialized to target specific information.

- *Write questions that will comprise the survey.* Two types of questions are used to collect information:

  1. Structured or fixed response

  2. Nonstructured or open questions

Each type of question has its own set of attributes. It is important to understand when and how to best use these questions.

Structured Questions

Structured questions offer the respondent a closed set of responses from which to choose **(Figure 11.12)**. Structured questions often appeal to researchers for the following reasons:

- They take minimal time to answer.

- Data collection is easier.

- Analysis is simpler than when using open-ended questions.

The following are considerations when designing structured questions:

- The researcher needs a thorough understanding of the subject matter being studied before she or he can develop a structured question that is valid and reliable; the respondent must be offered logical options as answer choices.

- Occasionally, responses such as "Other" at the end of a list of answer choices are appropriate because a respondent's answer does not fit into the offered categories.

- Similarly, adding "Don't know" to a response list for a question that some of the respondents may not be capable of answering will help ensure valid data is being collected. However, use the "Don't know" option sparingly. Try to ensure that respondents are capable of answering the majority of the questions on the survey questionnaire.

Figure 11.13, p. 294, is an example of a survey questionnaire used by a fire department seeking to determine public knowledge of the community's leading fire cause. Make sure that all answers are *relevant* to the question being asked. Irrelevant responses may distract the respondent and add unnecessary length to a survey questionnaire.

The list of responses to a question should be consistent. All responses should be similar so that no single response stands out to the respondent except the answer that is true for them. Consistency helps

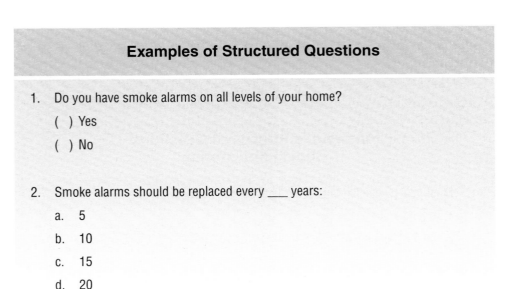

Examples of Structured Questions

1. Do you have smoke alarms on all levels of your home?

   ( ) Yes

   ( ) No

2. Smoke alarms should be replaced every ___ years:

   a. 5

   b. 10

   c. 15

   d. 20

Figure 11.12 Structured questions are simple to administer and evaluate but may lack depth of response.

ensure the survey is not leading respondents to a particular answer by making that answer different from the others. It also makes it much easier for respondents to find the answer that is relevant to them.

Sometimes a researcher is interested in obtaining a person's opinion. To capture varying degrees of emotion about a subject, it is best to use a rating question **(Figure 11.14)**. A rating question asks respondents to explain the degree to which they feel about something.

Answers in a structured question should not overlap **(Figure 11.15)**. One disadvantage of structured questions is that they do not capture new ideas or thoughts from the respondent. To solicit this type information, researchers often use nonstructured (open-ended) questions.

Nonstructured (Open-Ended) Questions
Nonstructured (open-ended) questions do not offer a list of answer choices **(Figure 11.16)**. Respondents are simply asked to write their response to a question.

Figure 11.13 The fire service can gauge awareness of local risks by using authentic data for responses.

Example of a Survey Question

1. The leading cause of fire in Liberty, USA, is:
   a. Portable heaters too close to combustibles
   b. Children playing with fire
   c. Unattended cooking
   d. Candle-related incidents
   e. I don't know

Example of a Rating Question

1. Please describe how you feel about the proposed ordinance requiring sprinklers in all new homes:
   a. Agree
   b. Disagree
   c. Unaware of proposal
   d. Don't have an opinion

Figure 11.14 A rating question is used when a researcher wants to obtain the degree of emotion a respondent has about a subject.

Answers to Structured Questions Should Not Overlap

1. Most fatal residential fires occur between the hours of:
   a. 6 p.m. and 11 p.m.
   b. 12 a.m. and 6 a.m.
   c. 7 a.m. and 11 a.m.
   d. 12 p.m. and 5 p.m.

Figure 11.15 The responses should not overlap by having the same information in two options.

Nonstructured questions are appropriate when exploring new ideas and the researcher is unsure what answers to expect from respondents. They can also be used to examine the opinion and attitude of a respondent toward a topic.

An advantage to using open-ended questions is that the researcher can gain more insight into the respondents' thoughts and ideas about a subject. The disadvantages to using open-ended questions is that it can be more time consuming and difficult to analyze the data.

Partially Structured Questions

In cases where the researcher has some idea of potential responses that may be generated, a **partially structured question** can be posed **(Figure 11.17)**. Conducting exploratory research on the subject matter being studied will help minimize the number of open-ended questions needed in a survey questionnaire. The following example applies to risk reduction:

A fire and life safety educator wants to examine citizen knowledge of existing fire causes within his or her community. Instead of using an open-ended format, the educator determines the five leading causes of fire and offers those choices in the form of a partially structured question. The choice "I don't know" is offered to help eliminate guessing. The educator can then conduct a follow-up interview in person to identify specific answers.

Tips for Creating a Good Survey Questionnaire

Many people are hesitant to answer questions about themselves, family, lifestyles, and home. A brief statement explaining why the information is being collected and how it will be used may encourage prospective participants to respond to a survey questionnaire. Instructions should be included with the survey questionnaire.

Example of a Nonstructured (Open-Ended) Question

1. What actions should be taken to reduce the number of fires started by people exhibiting acts of irresponsible behavior?

   _____

   _____

   _____

Figure 11.16 Nonstructured questions generate unscripted information for researchers.

Example of a Partially Structured Question

1. What is the *best* way for firefighters to reach your family with safety messages?

   a. Radio

   b. Television

   c. Community signage

   d. Internet

   e. Mail

   f. Telephone

   g. Direct visitation

   h. Other _____

Figure 11.17 A partially structured question features easy scoring and the potential to generate new information.

When designing questions, what seems obvious to the researcher may not be clear to the respondent. To help ensure that valid and reliable survey results are collected, include instructions on how to answer the questionnaire.

Asking individuals for personal or demographic information (age, race, income level, etc.) may make respondents feel that their privacy is being invaded and prevent them from completing a survey questionnaire. However, in many instances, this information is necessary for the research. If this type information is essential, it is best to place the questions at the end of the survey. Offer an explanation for why the questions are being asked and how the information will be used. Each question should be clearly and concisely worded so that there is no misunderstanding about what is being asked.

A very common mistake that will severely impact the validity of data is the inadvertent use of a double-barreled question. When writing a question, be sure to ask only one question at a time **(Figure 11.18)**. Use of a double-barreled question will skew data because it asks for a response in two areas and respondents will have to choose which to answer. To avoid this consequence, always ask a single question at a time.

When developing a survey questionnaire, make certain that questions are presented in a neutral manner. Care must be used so that respondents are not led toward a particular answer **(Figure 11.19)**. While the concept sounds simple, a developer may inadvertently phrase a question to reflect his or her underlying opinion.

Make sure that respondents will be able to answer the question being asked. The most common mistake is to ask questions that most people simply cannot remember. The following is an example of this:

— *What was the date that you last checked your smoke alarm?*

While this question seeks a specific answer, it is unlikely that many people will remember the exact date their alarm was checked. Most responses will probably be guesses rather than actual fact. Rephrasing the question to the following will make it much easier for the respondent.

— *When was your smoke alarm tested last?*

- During this past week
- Within the past month
- Sometime this year
- Over a year ago
- Not sure

Survey questions should be organized so that respondents (and interviewers if applicable) can focus their thoughts on one subject area at a time. Survey instruments should be user-friendly. A clean layout makes it easier for people to respond to questions and for the researcher to collect data. The method for marking answers should be explained in the directions and be clear to anyone who is administering or responding to the survey.

The best way to ensure that questions are well worded is to test them. Once a draft survey questionnaire has been developed, it should be pilot-tested among its intended target population.

Double-Barreled and Single-Format Questions

Double-Barreled Question

Are safety messages broadcast on radio and television an effective way to reach your family? ( ) Yes ( ) No

Single-Format Question

Is broadcasting safety messages on local radio an effective way to reach your family? ( ) Yes ( ) No

Is broadcasting safety messages on local television an effective way to reach your family? ( ) Yes ( ) No

Figure 11.18 Double-barreled questions are confusing to responders and inefficient for data collection.

Example of a Leading Question

Do you think that unattended cooking is the leading cause of fire in Liberty, USA?

( ) Yes

( ) No

( ) Not Sure

This leading question drives the respondent to the conclusion that unattended cooking is indeed the leading cause of fire in Liberty. A yes response to this question is the easiest, and many respondents may simply take the path that requires the least amount of thinking.

Figure 11.19 Leading questions skew data by encouraging participants to answer in a particular way instead of demonstrating knowledge.

Example of a Neutral Question

What is the leading cause of fire in Liberty, USA?

a. Children playing with lighters

b. Electrical appliance malfunctions

c. Smoking related

d. Unattended cooking

e. Don't know

Use of a neutral question helps reduce the chance of bias.

Testing a population sample of a dozen people is usually sufficient to examine if respondents (and interviewers if applicable) clearly understand the questions. Pilot-testing also allows the researcher to evaluate the capture of information needed for the study.

Direct Physical Inspection

Direct inspection is used when an evaluator wants to physically examine an environment in search of proof that behavioral change has occurred. Examples of this type of survey include:

- House numbering identification
- Presence, age, and operability of smoke alarms
- Home safety inspections

While direct physical inspection is labor intensive, it can provide a high level of proof that behavioral change has occurred among target groups. Direct inspection is well suited for examining living environments and lifestyles.

Observational Surveys

Observational surveys are used not only to assess knowledge recall but also to observe whether behavioral, environmental, or lifestyle changes are occurring among a target population. Direct observation offers strong evidence of impact because the evaluator physically watches the behaviors of those being studied.

Examples of well-suited observational surveys include the following:

- Seat belt usage
- Car seat installation
- Protective helmet usage
- Bicycle operation

Both direct inspection and observational surveys reveal valuable information about behavioral change. While each is labor intensive and requires a time commitment, they are less intellectually challenging than writing a valid test or survey questionnaire because they require simple data collection about the studied behavior.

Evaluation instruments for inspection and observational studies do not have to be complex. Many designers use check-off sheets or other simple recording instruments. Whatever the format, the tool must be user friendly and relate to the behavior change of interest.

As with all other forms of evaluation, inspection and observational studies must compare baseline data to conditions that are present after a program has occurred. Post-program data is then compared against a valid standard of performance, such as national data.

Example of an Observational Survey

A fire department that wanted to evaluate the effectiveness of a house-numbering initiative conducted the house numbering initiative and formatted it as an observational survey. The initiative included educational, media, and code compliance components.

Steps Used in the Process

- The fire department physically located, observed, and documented the addresses of 200 homes in its community that lacked or displayed substandard house numbers.

- One year after all program components were in operation, the fire department revisited the same 200 homes to observe if changes had been made to house numbers.

- Improvements meeting the standard of compliance were noted at 100 of the homes visited. This 50% increase proved that the house numbering initiative was positively impacting the community.

NOTE: Sometimes a fire and life safety educator may choose to design an instrument that combines a questionnaire with an inspection or observational survey. This strategy is acceptable if it follows the prudent design criteria covered in the previous section.

Measuring Legislative Actions on Public Policy

In addition to public education, a comprehensive risk-reduction strategy also involves the adoption of ordinances, codes, and standards that require the use of safety technology or mandate behavioral change. Legislation that enacts public policy in support of risk reduction is a measurable form of impact.

The adoption of any type of legislation takes research, planning, and collaboration with elected officials. Adoption of public policy also takes time. State laws require greater levels of approval than local ordinances. Federal legislation is more complex than state actions.

Often, a legislative proposal may have to be introduced several times before it is enacted. Fire and life safety educators who help draft legislation should not become discouraged if a proposal is not accepted on its first introduction **(Figure 11.20)**.

Measuring Changes in Organizational and Community Culture

When an organization or community makes visible changes in support of risk reduction, it is exhibiting a measurable form of impact. Cultural changes are noted as impact because they result in behaviors that make positive things happen.

Examples of cultural change within an organization include:

- Increased time and staff are dedicated to risk reduction
- Resources are allocated to support risk reduction
- Creation of risk-reduction programs
- Willingness of staff to participate in reducing risk

Examples of cultural change within a community include:

- Inclusion of school-based programs in essential curriculum
- Requests for community-based risk-reduction programs
- Increased levels of awareness among target populations
- Evidence of behavioral, environmental, and lifestyle changes
- Reduction of incidents, morbidity, and mortality
- Resources provided in support of risk reduction
- Documented cultural changes supporting risk reduction
- Implemented evaluation strategies

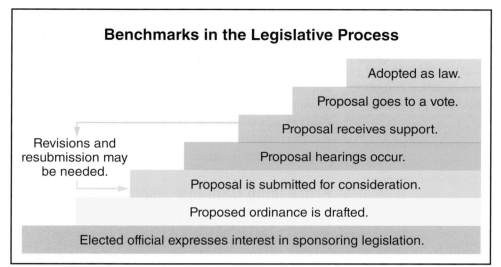

Benchmarks in the Legislative Process

Adopted as law.

Proposal goes to a vote.

Proposal receives support.

Proposal hearings occur.

Proposal is submitted for consideration.

Proposed ordinance is drafted.

Elected official expresses interest in sponsoring legislation.

Revisions and resubmission may be needed.

Figure 11.20 The process of proposing legislation has several steps and may take a substantial amount of time.

An **evaluation strategy** is a plan that details how a risk-reduction program will be examined for effectiveness. An evaluation strategy begins before a program is developed and continues throughout its life cycle. Process evaluation monitors a program's development, implementation, and outreach. Impact studies measure changes that are occurring among target populations as a direct result of the program.

Level II managers should create a plan that identifies how an evaluation strategy will be implemented. The plan should identify the following:

- Those who will be involved with the evaluation process
- The roles and responsibilities of each person or group
- A training strategy for team members
- Methodologies of how the evaluation process will progress
- Timing schedule for evaluation
- The amount of data needed
- How data will be processed into useful information
- How results of the evaluation will be shared

Identifying Who Will Be Involved with Evaluation

While Level II managers will likely conduct most levels of process evaluation, impact studies may involve people from outside the emergency services. Pretests and posttests are often administered by teachers in the school-based environment. Affiliate agencies such as coalitions and community groups may assist with surveys conducted throughout a municipality.

Regardless of who is involved, each group must understand his or her role and responsibilities to the evaluation process. Good training will accomplish this goal.

Training the Data Collector

The quality of any evaluation is dependent on the performance of those collecting data. Level II managers must be trained on how to administer the tool being used to gather data for evaluation. This rule applies to tests, surveys, and inspections.

Performance-driven school systems require measurement of instructional impact among students. This includes injury prevention curricula. Teachers who administer tests must understand why the examination is being given, how it should be delivered, and what will be done with the results.

If data collectors will be asking questions, clear direction must be provided so that each evaluator poses questions in the same manner. When doing physical inspection or conducting observational surveys, the criteria for what is being evaluated and how to record data must be clearly understood by those who will use the instrument.

Administering Pretests and Posttests

As the name implies, pretests and posttests should be administered before and after a lesson or program has been delivered. Pretesting usually takes place a few days before or during the start of a program. Posttesting may take place a few days or even a few months after a program's conclusion. Depending upon the availability of time and resources, a second posttest can be given several months or even a year after learners received a program. The longer the knowledge is retained by learners, the stronger the proof that lessons and programs are producing impact.

Proper organizational skills are needed to ensure valid and reliable data analysis. The best level of impact analysis occurs when an evaluator can compare the pretest and posttest scores of a specific person to that of group performance.

Surveys, Questionnaires, Inspections, and Observational Media

As with testing, surveys should be conducted before and after a program is in operation. Comparing baseline to post-program data is the only way that reliable and valid information can be obtained.

The following recommendations will help the evaluator design good instructions for the target audience:

- Ensure that participants understand the instructions. For written tests and skills tests, explain the instructions before giving the evaluation.

- Be sure that instructions are easy to read and concise. Also, see that the instructions are written at the educational and reading level of the target audience.

- Explain the purpose of the evaluation to the target audience. This is very important, especially with adults.

Collecting an Adequate Amount of Data

To prove reliable and valid, an adequate amount of data must be studied. Obviously, a larger sampling of data should equate to a greater degree of reliability.

Pretest and posttest scores from one classroom of students would not provide enough data to reliably assess if a lesson or program is having impact across an entire school system. The probability of obtaining valid data increases dramatically with a larger sample size: for example 150 out of 175 classrooms.

The same is true for surveys. Inspecting five homes for smoke-alarm compliance will not produce reliable conclusions about community-wide conditions. Increasing the number of inspections so that 25% of all homes within the community are visited increases the reliability of the study.

The availability of resources (including "people-power") often dictates how much time and effort can be dedicated to evaluation. However, this should not serve as rationale for omitting the task. The Level II manager should strive for the best effort that is realistic for the level of available resources. Programs that receive favorable consideration for funding are usually those that demonstrate measurable outreach, impact, and outcome.

Processing Data Into Useful Information

The raw data collected through tests and surveys has little meaning until it is compiled into a useful format. Turning facts into useful information requires accurate data entry and analysis.

Data collection for impact evaluation will likely involve multiple people. However, data entry into a collection system should be limited to a select group of individuals who are designated as "recorders." Recorders must follow guidelines for entry that are created in advance by a person or group knowledgeable in how to best capture data objectively.

Computer-based information collection software offers fire and life safety managers a variety of formats for recording and tracking data collected during impact evaluation. At development time of this manual, programs such as Microsoft Excel® and Access® were recognized as good options for handling data **(Figure 11.21)**. Both programs, as well as others, permit large quantities of data to be compiled and evaluated.

Figure 11.21 Spreadsheets and other data-handling software programs assist in the management of information collected during evaluation.

Entering and processing the responses from structured questions is obviously easier than interpreting an open-ended answer. However, before designing an evaluation instrument, consider if a limited number of open-ended questions may be important to the study. If so, decide in advance how to pose each question, interpret data, and enter the data.

Evaluating Change

A critical part of the evaluation process is determining whether change has occurred among the target group as a result of program delivery. Impact is demonstrated by changes in knowledge, behaviors, and lifestyles.

To prove knowledge gain, an evaluator compares the scores of a learner's pretest with those from a posttest. The strongest proof of impact is produced when an evaluator can compare the pretest and posttest scores of a specific person with a group's performance.

When examining knowledge gain, two types of calculations are used to interpret the data:

- Mean of scores
- Percentages

Calculating mean and percentages helps to clarify the data obtained in evaluation.

Mean of Scores

The mean of a set of scores is simply the average score. To calculate the mean, add all the scores of the test, and divide by the number of scores.

Percentage

Determining **percentages** is another calculation commonly performed during the evaluation process. A percentage is a part of the whole expressed in hundredths.

For example, consider a presentation on home escape plans presented to a civic group. There were 40 people in the audience. A week after the presentation, a survey was sent to each participant to determine whether or not they had completed a home escape plan because of the presentation. Thirty of the participants returned the survey. Of those, 20 had completed a home escape plan because of the presentation.

In this example, it is necessary to calculate two percentages:

1. Percentage of participants who returned the survey
2. Percentage of participants who did a home escape plan because of the presentation

To calculate the percentage of participants who returned the survey, divide the number of participants who returned the survey by the total number of participants who received the survey and then multiply by 100:

$$\text{Percentage (\%)} = \frac{30}{40} = 75\%$$

Based on this calculation, 75% of the participants completed the survey.

The next calculation is the percentage of participants who did a home escape plan because of the presentation. To calculate the percentage, divide the number of participants who completed a home escape plan by the number of participants who returned the survey:

$$\text{Percentage (\%)} = \frac{20}{30} = 66\%$$

Based on this calculation, 66% of the participants who returned the survey developed a home escape plan because of the presentation. This may not represent the actual number of participants who did the home escape plan because 25% of the surveys were not returned.

Another use of percentages is in the evaluation of skills test. For example, to evaluate a presentation given to 25 new fathers on proper placement of children in safety seats, calculate the percentage of fathers who successfully completed the skills test. Of the 25 fathers tested, 19 successfully placed the child in the safety seat during the skills test.

To calculate this percentage, divide the number of fathers who successfully completed the skills test by the number of fathers taking the skills test:

$$\text{Percentage (\%)} = \frac{19}{25} = 76\%$$

Based on this calculation, 76% of the fathers were successful in the skills test.

Interpretation of Data

Developing conclusions about program impact is based on an objective interpretation of evaluation results. After calculations have been completed, it is necessary to consider one or all of the following to develop a conclusion:

- The difference between the average pretest and posttest scores

- Any patterns in the scores such as specific questions that are missed, lack of improvement in any one area, or confusion about specific behaviors

- The differences in scores from one presentation to another or from one target audience to another

- The outcome objectives for the presentation

The desired outcome (as identified in the learning objectives) is compared with actual knowledge gain. Previously defined benchmarks determine program success or establish the need for remedial or repeated programs.

Each type of fire and life safety education presentation or program presents different evaluation needs and criteria. Regardless of the type of presentation, it is important to take the time to carefully review all the information and the meaning of the information.

Tips for Interpreting Results of an Evaluation

Make sure that the evaluation method is appropriate for the presentation.

- Develop a good evaluation strategy before the presentation.

- Seek help during the planning stage if assistance is needed to develop an evaluation tool.

- Explain the purpose of the evaluation to the target audience, especially if they are adults. This will help to ensure that the audience provides accurate and serious responses.

- Consider each piece of information gained from the evaluation. Consider also the evaluation results of other similar presentations.

- Ask why if the evaluation indicates the outcome objectives were not achieved. Think about how the presentation affected the outcome. Could program changes improve the presentation?

- Ask for help from an experienced resource if the results are unclear or if it is difficult to develop a conclusion. The results of the evaluation could have a significant impact on the presentation. Do not make presentation changes based on invalid conclusions.

Assistance with Evaluation

Many fire and life safety educators use commercial life safety curricula such as products developed by the National Fire Protection Association® or the Home Safety Council. Most programs of this type come with evaluation instruments as well as an evaluation strategy. Take advantage of the accompanying evaluation instruments, which have already been validated and are designed to specifically evaluate the information presented in the program.

The best local resources for help with evaluation are other professional educators. Teachers, college professors, principals, and injury prevention specialists routinely develop and implement evaluation instruments. These resources are generally qualified and willing to provide help with fire and life safety programs.

Personnel from other local and state groups and agencies are potential resources for help with evaluation:

- County health departments

- State extension offices

- County and state fire marshals

- State fire training agencies

- Marketing firms and other consulting groups

- Fire and life safety educators

- Local governmental analysts

- University or community colleges

- Fire Corps members

When designing a risk-reduction lesson, program, or strategy do not forget to budget for evaluation costs. Experts recommend adding 10 to 20% of the total program cost for evaluation.

Reporting Results of Impact Studies

Once an impact study has been completed, results should be reported to staff, decision-makers, and the community at-large. An evaluation report does not have to be lengthy or technical. It should be written in simple, straightforward language and include the following:

- The purpose of the evaluation (what it set out to prove)
- Type of evaluation conducted (questionnaire, interview, observational survey)
- Explanation of the evaluation instrument used
- Profile of the population(s) studied
- Number of participants
- Criteria of what was examined during the study
- What was proven as a result of the evaluation
- Challenges associated with the study
- Results that are documented in an objective, nonbiased manner

Chapter Summary

Evaluation is a planned process that is used to measure the success and challenges of risk-reduction lessons, programs, and initiatives. A good evaluation process requires careful planning on the part of Level II managers. In some cases, evaluation will require the assistance of other educators. In all cases, evaluation is a valuable tool that should be an integral part of every program.

Evaluation should be an ongoing process that is integrated into all risk-reduction strategies. The information gleaned from evaluation forms the basis of an ongoing and continually updated action plan. Evaluation must be given the same importance as any tool or process used by fire and life safety educators. Effective evaluation is the only way to know whether presentation and program outcome objectives are being achieved.

Review Questions

1. What is the process for developing an evaluation strategy to measure the outcomes of a risk-reduction program?

2. What is the process for designing an evaluation instrument that measures the outcomes of a risk-reduction program?

3. What is the general procedure for implementing an evaluation strategy for a risk-reduction program?

Key Terms

Baseline Data — Data collected before a lesson or program is implemented.

Direct Inspection — Used when an evaluator wants to physically examine an environment in search of proof that behavioral change has occurred.

Evaluation Instrument — An instrument designed to collect data so changes in knowledge, behaviors, environments, and lifestyles can be evaluated.

Evaluation Plan — Component of an intervention strategy that includes the problem statement, goal, and a series of measurable objectives that support the goal.

Evaluation Strategy — Plan that details how a risk-reduction program will be examined for effectiveness.

Nonstructured (Open-Ended) Question — A question that does not offer a list of answer choices. Respondents are simply asked to write their response to the question.

Observational Survey — Used when evaluators want to observe if behavioral, environmental, or lifestyle changes are occurring among a target population.

Partially-Structured Question — Used in cases where the researcher has some idea of potential responses that may be generated by respondents.

Percentage — Part of a whole expressed in hundredths.

Structured Question — A question that offers the respondent a closed set of responses from which to choose.

Survey Questionnaire — Survey that uses a series of questions to obtain data from respondents.

Chapter 11 Notes

The process of evaluation – National Fire Academy Risk Reduction Curriculum

Science Buddies. The Kenneth Lafferty Hess Family Charitable Foundation.

1. Demonstrating Your Program's Worth – A Primer on Evaluation for Programs to Prevent Unintentional Injury. Centers for Disease Control and Prevention. March 2000.

2. Public Fire Education Planning – A Five Step Process. Federal Emergency Management Agency. August, 2002.

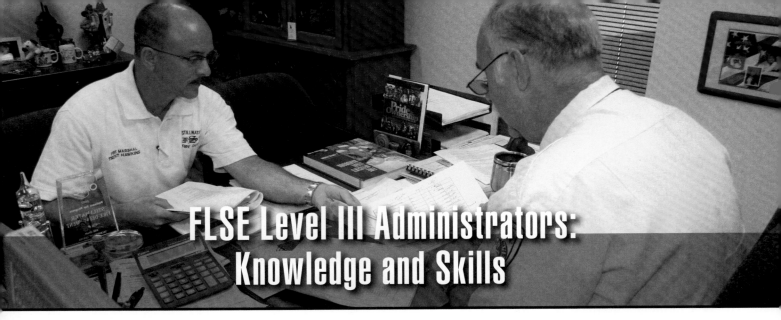

FLSE Level III Administrators: Knowledge and Skills

Chapter Contents

chapter 12

Key Terms

Job Performance Requirements

This chapter provides information that addresses the following job performance requirements of NFPA® 1035, *Standard for Professional Qualifications for Fire and Life Safety Educator, Public Information Officer, and Juvenile Firesetter Intervention Specialist*, 2010 edition.

NFPA® 1035 References

6.1.2

7.1.1

Learning Objectives

After reading this chapter, students will be able to:

1. Explain the purposes of organizational policy and procedures (NFPA® 1035, 7.1.1).

2. Explain the five types of prevention interventions (5 Es) (NFPA® 1035, 6.1.2).

3. Explain the reasons prevention interventions work most effectively when used in tandem with one another (NFPA® 1035, 6.1.2).

4. Summarize the four levels of prevention recognized by public health officials (NFPA® 1035, 6.1.2).

5. Compare and contrast the difference between the terms "Pub-Ed" and "Community Risk Reduction" (NFPA® 1035, 6.1.2).

6. Explain how societal and risk trends can be predicted and addressed using a community-based approach (NFPA® 1035, 6.1.2).

Chapter 12
FLSE Level III Administrators: Knowledge and Skills

Case History

A fire department serving a community of 57,000 worked hard to promote the use of smoke alarms in its community. Over ten years, it invested over $70,000 in billboards, street signs, apparatus posters, television commercials, and radio ads that encouraged citizens to equip their homes with smoke alarms. It has been the only prevention strategy used by the department.

Despite its large investment in advertising, the department continued to respond to over 200 significant residential fires each year. Sadly, investigation revealed that only a fraction of the homes where serious fires occurred had working smoke alarm protection.

In an effort to reduce fire incidents and increase smoke alarm presence and operability, the fire department hired its first community risk-reduction officer (program administrator). Department leadership expected the new officer to help them develop and implement a comprehensive community risk-reduction plan.

The first task addressed was to analyze the department's policies and procedures pertaining to community risk reduction. It become readily apparent that in the department's procedures, community risk-reduction was not a priority. The officer worked closely with the fire chief, shift commanders, and company officers to create and adopt new procedures which allowed the fire companies to be more involved in community risk-reduction activities in their first response districts.

With this new support system in place, the program administrator created a community partnership to tackle the smoke alarm problem. A multipart strategy was implemented, which involved the fire companies. After a year, over 80% of the homes in high-risk neighborhoods had working smoke alarms. In the third, fourth, and fifth years of the program, there were no fire deaths or injuries in the high-risk neighborhoods, which was a significant decrease in the fire problem.

Level III administrators are expected to understand and advise educators in the lower two levels and actively participate in the advancement of risk reduction as an institutionalized priority. Reducing community risk is a process that requires knowledge, skill, and teamwork.

A quick review of the NFPA® 1035 levels of achievement regarding the fire and life safety educator follows:

- The Level I educator primarily presents programs developed by a Level II manager and must understand the relevant instructional methodologies and practice safe and ethical instruction. He or she must also be able to document and evaluate prevention activities so that informed decisions can be made about modifications to future programs.

- The Level II manager is responsible for creating community risk-reduction programs based on a plan established by the Level III administrator, as well as leading and evaluating programs. Leadership, program development skills, and an understanding of combined prevention interventions (Five Es) are important components of this process.

- The Level III administrator should master the skills necessary at the earlier two levels in order to effectively oversee the entire risk-reduction process. The primary responsibilities at this level are strategic in nature and will be explained at length in this and the next four chapters.

> When referring to the three levels of fire and life safety educators, the following terms are used: Level I is *educator;* Level II is *manager;* and Level III is *administrator.*

Most administrators performing tasks associated with Level III are experienced fire and life safety educators who have been leading fire and life safety initiatives for years. Although these educators perform administrative level duties, most still develop, deliver, and evaluate risk-reduction programs (**Figure 12.1**). Remaining an active practitioner allows administrators to maintain skill proficiencies.

This chapter provides a broad overview of professional development, organizational policy, budgeting, strategic planning, prevention interventions, and the future of reducing risk.

Enhancing Professional Development Through Continuing Education

People use personal experience and knowledge to refine a specific skill set. Both resources work in tandem to empower a person with insight and understanding of a subject. While experience does impart knowledge, formalized training can help enhance the depth at which a person understands a subject.

Analyzing risk issues and developing strategic solutions is a skill set that must be possessed by a Level III administrator. Advanced training can help educators obtain this skill set. Many local, state, and national institutions offer higher education opportunities for educators to refine their abilities to lead risk-reduction efforts (**Figure 12.2**). The opportunities available at the state and federal level are often low cost or free. Many offer college credit upon completion.

The Village Fire Company Model

The Village Fire Company Model is a decentralized approach to providing all aspects of fire protection to the community. This model places the responsibility of providing fire suppression, fire and life safety education, fire code enforcement, and community relations on the fire company personnel assigned to the first-due district (referred to as the "Village"). Personnel are taught how to identify specific risks and other quantifiable trends through data analysis as well as how to develop or select a prevention program to help manage each specific risk. Personnel are also trained in fire and life safety education, code enforcement, inspections, as well as to provide the support by department administration to manage those programs in their respective village.

The benefit of allowing the individual company personnel to coordinate and participate in community programs within their village is that the community members begin to recognize the fire company as "their fire company" and become more receptive to fire and life safety messages. The key to making this type of approach successful is convincing company personnel to take ownership in their village.

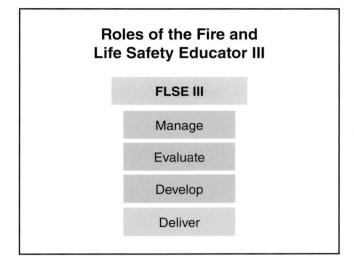

Roles of the Fire and Life Safety Educator III

FLSE III

Manage

Evaluate

Develop

Deliver

Figure 12.1 Level III administrators perform many functions within the risk-reduction process.

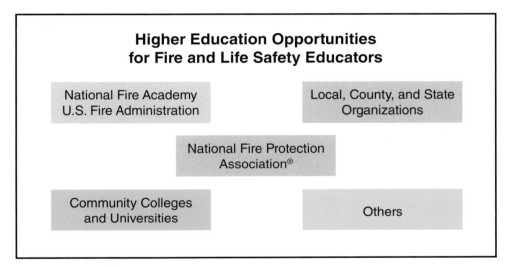

Higher Education Opportunities for Fire and Life Safety Educators

National Fire Academy U.S. Fire Administration

Local, County, and State Organizations

National Fire Protection Association®

Community Colleges and Universities

Others

Figure 12.2 Risk analysis and strategy development are two necessary skills that an administrator will need to develop through continuing education.

In addition to gaining valuable knowledge, an educator who seeks higher education sets an example for others to follow. Level III administrators are leaders who encourage and support the advanced training of subordinates.

Organizational Policy and Procedures

Most organizations have established policies and procedures that support their agency's mission. These guidelines are in place to help facilitate operations in a safe, ethical, and productive manner.

The Level III administrator should help create and be knowledgeable of his or her organization's policies and procedures, which outline how the agency's risk-reduction mission is to be carried out. Because the Level III administrator may supervise others, he or she must ensure that subordinates understand and comply with the organization's standard operating procedures **(Figure 12.3, p. 310)**. These procedures include, but are not limited to:

● Protocol for interacting with peers and the general public

● The organization's code of expected conduct and ethics

● Guidelines that promote a safe working environment

● Roles and responsibilities of Level I educators and Level II managers

● Purchasing guidelines of the organization

● Communication protocols for disseminating information

The most important skill required of the Level III administrator is the ability to create and lead an organization's risk-reduction process. The nationally

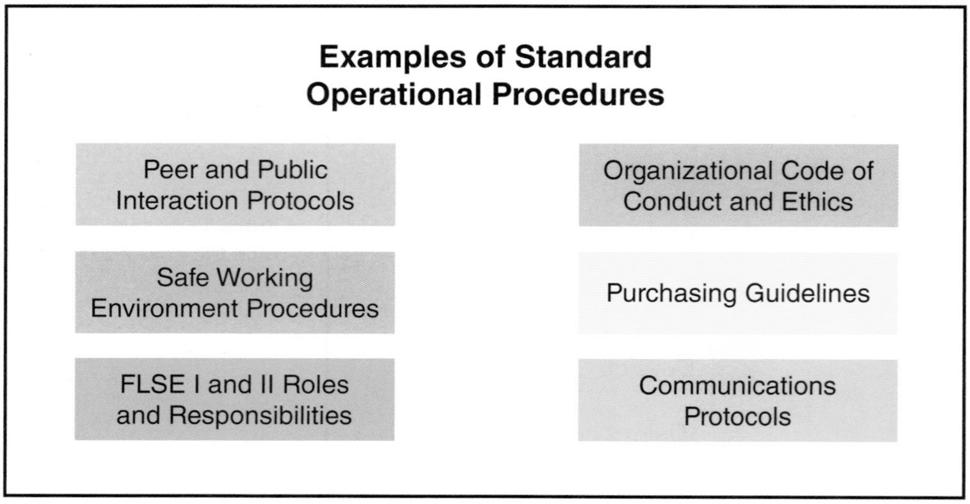

Figure 12.3 Standard operational procedures provide a framework of rules and expectations in an organization.

Examples of Standard Operational Procedures

Peer and Public Interaction Protocols

Organizational Code of Conduct and Ethics

Safe Working Environment Procedures

Purchasing Guidelines

FLSE I and II Roles and Responsibilities

Communications Protocols

recognized five-step planning process promotes a strategic approach to risk reduction. The model was discussed extensively in several previous chapters because educators operating at all levels must understand its importance and application.

The third step in the five-step planning process calls for administrators to identify prevention interventions that, when strategically employed, have logical potential to mitigate a selected risk. The intervention is one or a series of the Five Es (Education, Engineering, Enforcement, Economic Incentives, and Emergency Response).

Interventions are chosen after the risk has been analyzed to identify a common sequence of events that lead to its occurrence. Once a sequential pattern has been identified, the administrator can recommend steps within the sequence where interventions can be employed. It is a proven fact that use of multiple interventions has the best potential to mitigate an event.

Prevention Interventions

As a risk-reduction strategist, Level III administrators must be able to apply use of multiple prevention mediums. Prevention interventions are described as follows:

- *Education interventions.* Designed to raise awareness, provide information, impart knowledge, and ultimately produce a desired behavior. It is important to note that education provides a foundation for the entire prevention intervention system. People must be aware of a problem and understand how their actions can affect a solution through directed action. This includes populations who design engineering interventions or make public policy changes.

Education is the foundation of prevention and should be used as a core intervention strategy. However, used alone, education is often a weak intervention. The most effective strategies are those that involve combined use of education, technology, standards, codes, and adequate emergency response **(Figure 12.4)**.

- *Engineering interventions.* Designed to change vehicles, products, materials, and processes to make them less hazardous, or to alter an environment to make it safer. Examples related to fire safety include the various types of smoke alarms, flame-resistive furnishings, self-extinguishing cigarettes, and sprinkler systems.

- *Enforcement interventions.* Refer to all the ways in which people are required to act to mitigate risk. Examples related to fire safety include ordinances, laws, and building codes that require the installation of smoke detection and sprinkler systems.

- *Economic incentives.* Used to support the previously listed interventions. Examples of positive incentives include reduced insurance premiums for buildings having fire-resistive construction, sprinklers, and automatic notification systems. Examples of negative incentives include fines for violating fire codes.

- *Emergency response.* An important intervention that must never be overlooked. Because risk will never be completely eradicated, communities must have an adequately staffed, trained, and equipped emergency response system.

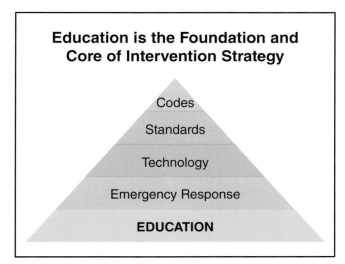

Education is the Foundation and Core of Intervention Strategy

- Codes
- Standards
- Technology
- Emergency Response
- **EDUCATION**

Figure 12.4 Education is a weak intervention on its own, but it provides a foundation and structure for other interventions.

Rationale for Combining Prevention Interventions

It is very tempting to rely on education as the only risk-reduction strategy. However, this practice is strongly discouraged.

Consider, for example, the fire problem in the U.S. In the late 1960s, over ten thousand people were being killed annually by fire. Thanks to the creation of smoke alarms, deaths dropped by several thousand within a few years. Yet, decades later, the U.S. continues to exhibit one of the worst fire death rates among the developed countries.

Factors contributing to residential fire deaths include:

- Lack of working smoke alarms

- Delayed 9-1-1 notification as residents attempt to fight a fire in progress

- Rapid spread of toxic smoke from combustible materials

- Absence of a pre-arranged family escape plan

Educational initiatives have been in place for many years; however, overall improvement has remained stagnant. Imagine the potential impact and outcome of requiring the following modifications to take place within residential properties and communities at-large:

- Installation of interconnected tamper-proof smoke alarms

- Residential sprinklers

- Alarms and sprinklers tied to automatic notification systems

- Fire-resistive building construction

- Fire-resistive furnishings

- Child-resistant lighters

- Stoves with burners that produce a restricted amount of heat

- Portable heaters that produce a restricted amount of heat

- Reduced insurance premiums for compliance with relevant initiatives

- Ordinances prohibiting clutter and large fire loads

- Stiff penalties for fires caused by grossly negligent behavior

- Fire departments whose staffing and response meets NFPA® standards 1710 and 1720

Though a tremendous undertaking, this strategy should be considered in the long-term vision for the emergency services. Many developing communities are already embracing this approach by enacting Adequate Public Facilities Ordinances (APFO) that support proactive and comprehensive risk reduction.

Educating the constituency and decision-makers builds a foundation for which higher-order initiatives can be proposed. However, it should be the goal of Level III administrators to move toward integration of combined prevention interventions as long-term risk mitigation reduction strategies.

Levels of Prevention

Level III administrators are also expected to be able to collaborate with public health officials to address risk-related issues. Understanding terminology common to public health broadens the administrator's outlook on how to mitigate risk in a strategic and collaborative manner.

Prevention is an active process of creating conditions that promote the well-being of communities. Public health officials view prevention as any activity which reduces morbidity or mortality from disease. The emergency services take a very similar view. Instead of limiting their focus to disease, they monitor preventable, human-created risks to life and safety **(Table 12.1, p. 312)**.

Table 12.1
Levels of Prevention

Level:	Purpose:	Examples:

Primary (Universal)	• Circumvent events that might result in injury, death, or property loss
	• Improve the well-being of a healthy population
		• Community education
		• Reinforces healthy behaviors and discourages unsafe/unhealthy lifestyles
		• Venues
		  – School-based programs
		  – Community-based programs
		  – Open houses
		  – Public service announcements
		  – Community-wide home safety surveys

Secondary (Selective)	• Mitigate or modify events to reduce their severity
	• Aimed at people who may appear healthy but might be at high risk
	• Confirmed high-risk populations:
	  – Very young children
	  – Older adults
	  – People with disabilities
	  – Populations affected by poverty
	• Other high-risk populations
	  – Smokers
	  – Populations with chronic medical conditions
	  – Substance abusers
		• Prevention interventions that are employed after an incident has occurred are forms of secondary prevention
		• Activation of smoke alarms, sprinklers and emergency response to incidents are examples of secondary levels of prevention

Indicated	• A component of secondary prevention • Involves a screening process to identify individuals who exhibit early signs of disease, behavioral or environmental problems that may place them at higher risk from preventable harm	• Screening for hypertension • Influenza vaccination clinics • Juvenile firesetting intervention programs • Inspections and home surveys in high-risk areas • Any initiative that targets confirmed high-risk populations
Tertiary	• Reduce the negative impact caused by a disease, injury, or condition to prevent further complications or recurrence	• Rehabilitation aimed at returning a functioning patient to society

Administrators are not expected to be **epidemiologists**. However, it is important to recognize that similarities exist between preventing chronic disease and the mitigation of community risk. The public health community is an excellent resource for collaboration on community-risk identification and development of mitigation strategies.

Public Fire Safety Education vs. Community Risk Reduction

The difference between the historical term **public fire education** and the more contemporary title of *community risk reduction* deserves examination during this introductory chapter for Level III administrators. The use of a strategic process to mitigate risk entails using all levels of prevention interventions strategically. As communities and risk issues diversify, many administrators are being called upon to examine risk in a broader scope. This includes evaluating the wide span of natural and human-created problems that currently threaten or have potential to endanger the communities we serve.

The United States Fire Administration places great emphasis on reducing the fire problem in the U.S. In addition, the USFA has introduced several broad risk-reduction benchmarks that call for the emergency services to take the lead in creating partnerships aimed at addressing "all-hazard" risks that threaten local communities.

The five step planning process coupled with use of integrated prevention interventions creates an approach that can be applied to most forms of natural and human-created hazards. Developing a mitigation strategy that includes an evaluation plan helps guide a risk-reduction team with a time-sensitive measurable approach to threat reduction.

Considering an "all-hazard approach" to risk mitigation is not a call for the fire service to abandon its long-standing mission of fire prevention. What is recommended is the formation of interagency partnerships to evaluate, prioritize, and plan to address local community risks in a strategic manner.

Administrators must become adept at soliciting and facilitating support from nontraditional sources so that collaborative partnerships are formed to enhance and expand risk-mitigation initiatives. While many partners may be external to the emergency services, they are important **stakeholders** in the overall health of a community.

Interagency Networks

The Home Safety Literacy Project brought the Home Safety Council, ProLiteracy Worldwide, and Oklahoma State University's Fire Protection Publications together to address fire safety and disaster preparedness among literacy-challenged populations. The project was further enhanced through receipt of two Fire Prevention and Safety Grants through the U.S. Department of Homeland Security.

Analyzing the Future and Planning Accordingly

Expanding risks, population diversity, economic fluctuation, and advancing technology are factors that can affect the vitality of a community and must be closely monitored by risk-mitigation strategists. Changes in risk occurrences will usually become evident as incident data are monitored over several years. Professional planners can predict population changes by monitoring migration patterns to and from a community. Economists forecast change by examining housing and employment patterns. This information is best obtained through open lines of communication with local government, population experts, and the community at-large.

An administrator must exhibit proficiency in analyzing short- and long-term needs of the community that relate to risk mitigation. Stakeholders with an interest in a safe and vibrant community are natural partners for risk mitigation.

Seeking **partnerships** from local government, target populations, community leaders, businesses, corporations, service groups, property owners, and investors is an example of how to broaden the effectiveness of a risk mitigation planning team **(Figure 12.5, p. 314)**. It also serves as a mechanism to expand the pool of resources available for addressing selected risks.

Viewing risk as a community problem also creates a rationale for using delivery systems that may previously have been overlooked by the emergency services. For example, many communities already have active neighborhood associations, Fire Corps, and other service-minded groups. As communities diversify, advocacy groups may have members who can offer expert advice on how to best address cultural and language diversity in an appropriate and effective manner.

Finally, the Level III administrator must be adept at predicting what future risk mitigation resources will be needed by his or her organization over a five to ten year span. As communities expand, so does the need for trained staff who can professionally create, lead, deliver, and evaluate risk prevention and reduction strategies.

Figure 12.5 A risk mitigation planning team should include a diverse panel of participants in order to represent as much of the community as possible.

Prospective Risk Mitigation Planning Team Partners

Investors

Local Government

Property Owners

Target Populations

Risk Mitigation Planning Team

Service Groups

Community Leaders

Corporations

Businesses

Chapter Summary

Advancing technology is generating a greater mass of message media that can be used to reach consumers with educational information. From buildings to vehicles, safety protection is being engineered into products that offer higher levels of passive defense from risk.

Many consumers not only support, but they expect preventive interventions to be engineered into their living environments. Administrators are obliged to support and help facilitate these higher-order enhancements. Safer communities are created when local government, the emergency services, and community members work in synergy to mitigate risks.

Review Questions

1. What is the purpose of organizational policies and procedures?

2. What are the five prevention interventions?

3. Why do prevention interventions work most effectively when used together?

4. What are the four levels of prevention recognized by public health officials?

5. What is the difference between the term *public education* and *community risk reduction*?

6. How are societal and risk trends predicted and then addressed using a community risk-reduction approach?

Key Terms

Epidemiologist — A professional who scientifically analyzes the occurrence of morbidity and mortality.

Partnerships — Joining forces with other groups to address common interests.

Public Fire Education —A systematic approach to designing, implementing, and evaluating community safety education programs.

Stakeholders — People, groups, or organizations that have vested interest in a specific issue.

Chapter 12 Notes

Integrated Prevention Interventions. National Fire Academy Risk Reduction Curriculum.

NFPA® 1710: *Standad for the Organization and Deployment of Fire Suppression Operations, Emergency Medical Operations, and Special Operations to the Public by Career Fire Depatments.* National Fire Protection Association, Quincy, MA.

NFPA® 1720: *Standard for the Organization and Deployment of Fire Suppression Operations, Emergency Medical Operations, and Special Operations to the Public by Volunteer Fire Departments,* National Fire Protection Association, Quincy, MA.

FLSE Level III Administrators: Administration

Chapter Contents

chapter 13

Key Terms

Job Performance Requirements

This chapter provides information that addresses the following job performance requirements of NFPA® 1035, *Standard for Professional Qualifications for Fire and Life Safety Educator, Public Information Officer, and Juvenile Firesetter Intervention Specialist*, 2010 edition.

NFPA® 1035 References

7.2.1

7.2.2

FLSE Level III Administrators: Administration

Learning Objectives

After reading this chapter, students will be able to:

1. Explain how to develop an organization's fire and life safety education budget. (NFPA® 1035, 7.2.1)

2. Describe the two sections or categories of an operating budget. (NFPA® 1035, 7.2.1)

3. Describe how to determine and justify operating costs in a program budget. (NFPA® 1035, 7.2.1)

4. Describe alternate systems of program development and delivery that can be used to support a risk mitigation strategy. (NFPA® 1035, 7.2.2)

5. Explain how to sustain a risk-mitigation strategy through use of nontraditional approaches. (NFPA® 1035, 7.2.2)

Chapter 13
FLSE Level III Administrators: Administration

Case History

In the early 1990s, the Las Vegas (NV) Fire and EMS community decided to tackle the challenge of low cardiac arrest survival rate in the community. The city had a dismal survival rate of around 4 percent. As part of a Hotel Life Safety Program, a simultaneous effort by Clark County Fire Department and Las Vegas City Fire Department trained hotel security guards in hotels and casinos on the Las Vegas strip and in downtown Las Vegas in the use of automated external defibrillators (AEDs). Staff from the Clark County Fire Department coordinated the scheduling, solicited vendors, and marketed the program to the hotel casino executives. Firefighters and paramedics provided the instruction, and the initial deployment of the AED was provided through a grant from Physiocontrol.™

In July 1997, a 63-year-old North Carolina textile worker named Thurman Austin came to Las Vegas with his wife. Mr. Austin gambled until late, rose early, and smoked practically nonstop. He thought little of an episode of chest pain that came and went. As Mr. Austin played slots one afternoon at the Stardust, he blacked out and cracked his head on a machine as he tumbled to the floor. In less than three minutes, Stardust security officers were delivering a shock to Mr. Austin using an AED. Prior to the ambulance arrival, Mr. Austin regained consciousness. He was telling his story to the media the next day.

Las Vegas casino security officers have restored the heartbeats of about 1,800 gamblers and employees in the past ten years, according to the Clark County Fire Department. The survival rate has risen to 74 percent when a defibrillator is used within three minutes of the patient collapsing.

Today, community standards are in place putting an AED within 90 seconds of anyplace on the property. The program has spread to the suburbs of Henderson and North Las Vegas and has continued to be supported by EMS or fire and life safety educators in the metropolitan Clark County. Henderson, Nevada, has placed AEDs in police cars. The AED has become commonplace in most federal and public buildings. Most of this effort was due to congressional testimony provided by Clark County Fire Department EMS and public education personnel.

Source: Valenzuela, Terence D et al. "Outcomes of Rapid Defibrillation by Security Officers after Cardiac Arrest in Casinos." New England Journal of Medicine. 343, No 17, (2000): 1206-9.

Level III administrators oversee the entire risk-reduction process. Leading that process requires the ability to develop a comprehensive budget to support risk reduction. This chapter provides specific information on budgeting and formulating alternative systems of program development and delivery. Both are important administrative components of a risk-reduction process.

The Level III Administrator and Budget Proposals

Most municipalities require budget proposals to be submitted several months in advance of the actual fiscal starting date. This action is necessary so decision-makers have adequate time to discuss and make disposition on proposals. Systems of government usually require municipalities to submit a balanced budget by a specific date, which is often called a **milestone budget date**.

The Level III administrator should have his or her proposed risk-reduction budget submitted to superiors well in advance of internal deadlines

(Figure 13.1). Continuing evaluation of community risk issues, trends, and mitigation strategies guide the Level III administrator to an awareness of budgetary needs. As the developer of his or her department's risk-reduction budget, the Level III administrator needs to understand how to determine and justify monies needed to subsidize the entire risk-reduction process.

Finances for public safety are usually drawn from a **general municipal fund**. The general fund provides revenue and expenditures of unrestricted municipal purposes and for all necessary financial transactions not accounted for in any other fund.

The general fund is usually the largest and most important accounting activity managed by a community or organization. Financial support of this fund is received from a variety of sources, including property taxes, earnings and profits taxes, utility taxes, service charges, interest and rental income, grants, business licenses, permits, and franchise fees.

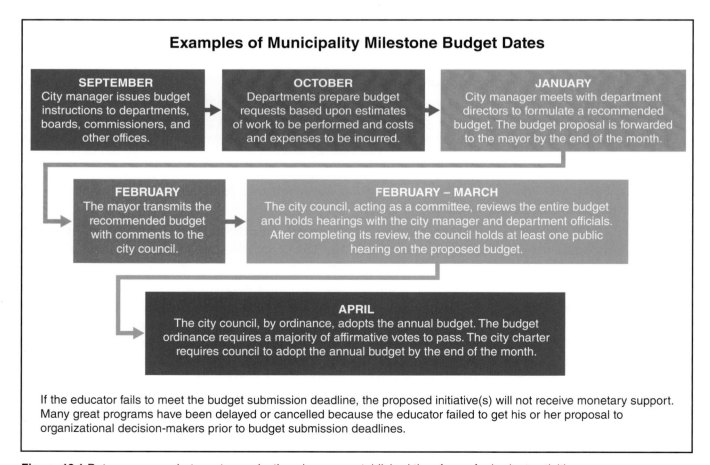

Examples of Municipality Milestone Budget Dates

SEPTEMBER
City manager issues budget instructions to departments, boards, commissioners, and other offices.

OCTOBER
Departments prepare budget requests based upon estimates of work to be performed and costs and expenses to be incurred.

JANUARY
City manager meets with department directors to formulate a recommended budget. The budget proposal is forwarded to the mayor by the end of the month.

FEBRUARY
The mayor transmits the recommended budget with comments to the city council.

FEBRUARY – MARCH
The city council, acting as a committee, reviews the entire budget and holds hearings with the city manager and department officials. After completing its review, the council holds at least one public hearing on the proposed budget.

APRIL
The city council, by ordinance, adopts the annual budget. The budget ordinance requires a majority of affirmative votes to pass. The city charter requires council to adopt the annual budget by the end of the month.

If the educator fails to meet the budget submission deadline, the proposed initiative(s) will not receive monetary support. Many great programs have been delayed or cancelled because the educator failed to get his or her proposal to organizational decision-makers prior to budget submission deadlines.

Figure 13.1 Dates may vary, but most organizations have an established time frame for budget activities.

Nonprofit volunteer departments often use budgetary practices similar to the municipal government. Funding for prevention programs may begin in a general type fund and then be channeled through a committee or other oversight system.

The general fund has categories through which monies are allocated for use. In municipalities, funding for risk reduction is usually dispersed through a category entitled "operating budget."

Operations Budget

Expenditures in an operations budget usually include operating and personnel costs. Operating costs are the expenses needed to help create, evaluate, and sustain a risk-reduction strategy **(Figure 13.2)**. In general, the largest expense of municipal government is personnel costs, which include salaries, wages, and benefits.

Operating Costs

Before formulating a budget for risk mitigation, the Level III administrator should meet with his or her superiors who are responsible for submitting the budget for the entire division or organization. This action is necessary to help ensure that the administrator is submitting requests in a manner that corresponds with organizational protocol.

Administrators should be aware that the preferred format of budget proposals is unique to each organization. Several software interfaces offer programs that greatly aid in the collection of data. For best results, administrators should consult with staff members who are already doing similar jobs before creating a new system.

The Level III administrator should have itemized budget summaries of each risk-reduction program that comprises the overall strategy. The summaries do not have to be included in the budget proposal but should be available for review should superiors have questions related to specific programs or initiatives. (**NOTE:** An example of an itemized budget for a *specific* risk-reduction program can be found in Chapter 8.)

Personnel Costs

An employee is paid a salary or wage in order to perform a level of service, as well as to receive benefits such as health insurance and retirement contributions paid on his or her behalf.

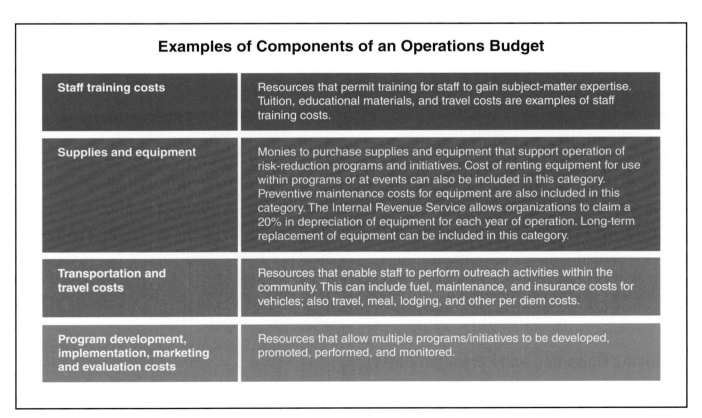

Examples of Components of an Operations Budget

Staff training costs	Resources that permit training for staff to gain subject-matter expertise. Tuition, educational materials, and travel costs are examples of staff training costs.
Supplies and equipment	Monies to purchase supplies and equipment that support operation of risk-reduction programs and initiatives. Cost of renting equipment for use within programs or at events can also be included in this category. Preventive maintenance costs for equipment are also included in this category. The Internal Revenue Service allows organizations to claim a 20% in depreciation of equipment for each year of operation. Long-term replacement of equipment can be included in this category.
Transportation and travel costs	Resources that enable staff to perform outreach activities within the community. This can include fuel, maintenance, and insurance costs for vehicles; also travel, meal, lodging, and other per diem costs.
Program development, implementation, marketing and evaluation costs	Resources that allow multiple programs/initiatives to be developed, promoted, performed, and monitored.

Figure 13.2 An operations budget includes operating and personnel costs.

The salaries of most full-time risk-reduction educators are based upon a 40-hour work week. Exceptions sometimes occur in the case of negotiated contractual agreements between labor groups and municipalities. Overtime pay is due employees whose weekly work hours exceed set standards. In general, overtime rates are usually 1.5 times the employee's hourly rate. Level III administrators need to understand overtime budgeting so that compliance with the nationally recognized Fair Labor Standards Act (FLSA) is maintained. The FLSA is a federal law requiring employers to compensate employees at a pay/comp rate of time-and-a-half for services performed off-duty in the local community on behalf of the agency where the individual is employed.

A full-time person costs an organization more than what is paid in salary or wages. The common costs of employing a person often include the following:

- Federal, state, and local taxes
- Social Security and Medicare contributions
- Insurance and workers compensation coverage
- Sick leave
- Holiday and vacation time
- Retirement, pensions, and deferred compensation options

Human resource managers and finance officers can offer valuable advice on how to calculate the cost of hiring an employee. A general rule for estimating the total cost of an employee (salary plus benefits) is to add approximately 20% to the projected base salary of staff employed full time **(Figure 13.3)**.

Volunteer organizations should also be aware of personnel costs. Many organizations employ full-time staff to ensure response to emergency calls. Assigning paid staff to help plan and deliver risk-reduction activities provides an excellent strategy to show added value to the investment of hiring full-time personnel. In busy organizations, it may be necessary to budget for back-filling the position of the staff member assigned to risk-reduction duties so that calls for emergency response may continue to be answered.

Justifying Operating and Personnel Costs

Facilitating a successful risk-reduction process requires the use of resources. Level III administrators should be skilled in determining and justifying the operating and personnel costs needed to support the

risk-reduction process. This is best accomplished by communicating to decision-makers how proposed mitigation initiatives will impact the community in a positive manner. Referencing a pre-established action plan will help strengthen this justification.

Estimating Total Cost of An Employee

($45,000 is used as an example of a position's base salary. Actual salary will vary.)

		$45,000
Step 1: determine 20% of base pay	X	.20
		$9,000
		$45,000
Step 2: determine estimated total cost	+	$9000
		$54,000

Figure 13.3 Full-time personnel are paid more than just a base salary.

What This Means to You

A Level III administrator monitors the entire process of an organization's risk-reduction strategy. In addition to monitoring program development, outreach, and impact, you should conduct an annual review of the organization's response history. This action allows you to examine the effect that mitigation initiatives are having on the occurrence of incidents.

Having accurate knowledge of the overall program outreach, impact, and outcome produced by the organization's risk-reduction strategy allows you to compare program costs against benefits. This is where a well-written evaluation plan becomes invaluable.

It is prudent to examine the number of staff hours that are invested into each risk-reduction activity. This strategy allows staffing costs to be compared with program activity and impact that is being created.

Once a budget is approved, it can be difficult or sometimes not legally possible to reappropriate funds that are dedicated to specific activities. Conducting ongoing cost/benefit analysis will help you make informed decisions about future resource requests and appropriations.

Because you are responsible for the organization's entire risk-reduction process, it is imperative to have open communication with departmental leadership **(Figure 13.4)**. You must understand the organization's long-term plan, priorities, and challenges that may impact future goals.

Figure 13.4 Information sessions help everyone maintain current budget expectations.

Tracking, evaluating, and reporting the progress of the organization's overall risk-reduction process is the responsibility of a Level III administrator. Monitoring the evaluation results of life-safety programs allows the Level III administrator to conduct ongoing cost/benefit analysis on all activities. It can also generate data that proves initiatives are working, thereby creating a rationale for continued or increased levels of support.

Presenting a Budget Proposal to Decision-Makers

The Level III administrator will make an annual budget proposal for the organization's entire risk-reduction strategy to his or her superiors. In addition, presentations to higher level municipal decision-makers may be needed throughout the budget appropriation process.

Developing a well-prepared, easy-to-understand presentation is essential. This applies to both written and verbal presentations. Fact-based rationales, a good plan, clear visuals, and quality printed materials are components of an effective presentation.

The time allotted for the budget presentation may be rigidly defined. Regardless of the administrator's level of formal education, there is no excuse for unprofessional work. Computer programs offer spelling and grammatical help, and multimedia programs enhance the educator's ability to help decision-makers visualize what they are being asked to fund.

An administrator is required to exhibit proficiency at managing the funding for his or her organization's entire risk-reduction process. Regardless of size, most organizations have specific guidelines on how budgeted monies can be spent. If the organization is part of a larger municipality, the local government has even more requirements that must be followed.

Laws often govern how the municipality spends money. These check-and-balance systems are in place as a safeguard for public funds. Accountability and accurate record-keeping are responsibilities of both Level II and III fire and life safety educators.

Most organizations have a purchase requisition system that is used when dispersing funds for a budgeted item. The system usually requires the use of purchase orders and a competitive bid process for items exceeding a specific amount set by the organization. In addition, when using funds acquired through grants, it is imperative to carefully follow and adhere to all guidelines of the grant.

Alternative Systems of Program Development and Delivery

Facilitating an organization's community risk-reduction process is a complex job that requires the Level III administrator to have training and experience. It also requires resources to support the process. While it is a responsibility of the organization to budget resources that support comprehensive risk-reduction initiatives, Level III administrators need to maintain proficiency in designing alternate systems of program development and delivery.

Terminology in Strategic Networking

A Level III administrator must exhibit the ability to formulate alternative systems of program development and delivery so that the **fire and life safety strategy** is sustained in the community through nontraditional approaches. Alternate systems of program development are strategies that seek collaboration from sources external to the emergency services to help develop risk-reduction programs and initiatives.

An *intra-agency* network is collaboration between departments from within the same municipal organization. If the activity occurs between several agencies from within a community, it is called an *interagency network*.

A fire and life safety strategy is a series of activities, programs, and initiatives designed to reduce identified risks within a community. Forming alliances with groups from outside the organization to which the educator is associated is considered a nontraditional approach to risk reduction.

The concept of using alternative systems and nontraditional approaches to risk reduction is not new to the functioning of emergency services. It simply means expanding traditional ways of developing and delivering programs to incorporate the use of external resources. These resources can take the form of products, funding, in-kind services, and other resources **(Figure 13.5)**.

The benefits of networking with other groups and organizations were discussed in several earlier chapters. The concept is revisited here because the formation of partnerships is essential when seeking help from nontraditional sources.

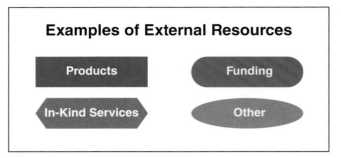

Examples of External Resources

Products

Funding

In-Kind Services

Other

Figure 13.5 Strong partnerships with external organizations pay benefits in more than just increased funding for initiatives.

There are many people and organizations external to the emergency services that have expertise in program development, resource acquisition, marketing, delivery, and evaluation. Level III administrators should consider identifying, recruiting, and using this expertise to advance risk-reduction activity at the local level.

Program Development

In a previous era (circa 1970) of fire prevention, there were a very limited number of partners available to help advance safety-education initiatives. However, this situation changed through the efforts of the federal government, nonprofit institutions, schools, and a small army of dedicated prevention advocates.

Risk-reduction advocates now have a wide variety of resources available as they search for ways to develop a fire and life safety program that will meet their community's needs. These opportunities exist at both the school and community-based levels.

Level III fire and life safety administrators need to be proficient in making decisions regarding whether to purchase predeveloped products, modify existing material, or create custom work. Before asking staff to develop material, administrators should ensure that Level II managers consider external resources that can be used as is or adapted to fit local needs. A cost/benefit analysis can help the administrator make fiscally responsible decisions.

Whether purchasing, modifying, or creating a program, administrators must ensure that it has been evaluated for its educational and behavioral content. The program should show promise at serving local needs and being cost effective. When considering cost effectiveness, examine the amount of effort and expense that would be needed to purchase or modify an existing program versus creating one from scratch.

Sources for Predeveloped School- and Community-Based Life Safety Programs

- **National Fire Protection Association (NFPA®)**: Offers a wide variety of predeveloped school- and community-based life safety educational programs that are age and target audience specific.

- **United States Fire Administration (USFA)**: Offers fire safety education materials to the emergency services and the general public at-large. Materials are available for both school- and community-based use.

- **National SAFE KIDS Campaign**: Materials and programs that target preventable injury among children age 14 and under.

- **Home Safety Council**: Produces a variety of materials that target preventable injury among specific populations. It also offers information on risk issues that affect the general public.

- **Insurance Companies**: Many companies provide prevention materials and programs that target fire and other preventable risks.

- **School-Based Health Curriculums**: All schools have a curriculum that addresses health. Fire and other preventable injury topics are often included in this curriculum.

- **Advocacy Groups**: Many areas have advocacy groups that address specific life safety issues including water safety, fall prevention, and other topics as addressed in Chapter 2.

Networking with peers at the local, state, and national level can help identify school and community-based programs that have proved successful in other locations. This strategy can also lead to obtaining programs used in other areas that may be adapted with permission for local use.

When considering development of school-based material, it is wise to seek collaboration with local education officials. Professional educators should be trained to evaluate and select material for inclusion as school curriculums **(Figure 13.6)**. Emergency services personnel can offer vital input about the educational and behavioral soundness of the material.

Professional educators are also excellent resources for help when developing a fire and life safety program. Although the research and development of educational materials is a Level II skill, the Level III administrator must ensure that the task is being done correctly. All programs must be proven educationally sound, behaviorally correct, and cost efficient. This rule applies to all school and community-based programs **(Figure 13.7)**.

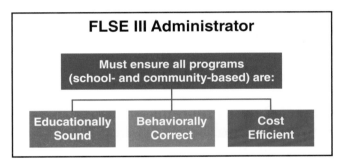

Figure 13.7 All educational programs have requirements in common that must be ensured.

Figure 13.6 Professionals can learn from each other to enhance programs for their target audiences.

Creating an interagency network of organizations that work together to address fire and other preventable injury expands the pool of experts who can help the Level III administrator make informed decisions about using alternative forms of program development and delivery. Cooperation, communication, synergy, and broad-based support ultimately results in greater levels of program outreach, impact, and outcome.

Program Delivery

The best developed programs are ineffective without resources that permit program delivery. Outreach, impact, and outcome are impossible without the resource of people for program delivery.

Earlier chapters presented suggestions for recruiting, training, and evaluating staff from within local agencies to deliver prevention programs. These principles and a few others apply when seeking assistance from external organizations. When asking for assistance with delivery of school or community-based programs, the Level III administrator must have a mechanism in place to recruit, screen (if applicable), train, mentor, and evaluate participants. The following section presents information to consider before designing an alternative system of delivery for school and community-based risk-reduction programs.

School-Based Programs

School-based programs are delivered within a school system. They include in-class lessons, after-school programs, and outreach initiatives. These venues remain effective media for empowering children with lifesaving skills and reaching families with preventative information.

Emergency service organizations that lack a fire and life safety educator sometimes find it challenging to find personnel who are interested in performing school-based services. Metropolitan departments often find it difficult to plan school visits due to large call volumes. A viable option is forging a partnership with schools where professional teachers or parent volunteers can teach safety lessons. The following section discusses potential options for seeking alternatives to emergency service staff presenting school-based programs.

Professional Teaching Staff

Professional teachers are trained in the use of lesson plans and delivery of age-appropriate instruction. Teachers are also experienced at working with special needs students and understand the determinants that drive a school's standard operating guidelines. Professional teachers are also likely to embrace the need for program evaluation because they work in performance-driven school systems.

There are some potential challenges to consider when asking schools to deliver prevention lessons. Curriculum determinants, such as student performance outcomes, often place extreme pressure on teachers. This stress can lead teachers and administrators to politely decline involvement in optional prevention programs in favor of investing time to meet required performance standards.

As discussed in the Level II section, the ultimate aim of the emergency services should be to integrate fire and life safety education into the school's essential curriculum. All school systems have a required health curriculum for students. Various levels of fire safety, injury prevention, and emergency preparedness are usually included in this curriculum. It is important for administrators to have a strong and positive relationship with the local school system so that they can influence the amount and quality of safety education being presented.

Performance Outcomes

School curriculum is driven by the need to demonstrate performance outcomes. Gone are the days of taking a fire truck or ambulance to the school for show and tell. Schools expect, and should be granted, the opportunity for measurable knowledge gain among students.

In many communities, teachers or trained school-based volunteers are assisting the emergency services by presenting safety curriculums to students. Emergency responders visit schools as a follow-up to lessons and to reinforce learning objectives **(Figure 13.8)**.

School-Based Volunteers

Schools often rely heavily on parents, older adults, and volunteer mentors to supplement classroom teachers. School-based volunteers, after undergo-

Figure 13.8 Emergency responders visit schools to confirm that students remember life-saving skills and behaviors.

ing background screening, quickly become valued assistants to their local school, teachers, and students. Many communities enjoy a waiting list of school-based volunteers eager to empower students with knowledge and skills. Whether presented by professional teachers or school-based volunteers, life safety programs must be conducted in a safe, efficient, and competent manner.

The Level III administrator does not have to be directly involved with recruiting, training, or evaluating those who perform alternative forms of program delivery.

However, the administrator is ultimately responsible for ensuring that the instructional delivery, outreach, and impact are evaluated, reported, and enhanced according to need.

Volunteerism in the United States

Volunteers have comprised the backbone of the emergency services for more than a century. While economic factors and social influences have negatively impacted volunteerism in some parts of the United States, the spirit of community service remains strong in others.

Volunteers external to the emergency services provide an alternative nontraditional form of program delivery. The following provides suggestions on preplanning, recruiting strategies, and sustaining alternative forms of program delivery.

Preplanning:

- Create a recruitment plan before recruiting volunteers.

- Define the purpose of involving volunteers as team members before initiating recruitment efforts.

- Identify what positions are needed to accomplish program objectives.

- Consider what skills are needed by prospective volunteers to perform specific tasks.

- Develop a job description that clearly defines what duties the volunteers will perform if they choose to become involved. Use clear, concise language to describe what needs to be done to carry out the assignment. If applicable, describe personality traits and specific personal skills that are desired.

- Define where and when the volunteer will deliver programs. Describe the audiences with which the volunteer will be working.

- Specify the training and orientation that the sponsoring agency will provide.

- Clearly emphasize costs or special requirements that are expected of the participant.

- Clarify the time commitment that will be needed to fulfill the assignment.

- Define the benefits of volunteering to perform services. Examples may include personal satisfaction, the ability to help others, community involvement, learning new skills through training, serving as a positive role model for others, and meeting new people. Highlight these items for inclusion in recruitment efforts.

- Plan for and build a career ladder of experiences and successes for volunteers. Develop a communication strategy so that volunteers will receive feedback on their efforts.

- Decide how volunteers will be evaluated. Develop a mentoring strategy so that each new participant is paired with an experienced staff member.

- Train a group of speakers from the lead organization who can articulate why assistance is needed. These speakers should be good communicators who are truly interested in recruiting volunteer assistants for alternative forms of program delivery.

- Conduct a needs assessment to determine what perception the public presently has of the organization. This directly affects recruiting efforts. If negative perceptions exist among potential volunteers, develop a strategy to address such challenges.

- Determine logical places to conduct recruitment efforts. Networking with peers and other organizations may help identify good places to begin. When recruiting for help in a specific geographical area, such as a neighborhood, examine a cross section of sources such as businesses, churches, local government, and residents.

Recruiting Strategies:

- Recruit groups rather than individuals. This strategy is particularly effective with younger volunteers and very active adults who may not have spare time for a new commitment.

- Create short-term commitments. Many people are afraid of getting tied into a volunteer commitment that exceeds their availability of time. A person or team may be willing to become involved if their commitment of time could be staggered or rotated.

- Encourage family units to volunteer together. The job can be structured to emphasize skills that can be taught and experienced among family members. These situations should be designed around short-term opportunities that offer challenging and interesting assignments for various age levels within a family unit.

- Recruit corporate involvement. Teams from corporations with the same program emphasis will come together for a short-term assignment where

visibility for their companies can be seen. Teams may wear shirts or hats with their company logo on them. Their work can be captured through photos.

- Consider high school and college students. Many school and university systems require students to complete a specified level of volunteer service prior to graduation. Colleges often seek co-sponsors for internship programs so that students gain practical work experience related to their field of study.

Today's workforce includes employees whose working hours may be different from the traditional 9 to 5 arrangement. Do not overlook people who may work evening, night, weekend, or swing-shift hours.

Finally, decide how many volunteers are needed to meet the defined needs of the program before beginning recruiting. Be prepared for contingencies such as an overwhelming response of people willing to help.

Community-Based Programs

Community-based programs are risk-reduction initiatives conducted throughout a community that do not involve working with a school system. Examples of community-based programs include block parties, car seat safety clinics, home safety inspections, and smoke alarm installations **(Figure 13.9)**.

While most emergency service organizations collaborate with their local school system at some level, community-based programs are sometimes neglected because they are viewed as too time and labor intensive. Considering an alternate nontraditional approach to their development and delivery may create innovative opportunities to advance risk-reduction initiatives throughout the community.

Competition for a person's time, attention, and resources can be fierce in today's society. Although it can be a challenging process to formulate partnerships, the emergency services offer one of the best rationales for groups to consider: Helping to advance these initiatives can improve the safety, health, and vitality of the entire community. The following section offers venues to think about when considering an alternate form of program delivery for a community-based program:

- *Service groups* — The primary mission of these groups, such as Lions clubs, American Legions, and other fraternal organizations, is to offer some form of service to the community. While service groups in many larger cities often struggle to sustain membership, those in many smaller communities remain an integral component of the community.

Most service groups cannot offer substantial quantities of financial assistance. However, they may be able to muster a significant cadre of volunteers willing to perform various levels of outreach activity within the community.

- *Youth groups* — Groups usually comprised of middle and high school students and adult advisors. These groups include scouting, 4-H, Future Farmers of America, honor societies, and groups organized to perform student service learning activities. When used appropriately and with an adequate supply of trained adult mentors, a well-organized youth group can offer an enthusiastic alternative staffing resource supplement.

- *Corporate groups* — Financial support is not the only resource that the business and corporate world can offer the emergency services. Many businesses and corporations are very interested in providing some level of service to their community.

Figure 13.9 Community-based initiatives bring safety messages to individuals outside of a school system.

A business, industry, or corporation does not have to be a large conglomerate in order to offer a valuable service. Often, it is the small to mid-size business or local staff from a nationally recognized organization that can offer the greatest level of "people power" to deliver services.

- *Labor organizations* — Labor organizations are comprised of members who belong to a specific or group of unions. Unions are organized groups that represent the interest of employees who work for a specific company or municipality. As with corporations, many labor groups are willing to become involved in activities that have potential to make a positive impact on the community where they are employed. Many even have committees that consider requests for assistance.

- *Faith-based organizations* — Churches and other faith-based organizations are often interested in performing services that benefit the overall well-being of a community. Many communities have a council of churches so that pertinent information can be shared and networking opportunities created. The leadership of a congregation is usually aware if such a council exists.

- *Neighborhood associations* — Neighborhood associations are comprised of residents living in a specific geographical area who come together to address common interests. Many associations include members who are active and very interested in the overall well-being of their neighborhood. Associations are often a logical place to begin when searching for an innovative way to reach residents of a specific area.

- *CERT and Fire Corps* — Community Emergency Response Teams and Fire Corps are two nationally recognized programs that were created by the U.S. government after the events of September 11, 2001. The concept of CERT and Fire Corps is similar. CERT seeks to empower the lay public with knowledge of how to sustain itself and assist local responders during times of disaster situation or domestic terror. Fire Corps calls for the creation of ways for the public to assist their local emergency services with resources. The emergency services in many communities are encouraging local CERT and Fire Corps groups to become involved in fire and life safety outreach programs.

The Fire Corps Program

The Fire Corps program, created in December 2004 under the umbrella of Citizen Corps, is a nationally recognized program that supports and supplements fire and EMS departments through the use of citizen advocates.

Fire Corps members can assist with a variety of fire safety projects and activities, from helping with smoke alarm installation programs, conducting fire safety presentations, assisting at large events such as safety fairs, helping with data analysis and web page development, along with many other fire safety activities.

Fire Corps can enable a department to increase the level of fire safety programming, allowing for the opportunity to reach more people in a community with fire safety efforts. It can also allow the fire and life safety educator to have more time to concentrate on other tasks.

Johnson County RFD #1 Fire Corps

Johnson County RFD#1 Fire Corps members, with over 100 plus University of the Ozarks Phi Beta Lambda members, assist the department's firefighters with its fire and life safety education program. These members, representing 23 different countries, reach not only those in the US, but they also take the fire safety practices learned back to their own countries.

Started in March 2005, these Fire Corps members participated in almost 300 hours of fire safety education training each year. As of 2006, their efforts have helped the department realize a 34% decrease in residential property loss.

Phi Beta Lambda is a national collegiate organization of students preparing for careers in business and injury-related fields. One of the arms of its mission is a community service component. Consider contacting your local college or university to find other community service based organizations that might be willing to assist your department with its fire and life safety efforts.

Local Government

Most local governments have several departments that perform basic services within the community. Examples include fire, EMS, police, utilities, public works, community development, and public information. Forging an intra-agency partnership can create multiple ways to deliver risk-reduction initiatives through the cooperative efforts of a municipal organization.

Interagency Partnership

This type of collaboration involves identifying and working with other community-based organizations that have similar missions or contact with target populations that the educator is interested in reaching. Examples of organizations include Community Action Councils, advocacy groups for older adults and those with disabilities, social service agencies, health care institutions, and housing authorities.

The first step when considering a partnership to advance program outreach is to conduct research. In addition to having a risk-reduction strategy, the Level III administrator needs an understanding of the potential resources present within his or her community.

Once potential partners are identified, the administrator must create a rationale for why the outside agency should participate and how their support will be utilized. The Level III administrator must also commit his or her organization to training, evaluating, and mentoring those who agree to help.

Chapter Summary

Overseeing the entire risk-reduction process of an organization requires the ability to develop a comprehensive budget that supports public safety efforts. Level III administrators must possess the ability to develop a budget that includes and justifies operating and personnel costs. Understanding the organization's operating plan and budget process and having open communication with executive officers empowers the Level III administrator with knowledge to perform these proficiencies.

Society places increasing demands on the emergency services. Increased call volumes, training requirements, and domestic security issues can challenge an organization's pool of available resources.

As the administrator of an organization's entire risk-reduction process, the Level III administrator should be proficient at facilitating nontraditional approaches to the development and delivery of risk-reduction initiatives. Knowing one's community and establishing relationships with organizations external to the emergency services is essential to developing partnerships that can advance risk-reduction through alternative delivery media. Communication, cooperation, and commitment are three of the most essential components that comprise a successful alternative or nontraditional form of evaluation.

Review Questions

1. What is the process for developing an organization's fire and life safety education budget?

2. What are examples of operating and personnel costs within an organizational budget?

3. What are some methods for determining and justifying operating costs?

4. What are alternative systems of program development and delivery for a risk-mitigation strategy?

5. What are nontraditional methods that can be used to sustain a risk-mitigation strategy?

Key Terms

Community-Based Program — Activities that support an overall risk-reduction strategy and occur throughout a community.

Fire and Life Safety Strategy — A series of activities, programs, and initiatives designed to reduce identified risks within a community.

General Municipal Fund — The largest and most important accounting activity managed by a community or organization. The fund provides revenue and expenditures of unrestricted municipal purposes and all financial transactions not accounted for in any other fund.

Milestone Budget Date — A date by which municipalities are required to initiate actions on budget proposals. Governances usually require municipalities to submit a balanced budget by a specific date.

School-Based Program — Activities that support specific outcome objectives of a curriculum presented within a school system.

FLSE Level III Administrators: Planning and Development

Chapter Contents

Key Terms

Job Performance Requirements

This chapter provides information that addresses the following job performance requirements of NFPA® 1035, *Standard for Professional Qualifications for Fire and Life Safety Educator, Public Information Officer, and Juvenile Firesetter Intervention Specialist*, 2010 edition.

NFPA® 1035 References

7.3.1

7.3.2

7.3.3

7.3.4

7.3.5

Learning Objectives

After reading this chapter, students will be able to:

1. Plan and develop an organization's entire risk-reduction strategy. (NFPA® 1035, 7.3.1)

2. Create an interagency collaborative fire and life safety education partnership that supports mitigation of a specific fire or injury issue within the community. (NFPA® 1035, 7.3.2)

3. Project and plan for emerging trends and risk issues that may challenge the local community. (NFPA® 1035, 7.3.3)

4. Propose public policy to decision-makers who support mitigation of a specific risk issue(s). (NFPA® 1035, 7.3.4)

5. Develop a marketing plan so that awareness of risk issues and solutions is created within the community. (NFPA® 1035, 7.3.5)

Chapter 14
FLSE Level III
Administrators:
Planning and Development

Case History

The city of Shreveport, Louisiana, reported seven fire fatalities in 2008. Those fatalities included three children under the age of 7 and three adults over the age of 65. The other fatality was 53 years old.

According to fire officials, it is believed that at least five of the seven fatalities could have been avoided. The deaths occurred as a result of carelessness or an oversight on someone's part.

Most of the fatalities, as well as many of the fires in Shreveport, occur in neighborhoods where a majority of the residents are living below the poverty line. Shreveport officials found that children and the elderly are at most risk for being killed or injured in a fire.

Organizations such as the National Fire Protection Association® and the United States Fire Administration have conducted research that draws the same conclusions. However, having local information and local officials involved in the research process makes the message more personal and more relevant to those living in the community.

Planning and developing risk-reduction initiatives are the primary tasks assigned to the Level III administrator. This leadership responsibility is crucial to the work that is carried out by the risk-reduction section of the fire agency. Planning and development tasks should be taken very seriously and are a part of the daily activities of the Level III administrator. This responsibility also includes planning and developing the supporting components of the program that will make it successful. Having a specific risk-reduction strategy enables everyone in the agency, from management to the recruit firefighter, to know the focus of the department's risk-reduction strategy and what their roles are in the process.

Level III administrators lead and direct the activities of the risk-reduction team and the strategies that are employed. The Level III administrator sets the tone for the risk-reduction work, and planning can lead to an increase in the effectiveness of the work being performed. In many jurisdictions, the individual performing Level III duties may be serving in the roles of a Level I educator and Level II manager as well. The Level III administrator serves as an educator, a planner, an administrator, a manager, and of course, a leader **(Figure 14.1, p. 336)**.

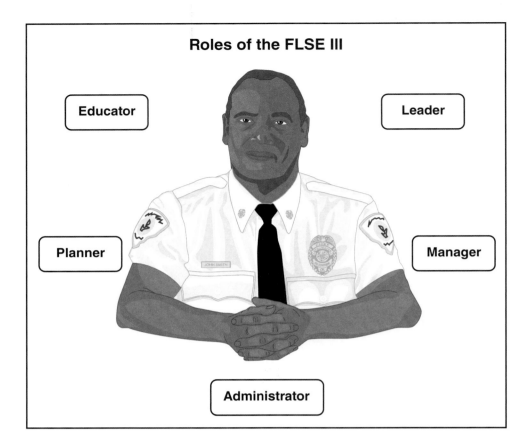

Figure 14.1 The Level III administrator juggles several roles within the risk-reduction department.

Roles of the FLSE III

Educator

Leader

Planner

Manager

Administrator

Developing a Comprehensive Risk-Reduction Strategy

A Level III administrator must be proficient at developing an organization's overall risk-reduction strategy. The strategy includes program goals, design methodologies, implementation activities, evaluation methods, and resource appropriation. The strategy should include community education as its foundation. It should also involve other aspects of an effective prevention strategy that includes engineering, enforcement, economic incentive, and emergency response.

For the leader of the risk-reduction campaign, this is one of the most important skills that can be understood and developed. Without a leader who is proficient at creating, implementing, evaluating, and sustaining the overall risk-reduction initiatives, the process is likely to be less effective or may even fail.

In order to be effective in the risk-reduction process, Level III administrators must follow a specific process for the design, implementation, and evaluation of the risk-reduction initiatives. The steps involved in successful programming are explored at length in this chapter **(Figure 14.2)**. The steps for the develop-

ment, implementation, and evaluation of successful risk-reduction programs include:

- Building support for community risk reduction
- Preparing for risk reduction
- Assessing community risk
- Identifying intervention strategies
- Taking action
- Evaluating the program

Building Support for Community-Risk Reduction

In order for any risk-reduction program to be successful, there must be support from both the organization and community. The Level III administrator must be a catalyst who is willing to lead the risk-mitigation process on behalf of his or her entire organization. An important starting point requires building equity for risk mitigation within the organization. This equity is built through leading by example and empowering others with the skills needed to become champions of reducing community risk.

The Level III administrator is a skillful planner who designs strategies that incorporate all levels of

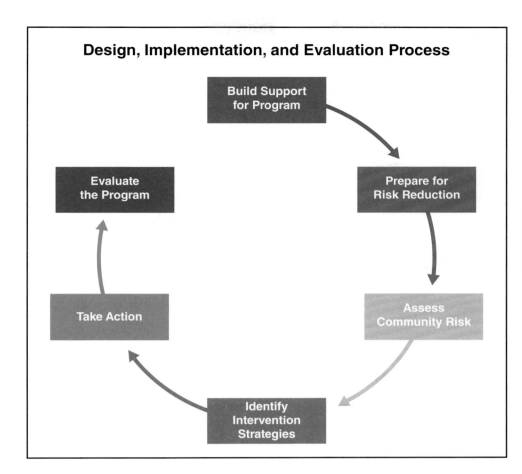

Design, Implementation, and Evaluation Process

- Build Support for Program
- Prepare for Risk Reduction
- Assess Community Risk
- Identify Intervention Strategies
- Take Action
- Evaluate the Program

Figure 14.2 This process represents a logical and proven order for the life span of an initiative.

preventive interventions. Once strategies are implemented, they are evaluated and adjusted according to need. Finally, the leader is committed to seeking resources that support the overall risk-reduction process. These resources include the following:

- Attention from decision-makers
- Time committed to risk reduction
- People to perform services
- Money to support the process

After the organization has embraced risk reduction as a core value, the Level III administrator can involve the community in the solution process. This is accomplished through identification of stakeholders from the community who have common interests in local risk issues. As part of the recruiting process, the administrator educates stakeholders so that they develop a vested interest in mitigating risks. Together, risk-reduction leaders, stakeholders, organizational, and community decision-makers can act as a planning team to help prioritize risks and develop a long-term intervention strategy.

Preparing for Risk Reduction

The goal of this section is to create a champion who is committed to advancing risk reduction in his or her community. The following steps are included in preparing for risk reduction **(Figure 14.3, p. 338)**:

1. Understanding risk reduction
2. Accepting personal responsibility
3. Developing a personal vision
4. Evaluating authority and politics
5. Developing a project plan

Understanding Risk Reduction

As described in earlier chapters, the process involved in successfully lowering the risk factors in a community requires vision, planning, interventions, evaluation, and resources. Risk reduction cannot be accomplished effectively by one person. Building an organizational and community culture supportive of risk reduction is essential to long-term success.

The Level III administrator knows that to be successful, an organization needs strong, dynamic leadership. Those most effective at leading others do

Preparing for Risk Reduction

Developing a project plan

Evaluating authority and politics

Developing a personal vision

Accepting personal responsibility

Understanding risk reduction

Figure 14.3 These steps work together to give the administrator the information he or she needs in order to create a successful initiative.

so by example and are subject-matter experts in the field of risk reduction. Training and higher education are key ingredients in learning how to lead a successful risk-reduction process. Supporting training opportunities for subordinates helps empower others with the skills needed to reduce risk.

Accepting Personal Responsibility

The responsibility of risk reduction cannot be taken lightly. Each year, around 3,000 people die as a result of uncontrolled fire, and approximately 100 firefighters die in the line of duty. (These averages do not reflect the events of September 11, 2001.) Billions of dollars in property are also lost. Add to this the losses due to preventable injury — such as those resulting from motor vehicle crashes, poisonings, falls, and drownings — and the numbers are staggering. The ultimate aim when seeking institutionalized support for risk reduction is for staff at all levels to accept prevention as a personal responsibility. The rationale for doing so is hard to refute. The ultimate mission of the fire service industry is to save lives and prevent loss. Safer communities also lead to safer responders and increased levels of community vitality.

By accepting personal responsibility, the Level III administrator makes a commitment to ensure that risks affecting the community are identified, sequenced, and prioritized. Populations at risk are

examined and mitigation strategies formulated. Action plans are then implemented, evaluated, and adjusted according to need. This includes making sure that subordinates have the basic tools needed to perform services.

Long-term results require careful planning, willingness to modify strategies, and patience for strategies to prove successful. It is also important that an administrator realizes there will be challenges to the process, both internally and externally.

Finally, the leader is passionate about convincing others that following a proven risk-reduction process is well worth the investment of attention, time, and resources. The reward will be realized through documented program outreach, measurable impact, and the overall reduction of loss in a community.

Developing Personal Vision

Personal vision involves thinking ahead to imagine what the future *could* be like if certain actions were taken. In the context of risk reduction, it begins with envisioning what a safe community would look like and what actions would be required to accomplish the vision.

Before setting out to develop a risk-reduction strategy, the Level III administrator should reflect on present conditions, both internally within the organization and externally throughout the community. The following are examples of questions the administrator should consider:

- What are the current risk issues that challenge the community?
- What populations are affected?
- What level of internal support for risk reduction is currently present within the organization?
- What level of internal support is present in the community?
- What barriers will act as constraints to the program's success?
- What factors will serve as catalysts to success?
- What actions are currently being taken to reduce risk?

While leaders can create their own personal vision, they should not keep it a secret. When they communicate their vision to their subordinates, superiors, and the organization, they ensure that everyone is moving in the same direction and working toward the same end. Many great actions taken by entire organizations began with one person's vision of what could become reality through specific actions. The strategy for using a personal vision as a powerful resource will be explained in the next chapter.

Evaluating Authority and Politics

The Level III administrator should have a voice in organizational policy development that applies to preventive services. An open line of communication must exist between the Level III administrator and the organizational leadership. This communication mechanism is essential to institutionalizing risk reduction as a core value.

The Level III administrator also needs to understand the levels of legitimate authority within the organization and the position that his or her role holds. Legitimate authority is the level of authority required to issue directives and deploy resources.

While cooperative support (as opposed to mandated actions) is certainly advocated, it can be challenging for a leader to advance risk-reduction initiatives without some form of legitimate authority. Level III administrators must know what actions they are permitted to direct and the level of decisions that can be made without consulting superiors. The Level III administrator should continually monitor the political climate between the chief executive officer, mid-level management, and line staff. This knowledge allows the administrator to be aware of internal organizational determinants that may have an impact upon risk-reduction initiatives. It is also prudent for the administrator to identify, understand, and monitor the external attitude held by the community and decision-makers toward community risk reduction.

As discussed in previous chapters, organizational equity is created by dynamic leaders who follow through on plans. These leaders rally others within the organization to support a project and empower them with the skills and resources to succeed. Community equity is created when members of the community at-large notice behaviors that demonstrate the organization is acting on behalf of those being served.

The Level III administrator must always be aware of the support present for risk reduction, both internally and throughout the community. The road to institutionalizing prevention as a core value is a journey — not a defined destination. Be prepared for challenges and adjust strategies according to needs.

Developing a Project Plan

Developing a project plan is the final component in preparing for risk reduction. The following components address how the project will proceed:

- Seek approval to proceed with the project.
- Convene a leadership team with representatives from both inside and outside the organization. This group will be the core team members, perhaps four to five people, who will work on the initiative over a long-term basis.
- Identify the stakeholder group. Members of this group have an interest in the outcome of the process and are directly affected by the risk issue.
- Outline a planning schedule. Having a good "plan for planning" sets the tone for the rest of the process.

Assessing Community Risk

This step of the risk-reduction strategy promotes actions that a Level III administrator should ensure takes place as part of a thorough and objective community risk assessment. These actions must occur before a mitigation strategy is designed. The assessment must be accurate, or it may skew the identification of conditions that are affecting a community and its people. The goal of this section is to create an outcome objective that identifies a desired level of risk to be attained through the risk-reduction process.

Analyzing the Community

Level II and III fire and life safety educators are expected to possess a thorough understanding of the community's demographics, which include:

- Population distribution
- Economics
- Social and cultural influences
- Educational levels
- Employment conditions
- Community development

In addition to knowledge of the community's demographics, Level III administrators need to understand the fire and injury risk problems in their community as well.

Identifying Hazards and Causal Factors

Risk sequencing studies the series of actions leading to the occurrence of a risk event. It is an evaluation that is performed so that logical places for intervention can be identified. As a mentor of subordinates, the Level III administrator should encourage all fire and life safety educators to also explore the wider picture of risk causation. A targeted risk should be examined for underlying causation such as social, cultural, or economic factors that may be contributing to occurrences. Collecting reliable data and performing objective analysis of risk are considered some of the most important components of a prevention planning process.

As part of the analysis process, evaluators should search for factors common in the occurrence of multiple types of risks. This strategy helps uncover factors common to multiple-risk causation. Conducting post-incident interviews with those directly responsible for causing the risk will help Level III administrators search for underlying factors.

The Level III administrator should consider using company-level personnel and community partners, such as law enforcement, to help identify community risk **(Figure 14.4)**. While their input is typically

Figure 14.4 Community partners will have a slightly different perspective on the same concerns as the Level III administrator.

anecdotal rather than empirical, the value of their insight into what is happening in their respective districts is immeasurable.

Assessing Vulnerability

Once the organization has a general idea of risks that are affecting its community, Level III administrators should examine who is most vulnerable. In addition to studying the population at-large, the Level III administrator must examine how incidents are affecting confirmed high-risk populations.

When assessing vulnerability to risk, it is important to consider the impact each risk is having, or has potential to have, over a specific population. For example, fires started by pre-school age firesetters often take the lives of those young people. Older adults are more affected by injuries from falls than perhaps younger adults. Individuals in a lower socioeconomic bracket are less able to afford safety equipment, such as child restraint seats and bike helmets, than those with a greater income.

It is also important to examine the types of risks accounting for the greatest level of concern. In most communities, fire does not cause the greatest number of injuries and death, yet it may be the main focus of the agency's risk-reduction program.

Many organizations perform a level of proactive risk reduction. As the leader of the organization's risk-reduction process, it is important to be aware of the potential ramifications of not addressing the most critical or most frequent community risk issue.

Establishing Priorities Based on Rated Risks

Risk is prioritized by studying the frequency of occurrences, rates of rise, morbidity, mortality, and the cost generated by incidents. Because the review of data drives the decision on priorities, the Level III administrator must ensure that objective reporting and evaluation occurs.

Reaching consensus on which risks to prioritize is an important component of the planning process. This action creates a "shotgun" approach to mitigation with resources being spread thin while trying to reduce multiple risks simultaneously. A more effective strategy is to prioritize one or perhaps a few risks that share common root causation factors. The following sections explain how to prioritize these risks.

Defining Acceptable Levels of Risk

At first, the concept of defining an *acceptable level of risk* may seem abstract. However, no matter how well organized and resource-equipped a risk-mitigation strategy may be, preventable occurrences will never be completely eradicated. Believing that a specific risk occurrence can be completely eliminated will only result in disappointment for those trying to stop it.

The ultimate aim is to set a measurable level of reduction that is realistic to achieve. The only way to create a benchmark for reduction is to begin with a baseline level of information about the risk issue being considered.

The Level III administrator must ensure that reliable data is collected and evaluated objectively by subordinates. This task must occur before a planning team convenes to discuss setting an acceptable level of measurable reduction.

When considering what an acceptable level of reduction may be, it is important to examine several factors:

● What are the root factors leading to the causation of the risk?

● Are there social, cultural, political, or economic factors that make reducing the risk more complex?

● What level of resources can the organization and the community commit to reducing the risk?

While envisioning a significant reduction of the selected risk over the long term is encouraged, it is acceptable to pursue a modest level of decrease in the shorter term of three to five years.

The Level III administrator should not create the benchmark of desired reduction alone. This action is best accomplished through direction from a risk-reduction planning team. The goal is to reach consensus on what is a reasonable and attainable level of reduction.

Why create the benchmark of an acceptable level of risk? If an organization is not taking the lead to reduce an existing level of risk, the community may believe that what is occurring is acceptable. This can lead to a culture of acceptance that transcends to decision-makers and even the organization itself.

Creating a Risk-Reduction Outcome Objective

An outcome objective is establishing the desired level of measurable reduction for a specific risk over a set amount of time. An outcome objective creates a benchmark against which risk-reduction strategies may be measured. Once an outcome objective has been created, an intervention strategy to reduce the specified risk can be developed.

Identifying Intervention Strategies

This component of the model promotes developing a strategy that defines how the risk-reduction process will be conducted. The Level III administrator has an important role in developing this strategy, as he or she is ultimately responsible for deciding what interventions will be used. The ultimate goal of this component is for a planning team to design an intervention strategy to reduce an identified risk.

Identifying Potential Strategies

Reviewing the sequence of events common to most occurrences of the identified risk begins the process of selecting potential intervention strategies. The sequence is examined to reveal places where various interventions may be used to interrupt the chain of events leading to the event.

The planning team should review underlying factors such as social, cultural, and economic factors that may contribute to the occurrence of the identified risk **(Figure 14.5)**. Having a team with diverse membership is important so that creative ways of intervention can be explored.

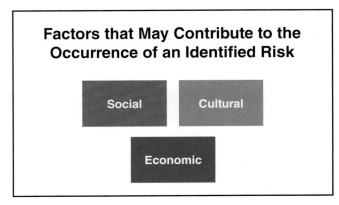

Figure 14.5 Underlying risk factors may create or contribute to a risk occurrence.

Using a diverse team can be beneficial when seeking to facilitate partnerships with local government, corporations, business, industry, and target populations. Partnership can also help advance the levels of intervention available for the process.

Analyzing Cost vs. Benefit

Once possible interventions have been identified, the Level III administrator should lead the process of performing a cost/benefit analysis on each proposed strategy. The cost of each potential intervention is compared with the potential benefit that may be realized. Open communication between the organization's leadership and the Level III administrator is essential during this process. As discussed in several preceding chapters, there are many costs associated with risk reduction. Leaders must consider the cost of people, equipment, time, attention, and sometimes even political action.

It is very important for those conducting a cost/benefit analysis to remain focused on seeking long-term sustainable solutions to the identified risk. While less expensive and time-saving solutions may show promise in the short term, a Level III administrator should encourage the organization to consider the long-range benefits of investing resources into strategies that may produce stronger outcomes over time.

Selecting Risk-Reduction Strategies

Upon concluding a cost/benefit analysis, the planning team should reach consensus on the strategies that will be used to reduce the selected risk. The Level III administrator is responsible for ensuring that a series of combined prevention interventions are slated for use.

The ultimate goal is to create an intervention strategy that includes a series of integrated lessons, programs, activities, and initiatives that produce measurable impact. The impact is measured through monitoring outreach, knowledge gain, and behavioral and lifestyle change.

The Level III administrator must ensure that program delivery, program outreach, and program evaluation are all being appropriately performed. Done well, the intervention strategy should lead to long-term reduction in fires and preventable injury.

Developing an Evaluation Strategy

An evaluation plan for a reduction strategy is more comprehensive than one that outlines a single risk-reduction program because several initiatives are likely being used to combat an identified risk issue. An evaluation plan is designed to measure the success of reaching the objectives developed as a part of the risk-reduction strategy planning process.

How to Write Objectives

An effective way to write objectives is to use the SMART acronym. Objectives should be written so that they are:

- **S**pecific — Write a concise statement of desired action.
- **M**easurable — Identify a quantifiable level of change.
- **A**ttainable — Ensure that they are completed in the time frame allotted.
- **R**elevant — Make sure that they are related to the overall program goal.
- **T**ime sensitive — Identify a specific timetable for completion.

An evaluation plan that is comprised of SMART objectives creates a measurable road map to risk mitigation.

Collecting baseline data is a prerequisite to performing any level of impact or outcome evaluation. Knowledge levels, human behaviors, and environmental conditions must be evaluated before an initiative begins so that baseline data can be compared against post-initiative data. This level of action can be labor intensive, but it should not be overlooked.

One of the most important duties of a Level III administrator is to ensure that an evaluation plan is written and followed. Enlisting support from a planning team when developing a comprehensive intervention strategy helps ensure objectivity and expands the pool of resources available to the administrator.

Taking Action

This component identifies the resources needed for actions to occur, when implementation will take place, and who is responsible for task completions. It also defines levels of approval needed if policies related to risk-reduction are to be created or modified. The ultimate goal of this component of the model is program implementation.

Identifying Needed Resources

Having adequate resources is essential to facilitating a successful risk-reduction process. Those who develop, deliver, evaluate, and supervise reduction initiatives need basic tools required to perform services. Adequate resources include:

- Support from the organization and interest from the community
- Time, people, funding, equipment, tools, and materials dedicated to risk reduction

Resource acquisition for risk-reduction initiatives is ultimately the responsibility of the organization's chief executive officer. However, the lead person in charge of risk reduction should identify what resources are needed. Requests should be made in accordance with organizational protocol and in a time-sensitive manner. The Level III administrator must be able to justify the resources requested for each component of a risk-reduction strategy. This includes costs such as operating and personnel expenses.

Developing an Implementation Schedule

An implementation schedule identifies when activities that support the risk-reduction strategy will be performed. The schedule should reflect the proposed timelines identified by the planning team's objectives for the initiative and its evaluation **(Figure 14.6)**.

The most immediate actions to be accomplished are usually identified through process objectives. The objectives state timed benchmarks for actions such as program development, implementation, and delivery to occur. Monitoring of these activities begins immediately.

Impact objectives call for action such as evaluating knowledge levels, behavioral change, and lifestyle modifications. Activities to evaluate impact include testing, observation, and surveys. The implementation of activities such as testing to measure knowledge level changes may need to begin soon after program activity is initiated. Other activity such as monitoring behavioral, environmental, and lifestyle changes may take place over a longer term.

Outcome evaluation measures changes in the occurrence of fire and injuries over time. However, its implementation may not begin for up to a year after reduction initiatives have been initiated.

It is important for a planning team to maintain a realistic outlook of how long it will take to accomplish the development, implementation, delivery, and evaluation of a risk-reduction strategy. A Level III administrator should encourage his or her planning team to consider potential challenges and adjust implementation benchmarks accordingly.

Patience and a realistic concept of time are important attributes to possess when leading a strategy that seeks to reduce risk. Activity and program deliveries can bring educational outreach rather quickly. Higher order initiatives that use engineer-

Figure 14.6 Creating a schedule visually shows how the implementation timelines are interdependent.

ing, technology, and enforcement will take longer. This is particularly true when seeking legislative changes for codes, ordinances, or laws relating to risk reduction.

Assigning Responsibility

During this component, the planning team identifies who will be responsible for completing specific activities associated with the implementation of the risk-reduction strategy. The time frame of when actions will occur is also clarified.

A major contributing factor that can lead to a dysfunctional risk-reduction strategy is failure of people to perform assigned tasks in a timely manner. This is especially true during the planning and implementation phase of a strategy. Those who have been given tasks need to be held accountable for meeting deadlines. During the pre-implementation stage of a strategy, the planning team should clarify the expectations of each person who has responsibility for performing an assigned task.

People who have accepted responsibilities need the authority to perform the necessary actions. The Level III administrator and organizational leaders should support subordinates who may need the power of legitimate authority to ensure that a task is completed in a timely manner.

Gaining Policy Approvals

The Level III administrator is responsible for assisting with two important levels of policy that support a risk-reduction strategy:

1. Internal organizational policies that promote behaviors supportive of community risk reduction

2. Public policy that supports the risk-reduction strategy

The concept of organizational equity has been discussed in previous chapters. The Level III administrator is responsible for working both formally and informally with organizational leaders in the development and implementation of policies supportive of risk-reduction efforts relevant to all organizational members.

Public policy encompasses the laws requiring specific actions or behaviors to occur. Legislation or ordinances requiring installation of smoke alarms and sprinkler systems are examples. In addition to laws, public policy is also found in less official forms.

Gaining approval from a school system to include risk-reduction education in its essential curriculum is a form of public policy. This concept will be covered later in this chapter.

Regardless of the type or level of policy adoption being sought, planning and patience are essential to a successful outcome. Decision-makers at all levels must understand why a policy is needed, its probable effects on constituents, and the overall long-term benefits of adoption.

Evaluating the Program

This component defines how the risk-reduction strategy will be evaluated and what should be done with the results. It culminates with recommendations of how to use evaluation results to recommend future modifications to this strategy.

Evaluating Results

Evaluating program activity, impact, and outcome represents the most accurate way of determining that the strategy is producing the desired results. It is also the most effective way to reach conclusions about the need to modify components of the strategy.

Process evaluation monitors program development, implementation, delivery, and outreach. This level of evaluation is often referred to as "program monitoring." Process evaluation begins in the planning stages of the strategy and provides important short-term results.

The Level III administrator must insist that those who develop, present, and evaluate risk-reduction programs document their activity. Leaders of the reduction strategy should review this data regularly to monitor program activity and modify actions according to need. The Level III administrator must ensure that subordinates perform impact evaluation accurately and objectively. Baseline data is required so that conditions existing before a strategy is implemented can be compared to those present after programs or initiatives are in place. Impact evaluation measures knowledge gain, behavioral, environmental, and lifestyle changes.

The Level III administrator should regularly review evaluation data of the risk-reduction programs and initiatives. This action is important so that the planning team and other decision-makers can consider potential modifications to components of the strategy as needed.

Outcome evaluation tracks the changes in the number of incidents related to the targeted risk over a specified time period. Outcome is also evidenced by anecdotal stories that positive actions took place or incidents were prevented as a direct result of a risk-reduction program.

It will take several months and perhaps a couple of years for a risk-reduction strategy to show statistically sound proof of program impact. Evaluation of outcomes will take longer; it will take at least three to five years and even as long as ten years.

The Level III administrator must understand the need for skill, patience, and tenacity when overseeing the evaluation process of an organization's entire risk-reduction strategy. He or she should set an example for subordinates by scheduling regular reviews of the process, impact, and outcome being created by programs and initiatives of the overall risk-reduction program.

Reporting Results

As administrator of the organization's overall risk-reduction strategy, the Level III administrator needs ongoing reports from subordinates on the progress of all prevention initiatives that are being conducted. In turn, the administrator should regularly prepare a report that summarizes the process, impact, and outcome being created by reduction strategies. Those receiving reports should include, but not be limited to, planning teams, delivery staff, organizational leadership, government and political decision-makers, community stakeholders, and the media when applicable.

Modifying Risk-Reduction Initiatives

A primary objective of evaluation is to enhance a process for an accurate and objective review of a risk-reduction strategy. The ultimate goal of the process is to identify steps where the strategy could be enhanced in order to create a more effective process, impact, and overall outcome.

The Level III administrator is ultimately responsible for ensuring that his or her organization follows an organized process of evaluating risk-reduction strategies and acting on the findings. Committing to this process creates a cycle whereby risk-reduction strategies can be enhanced to their fullest potential. It also serves as proof that an organization is proactively addressing risk to its fullest potential.

Creating Partnerships for Successful Initiatives

Most successful intervention strategies include the creation of collaborative partnerships across inter-agency lines. Partnerships are an essential part of any successful community risk-reduction initiative for both Level I and Level II fire and life safety educators. As indicated in the previous section, it is important to bring together a planning team to help design the risk-reduction initiatives. The responsibility for designing and creating these community and interagency partnerships is tasked to the Level III administrator.

Collaborative partnerships are essential to achieving the goals of any community risk-reduction program. These partnerships are purposeful relationships between agencies and organizations in the community that are committed to the risk-reduction effort and whose mission is in line with that of the initiative. The members of the partnership should be committed to working together toward a common goal. Partnerships or coalitions may be formed to influence or develop public policy around a specific issue, to change people's behavior, or to build a healthy community.

A number of organizations or individuals may be working in a community to address some or all of the issues included in the emergency service's risk-reduction initiative. If the approaches are different or the agencies do not cooperate or collaborate, little may be accomplished as they may be working against each other. However, if they are working together and agree on a common goal and a common way to approach the issues, the impact is more likely to be significant.

The Community Tool Box publication of the University of Kansas[1] gives significant insight into the development of coalitions and partnerships. It provides the following reasons for the development of a community coalition:

- *To address an urgent situation.* Is there a particular fire or injury issue that has reached a critical stage in the community, such as juvenile firesetting or driving under the influence?
- *To empower elements of the community to take control of the future.* Using coalitions to address the fire or injury risk issues in a community contribute to the health of a community's future.

- *To obtain or provide services.* Perhaps a community does not have a risk-reduction plan or have a fire or other community agency that is committed to the prevention of injury and fire.
- *To bring about more effective and efficient delivery of programs and eliminate any unnecessary duplication of effort.* By partnering with all players involved in a particular risk issue, efforts are organized and focused, and responsibilities are divided and coordinated.
- *To pool resources.* By partnering together, agencies can accomplish what they might otherwise not be able to manage alone.
- *To plan and launch community-wide initiatives.* Coalitions can unify long-term efforts for risk-reduction initiatives in a particular community or neighborhood.
- *To create long-term, permanent social change.* This is the crux of risk-reduction initiatives. A coalition that involves diverse groups and cultures can sometimes accelerate the process of change in a community.

Additionally, creating partnerships can help revitalize the efforts and energies of those individuals who are trying to do too much by themselves. Members of a coalition can help provide a new source of energy and ideas for an effort. Simply put, by creating partnerships, the risk-reduction initiatives are much more likely to be successful and reach the intended goal.

General Steps for Convening a Coalition

Much like risk reduction, organizing a coalition must follow a certain set of procedures or processes. Effective coalitions do not just come together by accident or without planning. The following sections provide a process for beginning a coalition.

Gathering a Core Group of Individuals

When the Level III administrator sets out to create a coalition for the risk-reduction issues that have been identified by the host agency, the first step is to bring together a core group of individuals whose representation is essential. This core group should include representatives of stakeholders from the community who have an interest in the success of the coalition's efforts.

Stakeholders will include individuals who are most affected by the issue. It is unfair and unwise to make decisions about people's lives without including

them in the process. Stakeholder groups also include those who are charged with carrying out community functions that are related to the risk-reduction issues, such as law enforcement agencies, social services, public health agencies, and any other agencies or organizations related to the risk-reduction issues being addressed.

The initial core group should also include community leaders. These individuals should be highly credible in the community, such as clergy and business or civic leaders, who can influence large numbers of community members. In addition, there should be room for community policy makers, such as local political leaders, state representatives, and others in policy-making positions. This will not only add credibility to the coalition but also increase the chance that the policy will positively influence the community.

Using a core group to initially lead the risk-reduction effort provides more contacts and community knowledge than one individual might provide. It also gives the coalition more credibility among potential members and makes finding coalition members an easier process. Additionally, the use of a core group shows that the risk-reduction effort has support from a wide variety of community sources.

Some jurisdictions have specific policies which prohibit anyone but the department head from officially representing the organization and/or from making formal commitments of staffing and other resources. The Level III administrator must be familiar with such policies and ensure that they are followed when working within a coalition.

Identifying Potential Coalition Members

Once the core group has been selected and engaged, other potential members for the coalition may be available, including the following:

- Individuals in a particular community without whom nothing gets accomplished
- Individuals who share a particular interest in a risk-reduction issue because it has touched their lives or the lives of their loved ones
- Individuals or organizations that want to be involved in a community effort that helps others

Coalition members should be those who are most affected by or concerned with the problem being addressed.

Recruiting Members to the Coalition

The core group can brainstorm a list of possible members and identify those who are known by them personally. Potential members can be contacted by phone or e-mail, and with personal letters and face-to-face visits. Direct contact is the best way to recruit members and will have the best results **(Figure 14.7)**. When contacting individuals about coalition membership, it is important to offer compensation for their time and effort. This may be an offer to work in a small group or to contact their local political leader. It is also important that the work of the coalition is described with specificity. People like to know what they are getting into and that their time is being spent wisely.

Figure 14.7 Meet potential coalition members in person whenever possible.

Planning and Holding an Informational Meeting

Once potential members have been contacted, the first meeting can be held. The first meeting of a coalition is an important one. It needs to get people excited and energized about the issues being discussed. It is important that the meeting gets the coalition off to a good start.

The first meeting should have a specific agenda. Items to include on the agenda should be:

- *Introductions.* All members of the group should briefly introduce themselves, including their organizational connection and the nature of their interest in the risk issues being discussed.

- *Issues.* A statement should be developed or at least discussed that defines the issue (or issues) around which the coalition is being developed.

- *Structure.* An outline should be presented explaining how the group will be run and organized and the type of things it will do.

- *Vision.* This will start the process of developing a mission and vision statement for the group that will guide its work.

- *Procedures.* This should include the formation of an action plan or at least the development of a small group to work on the action plan for the organization.

- *Meeting schedule.* A regular meeting schedule may be established or at least the date and time for the next meeting. In addition, people should leave the meeting with a sense of accomplishment and actions to be taken for the next meeting.

As the coalition's founder, the Level III administrator should follow up on the items discussed in the first meeting. This might include the distribution of meeting minutes to the members and sending invitations to those who might not have been able to attend. Progress on tasks that were assigned at the first meeting should be monitored by an offer of assistance or involving other individuals who have expertise in the area.

Identifying the Vision and Mission of the Partnership

In order to keep the coalition moving forward, it is important that information is gathered about the problem (as it becomes available), the issue, and the community. The more information that is available, the easier it is to define a problem and for the group to plan an appropriate intervention strategy. Vision and mission statements must be completed and agreed upon by the entire group. This is an important step, as these documents will be the foundation of the coalition and serve as a reference for the group on particular issues or initiatives.

Designing the Structure of the Coalition and Electing Officers

The group should solidly define the structure of the organization. The structure can range from very informal to very structured. There may be a need to write bylaws for the group or to provide another way to formalize the mission and goals of the group. Depending on the structure, officers may need to be elected. Or, some type of coordinating or steering committee should be formed to serve as a governing body for the organization.

Setting Goals and Considering Resources
Goals for the work of the group should be determined. Again, this might be the work of a small group, but they should be agreed upon by the entire organization. Agreement on the goals for the organization will also help to determine what resources may be needed, such as financial, informational, or material.

The following are some general recommendations for getting the organization going:

- *Communicate constantly.* Keep the lines of communication open among the members of the coalition, the media, and the community. No one should feel left out of the loop.

- *Be inclusive.* Make the coalition open to anyone in the community. Try to involve all members of the coalition. People need to feel ownership of the coalition in order to work harder to achieve its goals.

- *Network.* Continue to invite people to the coalition. Involve other groups in the community.

- *Set concrete, reachable goals.* Success in achieving goals early can help the coalition develop strength for later years.

- *Be creative about meetings.* Have fun. Have themes and exciting presentations. Rotate responsibility for each meeting's special feature among different members.

- *Be realistic and keep promises.* Before promising, be sure that it is possible. Be sure that what is promised gets done.

- *Acknowledge diversity among the members.* Not all members will agree with everything that the coalition wants to do. Make sure to use diversity as a source for discussion, and respect the opinions of others.

- *Praise, reward, and celebrate.* Celebration of success, through individual or group awards, is a great way to bond coalition members together. Celebration of achievement will help the coalition grow and develop.

It is the responsibility of the Level III administrator to organize the coalition, and the Level II manager is tasked with the responsibility of facilitating the coalition. However, this needs to be a partnership in leadership between the two individuals, as involvement of both levels indicates a total commitment from the host organization.

Barriers to Creating Coalitions
Creating coalitions aids the implementation of successful risk-reduction programs. However, the creation of successful coalitions may not be without barriers or obstacles. It is important to be aware of some of the obstacles and ways to overcome them. The University of Kansas' Community Tool Box lists the following as potential barriers to forming coalitions:

- *Turf issues.* Sometimes organizations are sensitive about sharing their work, funding, and time. As the coalition's creator, the Level III administrator may need to convince organizations that working together will benefit everyone and better address the issues. Organizations may need to be encouraged and shown that not only are they sharing their work, time, and money but that other organizations will be contributing theirs as well.

- *Bad history.* There may have been past experiences among individuals, organizations, or the community as a whole that were not positive or successful. This may lead to the belief that working together is simply not possible. The new coalition may have to work through this history before it can actually begin its work.

- *Domination by professionals or other "elites."* There may be those who, due to their status, education, or political level, feel that they have all the answers and will neglect to involve those people most affected by the issue or problem. It is up to the Level III administrator to create an atmosphere of participation and rein in those who believe they have all the answers.

- *Poor community involvement.* In some communities, this may be the first time that agencies have worked together and with the community at-large. A trusting, productive relationship may need to be established.

- *Funding.* In seeking funding, the coalition must make sure that the funding source does not push the organization in the wrong direction or away from its vision and mission.

- *Failure to create or provide leadership.* Coalitions need a particular kind of leadership that promotes collaboration among the members. Training and mentoring from outside may be necessary to provide the appropriate leadership to allow the organization to grow and prosper.

- *Perceptions about working together.* There may be the perception that the costs of working together outweigh the benefits. In this case, the Level III administrator must find ways to increase the benefits and decrease the costs for those organizations or individuals.

By understanding the potential barriers to creating successful partnerships, the Level III administrator can plan for and overcome them. This will increase the chances for success. Not all barriers can be planned for or anticipated, but being aware of the possibility can allow the organization's leadership to minimize the impact or solve the situation that is causing the barrier prior to it becoming a hindrance to the success of the organization in reaching its goals.

Public Policy and Its Role in Risk Reduction: The Level III Administrator's Responsibility

As has been discussed in earlier chapters, risk-reduction strategies must involve the use of all five Es: education, engineering, enforcement, economic incentive, and effective emergency response. Part of any engineering or enforcement aspect of risk reduction involves the introduction of new public policy or a change in existing policy. This policy may be national, state, or local and may be considered formal or informal.

The Importance of Public Policy

Policies are written or unwritten guidelines that governments, organizations, institutions, communities, or individuals use when responding to issues or situations. Policy can take different forms. It can be in the form of official government policy that is discussed publicly and written down, such as laws or regulations. Unofficial government policy includes those unspoken attitudes and assumptions held by policy makers. These attitudes can become part of the culture and may be incredibly difficult to change. Other policies include those made by government bureaucracies and public services or policies of private

foundations, funders, and businesses. In addition, there may be policies adopted by the community as a whole, which are influenced by the opinions of community leaders and public opinion.

Creating a Strong Partnership

- Gather on a regular basis with a clear purpose, and start and end on time.
- Define roles and responsibilities for all of the partners.
- Form active committees so that partners are involved in the issues of concern to them.
- Develop bylaws that reflect the mission of the partnership.
- Ensure consistent and clear communications among all partners.
- Preserve shared leadership and responsibility by delegating meaningful tasks and timelines that are reasonable.
- Build social time into the gatherings for networking.
- Recognize hard work and dedication through celebration and fun activities.
- Agree on fiduciary responsibilities and develop a budget for the partnership.
- Build relationships with elected officials and other key community leaders to gain support for the organization and its mission.
- Recruit technical assistance and support if resources are needed from outside the partnership.

Source: Department of Health and Human Services, State of Missouri

What This Means to You

Many states and local jurisdictions are in the process of promoting, through policy and legislation, a ban on the sale of novelty lighters. Check your state or local community for current legislation. Novelty lighters look like toys and carry an attraction for children. Many times, children mistake such items as toys, not realizing the danger that is present. The use of such lighters has led to many fires and multiple fire deaths. Through coalitions formed for such a purpose, the active lobbying for the legislation has been successful in many states and communities. This is just one example of how individuals and coalitions can affect risk reduction through a change in public policy.

Changing policies can be a crucial strategy in implementing community interventions. Many times policy makers, legislators, local politicians, and leaders do not understand the risk issue and its affect on the community. They may have other reasons for maintaining outdated policies. A change in policy may be one way to implement interventions or to fund such initiatives.

As discussed in Chapter 8, the role of the Level II manager is to prepare public policy changes that relate to local risk-reduction issues and recommend them to management for presentation. The Level III administrator presents these changes to national, state, or local level policy makers. This task is of great importance.

Prior to the introduction of any public policy, the following should have been researched, addressed, and presented:

- Explanation of the issue
- Justification for the policy
- Solutions to the problem, which should include economic incentives among others
- Benefit of adopting the policy
- Impact of adoption of the policy

It is the responsibility of the Level III administrator to review the information that has been provided by subordinates and give validation if necessary. The appropriate arena for the introduction of the policy must be researched and determined, as well as the proper procedures to be followed when seeking introduction and adoption of the policy.

Policy change can be time-consuming and difficult. Change starts with the assumption that the present policy, or a lack of policy, is unacceptable, and a change is needed to achieve the mission and goals of the risk-reduction initiatives. Policy change is possible when those individuals and groups behind the change care enough to persevere.

Eight Steps to Policy Change

Researchers have identified eight steps or guidelines that should be followed for introducing new policies or policy changes. While these steps are broad and general, they serve to help individuals and groups understand how to determine the appropriate strategies for addressing changing policies. The eight areas — identified as the Eight Ps of Policy Change — are as follows:

- *Preparation.* Those individuals involved in changing policy research the issue to gather as much information as possible. The Level III administrator and the coalition being represented must include experts on the issue, the individuals affected by the issue, and those involved in the solution. In addition, Level III administrators must be very familiar with the current policy and know who makes and influences the policy. Finally, preparation for changing policy must include knowledge of allies and opponents, who is inflexible, and who is open to discussion. Being prepared means having the knowledge to counter any argument or attack against the new policy.

- *Planning.* Strategic planning is essential to ensure that changing policies is a necessary and appropriate part of the risk-reduction initiative. As a part of the implementation process, Level III administrators should engage in a strategic planning process that involves the coalition that was originally formed to address the issue and may include other community members. Planning is essential to the introduction of a new policy in any forum.

- *Personal Contact.* This involves establishing and maintaining personal contact with those who influence or make the policy. This might be the local elected and appointed officials, individuals at regulatory or funding agencies, and both national and state legislators and their aides. Personal relationships are the key to being a successful advocate and finding success in changing policy. Other contacts that may be established include those with media representatives, directors at community-based organizations, and key individuals in the community.

- *Pulse of the Community.* Before policy can be introduced, the Level III administrator must understand how the community feels. This includes what the community will support, what they will resist, and how they can be persuaded. Policy is more likely to be adopted or changed if it is what the community wants.

- *Positivism.* Policy that contains positive economic incentives, such as rebates or tax breaks, is more readily accepted than one that contains negative economic incentives such as special taxes or fines. Accent the positives of the policy change. The policy should ensure that people are rewarded for doing the right thing and not punished for doing the wrong thing. Benefits of the policy can be economic, social, psychological, or physical.

- *Participation.* When suggesting policy change, it is important to involve as many people in the community as possible. This can be done with the strategic planning group previously mentioned and should serve the same purpose that the coalition has already established as its mission statement.

- *Publicity.* Keep the community informed and keep a high profile of the issue and policy solution. Use the media, internet, community connections, and any other available sources to make the community aware of the policy-change efforts and to understand why the change is necessary. Publicity will help gain and maintain community support.

- *Persistence.* It takes a long-term commitment to achieve policy changes, and the Level III administrator must be prepared to keep at it for as long as it takes.

Policy change or adoption is one important step on the road for addressing risk-reduction issues in a community. A change in policy can actually change people's minds and attitudes. Sometimes it is the shortest road to such change, which ultimately results in a reduction in the risk issues in a community.

Effective Implementation Using Marketing Strategies

Implementation strategies for risk-reduction interventions are a crucial component of successful outcomes for the program. Implementation must include a process for informing the community about the program and its elements. Successfully informing the public about an initiative is one of the first steps in changing behavior relating to the risk.

Commercial marketing strategies have been used very effectively for many years to sell products and services to the public. In recent years, these same strategies have been successfully applied to public health and injury issues. Social marketing has been used by public health and safety agencies to create awareness, provide education, and change behaviors.

The Virginia Graeme Baker Pool and Spa Safety Act

In 2007, President Bush signed into law the Virginia Graeme Baker Pool and Spa Safety Act. This legislation was the result of the work of one individual, Nancy Baker. Mrs. Baker lost her daughter, Graeme, to drowning when the powerful suction of a drain in a hot tub trapped the 7 year old under the water. Mrs. Baker began a three-year campaign to established anti-entrapment safety standards for pools and spas and created incentives for states that adopted the national legislation. Mrs. Baker began her work by conducting research into the issue and found that other children had also fallen victim to the powerful force of drains in hot tubs and spas. She began working with Safe Kids Worldwide, a national coalition working to prevent unintentional injuries for children. She also built partnerships and relationships with those in legislative positions at the federal level. The work of Mrs. Baker is just one example of what one individual can accomplish through diligence and perseverance.

Source: Safe Kids Worldwide

Social marketing is a term that refers to the application of commercial marketing strategies and techniques to health issues and social problems. While the focus of commercial marketing is to change people's behavior for the benefit of a producer or merchant, the focus of social marketing is to change people's behavior to benefit themselves, the community, or society as a whole. The same strategies that achieve results in the commercial arena can be used to achieve success within the area of risk reduction and prevention. With social marketing, members of the risk-reduction team can reach the target audience more effectively, customize messages for the target audience, and create longer lasting behavioral changes in the audience. Social marketing should be used when trying to change the behavior of large numbers of people, when the change is taking place over a long period of time, and when there are resources necessary for a comprehensive campaign. Social marketing is an overall approach to risk-reduction work and not a short-term project. The use of social marketing techniques will affect how fire and life safety educators approach their work as a whole.

Example of Social Marketing: Smokey Bear

The Smokey Bear campaign is the longest running public service campaign in U.S. history. It is a clear example of social marketing at its best. Smokey's forest fire prevention message remained unchanged for 50 years until April 2001, when the Ad Council updated his message to address the increasing number of wildfires in the nation's wildlands. However, the campaign information, posters, and even Smokey himself has been adapted over the years to meet the needs of the times and the environment. The message, "Only You Can Prevent Forest Fires," is just part of the work that has been done by the U.S. Forestry Service. Smokey is working to change a specific behavior (carelessness with fire) and his message is targeted at a specific group (children ages 6 to 10 years old). The campaign reduces the barriers to the positive behavior, which are deemed to be ignorance and "it's no fun." The message is supported by information at campsites for parents and caregivers, where it is reinforced. Smokey provides information through a variety of media – internet, commercials, video, posters, and roadside billboards. Smokey Bear has proven to be one of the most successful and recognizable fire prevention campaigns that uses social marketing techniques.

Source: U.S. Forestry Service

The focus of social marketing is the consumer. This is the audience whose behavior needs to be modified or altered. Social marketing campaigns must first start by examining the beliefs and attitudes of the target audience in order to affect the decision-making process of these individuals. To change or adopt a behavior, the target audience must:

- *Receive and understand the message.* It is important to gain the attention of the target audience in order to create awareness and interest. The target audience must also understand the issue. It needs to be conveyed in language they understand and make sense within the context of their lives.

- *Change attitudes and conditions.* The recipient of the message must form a positive attitude or frame of mind about the behavior. The campaign should start the audience thinking about the positive outcomes that can be gained by making the change and adopting the desired behavior.

- *Be motivated to change.* It is not enough to simply think about the change. The social marketer must instill in the audience the intent to change. The campaign must transform thoughts into action. Motivation requires knowledge of the audience and what is important to them.

- *Be empowered to act.* Barriers must be removed, and members of the audience must understand that the change is within their power and capability. They must also be aware that the necessary supports are in place to assist them when needed.

- *Receive reinforcement for the behavior.* There must be some benefit from having acted so that the desired action will be repeated. The more immediate the benefit, the more likely the behavior is to be repeated and the change permanent **(Figure 14.8)**.

Because social marketing campaigns are based upon commercial marketing principles, a discussion of those principles is in order. Whether commercial or social, marketing is about persuasion. While it might seem out of place to talk about marketing and risk reduction together, the basic principles of commercial marketing apply to risk-reduction initiatives in the community.

Four basic principles of any marketing campaign are commonly referred to as the "Four Ps" **(Figure 14.9)**. While some experts in the field have developed additional principles, these four are basic to any marketing campaign. The Four Ps are **product, price, place**, and **promotion**:

- *Product.* The product is what is being marketed. In commercial campaigns, this is usually an item or service that the target audience will purchase or use. For social marketing, the product is the behavior that members of the community should modify or adopt.

- *Price.* This is the cost of the product. For social marketing, there may not necessarily be a dollars-and-cents price for a product. It may be a question of time or the effort that the target audience will have to put forth to make the change or adopt the desired behavior. Price in a social marketing campaign is not always easy to quantify, but it is still a determining factor for the target audience. The social marketing campaign must examine these costs and try to reduce them for the target audience.

To Change or Adopt a Behavior, the Target Audience Must:

Receive and understand message

Change attitudes and conditions

Motivate people to change

Feel empowered to act

Receive reinforcement for behavior

Figure 14.8 The end result of intervention should be a change in behavior.

The "Four Ps" of a Marketing Campaign

Product

Price

Place

Promotion

Figure 14.9 The four principles of marketing apply to social campaigns because persuasion is the goal of both.

- *Place.* In a social marketing campaign, *place* may refer to barriers that prevent the target audience from adopting the behavior. It may also refer to accessibility of the supports that provide the audience with the ability to make the change. The less people have to go out of their way to make the change, the more likely they are to make it. Many times, it may be necessary to bring the product to the people in a place that is familiar to them.

- *Promotion.* Advertising that is done to create awareness of the issue and provide the solution is called promotion. This could be through formal media such as television or newspaper, or it could be informal such as by word of mouth. Word of mouth and personal visits may make a greater impression on the target audience than the best commercial or printed ad.

It is important to remember that advertising alone is not social marketing. It takes all aspects of the social marketing campaign to create a change in the behavior of the target audience. Many successful social marketing campaigns have employed a variety of means for promoting the behavioral change. Examining each aspect individually should help with understanding how they will assist with the risk-reduction campaign.

Developing a social marketing campaign for the community is not a difficult process. While the Level III administrator may understand the problem, it is important that all parties involved also understand it. This includes other fire and life safety educators,

Health Marketing

A new trend in public health is the use of health marketing as a means for creating, communicating, and delivering public health initiatives to the general public. Much like social marketing, health marketing uses the science and strategies of commercial marketing. Concepts of marketing research, marketing strategies, mass communication, public affairs, journalism, and instructional design are all incorporated into the health marketing practice. The Centers for Disease Control is the front-runner in promoting health marketing as a means for changing or improving health. The National Center for Health Marketing was established in 2004 by the Centers for Disease Control, and its health-marketing efforts provide examples of other health-marketing programs.

management, members of the coalition, and the target audience. The problem should be written down so that there is no misunderstanding from any members of the team. It also should be defined broadly, which will allow for more suggestions for improving the situation or resolving the problem.

Once the problem has been defined, goals must be established. Goals are the objectives of the risk-reduction initiative. They should establish what is to be achieved by the campaign within a given time frame. Goals should not be so broad and over-reaching that there is difficulty achieving success. Smaller goals should be set so that the group sees results and is encouraged to continue the work.

Identifying the Target Audience

Another part of problem definition is identification of the target audience. Many times the primary audience is easily identified as the population who is most affected by the risk issue. However, there may also be a secondary audience — one who has the ability to affect the behavior of the primary audience. One example of a secondary audience would be the parents of preschool children (primary audience) because younger children do not control their environment. Another secondary audience includes caregivers of older adults, with the older adults themselves serving as the primary audience **(Figure 14.10)**.

It may be necessary to divide the target audience into subgroups, depending upon how different groups will respond to the marketing strategies. Groups may need to be divided based upon age, gender, race or ethnicity, past behaviors, economic status, or geographic location. The number of subgroups or the basis for the division will be contingent upon the audience and the behavior being promoted.

Defining the Target Audience

Once the audience has been identified, it is important to understand the audience. Social marketing focuses all attention on the target audience, so it is important to understand what is important to this group: how they feel about the problem and the barriers to solving the problem, which may be real or perceived; and what will convince them to change their behavior.

To accomplish this step requires the campaign developer to observe the target audience and their behaviors, conduct surveys and interviews, and sponsor focus groups. Involving key members of the target audience in the coalition or campaign development will be helpful in addressing this step of the planning process.

Communicating with the Target Audience

Once the problem has been identified, it is time to choose the appropriate strategies for the marketing campaign. This can be done through brainstorming

Figure 14.10 Identifying primary and secondary audiences allows educators to tailor a message to those most at risk as well as to those who can act on it.

sessions by identifying the different options available to make the behavioral change more attractive and affordable. There may be different strategies that will effectively reach the different subgroups of the audience that are targeted by the campaign. The Level III administrator also must decide how many resources are available and where those resources should be concentrated.

It is important to always keep in mind that these strategies must be measurable and should decrease the attractiveness of the competing behavior or increase the attractiveness of the desired behavior. These strategies should also improve the ability of the target audience to make the behavioral change.

When choosing the strategies for the campaign, the Level III administrator must also decide which is the best channel of communication (television or newspaper) for the target audience. It should also be decided if presentations by experts or face-to-face visits would work best. By knowing the target audience, it is easier to determine how they will best be reached.

Once the strategies have been chosen, it is time to implement the campaign and begin evaluation procedures. Evaluation is a continuous process, especially given the long-term nature of social marketing campaigns. There must be a continuous modification of the campaign as evaluation results are received.

When evaluation has been received and modifications made, the program must continue. Administrators must be vigilant in their efforts to promote and update their program's results. Due to the nature of their mission and goals, social marketing campaigns may never end.

A Successful Example of Social Marketing

The Tuscaloosa (AL) Fire and Rescue Service uses social marketing techniques to motivate residents in high-risk communities to change or modify their behavior. A study of Tuscaloosa's ten-year fire record showed that 80% of the city's emergency calls occurred in two communities. Demographic research indicated the populations of these communities had economic, social, and cultural factors different from nearby areas with fewer emergency calls. Although the existing fire and life safety program was effective in many communities, it was not affecting needed behavior change in high-risk areas.

Research results were discussed with partners in the high-risk communities — residents, station personnel, elected officials, school principals, and others — to help develop a strategic, proactive, and innovative campaign titled Project FIRE (Fire and Injury Reduction Education).

One of the most popular aspects of Project FIRE is an adopt-a-school partnership among neighborhood fire stations and elementary schools. Firefighters visit each classroom monthly during the school year to deliver fire-safety lessons taught through activities and games. Students participate in training on smoke alarms, escape drills, firefighter careers, holiday safety, water safety, cooking safety, safe use of portable heaters, calling 9-1-1, and many other fire and life safety topics. Project FIRE also includes a smoke alarm installation program, educational events for older adults and caregivers, programs for children with autism spectrum disorders, and other programs for high-risk groups.

Project FIRE is a customized program and not a series of prepackaged one-size-fits-all presentations. While it is impossible to know the number of fires and fire-related injuries and deaths prevented by Project FIRE, there are measurable benefits and cost-savings. Project FIRE has cultivated a rewarding behavior change in neighborhood relationships. Firefighters are now more likely to be recognized as an essential, helpful, and trustworthy part of the neighborhood than before the program. From a fiscal perspective, targeting public education efforts maximizes use of limited resources to do the most good for the most people. A year-round program makes it easier to schedule events, order supplies in bulk, prioritize public education requests, and obtain additional funding.

Project FIRE fosters the changing role of the firefighter as a fire preventer. In the Tuscaloosa Fire & Rescue Service, fire and life safety is everyone's responsibility and everyone contributes to its success.

Source: Tilda Mimms from Tuscaloosa (AL) Fire/Rescue

Strategic Planning

Many fire agencies spend multiple hours in strategic planning for the department's future. Many have strategic plans identifying issues, challenges, goals, and objectives for three years, five years, and ten years. Chiefs identify the issues and challenges so as not to be surprised by them and to maintain a state of readiness. Goals and objectives provide the department with direction and benchmarks for their achievement. Strategic plans also allow those forward-thinking fire administrators to share their vision for the department with other managers and personnel so that everyone is working together and heading in the same direction.

The strategic plan for a fire department should include risk-reduction activities. It is the responsibility of the Level III administrator to participate in this planning process. He or she should be able to project future issues and challenges for risk-reduction initiatives and what the fire and life safety issues will be for the community in the future. With these projections, the risk-reduction team can focus on lessening the effect of future issues before they become a high priority. Essentially, the risk-reduction section should have a strategic plan to stay on top of emerging trends and to plan and budget for the needs of the team working to effectively prevent fire and injuries.

In order to project future trends and issues for risk reduction, several areas must be examined continuously. Items that must be observed and studied include:

- The changing demographics of the community
- The status of housing, businesses, and industry
- The nature of the fire and injury problem, including local fire and injury issues and other regional, state, and national arenas

Community Demographics

The demographics of a community will alter the type of risks that will affect its residents. As demographics change, so do the risks. The Level III administrator, as the planner of risk-reduction initiatives, must keep aware of changing community demographics.

Most communities today are not static in their demographics. People leave the community and may not be replaced by people moving in. The age of the population, income levels, the ethnic makeup of the community, and the number of residents all will have an influence on the risk issues facing a community. If target populations are decreasing, again it will change the interventions and strategies needed to address the risk among the population **(Figure 14.11)**. Increases and decreases in the number of residents will affect the risk-reduction team, the issues to be addressed, and the methods used to address them.

An excellent source available to the Level III administrator is the U.S. Census, which provides relatively up-to-date information on community demographics. This information is accessible from the census web site (www.census.gov). The community's social service agency can also provide information on the number of individuals and families receiving public assistance. The school system can provide information on how class and school size is changing and can also provide information on the number of school children on free lunch programs. Comparing numbers from previous years can help establish trends in a community's demographics.

In order to provide for proper planning and development of risk-reduction programs, it is imperative that the Level III administrator consistently and regularly analyze the changing demographics of the community and make the appropriate adjustments to the focus and design of the risk-reduction program. This will ensure that the risk-reduction programs are targeting the high-risk areas and populations.

Status of Housing, Business, and Industry

The physical development of a community, or a lack thereof, will affect risk issues in a community. Areas to be examined include:

- *Age of housing.* As existing housing ages, the risk for fire and injury issues increases. If older housing is being replaced by newer housing, the risk issues will change and may even decrease. Occupancy types may change in older housing, that is, from a single-family residence to multiple-family apartments.

- *Density and type of housing.* If the number of housing units is increasing, the population density may be increasing as well, which increases the risk from fire. Additionally, it needs to be determined if housing is multi-family as opposed to single family and whether those statistics are changing as well.

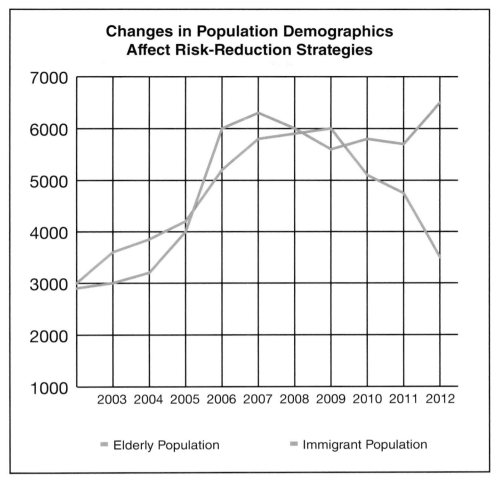

Changes in Population Demographics Affect Risk-Reduction Strategies

- Elderly Population
- Immigrant Population

Figure 14.11 Changes in community profiles will change the risks present in the community.

- *Business and industry.* Is new business coming into the community that can create additional risk or increase the population? Are businesses or industries leaving the community and not being replaced? These changes can have a profound affect on the fire and injury issues facing a community. If new industry is moving into an area, what type is it?

Different industries can also alter the risk issues in a community. Are buildings vacant? Are occupancies changing that can increase the risk to the residents in a neighborhood? Just as these factors will affect emergency response in the future, so will they affect risk-reduction issues and interventions.

Many communities have community development departments, planning departments, or industrial development agencies that can provide the risk-reduction planner with the type of information that is needed to help project future trends and issues for communities based upon their physical increase or reduction. Risk-reduction planners staying current on the changes in the community's buildings and the infrastructure for these buildings will be able to more accurately identify and project risk issues to be addressed in the future.

Nature of the Fire and Injury Issues

Planning for risk means staying current on changing fire and injury issues on a national, state, and local basis. Identifying the changing nature of fire and injury factors requires that the Level III administrator stay in touch with professional organizations and agencies in the field. Subscribing to professional publications, attending conferences and seminars, and networking with other fire and life safety educators are all excellent ways of staying up-to-date on the latest risk-reduction issues and solutions.

On a more local basis, fire and EMS response data can help the Level III administrator identify trends in the types of injuries occurring or the factors leading to hostile fires. This is true at the state level as well as at the local level. If an upward trend is identified in a particular classification of injury, the Level III administrator will have to determine who is receiving the injury, the root cause of the injury, and why the rate of injury is on the increase.

Planning for the future of risk reduction is not a task that is isolated from the daily activities of the Level III administrator; that is, it does not just happen once. It takes a concerted effort and should be a part of the regular routine of the Level III administrator. Reading, researching, and networking are all tasks which the Level III administrator must participate in for the proper planning and development of community risk-reduction initiatives.

The information developed from the projections should be shared with the leaders of the department as a part of their strategic planning process. If the risk-reduction team is adequately addressing risk and planning for addressing future risks, this may influence the plan developed by the organization's leaders. If this information is not shared with those in charge, risk reduction may become a lower priority for the organizational planners and therefore not receive the attention, personnel, or funding needed to be effective.

Chapter Summary

As the administrator of the fire and life safety activities of a fire agency, the Level III administrator must take the concept of planning and development of the risk-reduction strategy very seriously. Without proper planning, risk-reduction activities may not have the

focus needed to be successful. In addition, it is hard to properly evaluate the success of a program if there are no objectives or goals established.

Planning involves more than just developing the risk-reduction strategy. It is the responsibility of the Level III administrator to create a coalition to address the risk, promote public policy related to the risk, prepare a marketing plan for the risk-reduction initiative, and project future risk issues in the community. Planning is paramount to the effectiveness of any risk-reduction strategy and should be undertaken with great enthusiasm by those individuals given the responsibility. Effectiveness is demonstrated by a reduction in fires, injuries, and property damage, which is the mission of any risk-reduction team or organization.

Review Questions

1. What are the general steps for developing an organization's risk-reduction strategy?

2. What is the process used to create an interagency collaborative partnership for a fire and life safety education issue?

3. What methods can be used to project emerging trends and risk issues?

4. What is the process for proposing a public policy to decision-makers?

5. What is the process for developing a marketing plan designed to raise awareness on a risk-reduction issue?

Key Terms

Place — In identifying the place in a social marketing campaign, it may refer to barriers that prevent the target audience from adopting the behavior. Place refers to accessibility of the supports that provide the target audience with the ability to make the change.

Price — One of the four basic principles of any marketing campaign, which is commonly referred to as the "Four Ps." For social marketing, there may not necessarily be a dollars-and-cents price for a product. It may be a question of time or the effort that the target audience will have to put forth to make the change or adopt the desired behavior. Price in a social marketing campaign is not always easy to quantify, but it is still a determining factor for the target audience.

Product — The product is what is being marketed. In commercial campaigns, this is usually an item or service that the target audience will purchase or use. For social marketing, the product is the behavior that members of the community should modify or adopt.

Promotion — Advertising that is done to create awareness of the issue and provide the solution.

Social Marketing — Refers to the application of commercial marketing strategies and techniques to health issues and social problems. While the focus of commercial marketing is to change people's behavior for the benefit of a producer or merchant, the focus of social marketing is to change people's behavior to benefit themselves, the community, or society as a whole.

Chapter 14 Notes

1. Community Tool Box, University of Kansas (http://ctb.ku.edu) 2007

FLSE Level III Administrators: Education and Implementation

Chapter Contents

chapter 15

Key Terms

Job Performance Requirements

This chapter provides information that addresses the following job performance requirements of NFPA® 1035, *Standard for Professional Qualifications for Fire and Life Safety Educator, Public Information Officer, and Juvenile Firesetter Intervention Specialist*, 2010 edition.

NFPA® 1035 References

7.4.1

7.4.2

7.4.3

7.4.4

7.4.5

Learning Objectives

After reading this chapter, students will be able to:

1. Create accurate and specific educational messages suitable for a target audience and the risk issues of a particular community (NFPA® 1035, 7.4.1).

2. Establish clearly stated administrative policies for the risk-reduction program that are supportive of the organization's mission and federal/state/local regulations (NFPA® 1035, 7.4.2).

3. Create an awareness campaign within the organization that informs members of their role in the risk-reduction and prevention education strategies (NFPA® 1035, 7.4.4).

4. Create a training program for fire and life safety educators (NFPA® 1035, 7.4.3).

5. Create comprehensive reports for policy makers that clearly describe the educational strategies, goals, objectives, activities, impact, outcomes, and budgets of the risk-reduction division (NFPA® 1035, 7.4.5).

Chapter 15
FLSE Level III
Administrators: Education and Implementation

Case History

County executives and fire administrators recognized the upward trend of fire-related deaths and injuries of senior citizens in Montgomery County, Maryland. They determined that the best approach to identifying effective fire-safety strategies and procedures was to convene a focused, representative task force. A committee was formed of citizens with fire suppression experience and individuals representing senior citizens' interests and organizations. The group included representatives from the following:

- Residents of the county
- Senior citizen organizations
- Senior housing complexes
- Commission on Aging, Health, and Human Services
- Montgomery County Fire and Rescue
- Other social service organizations and agencies serving senior residents

The group made initial recommendations after six months and provided county officials with an annual report. A complete set of recommendations was presented approximately two years after the group's initial convening. Education was a critical component of each recommendation, citing a change in sociocultural attitudes regarding fire safety.

The success of this program comes from the involvement of community members and from those who work directly with the target population. It involved many aspects of the community, both public and private. It shows a commitment on the part of this community to the safety of its residents. It also demonstrates the importance of a focused, targeted process in developing interventions for the target population.

Source: Seniors at Risk: Creating a Culture of Fire Safety. Senior Citizens Fire Safety Task Force Final Report, September 2008.

As the risk-reduction professional advances from the level of Educator I to Educator II and then up to Educator III, the focus moves from education to management and then to administration. The Level III administrator may conduct few, if any, educational programs in the community.

However, the Level III administrator continues to function as an educator, although with a different focus. The target audience for the Level III administrator is mainly internal to his or her home organization, as opposed to external customers. Simply put, the Level III administrator's role is to perform the following tasks:

- Inform department members about risk-reduction initiatives.

- Report to management the results of the risk-reduction work.

- Educate the risk-reduction staff and other members of the organization about their duties and responsibilities.

In addition to the above, the Level III administrator in charge of the community risk-reduction program must educate all personnel in the fire agency about their roles in risk reduction and the outcomes of the work being performed in the community **(Figure 15.1)**.

As the program administrator, the Level III fire and life safety educator must be the expert on the community, its risk issues, and the initiatives being used to prevent or mitigate those risks. This information is imperative in the formation of the appropriate messages for target audiences. It also must be communicated to policy makers, government administrators, department heads, and all personnel so that each and every member of the department understands the importance of the risk-reduction activities.

In this chapter, the reader will find information about the development, vision and mission, and goals for the risk-reduction division. In addition, this chapter does the following:

- Discusses how to design a training program for a new fire and life safety educator

- Presents information on the concept of organizational equity and its importance in the risk-reduction efforts of the department

- Discusses other leadership concepts along with the development of reports of activities for managers and policy makers

Creating Messages for Risk Reduction

As was discussed in the previous chapter, the Level III administrator is responsible for designing, developing, and evaluating the risk-reduction program for the department. This includes understanding the community, identifying the major risk issues, determining the appropriate audiences and delivery methods, and evaluating the overall efforts of the risk-reduction activities. Throughout the planning process for the risk-reduction initiatives, the Level

Figure 15.1 The Level III administrator is the expert on the community, its risk issues, and the initiatives in operation to address those risks.

III administrator must determine the messages that are appropriate for the identified risks and the target audiences.

In Chapter 2, a wide variety of fire, life safety, and disaster preparedness messages were presented. In most instances, the positive behaviors for the various situations do not change. However, the message may need to be adapted for the audience and how the message is presented may have a great impact on the effectiveness of the message **(Figure 15.2)**. This means that a message about testing a smoke alarm will be different for younger children than for adults in that young children should not be encouraged to test the smoke alarm on their own.

There is a difference between the terms *behavior* and *message*. The behavior is the life-safety action that is needed to prevent the incident or mitigate the damage. The message is how the behavior is performed or carried out. "Stop, drop, and roll" is the desired behavior for extinguishing clothing fires. The step-by-step instruction for carrying out the stop, drop, and roll procedure is the message. For some audiences, this is an appropriate message. For others, such as those that have physical disabilities or are older adults, this might not be an appropriate message for extinguishing clothing fires. It is up to the Level III administrator to determine the appropriate message for the targeted audiences.

When creating messages about a specific behavior, the Level III administrator must ask the following questions:

1. *What message is more commonly used?* Using nationally accepted messages is clearly better than trying to invent new messages. Nationally accepted messages tend to have more validity since they are reviewed by educators from various organizations throughout the nation. Nationally accepted messages also provide consistent language between various fire and life safety materials and programs. Before creating a new message, the Level III administrator needs strong evidence that a change is needed and the new message is correct. Using a more common message will also prevent confusion among the target audience. If they hear the old message and the new message, they may become confused and therefore do nothing. As an example, some jurisdictions encourage individuals to change the battery in their smoke alarms twice a year, while others promote changing the battery once a year. To promote consistency, educators should promote reading the manufacturer's instructions and changing the battery according to those instructions.

2. *What action is simplest for people to remember*? Messages must be simple for people to remember them. When creating a message, test it with the

Figure 15.2 The presentation of a message can be as important as the content of the message.

target audience to make sure that people remember it and actually perform the behavior correctly.

3. *What action is the easiest for people to perform?* In an emergency, people will do what is easiest and natural. Messages must seem natural and not be complicated or tedious.

4. *Is it the right message for the target audience?* Messages may differ slightly for different age groups and may vary greatly from audience to audience. Messages will vary depending upon the living arrangements of the target audience, the type of dwelling, and even culture or heritage. An example would be the use of candles. Many cultures use candles for religious purposes and will not be as likely to extinguish them when leaving a room or may not keep them a 1-foot distance from combustible items. Messages may also vary depending upon geographic location, climate, and population density such as rural versus urban neighborhoods.

What This Means to You

In a small fishing community in rural Alaska, women light candles and place them in the window of their homes when their husbands go out to sea. The candle burns until the husband returns. It is your job to educate these families about how the candle can be burned safely; that is, without the curtains drawn or away from combustible items. It is unreasonable and insensitive in this culture to ask the family to extinguish the candle. You must understand the cultural beliefs of the audience as it pertains to particular messages. When working with these individuals, you must honor and respect various beliefs.

What makes a good message? The Centers for Disease Control has conducted research to try and answer this question. According to this research, messages must be closely targeted and take into consideration the unique characteristics of the target audience including their culture and beliefs. Developing effective messages requires that the Level III administrator have an understanding of the target audience's perception of the issue and possible reasons why standardized messages may not be effective. Good messages must demonstrate advocacy, empathy, and creativity. Effective messages require the developer to think like a member of the target audience and understand their reasoning processes. According to the CDC,[1] a good message is one that works within the audience's value system and demonstrates credible and persuasive reasoning. An effective message requires recognition on the part of the target audience; they must be able to "see themselves" in the message.

An effective way to create messages that are appropriate for the target audience is to include members of that audience in the development process. If one is designing messages for a special needs audience, who knows better about their capabilities or restrictions than members of that audience! This will involve the use of focus groups or other community members acting in an advisory capacity **(Figure 15.3)**.

Messages to the target audience must be relevant, clear, and concise. Emphasis should be placed on the content and not just the method. Messages should be developed for a specific audience, taking into consideration its cultural ideas, practices, and feelings about death, illness, and fate. In order to create the most effective message, the Level III administrator needs to draw upon the expertise from the target audience and those working with the audience to determine how the audience will best receive the message. Effectiveness requires a variation of the message to meet the needs of the audience receiving it.

Adapting Messages for the Audience

Tilda Mims, public safety educator for Tuscaloosa (AL) Fire & Rescue Service, relates the following about messages: "In high-risk areas, the audience is in a very different place, economically and culturally, than what many people in the fire service grew up with themselves. We were in a class talking about getting low and crawling, and a little girl said, 'That's what you do when they're shooting outside.' We were floored. So I just said, 'Tell me about that.' She said, 'Well, the bullets come through the walls.' So we had to change the message, and we said, 'Well, when what you're afraid of is inside the house, you have to get out. When what you're afraid of is outside, then you stay inside.'"

Source: IAFC *On Scene*, March 25, 2008.

Figure 15.3 Focus groups allow knowledgeable community members to contribute to initiatives that will benefit the community at-large.

Establishing Administrative Policies for the Risk-Reduction Program

As the administrator of the risk-reduction program and its activities, the Level III administrator must develop goals and policies that govern risk-reduction activities. These goals and policies must be in line with the department's policies and federal, state, and local regulations. Most importantly, the stated administrative policies created for the risk-reduction program must support and be compatible with the organization's mission.

Written policies and procedures permit everyone in the division, and in the organization, to understand how risk-reduction activities are scheduled and conducted. Through stated policies and procedures, individuals can understand the priorities of the department in working with the different audiences in the community. Most fire departments have some kind of **standard operating procedures** (SOPs) or standard operating guidelines (SOGs) for many of their operations and activities, and risk-reduction activities should be no different.

Vision Statement

The first step in developing goals, procedures, or policies for fire and life safety activities is the creation of a **vision statement**. A vision statement is a descrip-

tion of the ultimate results of the work of the fire and life safety educators, which for any risk-reduction program is a safer and healthier community.

The vision statement provides a picture of the future and its potential. The vision provides an ultimate goal to work toward. It provides motivation for the work and a reason for commitment. By creating a vision statement, all members of the risk-reduction team, and the entire department, can have a picture of the overall objective and goal of the activities being conducted. The vision may include idealistic phrasing to which the organization can aspire, though it may not realistically achieve. Through the vision statement, all members of the agency can understand the hopes and dreams of the risk-reduction leaders. The vision provides the basis for the goals, objectives, and strategies of risk reduction in the community.

When creating the vision, the Level III administrator should set hopes and aspirations high by doing the following:

- Dream and capture the passion that is so prevalent among those who commit their careers to risk reduction.

- Examine the values of the organization and the community.

- Share the vision with the members of the team, as well as the entire organization. The vision statement should consider the community and its risks, the organization's mission statement and goals, and the goals and objectives of the local governing body.

Mission Statement

The establishment of the vision statement leads to the creation of a **mission statement** and goals. While the vision statement looks to the future, the mission statement refers to the present state of the risk-reduction division. It provides a meaning for the existence of risk-reduction work and allows the entire organization to understand the importance of the work being performed. All decisions about risk-reduction work, whether they are made in the stations, at officers' meetings, or by risk-reduction practitioners, should be based upon the tenets of the mission statement. That is, the mission statement should drive decisions about risk-reduction activities, and all activities should strive to meet the mission of the risk-reduction division.

Goals

Once the vision and mission statements have been established, the goals for the community risk-reduction program should be established. Goals for the work of the risk-reduction division should relate to the targeted programs and audiences and should be based upon one-, three-, and five-year achievements. Goals for the division may also relate to internal or organizational challenges or issues, such as increasing the number of individuals in the risk-reduction division, or the purchase of capital items such as a fire safety house or a fire and life safety education center **(Figure 15.4)**.

This process is similar to the strategic planning process for the entire agency. While it is simply one piece of any department's work, establishing the vision, mission, and goals for the community risk-reduction division allows this information to be successfully conveyed to all department members so that each individual understands his or her role in the process of risk reduction and the organization's commitment to the concepts of prevention and mitigation in the community.

Standard Operating Procedures

Once the vision, mission, and goals are established, a procedure should be established for the planning, scheduling, and development of presentations, activities, and other events relating to risk reduction. Because most departments have some form of standard operating procedures (SOPs) for many activities, it is up to the Level III administrator to develop the same standard procedures and policies for risk-reduction work.

Developing a procedure is not difficult, and it is important to have one in place. An SOP for education and risk-reduction activities should include the following:

- Process for requesting and scheduling events and activities, both for risk reduction and for public relations
- Procedure for requesting the scheduling of an activity or event
- Priority in which events will be scheduled (which should relate to the goals and objectives identified for the overall risk-reduction program)

Figure 15.4 Goals of a risk-reduction initiative may include the purchase of large-scale equipment.

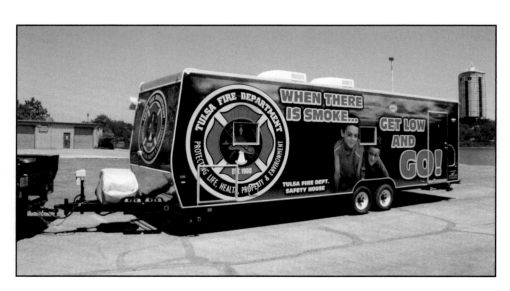

- Handling of requests from other jurisdictions or for those activities that might not be considered education, but are good public relations

- Guidelines that relate to how the event or activity will be conducted, what is expected of those working at the event, who will take care of supplies, etc.

- Information about the evaluation of the event and proper documentation

For a smaller department or one that is volunteer, it may not seem like this document is necessary. However, in order to have a focused and targeted risk-reduction program, each member of the agency should have an understanding of the rules and policies for scheduling activities and events so that there is no conflict and to ensure that events are adequately staffed and in line with the mission and goals of the risk-reduction division.

As the risk-reduction division grows, it may become necessary to establish internal policies and procedures for the staff. Topics may include proper dress code, equipment maintenance and check-out, emergency situations (including calling in sick), work hours, and any others that may be applicable. Having these procedures in place will help the division run smoothly, effectively, and efficiently.

Clarity is important when developing any type of policy or procedure. There should be no confusion about the particular procedure or process. Once the policy has been developed, someone outside the risk-reduction division should read the policy to ensure that it is understandable. Simplicity is also important. If the procedure for scheduling events is time consuming or complicated, individuals may not follow it or schedule events.

Ideally, things will run smoothly when it comes to risk-reduction activities, but this is not always the case. Planning ahead for obstacles or challenges can help divert them from occurring or minimize their impact.

Creating Awareness and Building Organizational Equity

Once the vision, mission, and goals have been established for the community risk-reduction division, they must be communicated to the members of the organization. Each individual within the organization has a part to play in the successful achievement of the goals of risk reduction. It is imperative that each member understands that role and accepts the responsibility for the duties that have been assigned to him or her. If members do not understand what is happening and why, it will be difficult to gain support for the program. Without the support of the department's members for risk-reduction activities, it will be very difficult to achieve success in reaching the goals that have been established.

Part of the role and responsibility of the Level III administrator is to develop and maintain a positive organizational culture that will support the work of risk reduction. While each and every member of the organization may not be actively performing risk-reduction activities on a daily basis, all must have a grasp of the organization's commitment to risk reduction and the goals and objectives of the risk-reduction work. All members must actively support that work and be committed to the end result.

Most fire organizations are not created with an instant commitment to community risk reduction. Fire agencies will fall somewhere along a continuum from the organization that has no support for risk reduction and performs few if any fire and life safety activities to the organization that is actively committed to risk-reduction work in every way and has institutionalized the concept. It is the responsibility of the Level III administrator to be the advocate for creating and maintaining the organization's commitment to the program. Before change can be expected in the community, change must occur in the organization.

The fire agency is the role model for the community. The members of the agency and its policies and programs must reflect a commitment to risk reduction. If there is no commitment, the goals of the risk-reduction program will not be met. By not meeting the goals of risk reduction, there is a failure to serve the best interest of the community's members.

Efforts to change the organization's view of risk reduction must come from all levels. These efforts need to target senior leaders, company and battalion officers, firefighters, and all civilian personnel. When members of the organization support risk-reduction activities, that support must be rewarded. There should be positive consequences for those who embrace community risk reduction and contribute to the success of the initiatives.

Those tasked with promoting this change effort must understand that it is not an easy task, but it can be achieved with commitment and perseverance.

The Level III administrator is responsible for creating an awareness within the fire organization and providing information on the role of each and every member in the fire and life safety education process. This responsibility will require that the administrator examine the culture of the organization and address areas where changes may be needed in order to fully promote the educational goals and policies. Change must come from within the organization in the support and implementation of educational programs and strategies.

How does one go about changing the organization's culture? How does the Level III administrator market the concept of risk reduction within the organization? There are eight building blocks for creating and maintaining organizational change that have been identified in the National Fire Academy's Executive Fire Officer curriculum. They are as follows:

1. *Recruit support.* The Level III administrator must gain the support of formal and informal leaders within the organization. Change must occur at all levels, but it may be the most powerful at the company and battalion levels. In some departments, this may also include unions and auxiliary organizations. Find individuals who are interested in fire and life safety education and have a willingness to assist. Some members may have a special skill or interest in one particular aspect of risk reduction, such as working with older adults or participating in health fairs. Look for those key leaders in the department and recruit their support, remembering that support is something that is earned.

2. *Empower members.* Agency members must be empowered to provide risk-reduction services when and where the opportunity presents itself. By allowing individuals to perform such duties and providing the resources for them, there is buy-in for community risk reduction at the various levels. Engine companies should not have to ask their supervisors if they can install a smoke alarm at a residence or have lunch at a school. They should feel empowered to do so, within the parameters of their chain of command and operating procedures, and the Level III administrator should encourage these activities and support them.

3. *Establish goals.* Establishing a mission statement, goals, and objectives has already been discussed. However, if these are not a part of the organization's overall goals and objectives, it will be difficult to achieve a cultural change. If the concept of risk reduction is not included in the organization's mission and goals, it is up to the Level III administrator to campaign for its inclusion.

4. *Promote positive organizational attitudes.* The promotion of positive attitudes must come from all levels of the organization, especially department leadership. What is done is often more effective than what is said. When the actions of leaders support risk reduction, then other levels of the department will as well. Promoting positive attitudes also means overcoming negative attitudes. Regular communication with personnel and correction of any misinformation that may exist can accomplish this objective **(Figure 15.5)**.

5. *Establish a budget for risk reduction.* When funds are budgeted, this shows an interest in and commitment to risk-reduction activities. Alternatively, when there are no funds committed to fire and life safety activities, few in the department will view them as important. Sharing funds for fire and life safety education with other divisions, such as inspections or training, will not have the impact on the organizational culture that a separate budget will have. Level III administrators may find the need to lobby for a separate budget and their own designated funds.

6. *Establish job requirements.* If risk reduction is the responsibility of all employees, then it should be built into each job description. A look at the professional qualification standards published by the National Fire Protection Association® reveals that for Firefighter[2] and Fire Officer[3], fire and life safety education is a requirement. With the requirement comes the need for training. Of course, this is critical for recruits during their training process, but it is also needed for those who may not have had such training earlier in their career. The Level III administrator must be prepared to deliver this training and actively campaign for the opportunity to deliver the training to operations personnel as well as civilian personnel. Level III administrators should establish strict requirements for those wishing to enter into the risk-reduction division to demonstrate that it is a job that not just anyone can perform effectively.

Figure 15.5 Regular communication among all levels of an organization can promote risk-reduction and positive attitudes.

7. *Establish professional development.* In some departments, risk-reduction work may be seen as a dead-end assignment or for one on light duty or waiting for retirement. Level III administrators must work to change this view and seek upward mobility within a department. Level III administrators must present themselves in a professional manner and as a member of the fire service team. They should seek professional development not only in the field of risk reduction but in other areas including leadership, management, and organizational operations. This may mean that the Level III administrator needs to contact the local community college for information on supervision and management classes. Educators should attend training seminars and other classes that relate to all aspects of fire department operations, not just risk-reduction activities. By doing so, the Level III administrator is in a better position to interact with chief officers and fire department management on risk-reduction activities and other related activities.

8. *Communicate to all members.* This may be the most important element in changing organizational culture and educating members about the risk-reduction services of the department. Lack of communication is the most common reason that efforts to change fail. Members of the department must be informed about risk-reduction activities, the successes and failures of those activities, and

the benefits of risk reduction to the community and to the department. The Level III administrator must communicate all important aspects of risk reduction to each person in the department, so that everyone understands their role. If department members do not understand what is happening or how they fit into the overall success, they are less apt to buy into the concept of risk reduction as a part of their job.

Even if the Level III administrator can successfully set the stage for risk reduction, support of the department's personnel is a key ingredient to a cultural change. This support may take months or even years to build. The Level III administrator must work continually to build organizational equity.

When the Level III administrator and the risk-reduction staff work to help meet the needs of the department's members, organizational equity is developed. Organizational equity does not happen by accident and requires certain responsibilities on the part of the Level III administrator and the risk-reduction staff. The Level III administrator must ensure that everyone in the risk-reduction division is doing his or her part and not simply delegating.

Much has been said about the importance of the demographics of the community. It is also important for the Level III administrator to look at the demographics of the organization. An important question to ask is what department personnel feel comfortable doing in risk-reduction activities. For example, not everyone feels comfortable making presentations, and some prefer behind-the-scenes activities. Other questions to ask include the following:

- What are the challenges within the organization that could affect the attitude toward risk-reduction activities?
- What is the past experience in the organization with risk reduction?
- What has caused any bad experiences involving a risk-reduction specialist or activity?

The Level III administrator must work with both formal and informal leaders to understand the point of view of the department's personnel toward risk reduction and to be sympathetic and understanding of their needs and concerns.

The Level III administrator must be able to communicate to staff and leadership the vision or plan for risk reduction and how everyone, including the risk-reduction staff, fits into that plan. Every departmental employee must understand the community's risk issues and the sequence of events that is causing the problem. The Level III administrator should communicate what resources, including personnel, are needed to get the job done.

In building organizational equity, the Level III administrator must recognize and accept the leadership role of the position. While the position may not carry a rank, such as lieutenant or captain, the Level III administrator is a key leader in the department. As such, this individual should lead by example. Those who continually delegate tasks will not be as readily accepted as those who do their share of the work. There must be a plan, addressing where risk reduction stands in the community and how it needs to be handled. The Level III administrator needs to develop the concept of customer service within the department. An individual in this position must also have a presence throughout the organization. Staying in the office is not the way to build organizational equity. Getting out to the individual stations, visiting with the department's members, and assisting with their activities will have a much greater influence.

There are two important points to remember:

1. *Always say thank-you.* This cannot be emphasized enough. Say thank-you to those who assist with programs, who schedule and plan, and the folks who bring apparatus or vehicles. Express appreciation for their work and their assistance. Thank the staff who work in risk-reduction efforts.

2. *Seize every opportunity to recognize and give credit.* When promoting or reporting on risk-reduction activities, give credit to those who participated. Use meetings, ceremonies, employee newsletters, memos to supervisors, and media press releases to recognize and give credit to station personnel. Give credit where credit is due!

The people in the department can be the most important resource and asset when it comes to community risk reduction. They can make or break the risk-reduction activities being performed and can have a huge impact on the success of the activities. The Level III administrator must continually work to create awareness among the members about the efforts taking place in risk reduction and to reward the successes and positive behaviors that are the result of the efforts of the department's work.

Training New Educators

The Level III administrator must ensure that all members of the risk-reduction team are properly trained. This includes training on job responsibilities, policies and procedures regarding risk-reduction activities, and performance measures relating to conducting fire and life safety programs. It is up to the Level III administrator to provide the Level I educators and Level II managers with the information and tools that are needed to perform the work effectively. This is true whether those individuals are a part of a risk-reduction division or line firefighters assisting with fire and life safety educational programs.

There is a distinct difference between training and education. Training usually involves gaining a skill, while education involves gaining knowledge, facts, concepts, and principles. Many times the two are intertwined in that knowledge, concepts, and principles are necessary to perform the skill effectively. This is the case with successful fire and life safety education programs. However, it is usually not the Level III administrator's responsibility to provide the education but to train new members of the prevention team.

It is up to the Level III administrator to see that those new to risk reduction receive the education needed to effectively perform fire and life safety education. Concepts presented earlier in this manual such as stages of development, learning theories and styles, evaluation, and lesson planning are examples of educational concepts necessary for the effective fire and life safety educator to understand before engaging in program delivery.

Once the education has been received, the new educator is not necessarily ready to deliver fire and life safety presentations. The Level III administrator must provide the skills training that is required for those who will be conducting educational programs. This includes the processes relating to risk-reduction activities, such as scheduling, planning, documentation, and even public speaking skills.

Training of new educators is an important responsibility of the Level III administrator and one that should not be taken lightly. Much of the success of a new educator depends upon the management and leadership provided by the Level III administrator.

A variety of methods can be used to provide a successful training experience. The method for training new employees will depend upon the resources available to the Level III administrator, including others trained in risk reduction. The proper training method may also depend upon the individual who is to be trained:

- Is this an individual who will be a full-time risk-reduction educator or someone who will be assisting with risk reduction in addition to other job responsibilities?

- Is this someone who has fire or EMS experience or someone who is new to the service?

The type of training will depend upon the circumstances and resources available. In order to provide for the optimum training experience, the Level III administrator must employee a variety of methods. These may include:

- Coaching
- Mentoring
- Peer assistance
- Leading by example

Coaching

While the term **coaching** is usually used in reference to sporting events, it certainly has relevance when talking about training and leading. Coaches, even in sports, give directions and provide expertise and advice with the goal of leading a team to victory.

Management or Leadership: Which Is It?

Experts feel that management and leadership are two different fields. Leadership should bring about useful change, while the purpose of management is to provide stability, order, and efficiency. Leaders are visionaries. They help people stay focused on the mission and vision of the organization. Managers keep things on schedule, maintain budget constraints, and make programs work efficiently. One individual may be both a great manager and a skilled leader. In any case, both managers and leaders are needed for organizations to be successful. Mike DeGrosky, CEO of the Guidance Group, had this to say about leadership and management:

- *Leadership is an influence relationship; management is an authority relationship.*
- *Leadership establishes direction by developing a vision for the future.*
- *Leadership communicates vision.*
- *Leadership energizes people and inspires them.*
- *Effective leadership brings about positive, needed change.*
- *Management establishes the structure and delegates authority and responsibility.*
- *Management monitors results and solves problems.*
- *Competent management results in orderly and consistent results.*
- *Both are essential to organizational effectiveness.*

In the field of risk reduction, the Level III administrator must be a leader and a manager. It is crucial that the Level III administrator have the ability to establish and communicate a clear vision for risk reduction in the community, the ability to manage people and budgets, and to maintain order and efficiency.

Adapted from "Management not Leadership" by Mike DeGrosky, Wildfire Magazine

Coaching, when used in reference to training or instruction, refers to an intensive tutoring given to subordinates regarding a particular activity **(Figure 15.6, p. 374)**. Coaches in the training environment provide motivational correction, positive reinforcement, and constructive feedback to improve

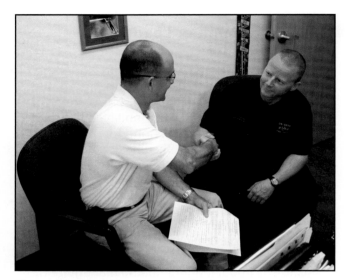

Figure 15.6 Coaching is one method of new employee training that provides motivational correction, positive reinforcement, and constructive feedback.

performance. Coaching can guide employees through learning challenges and direct them through skills performance, such as those skills necessary for an effective presentation.

The characteristics of self-confidence, humility, flexibility, and vision relate to positive, effective coaching and training in the following ways:

Self-confidence. In order to be an effective coach, Level III administrators must believe that they have the ability to make a difference in the team's performance. They also need to know that they *are* making a difference. In other words, they must be self-confident. Effective coaches must be able to focus on leading rather than just being a "friend." Effective coaches must stay on top of their own expertise, skills, and knowledge in order to share with others and lead them in effective risk-reduction work.

Humility. In contrast to self-confidence, effective coaches must possess humility. Without the team, there is likely to be little or no success in reaching the risk-reduction goals that have been set. The Level III administrator, as previously stated, often does little in the field in the way of risk-reduction activities. It is imperative that the team be sufficiently trained and empowered to be successful. The goal of the Level III administrator is to do everything possible to see that subordinates succeed, which will most certainly lead to an effective community risk-reduction program.

Flexibility. Effective coaching requires flexibility in training approaches. Just as all individuals do not learn in the same way, employees may respond differently to the various approaches that are used in training. Some employees may need to be challenged more than others and some may need more direct supervision. In the early stages of the training process, most employees will need more direct instruction, but this is not always the case. It is up to the Level III administrator to determine the appropriate training approach at a given point in time, understanding that these approaches may change as tasks change, employees lose their motivation, or goals are reached.

Vision. The final attribute of the effective coach is the ability to have vision. Vision has been a much-discussed concept in this unit for the Level III administrator. Effective leaders must be able to visualize the big picture and to see beyond the individual to his or her potential. Individuals with vision are able to see a subordinate's potential and help that individual reach that potential. Each individual's uniqueness must be recognized and utilized.

In addition, to be effective, the leader/coach must:

- Have regular interaction with each team member.
- Accept individual differences while encouraging teamwork.
- Demand the best from everyone.
- Hold people accountable.
- Praise and reward good performance.
- Trust and respect each individual.
- Listen to everyone's ideas.
- Be willing to compromise.

Mentoring

Mentoring is another method of training for new employees. Mentoring involves placing a new employee under the guidance of a more experienced employee. This form works well when there is more than one individual responsible for risk-reduction activities.

A mentor acts as a tutor, guide, and motivator for the new risk-reduction educator. Mentors will guide the actions of the new employee outside the office, for example, while giving presentations, at planning meetings, and when working at risk-reduction events. They also act as a "go-to" person when the new employee has questions about processes or procedures.

Access to a mentor provides a positive role model for the new risk-reduction educator. Mentors can help individuals overcome challenges or challenge themselves as the case may be. Mentors monitor achievements of the new employee and can assist in identifying specialized training needs.

Most often the mentor is not the new employee's direct supervisor. While this is not a hard and fast rule, caution must be used. The designation of the supervisor as mentor should in no way restrict an employee from seeking additional counsel or guidance from other professionals. According to the U.S. Air Force, the mentor should be a "trusted counselor or guide," and in many situations, the most logical individual to serve as mentor is the supervisor. This can also create a workload burden for the supervisor and cause stress to the new employees when they have concerns or issues with their supervisor. Again, decisions concerning mentoring assignments should rest with the individual organization, its needs, and its resources.

It may be that the mentor and the new employee seek out each other rather than being assigned. This might come as a result of a previous station assignment, or particular duty assignment. It may come about through similar interests or connections within the community. Whatever brings them together, it can certainly be a win-win relationship for both individuals.

Peer Assistance

Similar to the process of mentoring is **peer assistance**. By definition, a *peer* is someone of equal status in the organization. Peer assistance refers to the process of having employees of equal status assist others in the training process. Those who need advice and guidance can receive assistance from risk-reduction professionals who have a grasp of the knowledge and skills and have the ability to explain them.

A good example for peer assistance is a situation where there are two relatively new employees to risk reduction — one who is completely new to the fire service and one who transferred from another position within the organization **(Figure 15.7)**. The individual who is transferring may have more experience with risk reduction, and certainly with the department, than the new employee. The trans-

Figure 15.7 Peer assistance is characterized as a beneficial relationship of mutual support and information sharing.

ferring employee may be able to pick up on things faster simply because of the experience within the organization. The new employee may be able to provide the transferee with new insights or ideas because of recent training or past experiences. In many ways, peer assistance is an advanced form of team teaching. Peer assistance is used extensively throughout the teaching profession and is a good fit for risk-reduction specialists.

Leading by Example

While it may not seem like a means of training a new employee, leading by example can show the new employee what the job is all about. Some may prefer to use the term *job shadowing*, although this term is used mainly for students in a particular school-based program. In the context of risk reduction, leading by example provides more than just training for the new job. It can demonstrate commitment, passion, vision, and dedication to the work of risk reduction.

When a new employee is part of a training program for a new risk-reduction educator, leading by example allows the new employee to observe the Level III administrator in his or her role. This may require the Level III administrator to attend activities, events, programs, and other opportunities in order to demonstrate the "right way" of doing things for the new employee. The risk-reduction leader can demonstrate to his or her staff what it means to be a part of the risk-reduction team, particularly when it comes to decision-making, professional behavior, and commitment to the mission and vision of the organization.

Leading and training by example require many important behaviors from the Level III administrator, including:

- Modeling positive actions, attitudes, and behaviors that are desired from all employees of an organization

- Continuing research into developments, innovations, and ideas in the field

- Exercising diplomacy in all interactions

- Showing professionalism in information sharing

- Supporting the organization's management, mission, and goals

Training employees in the policies and procedures surrounding the risk-reduction initiatives is the easy part. This simply takes time and effort on the part of the supervisor or another employee. However, some things cannot be taught in a classroom. These include professionalism, compassion, and commitment — to name a few. These qualities are important to the fire service and particularly to those conducting risk-reduction activities in the community. The Level III administrator should demonstrate these qualities on a daily basis in his or her dealings with external customers, internal customers, and subordinates.

Reporting to the Agency

As a part of the internal marketing process for risk reduction, the Level III administrator will prepare numerous reports for members of the fire agency. Reports may be for senior management, all levels of management, and for the department as a whole. Communication is key to the process of institutionalizing community risk reduction as an attitude within the department. Earlier chapters explained the types of reports and their relevance. The significance of those reports will be explained in this section.

Most fire departments prepare strategic plans. These plans project one-, three-, five-, and even ten-year goals for the department. They also predict department needs, challenges, and obstacles so that those can be addressed before they are encountered. As was discussed previously, risk-reduction activities should be a part of the strategic plan. The Level III administrator is responsible for establishing goals, objectives, and strategies to combat identified fire and injury issues in the community. The Level III administrator should also develop a strategic plan solely for the risk-reduction division. This plan will guide the risk-reduction work and provide the foundation for reporting information to the agency and its members.

Members of the fire agency should be informed about the goals, objectives, and strategies of the risk-reduction plan. This will aid in the institutionalization of risk reduction in the organization. Just as important is the communication of successes, accomplishments, and achievements of fire and life safety events and programs. Senior management needs to be informed of the responsible use of budgeted funds and the successes and achievements that result from the use of those funds.

Monthly Reports

In Chapter 3, the concept of monthly reports and annual reports was discussed. The information provided by the Level I educator is crucial to the preparation of the reports that are offered to management. Monthly reports are a compilation of all of the activities of the risk-reduction division, or those who have the responsibility for risk-reduction initiatives. This might include the number of presentations delivered, the number of individuals contacted, the type of audience, and the amount of material distributed **(Figure 15.8, p. 378)**.

Monthly reports may also include information about the other activities of the fire prevention or risk-reduction division. These can include community events, such as health fairs and festivals, juvenile firesetter intervention programs, training classes, smoke alarm installations, and other tasks relating to risk-reduction strategies and interventions in the community. Program expenses and time devoted to particular events may also be included. The monthly report should also include evaluation information, including anecdotal stories or other outcomes.

Annual Reports

From monthly reports, the Level III administrator will prepare an annual report. Many fire agencies develop annual reports that are presented to a city council, county commission, or other governing body. Annual reports may become public documents, available on an agency's web page or published in the local paper. As a part of the annual report, the Level III administrator should design a report that will be included as part of the department's total report or can serve as a stand-alone document to provide management with an annual update of the activities of the risk-reduction division. In turn, this information can be shared with the members of the department so that those in operations positions can see the results of the activities in which they have participated. The annual report for the fire agency is a very important document in many jurisdictions, as decisions concerning budgeting and personnel may be based upon the information presented in this report. The same is true for the annual report of the risk-reduction division.

In order to demonstrate successes and accomplishments, goals, objectives, and strategies for the risk-reduction division must be clearly spelled out in the report. While information about the number of presentations given or the number of people attending is important, it is not relevant if it cannot be shown how the data fits into the overall mission of the risk-reduction division, and therefore the fire agency. This is where it must be shown that the vision, mission, and goals established for risk reduction are driving the activities, events, and other initiatives being conducted. This is also the point where the information collected from the evaluations becomes crucial in proving that risk-reduction activities are effective in the community. Information about the impacts and outcomes of programs, events, and initiatives is necessary to prove the worth of the risk-reduction division and the time, energy, and money that is spent in that field.

Formats for these comprehensive reports will vary from agency to agency. A format may be provided, or it may be left up to the Level III administrator to develop. Assistance from someone in the agency's administration may be helpful in making this report meaningful. The Level III administrator does not have to be the one who accumulates and compiles the information, but it is up to the Level III administrator to make sure that the report is accurate, meaningful, and a correct representation of the community risk-reduction program.

To get the most from the monthly and annual reports, the information should be shared with the entire agency. It is important to celebrate the successes, no matter how minor they might seem, because they provide incentive and motivation for participation in risk-reduction activities. Successes and achievements may also lead the way to increased funding or staffing for the risk-reduction work being conducted by the department.

Chapter Summary

Education responsibilities for the Level III administrator vary greatly from those for the Level I educators and Level II managers. The Level III administrator is viewed as the head of the community risk-reduction program and as such, has responsibilities other than those of planning and presenting programs and events. The Level III administrator is more focused on the organization, its members, and the risk-reduction staff. Training of new employees, reporting to management and policy makers, and generally leading the department into risk-reduction initiatives are tasks that fill the workday for the Level III administrator.

Smithville Fire and Life Safety Consortium
911 Post Drive
Smithville, Indiana

Public Education Monthly Report: November 2010

Public Education	Nov.	Oct.	YTD
Preschool Visits	25	31	100
Project SAFETY Visits	27	23	113
Safety Trailer Events	2	5	16
Basic Aid	0	0	62
Station Tours	4	2	15
Car Seats	1	4	40
Misc. Events	3	9	64
Total Public Education Events	62	74	472
Total Cancelled/ Rescheduled Events:	8	2	21

Total YTD contacts for 2010: 15102

Notables:
- Eight canceled events due to:
  - o Kidzone of Smithville closed its doors
  - o An emergency with the Public Educator with no one to cover Day Nursery
  - o A station tour that was rescheduled to January
- Fire Safety House Trailer has wrapped up its season
- Public Educator has applied for EMS Primary Instructor: Should receive cert in December
- The department provided "Camp Fire Safety" to the Local Cub Scout Pack. The pack then delivered dinner for the shifts at the stations.

Project SAFETY:
- Lesson for the month was E.D.I.T.H.
- Great job to John Sayers, Tim Todd, Jerome Middleton, Brett Copes, and Jim Matthews
- A special thank you to Joe Valentino and Connor Smith for help with the program this month
- Wrote December Holiday Safety lesson plan

Preschool Risk Watch:
- 25 lessons taught – Topic: Choking
- Designed and printed December newsletter
- Kidzone of Smithville closed

Grants:
- Fire Prevention and Safety Grant written for CPR Program
- CEDAP has not been awarded
- Filing a Polaris Ranger grant in December

Meetings:
- Joseph Simmons meetings
- Flexible spending account meeting
- Administration Meeting
- Fontaine Chevrolet wrap-up meeting for community awareness

Figure 15.8 Monthly reports are a compilation of the activity in the risk-reduction division over the course of one month.

These tasks are no less important than those that take place in the community. In fact, they may be more so. Without organizational support in attitude, budget, and personnel, the activities conducted in the community will be much less effective if at all. If training is lacking, then success will be lacking. The leadership of the Level III administrator will carry the organization far in the process of reducing risk from fire and injury to the members of the community that it serves.

Review Questions

1. What is the process for creating accurate and specific educational messages for a target audience?

2. What is the procedure for establishing and adopting administrative policies pertaining to risk reduction?

3. What is the process for creating a risk-reduction awareness campaign?

4. What is the process for creating an organizational training program for fire and life safety educators?

5. What is the procedure for creating a comprehensive report for policy makers?

Key Terms

Coaching — When used in reference to training or instruction, it refers to an intensive tutoring given to subordinates regarding a particular activity.

Mission Statement — The mission statement is about the present state of the risk-reduction division. It provides a meaning for the existence of risk-reduction work and allows the entire organization to understand the importance of the work being performed.

Peer Assistance — Refers to the process of having employees of equal status assist each other in the training process.

Standard Operating Procedures (SOPs) — Standard methods or rules in which an organization or a fire department operates to carry out a routine function. Usually these procedures are written in a policies and procedures handbook and all firefighters should be well versed in their content.

Vision Statement — A description of the ultimate results of the work of the fire and life safety educators. The first step in developing goals, procedures, or policies for fire and life safety activities.

Chapter 15 Notes

IFSTA **Company Officer**

IFSTA **Chief Officer**

IFSTA **Fire Instructor**, 7th Edition

NFA's Risk Reduction Curriculum

NFA's *Leadership: Strategies for Supervisory Success*

1. Centers for Disease Control. *Communicating about Chronic Diseases*. Chronic Disease, Notes and Reports, Vol. 11, No. 1, Fall 1998.

2. NFPA® 1001: *Standard for Fire Fighter Professional Qualifications*

3. NFPA® 1021: *Standard for Fire Officer Professional Qualifications*

FLSE Level III Administrators: Evaluation

Chapter Contents

Key Terms

Job Performance Requirements

This chapter provides information that addresses the following job performance requirements of NFPA® 1035, *Standard for Professional Qualifications for Fire and Life Safety Educator, Public Information Officer, and Juvenile Firesetter Intervention Specialist*, 2010 edition.

NFPA® 1035 References

7.5.1

7.5.2

FLSE Level III Administrators: Evaluation

Learning Objectives

After reading this chapter, students will be able to:

1. Describe the role and responsibility of the Level III administrator in the evaluation of the community risk-reduction program.

2. Perform evaluation at all levels of the risk-reduction program, particularly focusing on overall outcome evaluation.

3. Develop a health surveillance system or other similar system to monitor behavior and/or environmental changes that are a result of the community risk-reduction program (NFPA® 1035, 7.5.1).

4. Apply quantitative evaluation and qualitative evaluation to the fire and injury risk-reduction programs in the community to measure educational gain and behavioral change (NFPA® 1035, 7.5.2).

5. Prepare an evaluation report.

Chapter 16
FLSE Level III
Administrators: Evaluation

Case History

In 1995, the Department of Fire Services for the State of Massachusetts began a grant program for local fire departments, which was named Student Awareness and Fire Education (S.A.F.E.). The program was designed to place firefighters and educators in classrooms to provide fire-safety education to children. The mission and slogan for the program was "raising a fire-safe generation of children."

During fiscal year 2006, firefighters reached over 272,000 children in 272 communities. Over 836 firefighters were involved in teaching fire-safety education during classroom visits and community events. The children ranged in age from prekindergarten to 12th grade.

The average number of fire deaths of children under age 18 fell by nearly two-thirds, or 63%, since the start of the S.A.F.E. program. From the beginning of the program in 1995 to 2006, the average number of child deaths per year due to fire was 6.3. In the ten years before the program's implementation, the average number of child fire deaths per year had been 17.1. In fiscal year 2006, one child died in a fire in the state of Massachusetts. This decrease is attributed to consistent, comprehensive, statewide, school-based fire safety education.

This is an example of process evaluation, as well as outcome evaluation. Outcome evaluation takes time, in this case 11 years, but it was well worth the wait. This information, gathered in an annual report, ensures that the program will continue to be funded and encourages others to participate and support the effective work of this prevention effort.

Source: Massachusetts Department of Fire Services, S.A.F.E. 2006 Report

The importance of the evaluation process in community risk reduction cannot be overestimated. Presentations, events, activities, and other initiatives may be productive and a service to the community; however, without hard data from the successes, the true results cannot be determined. Without the proof that evaluation provides, one cannot say with certainty that the work of the community risk-reduction program is making a difference in the health and safety of community members. Oftentimes, it is that proof that allows the risk-reduction activities to continue, grow, and prosper.

Evaluation is important for a variety of reasons. First and foremost, it establishes the impact of the program on the target population. In addition, by conducting evaluation, problems with the program can be identified and the program improved.

Evaluation data can be used to market the program, gain support for the initiatives, and seek funding. With the use of evaluation data, the successful aspects of the program can be replicated. Showing positive evaluation results also helps to justify the program's costs. Evaluation is a large portion of the Level III administrator's responsibility. While the Level I educators and Level II managers may conduct process and impact evaluation, the Level III administrator's role is to determine, through effective evaluation techniques, if the risk-reduction work is achieving the objectives of the program.

Evaluation: A Review

Much information has been presented in this manual regarding the various levels, methods, and approaches to evaluation of risk-reduction programs. A review of this information follows.

Process Evaluation

Process evaluation is conducted for individual presentations and activities. Process evaluation begins as soon as the program is put into operation. This type of evaluation provides information about the service that has been provided, the nature of the service, and who received it. Process evaluation can also provide information about the strengths and weaknesses of the program, the populations that were reached, and if the implementation occurred as planned. Process evaluation methods include:

- Counting the number of presentations and events
- Recording the number of attendees at the presentations or events
- Tracking budget details
- Documenting the number of alarm installations or items given away
- Recording the number of media appearances or news articles

Impact Evaluation

Impact evaluation is the second level of the overall evaluation process. Impact evaluation measures the impact that a presentation, or series of presentations and activities, has upon the target audience. Impact evaluation answers such questions as:

- Has the audience learned anything?
- Has the program changed the target population's behavior?

- Has the program changed public policy?

Impact evaluation measures the changes in performance or behavior of the target audience. Impact evaluation may also measure the changes in the physical environment and measure changes in legislation or the enforcement of existing legislation.

Impact evaluation can be conducted by administering pretests and posttests to measure knowledge or educational gain. Observations can be conducted for the use of smoke alarms, seat belts, or bike helmets. Telephone surveys or mail surveys are a way of gauging environmental changes.

Outcome Evaluation

The final stage of the evaluation process is outcome evaluation. While impact evaluation measures knowledge or environmental changes, it does not measure whether those changes have made an overall difference in the fire and injury loss in the community **(Figure 16.1)**. The effects of risk-reduction activities may not be seen immediately, so outcome evaluation is long term, perhaps 5 to 10 years. Outcome evaluation measures significant changes in the reduction of deaths, injuries, incidents, and dollar loss from fires and unintentional injuries.

Methods for conducting outcome evaluation include monitoring the reduction in deaths, injuries, incidents and dollar loss through incident reporting systems, hospital and EMS patient reports, and other local data collection systems. Anecdotal information is another form of outcome evaluation. Letters from individuals, newspaper articles, and stories from parents or caregivers are all evidence of a long-term change in behavior that reduces the risk of injury or death.

Planning and Designing the Evaluation

As indicated in Chapter 14, the process of evaluation actually starts with the planning and designing of the community risk-reduction programs. The time to plan and design the evaluation is at the very early stages of program design. The development of objectives that are specific and measurable are the basis for the evaluation. Once the program has started, valuable baseline data has been lost.

The important question that the evaluation process should answer is whether the objectives were achieved. The process of evaluation, specifically

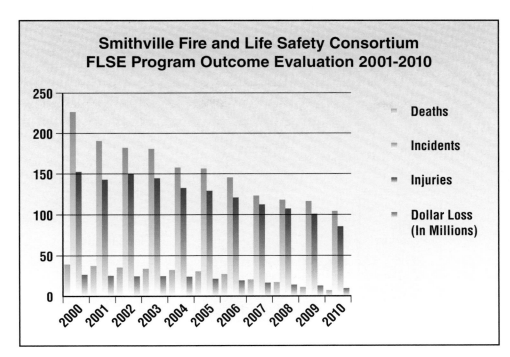

Smithville Fire and Life Safety Consortium
FLSE Program Outcome Evaluation 2001-2010

Figure 16.1 Outcome evaluation is the best indicator of an overall difference in the incidences of fire and injury in the community.

outcome evaluation, provides an answer to that question. Outcome evaluation is the main focus of the Level III administrator and is the main focus of the remainder of this chapter.

Outcome Evaluation and the Level III Administrator

The ultimate goal of fire and life safety programs is the reduction of deaths, injuries, and unintentional injuries. Because of this goal, the outcome evaluation process is a long-term commitment. It is not as simple as gathering baseline data before program implementation and then five years later, gathering more data. Many times fire administrators and other policy makers regularly need proof of the successes of the risk-reduction efforts in order to continue the funding and staffing of these activities.

Outcome evaluation uses statistical information to indicate that risk-reduction initiatives and interventions are working. The Level III administrator, when conducting outcome evaluation, must track the changes in the number of fires, injuries, and deaths that occur within the target area. This information may be gathered from the following list **(Figure 16.2, p. 286)**. This list is not all-inclusive; it simply serves as a starting point.

- Fire reporting systems
- Fire investigation reports

- Patient care reports
- Emergency room admission data
- Public health agencies
  Other sources include the following:
- Local agencies or organizations in a particular community that collect data related to fire and injury issues
- Additional statistical information based upon the nature of the issue being addressed
- Organizations that collect data on the target population, such as an elder care organization, that may be able to contribute additional information

If a program has targeted a particular neighborhood in the community, it may be possible to compare the statistics from the target neighborhood with the overall community-wide data. In order for the information to be statistically valid, this same information would need to be obtained as baseline data at the beginning of the risk-reduction process.

It is also possible to measure a change in the number of events based upon the issue that is addressed by the program. If the risk-reduction initiative is focusing on the use of bike helmets by children, it is possible there may not be a reduction in the number of children injured, but the extent of the injury may be lessened. Again, the data must be collected prior to the implementation of the program in order for the comparison to be a true representation.

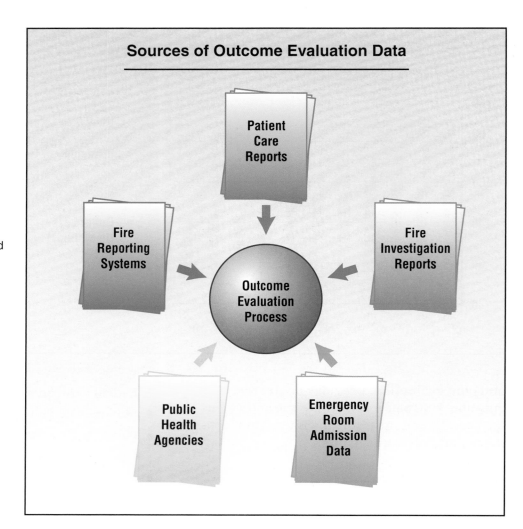

Figure 16.2 Outcome evaluation data can and should be pulled from a variety of sources in order to develop a complete picture of the community's risks over time.

Anecdotal evidence is great proof that risk reduction is effective, and it supplements or supports the statistical information. However, there may not always be such a story, or it might be too dated to have the needed effect. In addition, anecdotal stories are not always made known to the coalition or lead agency.

Quantitative vs. Qualitative Evaluation

Various types of outcome evaluation data can be collected. Data collected for the evaluation process can be categorized into two types: quantitative and qualitative. Both types of information are important in the evaluation process.

Quantitative Data

Quantitative data are pieces of information that can be counted mathematically and describe numerically the results of the risk-reduction process. Quantita-

tive evaluation answers the question "how many" or "how much" and uses numbers as the basis for the analysis process. Techniques for quantitative evaluation include surveys, questionnaires, statistical analysis, and examination of information on existing databases. Quantitative evaluation is good when determining what portion of the target audience has changed its behaviors relating to the target issues of a program by, for example, wearing seat belts or practicing home fire drills. Quantitative evaluation is used when comparing the baseline data to existing levels. It requires the use of statistical methods of analysis to properly interpret the results.

Qualitative Data

Qualitative data is best used to answer "how" and "why" questions and evaluates people's attitudes and opinions. It is mainly in narrative form as opposed to numerical. There is less emphasis on numbers and more emphasis on explaining why people think and behave the way they do in specific circumstances. Qualitative information is more subjective and may be harder to analyze and interpret. Qualitative data provides insight and promotes understanding of not only the way things are, but why.

Qualitative data is gathered from looking at what is happening, rather than asking questions about it. By conducting interviews and making observations, the collection of qualitative data provides insights into the experiences, behaviors, and opinions of the target audience **(Figure 16.3)**. Qualitative data collection uses open-ended questions that require more than a yes or no answer. If a focus group was convened as a part of the initial planning process for the program, the input of those individuals could provide valuable data for the evaluation process.

The collection of qualitative data may be more time-consuming and costly and may be more difficult to analyze. However, qualitative data can help to interpret or add substance to any quantitative data that is collected. When used for evaluation purposes, both qualitative and quantitative data have unique strengths and weaknesses. The use of both types of data can provide for a richer and more comprehensive understanding of the actual accomplishments of the risk-reduction programs.

Gathering the Data

No matter what model or system is used for the evaluation process, it will involve the collection of data. As a part of the planning process, the coalition must decide how the initiative will be evaluated, how the data will be gathered, and how the findings will be used.

The system for outcome evaluation needs to be appropriate to the initiative and easy to use. It should provide for consistent collection of data, accurate information, and credible findings. Team members need to decide what will be considered as evidence or relevant information to indicate the effects of the initiative. Indicators of success or criteria that can be used to judge the success of the program include the following:

- Program outputs
- Participation rates
- Levels of satisfaction
- Changes in behavior
- Community or system changes
- Improvements in community-level indicators, including incidence rates

The evaluation plan should also indicate how the quality of the data is to be assured. Evaluators will need to determine the appropriateness and integrity of the information gathered, including accuracy and validity. It should also be determined how much data will be needed to make an accurate and reliable determination of success. Other issues to be determined include who will gather the data, from what sources, during what time frame, and any precautions or permissions that may be needed.

Figure 16.3 Qualitative data provides insight and promotes understanding of the way things are and why.

Sources of data will vary according to each individual community and to the nature of the risk issue. A variety of methods exist to collect the data needed to conduct an appropriate evaluation. These include the following (Figure 16.4):

- Surveys about satisfaction and importance of the initiative
- Goal attainment reports
- Behavioral surveys
- Interviews with key participants
- Archival records
- Observations of behavior and environment
- Self-reporting, logs, or diaries
- Documentation system
- Community-level indicators of impact
- Case studies and experiments

Hierarchy of Outcome Measures

Frederick P. Rivara, M.D., Ph.D., a noted pediatrician and researcher, devised a hierarchy of injury prevention outcome measures. These measures include:

- Injury fatalities
- Injury cases admitted to hospital
- Injury cases treated in hospital emergency room
- All medically treated injuries
- Direct observation of behavior
- Monitoring of public policy or practice related to injuries and their prevention
- Measures of self-reported behavior
- Measures of knowledge, attitudes, beliefs, or intentions

The first four levels of the hierarchy represent measures of injury morbidity and mortality and are the most significant indicators of outcome. Measures of knowledge and attitude, while valuable information, are ranked lower in that these changes may not necessarily lead to a change in behavior.

Source: Injury Prevention: Meeting the Challenge

Once the data has been gathered, it must be sorted and compiled. Baseline data should then be compared with the new information and conclusions can be drawn. Stakeholders assisting with the evaluation process need to ensure that the conclusions meet the standards associated with evaluation. These could include any of the following:

- Standards that ensure the evaluation is useful and answer the questions that are important to the process.
    - Information included in the evaluation report must be clearly explained and described. The information should encourage follow-through and the use of the findings of the evaluation process.
- Standards that ensure that the evaluation data makes sense.
    - Steps of the process should be viable and pragmatic.
    - Evaluators must keep the procedures practical, and anticipate the different positions or interests of various community groups.
    - The process should be cost-effective and efficient.
- Standards that ensure that the evaluation is ethical and does not violate any rights or interests of those involved.
    - The evaluation should be complete and fair, reporting both successes and failures.
    - Evaluations should be designed to help the lead organization serve the needs of the community.
    - The evaluation process should respect the rights of all the participants in the process.
- Standards that ensure the accuracy of the data.
    - The collection process should be implemented in such a way that ensures that the data is valid and reliable.
    - It should include quantitative and qualitative data.
    - Conclusions drawn from the evaluation data must be justified.

Reliability and Validity of Data

Reliability and *validity* are two terms that are often used when discussing evaluation data and findings. In everyday English, **reliability** means dependability

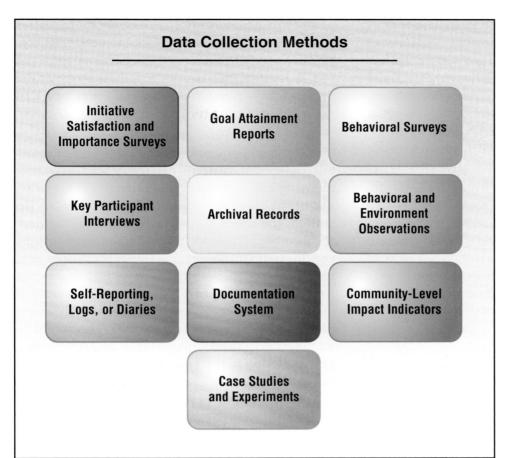

Data Collection Methods

- Initiative Satisfaction and Importance Surveys
- Goal Attainment Reports
- Behavioral Surveys
- Key Participant Interviews
- Archival Records
- Behavioral and Environment Observations
- Self-Reporting, Logs, or Diaries
- Documentation System
- Community-Level Impact Indicators
- Case Studies and Experiments

Figure 16.4 Data necessary for conducting an appropriate evaluation can be found in many different sources.

or trustworthiness. In research applications, reliability is the degree to which the method used to collect the data consistently measures what it is supposed to measure. This means that, if the same methods were used again and again, the results would still be the same.

Validity is the degree to which data measures what it is supposed to measure and, consequently, permits interpretation of the results. If attitudinal changes are being evaluated and one collects data on the number of smoke alarms installed, it might be hard to interpret these results as changes in attitude. The question is not whether the results are valid; it is if they are valid for the issue under scrutiny. The number of smoke alarm installations is definitely good information; however, more data would be needed to draw any conclusions regarding attitude changes.

Reliability and validity are complex statistical subjects. When designing and implementing the evaluation process, the Level III administrator should consult a research professional to assist in designing evaluation instruments and methods which can meet the test for reliability and validity. There may be

individuals at the local health department or nearby university who specialize in research. It is wise to find this individual early in the planning process to ensure validity and reliability of data. Discovering obstacles early and determininng workable solutions will ensure a smooth and effective evaluation process.

Systems for Evaluation

While the compilation of statistical comparisons is one means of evaluation, other methods have been developed. Examples of these include Service Efforts and Accomplishments (SEA) Reporting and a community health surveillance system.

Service Efforts and Accomplishments (SEA) Reporting

In the late 1990s, the Governmental Accounting Standards Board began promoting the use of an evaluation and performance reporting system called SEA.[1] Prior to this time, traditional financial reporting for government agencies involved reporting how much money was spent, how it was spent, and how many people were involved in the process.

Missing from this reporting was how well the money was spent, how efficiently it was used, and if it was used to further the mission and goals of the agency involved. Basically, the SEA system was implemented as a means for reporting the efficiency, effectiveness, and outcomes of government programs. Since that time, other governmental agencies, such as public safety agencies, have used the SEA system for their performance reporting. It is certainly applicable to evaluation reporting for community risk-reduction programs.

SEA reporting is not used to decide if a program is "worthwhile" but to determine if more funds are needed and if the level of service is adequate to meet the goals and objectives of the organization or program. SEA measures are related more to performance than to the merit of a program or division.

A drawback to the use of SEA reporting is that it is mainly quantitative data. It appears to attach a dollar amount to individuals' well-being and the quality of life in the community. Outcome evaluation is a five- to ten-year project; conversely, SEA reporting is a way of demonstrating outcomes on a more frequent basis and providing a continuing foundation for the risk-reduction program. The three basic elements to SEA reporting are as follows **(Figure 16.5)**.

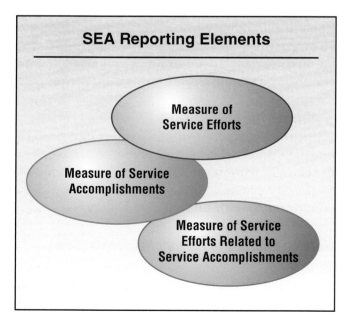

Figure 16.5 Service Efforts and Accomplishments Reporting determines if more funds are needed and if the level of service is adequate to meet the objectives of a program.

Measure of service efforts. These are the measures of the amount of financial and nonfinancial resources that are used to provide a service. For purposes of risk-reduction, this would include the cost of the programs, the number of employees involved, and the amount of equipment used.

Measures of service accomplishments. Measures of service accomplishments include both outputs and outcomes. Outputs are those measures that quantify the amount of a service provided. This might include the number of smoke alarms installed, the number of bike helmets distributed, the number of individuals contacted, or programs conducted. Outcomes are those measures that gauge the accomplishments or results that occur from the services provided. They provide a basis for how well the goals and objectives of a particular division or program have been met. This might be a reduction in the number of fires and fire deaths, or a reduction in the number of injuries.

Measures that relate service efforts to service accomplishments. This would include the amount of resources used per unit of output or per unit of outcome. These measures provide information on how much it costs to install a smoke alarm or distribute a bike helmet. These would be considered input-output measures. Input-output measures demonstrate the cost of the outcomes. It illustrates the cost for each unit of reduction in fires or injuries. Measures that relate efforts to accomplishments demonstrate efficient use of funds and can sometimes indicate a need for more personnel or funding.

Health Surveillance Systems

Another method of evaluating performance and outcome of community risk-reduction efforts is the design of a health surveillance system. Used in the public health arena, health surveillance is the ongoing systematic collection, analysis, and interpretation of health data. In most instances, this data is used for planning, implementing, and evaluating public health activities.

According to the Centers for Disease Control, injury surveillance is the continuing observation of all aspects of occurrence and patterns of injury to determine effective interventions. Timely analysis and interpretation of outcomes can be obtained and adjustments made, if necessary, through surveillance.

Injury surveillance data can be used to identify interventions, new risk issues, and high-risk groups, and assess the impact of the risk-reduction initiatives in the community. Surveillance systems can provide information about behaviors of community members and the effectiveness of the risk-reduction efforts.

Surveys and surveillance are not the same thing, although they are closely related. A survey is usually a one-time event and is often conducted through door to door visits, by telephone, or direct mail questionnaires. Surveys can provide baseline data and information about trends or outcomes only if they are repeated periodically.

In contrast, surveillance is an ongoing activity that can be built into the day-to-day operations of agencies. It is the best way to monitor trends, detect problems, and assess the results of risk-reduction interventions. With surveillance data, a risk-reduction specialist can design and apply appropriate interventions, but more importantly, the specialist can monitor the results and assess the impacts of such interventions.

The steps in creating a surveillance system are similar to those for creating a risk-reduction plan for the community. With a few additional steps, the planning process outlined in Chapter 14 can serve as the planning and development process for an injury surveillance system for an identified risk issue.

The World Health Organization (WHO) as well as the Centers for Disease Control (CDC) have identified the following steps as a logical sequence in developing an injury surveillance system. Each step is discussed at length in the following section, using a child passenger safety initiative as an example.

- *Define the problem.* Identify the nature of the problem that is to be the subject of the surveillance system. It can be general, or it can be very specific. This determines the structure and content of the surveillance system. It indicates what is to be placed under surveillance and also helps to identify sources of information. In the child passenger safety example, the information to be collected would relate to vehicle crashes and would include the number of children involved in vehicle crashes, the number that are injured, and the extent of the injuries. Other information might include the number of citations written by local law enforcement for violation of child restraint laws.

- *Collect the data.* Determine the pertinent details, which include demographic information such as age, location, nature of the injury, and any other information relevant to the outcome of the program. It might be necessary to collect information on all vehicle crashes where children are involved to determine what percentage are injured in crashes. It must also be determined who the appropriate data sources might be, such as local health departments, hospital emergency departments, and local law enforcement agencies.

- *Process the data.* Compile the information into a usable format. If an individual sorts through information on a weekly basis, he or she needs to extract the information related only to the subject of the surveillance.

- *Interpret the data.* Make interpretations once the data has been compiled. It might be found that the vehicle crashes involving children are occurring in a particular neighborhood, on secondary streets as opposed to highways, or within a particular high-risk group.

- *Report the results.* Present and distribute the results of the surveillance among the coalition or planning team members. Results may also be provided to policy makers or politicians as a part of the initiative.

- *Use the results.* This is the ultimate purpose of the surveillance system. Results are intended to help risk-reduction professionals respond to the problem under surveillance and measure the effectiveness of existing strategies for intervention. This allows for adaptations and revisions to the interventions to provide for more effectiveness. When a surveillance system is designed, it must have a purpose. The results must be presented in a format that is easily understood and analyzed.

- *Evaluate the surveillance system.* The system must be up-to-date and responsive to changing needs in the community. It needs to be dynamic, ensuring that it is producing the most accurate and relevant information. Many times the end users of the information are the ones who can most accurately evaluate the effectiveness of the surveillance system and any comments or suggestions should always be considered.

- *Keep the system up to date.* A regular evaluation of the system will require that the surveillance system be cyclical. That is, the steps must be repeated in order to keep gathering relevant and recent information. Health or injury surveillance is a continuous process, with the data obtained indicating trends in the incidences of the risk issue being addressed.

Good surveillance systems have several attributes that have been identified by the WHO, which include the following **(Figure 16.6)**:

- *Simplicity.* The data produced should be simple and straightforward. Forms used for data collection should be easy to use and easy to understand.

- *Flexibility.* The system should be easily changed when evaluation indicates that changes are necessary. Adding information or changing the target population should be easily accomplished.

- *Acceptability.* Staff, participants, and other stakeholders must be willing to participate in the system. Involving stakeholders in the design of the system will assist in securing the cooperation and commitment to use the system correctly.

- *Reliability.* Anyone using the data should have complete confidence in the accuracy of the information. The system should record injury events with all pertinent information, exclude all non-injury events, and detect all injury events within the target population.

- *Utility.* The system should be practical and affordable. It should not place a burden upon any one agency or individual.

- *Sustainability.* The system should be easily maintained and updated so that it continues to serve its purpose.

- *Timeliness.* The system should be able to generate up-to-date information whenever needed.

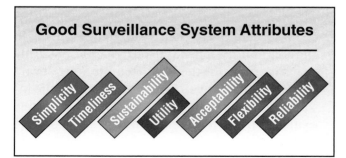

Good Surveillance System Attributes

Figure 16.6 Surveillance can be built into the ongoing activities of an organization, and should be definable by attributes identified by the World Health Organization.

Establishing an injury surveillance system as a part of the planning process for the risk-reduction initiatives is easily accomplished. It is an excellent tool for measuring risk in the community and the degree of success of a program. It will provide baseline data and provide continuing data on which to base the effectiveness of the risk-reduction initiatives being implemented. Including public health professionals or researchers in the design process will aid in the effectiveness and ease of implementation.

Centers for Disease Control Health and Injury Surveillance Systems

The CDC has used surveillance systems to provide information about behaviors relating to health and injury. Some of the systems they have developed include:

- *Behavioral Risk Factor Surveillance System.* This system monitors health behaviors and knowledge about tobacco use, physical inactivity, poor diet, alcohol use, violence, risky sexual behavior, and lack of preventive services. This long-running system provides data on health trends to assist public health agencies in directing monies to the appropriate risk-reduction programs.

- *Pregnancy Risk-Assessment Monitoring System.* This is an ongoing surveillance system that is part of the CDC's initiative to reduce infant mortality and low birth weight. A sample of mothers who have recently given birth are questioned concerning their attitudes about pregnancy, pregnancy-related violence, economic status, use of alcohol or tobacco, and HIV prevention.

- *Youth Risk Behavior Surveillance System.* This system is similar to the Behavioral Risk Factor System except that it targets risk behaviors among young people. Surveys are administered in local school systems and have the ability to be adapted to local needs.

These are just a sampling of the many health and injury surveillance systems being used in the public health field today. This is a system that is very applicable to the risk-reduction field and should be used as a form of monitoring and evaluation of community risk-reduction initiatives.

Source: Injury Surveillance Training Manual, CDC

Whatever system is designed for evaluation of the outcomes of the program, it must be systematic, statistically valid, and simple to understand. It must be ongoing, occurring at regular intervals.

Sharing Evaluation Results: The Evaluation Report

The results of the evaluation should be shared, celebrated, and used to make adjustments in the program. They should be shared with anyone involved in the community risk-reduction initiative. They must be honestly reported including not only the successes but any problems as well.

The report itself will vary, depending upon its intended audience. Reports to elected officials should be ongoing, concise, and emphasize the key points. Department personnel should be informed about the successes of the program with frequent updates. Neighborhood leaders have a vested interest in the information, as do the individuals living in the affected communities.

Decision makers who influence resources, target audiences, and elected officials should be informed of the results as well. The results of any enforcement initiatives should be reported to those administering the enforcements.

Some groups may require a more in-depth report, while some will require a simpler, less complex document. Numerous versions of the evaluation report may exist, in order to ensure that the information is useable and meaningful to its intended audience.

A variety of means can be used to communicate the information contained in the report **(Figure 16.7)**. These include the following:

- *Face-to-face meetings* — Allows for a personal exchange of information, which includes feedback to any questions. It works best for smaller groups and when persuasion about the risk initiative is required. However, it can be time-consuming. Having a fact sheet or short synopsis available for distribution will be helpful.

- *Public presentations* — Allows for information to be publicly shared. Reporting such as this is ideal for community groups or other large gatherings of people. Any presentation should be concise and address the key information. Any anecdotal stories should be used to personalize the information.

- *Written reports and briefs* — Allows for more in-depth sharing of information about the program and the evaluation results. Written reports should be geared toward their intended audience. If the report is for public health officials, it may be written differently than if for the general public. If the written report is for internal purposes, it may use photos and anecdotal stories to make the reports more personal and effective.

- *Video report* — Often the hardest to develop and present in a professional manner. This report puts the viewer in the position of the individual who is at risk and who was targeted by the program's interventions. This type of report can be used with news reports and public access channels.

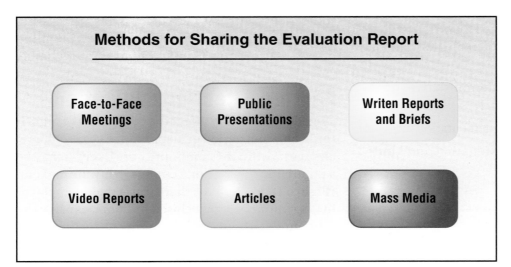

Figure 16.7 The Evaluation Report should be shared with interested parties, and these reports can be flexible and interactive.

- *Mass media* — The best method for reaching the public at-large. It usually takes the form of news stories. These stories focus on the community change and the reduction in risk to community members. Mass media reporting can also create interest in risk-reduction initiatives.

- *Articles* — Used to report the results to peers and other professional groups. Much like a written report, these articles must be written with the reader in mind. Most often, they will carry more information about the interventions used and the changes that were achieved.

In some cases, all that might be required is an executive summary or abstract. The executive summary should answer the following questions:

- What is the report about?
- Who wrote it and from where is it coming?
- What were the methods used to compile the report?
- Why was the program needed and how much did it cost?
- What did the program staff set out to accomplish?
- How was the program organized?
- What did the program accomplish?
- What implications do the findings have for the program and for community risk reduction?
- What are the conclusions, recommendations, and policy implications?

An executive summary can be a stand-alone document, or it can be used as a foreword to a more extensive report. It should be brief, two or three pages, and can be used by individuals who want information about the programs without having to read the whole report.

A more detailed report should contain information about the following:

- The community risk-reduction initiative being evaluated
- The design, planning, and implementation process
- Methodology used for the evaluation and kinds of data analyzed
- Presentation of the results
- Interpretation of the findings
- Conclusions, recommendations, and policy implications

The sharing of results is the best part of the evaluation process. It demonstrates the fruits of the hard work of the risk-reduction team and should be celebrated. Once prepared, the report should be available to any individual who has an interest in the community and its safety.

Making Program Modifications

Once evaluation results have been compiled and processed, they may indicate that a change is needed to the program. The question is not whether the program is worthwhile, but how can it be improved upon. It may simply be a matter of making it a better program or adding a dimension to make the impact even greater.

Once the evaluation report has been prepared and dispersed, the planning group should review the program objectives and review any feedback from the target audience on needed adjustments. If not already a part of the report, the group should seek input from the implementation staff on what changes or adjustments are needed. The group should then agree on the adjustments to be made, and make them. Of course, the program will need continuous monitoring with the changes.

There may be situations when the stated objectives have been met. If so, the program may be terminated and the focus moved to a new issue. Very rarely, however, will risk-reduction initiatives be terminated due to their complete success. The program may continue to be monitored, but resources diverted to other risk issues.

It may be that adjustments cannot be made for a variety of reasons including the lack of funding, resources, personnel, or even interest. In that case, the program should be terminated and a new planning process started to evaluate and address the risk issue.

Factors Affecting Evaluation

Outside factors may affect the evaluation results. If the evaluation period extends for five years or more, changes within the community are likely. It may be a population change or a change in ethnic makeup **(Figure 16.8)**. Perhaps there was a major employer in the community that closed its doors, causing the economic status in the community to decline. All of these changes can affect risk issues.

Project SAIFE

In 1998, the Centers for Disease Control (CDC), the U.S. Consumer Product Safety Commission (CPSC), the United States Fire Administration (USFA), and several other government and nongovernment organizations collaborated in an effort to prevent residential fire-related deaths. Research found that educational methods had an insignificant effect on the likelihood of owning a smoke alarm or having a functioning alarm. This was especially true of households in rural areas and those below the poverty level. The initiative, Smoke Alarm Installation and Fire Safety Education (SAIFE) Program, funded 16 states' participation in the program.

The program selected communities at greatest risk, identified local coordinators, and partnered with the local fire agencies. Participants worked in pairs visiting homes in the target areas, installing alarms, and delivering fire safety educational information. There were incentives awarded to the local program staff, and an evaluation process was completed.

Each state was required to track the number of homes canvassed, the number of homes where alarms were installed, and the number of people reached by educational messages. Additionally, the program tracked the number of fires in homes where alarms had been installed and the number of lives potentially saved as the result of an alarm alerting the resident to a fire. A six-month follow-up was conducted of 20% of the homes to verify that the alarms were functional and to determine if there had been a fire in the home.

The following list provides some of the outcomes for the program:

- 280,000 homes visited
- 212,000 smoke alarms installed in more than 126,000 high-risk homes
- 90% of alarms found to be functional upon follow-up
- 610 lives have been potentially saved as a result of an alarm that was installed from the program

Presently research is underway to determine how this program is associated with a change in knowledge, attitudes, beliefs, and behaviors associated with fire.

Source: Educational Research: Competencies for Analysis and Application

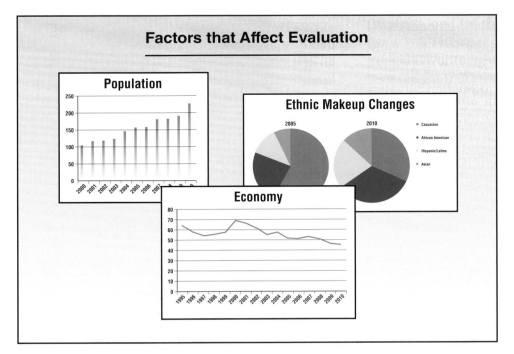

Figure 16.8 Communities can change drastically due to outside factors over the course of five years.

Factors within the lead agency may affect the program and its outcome. Perhaps the sole risk-reduction professional is out due to a lengthy illness. There could be a budget cutback within the department that forces the risk-reduction staff to assume other duties within the department.

It is important to look at changes such as these that can affect the outcome of the risk-reduction program. Changes in the makeup of the community can also change the risk issues as well. A variety of perspectives can be used to look at the data, such as on a per capita basis, that will help to control these outside factors. This information is not meant to explain deficiencies in the program or lessen the impact of results. However, it is important to use a critical eye and look at all aspects of the community, the program, and those implementing the program when drawing conclusions from the results of the evaluation process. Again, seeking the advice of a research professional can assist the Level III administrator in arriving at the most reliable and accurate results possible.

Challenges to Program Evaluation

When evaluation is overlooked, it is presumed that the interventions initiated are successful, without any evidence or support. The following reasons may explain why evaluation has been an overlooked tool for risk-reduction professionals:

Home Safety Literacy Project

An excellent example of evaluation at its highest level is the Home Safety Literacy Project. Research found that low literacy is a serious problem in the United States and adds to an individual's risk of fire or injury. Safety materials tend to be exclusively in English, in the form of text-heavy brochures and other handouts that are written at a sixth- to eleventh-grade reading level. This disparity is a serious barrier to learning necessary home-safety skills and to understanding and applying key fire protection and disaster preparedness measures in the home.

The Home Safety Literacy Project (HSLP) was developed by the Home Safety Council (HSC) to provide effective, low-cost fire safety and disaster preparedness education materials that can be used by adults at all reading levels. The innovative diffusion model pairs local literacy tutors with firefighters and other safety experts to deliver educational lessons and protective technologies (such as smoke alarms and disaster kits) to a high-risk audience. The HSLP was partially funded by the HSC with support from U.S. Department of Homeland Security and Fire Prevention and Safety Grants. HSC's national project partners include ProLiteracy and Oklahoma State University's Fire Protection Publications. The HSLP won the 2006 Health Literacy Award from the Institute for Healthcare Advancement.

In May 2006, 15,000 copies of the HSLP Project kits were made available to adult literacy teachers across the United States. The materials are highly illustrated with minimal text written in Plain English style. Based on a formative evaluation, HSC developed several levels (such as pictographs, two readers, and tabloids) and types (posters, tear pads, and brochures) of materials. Key messages include installing and maintaining adequate smoke alarms, practicing home escape plans, and preparing for natural and human-caused disasters.

HSC and independent evaluator Pacific Research Associates selected fifteen urban and rural communities to conduct a summative evaluation of the fire safety education component of the HSLP; an additional fifteen sites served as controls.

Documented results:

- Adult students in the Home Safety Literacy Project learned more fire safety messages than adult students who did not participate in the project.

- A greater number and percent of adult students in the Home Safety Literacy Project had smoke alarms installed in their homes than adult students who did not participate in the project.

- A greater number and percent of adult students in the Home Safety Literacy Project created fire-escape plans for their homes than adult students who did not participate in the project.

- Impact evaluation of the HSLP disaster preparedness materials in Arkansas, Tennessee, and South Carolina by Pacific Research Associates revealed that the number of adult students with written disaster plans quadrupled, and the number of disaster kits and contact lists tripled as a result of program participation. An *HSLP Facilitators Training Manual* based on pilot testing in these three high fire-risk states has been published.

- Size of the population
- Inadequate funds
- Lack of program staff trained in evaluation
- Lack of understanding of the importance of evaluation
- A focus on services rather than evaluation
- Concern about negative findings

It is the Level III administrator's responsibility to ensure that the challenges to the evaluation process are met prior to commencing the program. Outcome evaluation is the ultimate indicator of the achievement of the program's objectives.

Chapter Summary

As the coordinator for the risk-reduction program, the Level III administrator must take the task of evaluation seriously and with great enthusiasm. The Level III administrator should make good use of the resources in the community, including those public health or academic officials who can assist with the evaluation process. Evaluation must be planned early in the program's design process and should always revolve around the objectives of the program.

Review Questions

1. What is the role and responsibility of the Level III administrator in the evaluation of the community risk-reduction program?

2. What is the process for conducting a program evaluation for a risk-reduction program?

3. What is the process for developing a health surveillance system?

4. How are qualitative and quantitative evaluation methods used to measure educational and behavioral change?

5. How is an evaluation report prepared on a community risk-reduction program or initiative?

Key Terms

Reliability — A condition of validity; the extent to which a test or test item consistently and accurately shows the same results or scores given to a set of learners on different occasions or marked by different assessors or by the same assessors on different occasions.

Validity — Extent to which a test or any assessment technique measures the learner qualities (knowledge and skills) that it is meant to measure.

Chapter 16 Notes

1. Government Accounting Standards Board. Performance Reporting for Government. Found at http://72.3.167.245/aboutpmg/elements.shtml.

JFIS Level I Interventionists: Knowledge and Skills

▊ Chapter Contents

chapter 17

Key Terms

Learning Objectives

After reading this chapter, students will be able to:

1. Explain why juvenile firesetting intervention is a component of NFPA® 1035.

2. Explain the scope of America's juvenile firesetting problem.

3. Describe the profiles of juvenile firesetters.

4. Describe the components that comprise a successful juvenile firesetting intervention program.

Chapter 17
JFIS Level I Interventionists: Knowledge and Skills

Case History

Some juvenile firesetter intervention specialists (JFIS) find it chilling when they discover that a significant number of convicted serial killers were firesetters as juveniles. Did firesetting make them killing machines? No. Was it an indicator that future acts of antisocial behavior may be exhibited? Absolutely!

Consider the profile of a convicted killer who had been a juvenile firesetter and notice the progressive nature of the behaviors. Interest in fire started as a young child and was not addressed effectively (if at all) by parents. It continued through acts of curiosity-motivated firesetting. These acts were either unreported or inappropriately addressed. As the juvenile aged, he turned to firesetting as an anger-release mechanism. Again, his problem went unreported or was undertreated.

By the time the adolescent reached 16, a pathology had developed whereby the young man was starting fires to relieve stress and for recreation. He had started so many fires that he could not remember the details of them all.

A closer look at this young man's history of antisocial behavior would reveal more than just firesetting issues. Throughout his childhood and adolescence, he was hyperactive, often aggressive toward others, and sometimes defiant of authority figures. He received poor grades in school, stole things, and was often in trouble with authorities. He experimented with mind-altering substances.

By his 18th birthday, the adolescent had been adjudicated five times for various criminal acts. He spent his 21st birthday incarcerated for breaking into a store, stealing merchandise, and starting a fire to conceal the crime.

At age 25, the man was convicted of killing five young women over a period of three years. When asked at his sentencing why he had killed the women, he told the judge, "I was mad because they didn't pay any attention to me."

This case history is NOT intended to portray juvenile firesetters as potential serial killers. It is meant to exemplify the need for early childhood and parental education on firesetting prevention. It also shows the need for rapid identification and adequate response to juvenile firesetting behaviors.

Education is a major component of addressing community risk, including the problem of juvenile firesetting. People need to know a problem exists before they can take action. Residents, service agencies, schools, and the emergency services are target populations who need an understanding of America's juvenile firesetting problem and solutions.

Education: Addressing Community Risk

Education is the foremost component of primary (also called universal) prevention. As defined in Chapter 12, primary prevention is the process of preventing a problem from occurring. The frequency of juvenile firesetting behaviors can be reduced through combined use of school and community-based education. The JFIS I (with support from other educators) can heighten awareness within the community as to the scope of the firesetting problem. He or she can also provide critical preventive education to children, adolescents, parents, and caregivers.

Secondary prevention (also called selective or indicated prevention) is the process of reducing the impact of an incident that has already occurred. Early identification of firesetting, the intake process, interviewing, screening, and a variety of interventions are components of secondary prevention. In most communities, fire and life safety educators are credible interventionists on the frontline of this process **(Figure 17.1)**.

Community-Based JFIS Program

The JFIS I represents a logical team member in the quest to prevent and mitigate the effects of destructive juvenile firesetting. Preventing and addressing juvenile firesetting is often a challenging process that demands use of integrated community resources, especially law enforcement, juvenile justice, mental health, and social services. This is especially true when addressing complex firesetting cases.

It is highly recommended that a collaborative team of agencies are involved at the grassroots level when developing a community-based JFIS program. Leading the development (or being a primary copartner of such) is a Level II program manager.

In most communities, the fire department is the catalyst behind a successful firesetting prevention and mitigation program. The department's fire and life safety educators and fire investigators often serve as program leaders. Because juvenile firesetting is a community problem needing the cooperation of other agencies and organizations, it is not uncommon for other agencies such as juvenile justice officials, social service groups, mental health **clinicians**, public health organizations, or schools to take a leadership role in the battle to reduce firesetting **(Figure 17.2)**. The ultimate aim of a community should be to form a multidisciplinary collaborative team that will address the juvenile firesetting problem.

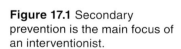

Figure 17.1 Secondary prevention is the main focus of an interventionist.

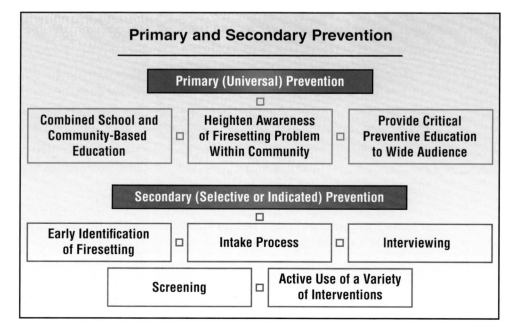

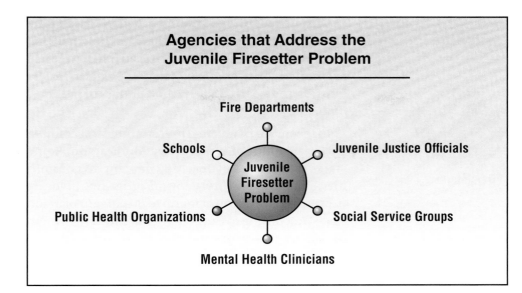

Agencies that Address the Juvenile Firesetter Problem

Fire Departments

Schools

Juvenile Justice Officials

Juvenile Firesetter Problem

Public Health Organizations

Social Service Groups

Mental Health Clinicians

Figure 17.2 Agencies outside of the emergency services may take a leadership role in firesetting intervention initiatives.

Just as a team is necessary to address issues at a fire scene, using a team of professionals to address a community's juvenile firesetting problem makes good sense in terms of effective resource utilization. Because juvenile firesetting can be a complex issue that is influenced by many factors, a team approach represents the best strategy to prevent or respond to the problem.

Whether practicing with a fire department, law enforcement agency, school, or community-based organization, the public education official has the opportunity and obligation to inform the population at-large about its community's juvenile firesetting problem. Being able to communicate how firesetting impacts the local community builds credibility for the educator and creates a foundation so other organizations see how they can help reduce the problem.

Framing the Problem of Juvenile Firesetting

Juvenile firesetting is *not* a new or mysterious affliction that affects a random group of children and adolescents. It is an age-old behavior that is now a better understood, often predictable, and sometimes preventable behavior which can be exhibited by virtually any child or adolescent regardless of gender, race, or family background. Juvenile firesetting is often influenced by family, social, environmental, and cognitive factors.

Firesetting is officially defined as: Any unsanctioned incendiary use of fire, including both intentional and unintentional involvement, whether or not an actual fire and/or explosion occurs.[1] The definition carries broad perimeters, so it includes incidents where no damages resulted. This is important because regardless of size, *all* firesetting incidents should be reported and addressed.

Juvenile firesetting can be a problem in any community. The scope of the problem is often influenced by population size and demographics of the community. Many U.S. communities have identified and are aggressively addressing their juvenile firesetting problem. Due to many factors, the problem can escape attention.

Underreporting of Juvenile Firesetting Incidents

According to the United States Fire Administration (USFA) and National Fire Protection Association® (NFPA®), the problem of juvenile firesetting is often underreported in the United States. This is, in part, because many parents do not report the first fire set by their child, particularly if the fire was minor and caused no real property damage. In addition, many parents are unaware that their community may have a program to address juvenile firesetting.

Another reason for underreporting is that many schools do not report all incidents of juvenile firesetting to fire officials. School officials may chose not to report child or adolescent firesetting behavior for fear of damaging the reputation of the organization. Community-based providers, such as mental health clinicians, may not report firesetting activity because of privacy issues or lack of knowledge about an existing **intervention** program.

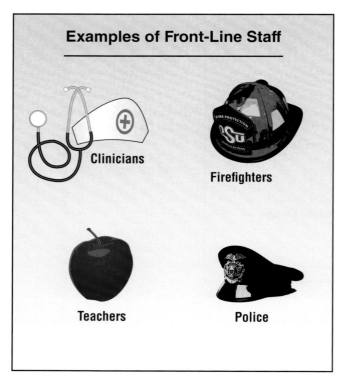

Examples of Front-Line Staff

Clinicians

Firefighters

Teachers

Police

Figure 17.3 Front-line staff have direct contact with people in situations where firesetting most often occurs.

Front line staff (including firefighters, police officers, teachers, and clinicians) should be trained to detect and report any level of firesetting incident **(Figure 17.3)**. In addition to being dangerous, juvenile firesetting has been identified as a behavior that was exhibited by many criminals found guilty of major offenses.

Executive fire officials need a thorough understanding of America's youth firesetting problem and recognized solutions. Decision-makers should be made aware that an informed public will likely bring an increase in the reporting of incidents. The increase in reporting is a positive sign that the community is responding to help address this dangerous behavior.

Variation in Data Collection

Variation of how incidents caused by juvenile firesetting are coded and entered into data systems can affect the tracking of firesetting behaviors. Many fire service data collection instruments offer such a wide range of ignition and fire cause factors to choose from that objective reporting of juvenile firesetting may become skewed. A solution to this problem is to standardize the definition and recording of firesetting incidents. These actions can be initiated at the local and state level.

Despite recording variability, at publication time of this manual, the Burn Institute® documented that annual child and adolescent firesetting in America accounted for over 40,000 fires, 150 deaths, 2,000 injuries and nearly $300 million dollars in property damage.

In recent years, juvenile firesetters have accounted for at least half of those arrested for arson. Some states report rates of nearly 60 percent. In communities lacking an intervention program, juvenile firesetting can account for up to 80 percent of arson cases. According to the Federal Bureau of Investigation (FBI), nearly one-third of those arrested were children under the age of 15. Five percent were under the age of ten.[3]

Roughly three out of every four children experiment with fire. Behaviors often involve experimentation with candles, stoves, fireworks, and cigarettes.[4] A major contributor to juvenile-set fires is a child having access to matchers or lighters. Three of every five child-set fires occur in bedrooms and involve ignition of bedding, mattresses, upholstered furniture, or clothing.[5]

Understanding Fire in Society

Because fire is such an important part of society, a child frequently sees fire used appropriately by caregivers and role models. Children, as young as age two, can develop a fascination with fire. This fascination (or curiosity) can be effectively addressed by parents through age-appropriate education.

Unfortunately in some households, a child may not always see appropriate use of fire, ignition tools, or receive preventive education. In addition, media influences such as age-inappropriate TV shows, movies, and even video games often sensationalize fire or portray it in a nonthreatening manner.

Once children become fascinated with fire, most want to learn more about it. If the fascination is not properly addressed through education, a child may attempt to make his or her own fire. This action often occurs in a secluded area of a home such as a bedroom or closet **(Figure 17.4)**. Unfortunately, young children have little understanding of burns or the consequences associated with an out-of-control fire. The reader should be reminded that once fire ignites combustible materials, it may double in size every thirty seconds.

Figure 17.4 Young children may experiment with fire somewhere secluded and full of combustible items.

Aggressive primary prevention that includes school and community-based education is the first line of defense in preventing juvenile firesetting. Early identification, screening, and intervention directed at the firesetter and his or her family is a critical form of secondary prevention. This demands cooperative support from parents, caregivers, and professionals from the fire, juvenile justice, social services, clinical fields, and school community.

Curiosity-Motivated Firesetters

It is often estimated that curiosity-motivated firesetting represents greater than 60% of all fires set by children. The **curiosity-motivated firesetter** is a child who is exploring his or her interest in fire through experimentation.

Most children experience fire interest between the ages of 3 to 5. This age group often asks questions focusing on the physical properties of fire, such as how hot a fire is, its color, or what makes it burn. These questions are similar to questions children have about the other physical elements in their environment; for example, children may ask why the sky is blue or what makes water wet.

Children also express their interest in fire through play. They may wear fire hats, play with toy fire trucks, and cook food on their toy stoves. This type of play is healthy and provides children with ways to explore and understand fire as a productive and useful part of their lives.

Parents and caregivers have the ultimate responsibility of educating children and protecting them from fire's power. Left untreated, repetitive firesetting behaviors often progress to more serious and frequent firesetting behavior. This reason, among others that will be discussed, is why aggressive fire prevention and swift intervention represent the most effective ways to reduce juvenile firesetting behaviors. Prior to examining how firesetting is best addressed, it is important to understand who is starting fires and why.

Who Are Juvenile Firesetters?

The majority of **juvenile firesetters** are ordinary children who are in need of a level of intervention. Most firesetters start their first fire while exploring a natural curiosity. If educational intervention does not take place, eight of ten children will continue to experiment, and the frequency of behavior may escalate.

Current Terminology

In previous times, the fire service often referred to curiosity-motivated firesetting as that of *fire play*. Consequently, the terms *fire play* and *firesetting* were used interchangeably. Child development specialists and educators object to the use of the word *play* in describing a child's negative behavior or misuse of fire and fire tools. According to these professionals, the word *play*, being a child's work or means of expression, should be associated only with positive learning activities.

The term *incendiary* was also often used interchangeably with *arson*. Professionals now recommend use of the term *intentional* to describe a fire set for a purpose. *Unintentional* refers to "not on purpose" and replaces the term *accidental*.

Comprehensive age-appropriate primary prevention such as preschool and elementary-level fire safety education is vitally important in preventing child firesetting. A concerning fact is that residential fires initiated by young children often cause more damage, injury, and death than those started by older children or adolescents. This is because young children often lack insight into why fire is potentially dangerous and how fast it can spread. Fortunately, the fire service has many effective educational programs at its disposal that have been developed, tested, and proven effective with preschool and elementary-age children.

Successful Primary Prevention in Portland, Oregon

In the 1990s, the Portland (OR) Fire Bureau launched a primary prevention program on fire safety directed at its preschool and early elementary level students. Over time, outcome data began to indicate the program's effectiveness. While this success story happened several years ago, the benefits of using age-appropriate primary prevention have strong relevance today.

Source: Public Education Officer Don Porth, Portland, Oregon.

Successful Education

Educational materials and messages that have proven most successful are those that are sensitive to the special growth and development needs of very young children. These programs include lessons that teach children why fire is a tool for adult use only and not a toy for a child's play. Programs should also include information on "what to do" if faced with an unsafe situation.

Providing age and intellectually appropriate education for parents and caregivers is also essential to the prevention process. Assigning children an inappropriate task for their age (such as retrieving a lighter or igniting an adult's cigarette) is a major contributor to child firesetting. It is often surprising to discover how little adults know about why children start fires and how to prevent the behavior from occurring. Sometimes in high-risk households, adults may lack insight into simple safety strategies. Education can be a powerful deterrent to safety illiteracy.

Experimental and Curiosity-Motivated Firesetting

If a child starts a fire, it is usually through experimentation with ignition sources such as matches and lighters. Many unsupervised fire starts are single episodes, motivated primarily by curiosity. Again, the leading causes of experimental or curiosity motivated firesetting among children are easy access to ignition materials and a lapse of supervision (sometimes only momentary) by parents or caregivers.

At least three distinct levels mark the chronological development of fire behavior in children: fire interest, fire starting, and firesetting. These categories of fire behavior represent increasing levels of involvement with fire.

Fire Interest

In general, a fire motivated by curiosity is unintentional. The fire is usually started with available ignition sources, and there is no typical target for the fire. If the fire gets out of control, the child or adolescent may attempt to extinguish the fire or seek help. Fires are usually set in an unsupervised secluded setting in or near a child's home and are relatively unsophisticated. In addition to age-related factors, cognitive challenges, such as learning disabilities and ADHD, can influence poor decision-making and spontaneous behaviors.

Curious and experimental firesetting refer primarily to young children, ages two through ten. The average age of a curiosity-motivated firesetter is five years old. However, investigators often learn that a fire started by an adolescent (or group of teens) was initiated because of boredom or the desire to experiment with fire tools in an uncontrolled environment.

While fascination with fire is a naturally occurring developmental sequence in children, setting fires is not. Led by proper parenting, effective education programs, and social interaction within their community, most children learn age-appropriate, fire-safe behaviors.

Fire Starting

In some children, fire interest leads to unsupervised fire starting and progresses to repeated firesetting. Children in the age range of 7 to 10 years who understand the rules of fire safety may continue to be involved in repeated firesetting without their parents or caregivers being aware of this activity. While the actual setting of fire is repetitive (and might involve a child as young as age 4), it may not represent any criminal intent. However, careful screening of the situation by a trained interventionist (and perhaps clinician) is in order to evaluate the potential for underlying psychological or social needs.

Firesetting

Curiosity-motivated firesetting can lead to more serious incidents if ignored. If a child or adolescent continues to participate in more than one unsupervised fire start, the probability of starting a significant fire increases dramatically. For this reason, it is critical for parents, caregivers, emergency services, schools, and the health community to understand that *all* incidents should be reported and addressed immediately.

Adolescents may be either boys or girls and may start fires out of curiosity. Their actions are sometimes prompted by curiosity, a desire to experiment, and carelessness. Sometimes it is a simple wish to explore the environment with little understanding of the consequences of uncontrolled fire. Again, cognitive challenges can influence poor decision-making and spontaneous behaviors.

Most adolescent firesetters who are truly prompted by curiosity do not intend to be destructive or to inflict damage on life or property. Many will try to extinguish the fire they start, and often it is the firesetter who initiates a call for help. The experimenting adolescent may initially deny or lie about their involvement with fire. However, if confronted by officials using an appropriate demeanor, they often show remorse for the event. Punishment, restitution for damages done by the fire, and accountability for these actions together with education will help deter further unsupervised experimentation with fire.

Problem Firesetters

The term **problem firesetter** categorizes types of fires started by juveniles who are not motivated by curiosity. This section profiles the subsets of problem firesetters.

The Delinquent Firesetter

In contrast to curiosity, some adolescent firesetters try to duplicate forms of dangerous behaviors seen in various media. **Delinquent firesetters** often target fields, mailboxes, Dumpsters™, and abandoned structures through acts of malicious mischief **(Figure 17.5)**. These behaviors often result in the creation of

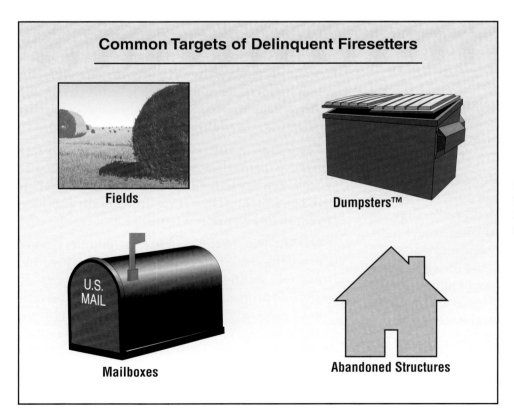

Common Targets of Delinquent Firesetters

Fields

Dumpsters™

Mailboxes

U.S. MAIL

Abandoned Structures

Figure 17.5 Delinquent firesetters may create hazards by acting out behaviors they've seen in movies and games.

costly and potentially lethal consequences through experimentation with accelerants or the construction of rudimentary explosive devices. While the internet provides a wealth of positive information, it can also provide knowledge of how to engage in destructive activity.

In some cases, adolescent firesetters may use fire to conceal a crime that has been committed. In many major cities, juvenile firesetting is often used as a rite of initiation for joining a gang.

Regardless of the magnitude of an event, the motives behind experimentation with fire and delinquent acts of firesetting must be immediately addressed. Left unchecked these actions have great potential for escalating into future acts of violence and other antisocial behavior. Comprehensive interventions such as age-appropriate, school-based educational programs coupled with punitive actions (with potential legal ramifications) are proven measures that often deter fire experimentation and **recidivism** by adolescents.

The Attention-Seeking Firesetter

Firesetting can be a very powerful way for juveniles to communicate the need for help. **Attention-seeking firesetters** start a fire in an attempt to bring attention to a stressful life situation such as depression, anger, or abuse. Intentional firesetting may be influenced by cognitive, psychological, or social problems. It can also be made worse by environmental factors such as access to ignition materials, lack of adult supervision, and family dysfunction. This type of firesetting is extremely dangerous because it often consists of a series of fire starts, both planned and spontaneous, that take place over several weeks, months, or even years. The severity of fires may vary.

In some problematic cases, there is an intention to destroy or harm property or people. Once a fire is started, the attention-seeking firesetter may not make an attempt to extinguish the fire or seek help. The fire acts as a symbol of a problem and signifies a cry for help in response to a stressful life experience or abuse.[6] The possible link between physical and/or sexual abuse, neglect, and firesetting has been investigated extensively by several states.

The attention-seeking firesetter (and his or her family) needs immediate intervention from a team of experienced professionals who can intervene appropriately. Intervention may include a combination of education, clinical (mental health attention), and social service support. **Adjudication** by justice officials may also be necessary.

NOTE: The JFIS component of NFPA® 1035 calls for both levels of intervention specialists to be proficient in determining the difference between a "simple" firesetting case and one that is "complex."

A curiosity-motivated child who has set fire to a piece of paper on one occasion is an example of a "simple" firesetting case. In contrast, a child who has set several fires in his or her home in response to other needs such as relief from an abusive environment would be classified as a "complex" case. Complex cases demand use of combined interventions from multiple agencies.

The Pathological Firesetter

Left unaddressed, juvenile firesetting behaviors can transcend into a **pathology** of continuing fire starts. In **epidemiology**, pathology is often referred to as the process of a disease. While juvenile firesetting is not a disease in itself, the behavior is a response to some level of need — be it curiosity- or problem-driven.

Pathological firesetting is very disconcerting because the perpetrator uses fire as a means for gratification without regard to others. A pathological firesetter may start hundreds of fires for many reasons. The term *pyromania* refers to a pathology whereby a person sets many planned fires for pleasure or to release stress. While the mental health community tends to reserve the term *pyromaniac* for adult offenders, left unchecked, juvenile firesetting behaviors can transcend into a pathology carried by a perpetrator to adulthood **(Figure 17.6)**.

Pathological firesetters represent an extreme danger to themselves, the community, and the fire service. If a firesetter's behaviors are identified as being pathological in nature, immediate multidisciplinary intervention is required.

NOTE: Due to the sometimes tenuous nature of problem firesetting cases, the family of juvenile firesetters should have reliable 24-hour access to a credible professional who can initiate intervention or referral during an emergency situation. Having this level of service available can often prevent an unstable situation from escalating into a catastrophe.

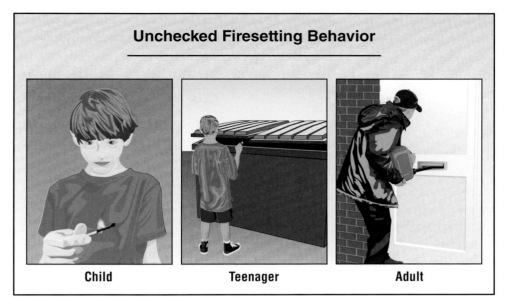

Unchecked Firesetting Behavior

Child   Teenager   Adult

Figure 17.6 Juvenile firesetting may begin with simple curiosity and escalate to a pathology over time.

Firesetters with Special Needs

People often connect the term "special needs" with some level of disability **(Figure 17.7)**. In the context of juvenile firesetting, the term references a young person challenged by one or more level of cognitive dysfunction. The term **firesetters with special needs** is presented here because of the ever-increasing empirical documentation that *many* juvenile firesetters (curiosity-motivated and problem-driven) are challenged by some form of special need.

It is well documented that cognitive challenges can influence dysfunctional behavior. Because all firesetting interventionists must be able to differentiate between a simple and complex situation, it is important to have knowledge of the many challenges that may influence human behavior.

The following section presents information on some of the major cognitive challenges that a firesetter and his or her family may face. This section is not designed to make the JFIS I an expert on clinical child psychology nor does it advocate attempting to diagnose cognitive challenges that may be affecting a firesetter. Its purpose is to highlight cognitive challenges that, when identified, may signal the need for consultation with a mental health professional or other behavioral specialist.

Attention Deficit Hyperactivity Disorder (ADHD)

Attention Deficit Hyperactivity Disorder (ADHD) is a condition that can interfere with a person's ability to cognitively focus on a topic; it can also influence

Special Needs in Juvenile Firesetters

ADHD	Learning Disabilities
Anxiety and Depression	Bipolar Disorder
Autism	Oppositional Defiant Disorder
Conduct Disorder	Antisocial Personality Disorder

Figure 17.7 Cognitive difficulties can influence dysfunctional behavior.

motor activity levels. Millions of people (especially children) are challenged by some form of ADHD. Some people are only affected by the attentive component of the disorder. This results in the person having trouble focusing and concentrating on a subject. If affected by the hyperactivity component, a person has trouble keeping still and may often make spontaneous decisions.

ADHD can influence juvenile firesetting in the following ways:

- If a juvenile has challenges with attention, he or she may have failed to adequately process fire safety lessons received in school.

- If challenged by hyperactivity, a juvenile may start a fire because the opportunity presented itself and potential ramifications for the action were not well thought out in advance.

Because ADHD is genetic and often runs in families, the household of a firesetter may need special attention from interventionists. This attention may be in the form of educational intervention for both the firesetter and his or her caregivers. In some cases, intervention from a behavioral specialist may be in order.

NOTE: Nearly 60 percent of juvenile firesetters may have a diagnosis of ADHD before their first referral to a firesetter intervention program.

- Nearly 90 percent of the "complex" firesetters have been assesed by a doctor, psychiatrist, or a counselor before their first referral.

- Nearly 40 percent of firesetters reported they had started *at least* three fires before their first referral.

Fire interventionists have long thought that approximately 85 percent of juvenile firesetters are in need of educational intervention only and are at low risk for repeat firesetting (recidivism). In contrast, emerging research seems to indicate that exactly the opposite may be true. Many of today's firesetters are already under the care of a doctor, psychiatrist, or a counselor *before* they are enrolled in a firesetting intervention program.[7]

Learning Disabilities (LD)

Nearly 20 percent of the U.S. population and nearly 30 percent of children with ADHD have a learning disability. A learning disability is a disorder that diminishes a person's capacity to interpret what they see and hear or to link information from different parts of the brain.

The interventionist should identify behavioral and learning challenges that are exhibited by the firesetter and his or her family early on during a screening process. This strategy allows the **interventionist** to develop intervention practices that consider the abilities and challenges of all parties involved.

Anxiety and Depression

Millions of Americans are affected by various levels of anxiety or depression. Low levels of anxiety (such as concern over taking a test) can serve as motivation for a person to take action that overcomes its source. High levels of anxiety (such as is caused by living within an abusive or dysfunctional household) can cause depression among children and adolescents. The root cause of many problem firesetting cases can be traced to a juvenile who is trying to send a signal that he or she is unhappy about one or more specific circumstances.

Bipolar Disorder

Bipolar disorder affects a person's mood cycle. A person with bipolar disorder often fluctuates between periods of intense highs and lows. Because bipolar disorder often accompanies other challenges such as ADHD, it can influence firesetting behavior. A juvenile who exhibits severe mood swings, has difficulties making appropriate decisions, and exhibits impulsive behaviors may be at greater risk of firesetting than other children.

Autism

Autism is an incurable cognitive disorder that affects approximately 5 out of every 1,000 children. Autistic children have difficulties with social interaction and communication (verbal and nonverbal). They often have difficulty interpreting what others are thinking or feeling because they are unable to observe or understand social cues, such as tone of voice or facial expressions.

Autistic children sometimes lack empathy and miss clues about appropriate behavior. In addition, they may demonstrate repetitive behaviors or have narrow obsessive interest in a certain topic. These behaviors can range in impact from mild to disabling. While a firesetting interventionist may not interact with a large number of autistic children over his or her career, the population deserves special recognition because of the potential of a juvenile becoming fixated on a topic such as fire.

Oppositional Defiant Disorder (ODD)

Up to half of juveniles with ADHD may carry the additional diagnosis of oppositional defiant disorder (ODD). Defiant juveniles can be stubborn and noncompliant and display outbursts of temper. They sometimes may even become belligerent. The juvenile with ODD is often argumentative with adults, refuses to obey directions from authority figures, and may sometimes become aggressive.

Due to their outbursts of negative behavior, defiant juveniles are often involved with problematic firesetting situations. Challenges such as ADHD, dysfunctional home environments, and peer pressure may increase the negative behaviors exhibited by a juvenile with ODD.

Conduct Disorder (CD)

Up to 40 percent of ADHD children may eventually develop a conduct disorder (CD). This pattern of antisocial behavior is more serious than oppositional defiance. Juveniles with CD frequently lie, steal, and fight with or bully others. They are also at greater risk of getting into trouble at school or with the police.

What makes the diagnosis of conduct disorder especially concerning is that the perpetrator often violates the basic rights of other people. A person with CD may be aggressive toward people or animals, destroy property, break into homes, commit thefts, carry or use weapons, start fires, or engage in vandalism. Juveniles with CD are at greater risk for substance use experimentation and later dependence and abuse.

Antisocial Personality Disorder (APD)

Antisocial Personality Disorder (APD) develops from a conduct disorder. It begins in childhood or early adolescence and continues into adulthood. APD is a pervasive pattern of disregard for, and violation of, the rights of others. To be diagnosed with this disorder, an individual must be age 18 or older as well as have a documented history of a conduct disorder before the age of 15.

Hallmark features of APD are deceit and manipulation. To prove an antisocial personality disorder, clinical practitioners must collect information from sources other than the individual being diagnosed. Due to the excess of their challenges, the antisocial person causes great concern for the professional community.

Family Influences and Firesetting

Family influences can have a direct impact on whether or not a child will set a fire. While juvenile firesetting can occur in any household, empirical evidence indicates that the behavior occurs more frequently in homes where a lack of both supervision and parenting skills exist.

Family dysfunction or lack of adult support can be factors that influence firesetting behaviors. Parents, legal guardians, or caregivers may be physically present in a home but emotionally absent. The family may be experiencing recent trauma or crisis.

In more extreme cases, drug and/or alcohol abuse may be evident among family members, including the firesetter. Physical and/or sexual abuse, neglect, and other antisocial adult behaviors may be occurring. Prior contact between the family and police is common. In summary, the home environment of many firesetters is chaotic. This is especially true in problematic, complex cases.

As part of the intake process, it is highly recommended that the interventionist includes a component to assess the safety dynamics in the firesetter's home environment. This is especially critical if the interventionist is considering a home visitation as part of the screening and intervention process. More information on this topic will be discussed in later chapters.

Response to a juvenile firesetting incident should begin by following a thorough **intake** process. This process involves gathering pertinent facts from the parent or caregiver such as what happened, who was involved, and (in their opinion) why the incident occurred. The intake process should also seek basic information on household demographics such as who resides in the residence and their relationship to the firesetter. Obtaining this information is essential for two reasons:

- Potential safety issues can be identified and considered if the interventionist is considering a home visitation.

- The interventionist can make an initial assessment on the level of firesetting situation he or she will be investigating.

Once a safe environment is ensured, the interventionist conducts a structured **interview** with the parents or caregivers of the child. This interview may be conducted at the interventionist's work location or the family's residence. This contact is important so that stresses on the family, patterns of supervision, discipline, and other environmental factors can be evaluated.

Observing the interaction of a family in their home environment, if possible, will often provide many clues as to why a child is setting fires. It is often a firesetting interventionist who discovers a household where child neglect or abuse is occurring. Again, if considering a home visitation, *always* perform a safety screening as part of the intake process before visiting the home of a firesetter.

The parents or adult caregivers of a juvenile firesetter are a target audience, equal in priority to the firesetter. Adults may lack insight or have inadequate knowledge of critical safety behaviors, such as the need to isolate ignition materials. The most significant factor in juvenile firesetting is that the firesetter has easy access to ignition tools such as lighters and matches. For example, data proves that more acts of firesetting occur in homes where parents or caregivers smoke.

Families of firesetters should receive comprehensive screening to ensure their home has an adequate number of working smoke alarms (less than ten years old) on all levels of the home. Consider recommending or providing and installing smoke alarms in the bedrooms of confirmed firesetters.

Many adults in high-risk households lack awareness that a child needs to learn how to safely coexist with fire in their everyday environment. Some parents may assume that the knowledge is taught to children in schools. For others, the concept of teaching safe behaviors to children may never occur to them. Interventionists can play a pivotal role in teaching parents how to prevent a child from setting a fire.

Professionals and Communities Taking Action

Many noted professionals continue to research factors that contribute to juvenile firesetting. These findings and proven mitigation strategies are being published regularly by credible sources. Many frontline practitioners and states are sharing their best practices around the world. This open exchange of information has led many communities to effectively identify, evaluate, and address their local problems.

While the professional community continues to publish groundbreaking research on firesetting intervention, work is still needed to close the gap between dated information and current best practices. When conducting research on juvenile firesetting,

Facts Regarding Juvenile Firesetting

The parents or caregivers of a firesetter may have preconceptions about the subject of children and fire. The following facts are presented to correct some of the myths associated with juvenile firesetting.

Facts Regarding Juvenile Firesetting

- Firesetting is not necessarily related to bedwetting and cruelty to animals.
- A firesetter will not "grow out of" the behavior.
- While most children have a natural curiosity about fire, they do not act on the interest and start a fire. Very few children have an obsessive interest in fire.
- There is always a reason for a fire start. That reason must be identified and addressed in an appropriate manner.
- Not all schools include fire safety as part of their essential curriculum.
- Burning a child's hand will not stop him or her from setting fires. It will only create fear and scars. It is also child abuse!
- Showing a child or adolescent pictures of dead bodies will not stop firesetting behaviors. This type of intervention only instills fear. In addition, it does not provide any information about safety rules and the appropriate use of fire.
- Scare tactics, such as having police officers or fire marshals threaten a child with handcuffs, are not an effective intervention strategy.
- An effective way to communicate the dangers and consequences of firesetting is through a reality-based, non-fear-oriented educational intervention. Physical examination of burned property in conjunction with age-appropriate education is being used successfully in many communities.
- Communicate to the firesetter in a nonthreatening, age-appropriate explanation the need for personal accountability and the consequences that will occur in conjunction with acts of firesetting. This directive, when presented from a respected official like a judge, police officer, or firefighter, is often very effective. However, the firesetter must respect the statement of the official as being true.

NOTE: Parents and caregivers of minors also need information regarding their legal and financial responsibility to acts of firesetting committed by juveniles entrusted in their care.

interventionists should use care to ensure that the information is current, valid, and published by a credible source.

The use of integrated preventive interventions (5 Es) continues to positively impact America's juvenile firesetting problem. The 1994 Consumer Product Safety Commission's child-resistant lighter standard led to a sharp decline in child firesetting-related deaths. In 2007, the Commission championed legislation requiring an increase to the small open-flame resistance for upholstered furniture and mattresses. Fires started by young children are nearly all small, open-flame ignitions. Therefore, these product requirements could make a significant difference in the remaining child-related fire problem.

Another emerging trend that has caught the attention of interventionists is the number of juvenile-set fires caused by novelty lighters. At development time of this manual, the states of Oregon and Arkansas were leading a nationwide effort calling for the Consumer Product Safety Commission to prohibit the sale and distribution of novelty lighters, which resemble toy versions of such common items as cell phones and footballs. Locally, the most effective juvenile firesetting intervention programs include participation from the fire service, law enforcement, justice officials, social services, mental health community, and schools. Open lines of communication, collaboration, and resource sharing exist among these groups in communities where a reduction in juvenile firesetting is being noted.

Communities that are successful have researched their firesetting problem and designed a comprehensive mitigation strategy that combines both primary and secondary level prevention. At the primary level, firefighters, schools, and community-based organizations work in tandem to provide age-appropriate fire safety education to selected target populations. When fires are started, an intervention team is in place to identify the problem, evaluate it, and intervene in an appropriate manner **(Figure 17.8)**.

Many communities use the following (or similar) format when addressing a juvenile firesetting incident:

- Identify the problem.
- Educate firefighters, police officers, mental health clinicians, social service workers, teachers, school counselors, parents, and the community at-large about the problem of juvenile firesetting.

Steps in Addressing Juvenile Firesetting Incidents

Step 4: Put Multiagency Agreements in Place

Step 3: Refine Reporting Systems for Early Detection

Step 2: Educate People about the Problem

Step 1: Identify the Problem

Figure 17.8 Communities with a good firesetting intervention program are able to respond quickly and efficiently to crises as they happen.

- Refine reporting systems so that early detection occurs.
- Put multiagency agreements in place that permit open lines of communication, cooperation, and **referrals**.

Intake Process

This is a process of collecting the initial comprehensive background information about the juvenile and family regarding the incident that brought the juvenile to the program. It also seeks background information on household demographics so that scene security can be assessed should the interventionist decide to conduct a home visitation.

Interview and Screening Process

An interview is the process of meeting with the juvenile firesetter and the family to determine the severity of the problem. Using an approved assessment tool, the interventionist interviews the firesetter and family members. The assessment tool is used to help the interventionist determine the severity of the problem. The assessment tool should be approved by the local **authority having jurisdiction (AHJ)** over firesetting events.

Intervention

This is a formal response to the firesetting behavior. It may include a combination of education, mental health counseling, medical services, social service support, or adjudication by the juvenile justice system. Ongoing assessment of each case is always performed. Every case of juvenile firesetting should receive follow-up. An open line of communication with the firesetter's family and referral agencies is essential.

Evaluation

While successful prevention and mitigation is being documented in many communities, others may lack any form of firesetter detection and intervention program. Sadly, in communities where a program is absent, up to 80 percent of intentionally set fires may be started by juveniles under age 18. Fortunately, nationally recognized organizations and other professionals continue to develop preventive strategies designed to be used at the local level.

JFIS Standard Levels I and II

The fire service has an ethical and often legal obligation to address the problem of juvenile firesetting. NFPA® 1035 devotes two sections (Levels I and II) to serve as a guide for the development, delivery, and leadership of juvenile firesetting intervention.

Level I outlines the **job performance requirements (JPRs)** for the entry level intervention specialist. Level II provides guidelines for program development and leadership. As with all NFPA® standards, the levels of responsibility and JPRs progress in ascending order. This manual provides supportive information that follows the JPRs as written.

As the intervention specialist gains experience, he or she will likely perform duties outlined in both levels of the standard. These duties will overlap and integrate with one another.

The following sections contain a succinct overview of the performance expectations of an interventionist meeting Juvenile Firesetter Intervention Specialist Level I. It is followed by a section profiling the expectations of a Level II program manager.

NOTE: A thorough explanation of specific performance standards applicable to each level will be presented in later chapters.

Juvenile Firesetter Intervention Specialist I (JFIS I)

The Juvenile Firesetter Intervention Specialist I manages the case of an identified firesetter so that screening, education, and referrals are initiated. Responsibilities of this position include the following, which will be explained in greater detail in the following chapters:

- Responds to inquiries, reports, or referrals from multiple sources regarding an identified or potential firesetter.

- Initiates contact with the legal caregiver of the firesetter and explains the program components offered by the local community. Schedules an intake/interview process to include the caregiver and firesetter.

  NOTE: The JFIS I must exhibit mastery-level ability in distinguishing a simple firesetting situation from a complex one. Simple firesetting situations are usually those that involve curiosity-motivated behaviors. Complex situations often surround problem firesetting incidents.

- Determines applicable education and referral interventions. Facilitates access to additional services as needed. The JFIS I, in consultation with his or her supervisor (JFIS II), determines and implements the specific education and referral interventions for each firesetter case. Intervention strategies may include referral to education programs, mental health screening, or justice system actions. Referrals may be single-system in nature or involve participation from several agencies.

- Performs (if qualified) educational interventions designed to deter recidivism. An example of a qualified interventionist would be the Level I Fire and Life Safety Educator as defined by NFPA® 1035.

- Monitors, documents, and evaluates program elements and firesetter progress. To be qualified as a JFIS I, it is necessary to meet all the job performance requirements of a Level I Fire and Life Safety Educator.

The JPRs include proficiencies in the following:

- The characteristics of fire and human behavior during emergencies
- Knowledge of fire causation and prevention
- Basic fire protection devices and systems
- The stages of intellectual growth and development
- Fire safety education, including hazard identification and correction

Additional **requisite knowledge** specific to JFIS I includes:

- Data collection systems
- Legal consequences associated with firesetting
- Federal, state, and local laws governing juveniles
- Regulations governing **confidentiality**
- **Family dynamics**
- Signs and symptoms of abuse or **neglect**
- Interviewing techniques
- Referral options to include justice system and mental health
- Program/agency policies and procedures

The successful JFIS I must be proficient in both oral and written communication, which includes the ability to apply interpersonal skills during interview sessions and educational interventions. The interventionist must be able to gather pertinent information and maintain data collection systems. The Level I interventionist must show expertise in recognizing risk, abuse, or neglect, and local laws governing the reporting of such.

Juvenile Firesetter Intervention Specialist II (JFIS II)

The Juvenile Firesetter Intervention Specialist II is responsible for organizing, leading, and sustaining a firesetting intervention program. He or she is also responsible for supervising Level I JFIS staff. In addition to meeting the job performance requirements of a JFIS I, the Level II program manager is responsible for the following:

- Supervise any JFIS I and other assigned personnel.
- Coordinate and evaluate training and personnel.
- Define target audiences and program goals.
- Establish and maintain interagency networks/coalitions.

- Develop, deliver, and evaluate education programs and awareness campaigns.
- Maintain and secure records of program components and firesetter case files.
- Exhibit mastery-level ability in distinguishing a simple firesetting situation from a complex case.
- Set the mission, goals, and objectives of the juvenile firesetter intervention program in consultation with an interagency network.
- Have knowledge of the federal, state, and local laws governing arson, abuse, and neglect.
- Understand organizational and community management, program policies, and procedures.
- Have proficiency in oral and written communication skills.
- Coordinate community resources, services, and participation of external organizations.
- Develop and manage a budget.

Many of the job performance requirements for a JFIS I and II are similar to the levels of responsibility in the NFPA® Fire and Life Safety Educator's job performance requirements. To prevent redundancy in this manual, the reader will be directed to reference previous chapters within this manual as mutual proficiencies are discussed.

Layout of the JFIS Section

Many individuals and nationally recognized organizations have made significant professional contributions in support of addressing the problem of juvenile firesetting. The NFPA® has been fortunate to have received this support. The JFIS component of NFPA® 1035 exists because of support from many individuals, communities, and organizations.

Chapters 17 through 25 of this manual follow, in sequential order, sections nine and ten of NFPA® 1035 that pertain to juvenile firesetting intervention. The reader should note that while new material pertinent to JFIS will be introduced, references will be made to information published in previous chapters.

In addition to reading this publication, the reader is encouraged to seek additional sources of education and practical training on the topic of juvenile firesetting. The National Fire Academy JFIS leadership courses are offered on campus in Emmitsburg, Maryland, and throughout the country in two-day deliverable formats. Many universities offer courses in child and adolescent psychology that empower students with enhanced understanding of factors that contribute to various levels of human behavior.

Chapter Summary

Because many firesetters have special needs, interventionists need a basic understanding of conditions that may influence cognitive function and human behavior. At development time of this manual, research identified that close to half of all juvenile firesetters exhibit one or more professionally diagnosed cognitive, neurological, or human-created challenge at the time they are referred to a juvenile firesetter program.

Creating, operating, and sustaining a successful JFIS program takes commitment, time, knowledge, organizational skills, patience, and tenacity. The United States, along with many other countries, is fortunate to have many model programs that are proving to be effective in reducing the occurrence of juvenile firesetting. While organizing several groups to work in synergy can be a challenging process, the potential benefits outweigh any associated struggles exponentially.

Review Questions

1. Why is juvenile firesetting intervention addressed in an NFPA® professional qualifications standard?

2. What is the scope of the juvenile firesetting problem in the U.S.?

3. What are the various profiles of juvenile firesetters?

4. What are the components that comprise a successful juvenile firesetting intervention program?

Key Terms

Adjudication — To hear or settle a case by judicial procedure.

Attention Seeking Firesetter — Starts a fire in an attempt to bring attention to a stressful life situation such as depression, anger, or abuse.

Authority Having Jurisdiction (AHJ) — An organization, office, or individual responsible for enforcing the requirements of a code or standard, or for approving equipment, materials, an installation, or a procedure.

Clinician — A degreed health professional who is licensed to perform specific services.

Confidentiality — A principle of law and professional ethics that recognizes the privacy of individuals.

Curiosity-Motivated Firesetter — A child who is exploring his or her interest in fire through experimentation.

Delinquent Firesetter — Starts fires because of boredom or peer or media influences. Fires may also be set to commit destruction of property, conceal a crime, or as a rite of passage into a group.

Epidemiology — Scientific study of the causes, distribution, and control of diseases among populations.

Family Dynamics — Structure and characteristics of a person's living environment, including relatives, caregivers, or other relationships and their interactions with each other.

Firesetter with Special Needs — Suffers from some level of cognitive disability or challenge such as ADHD. Any level of firesetter may have a special need that should be considered during a screening process.

Firesetting — Any unsanctioned incendiary use of fire, including both intentional and unintentional involvement, whether or not an actual fire and/or explosion occurs.

Intake — Process of collecting the comprehensive background information from the juvenile's family or caregiver regarding the incident(s) that brought the juvenile to the program.

Intervention — Formal response to firesetting behavior. It may include education alone or be combined with a referral to counseling or medical or social services. Juvenile justice sanctions are sometimes used (or required) as part of an intervention process.

Interventionist — Person who is qualified to perform a specific task, such as a juvenile firesetter intervention specialist.

Interview — Process of meeting with the juvenile firesetter and his or her family to determine the severity of the problem.

Job Performance Requirement (JPR) — Statement that describes a specific job task, lists the items necessary to complete the task, and defines measurable or observable outcomes and evaluation areas for the specific task.

Juvenile Firesetter — A person, through the age of 18, or as defined by the authority having jurisdiction, who is involved in the act of firesetting.

Neglect — Failure to act on behalf of, or in protection of, an individual in one's care.

Pathological Firesetting — Firesetters who have transcended through the firesetting profiles whereby they are now setting fires as a way to release stress.

Pathology — Manifestation of a problem into a deviating condition.

Problem Firesetter — Includes the profiles of intentional firesetting and firesetters with special needs.

Recidivism — Relapse into criminal behavior, such as firesetting.

Referral — Act or process by which an individual and/or family gains access to a program or community resources.

Requisite Knowledge — Fundamental knowledge one must have in order to perform a specific task.

Chapter 17 Notes

1. United States Fire Administration – National Fire Academy
2. Federal Bureau of Investigation, Uniform Crime Report
3. U.S. Fire Administration's National Fire Data Center
4. Used with permission from Don Porth
5. Burn Institute
6. NFA Juvenile Firesetter Intervention Curriculum

JFIS Level I Interventionists: Administration

Chapter Contents

Key Terms

Job Performance Requirements

This chapter provides information that addresses the following job performance requirements of NFPA®
1035, *Standard for Professional Qualifications for Fire and Life Safety Educator, Public Information
Officer, and Juvenile Firesetter Intervention Specialist*, 2010 edition.

NFPA® 1035 References

9.2.1

9.2.2

9.2.4

JFIS Level I Interventionists: Administration

Learning Objectives

After reading this chapter, students will be able to:

1. Explain why intervention of juvenile firesetting must follow an organized process (NFPA® 1035, 9.2.1).

2. Justify the importance of adhering to established protocols that govern the administration of a juvenile firesetter intervention program.

3. Describe how to perform specific administrative duties expected of a Level I Juvenile Firesetter intervention specialist (NFPA® 1035, 9.2.4).

4. Explain why the firesetter interventionist must exhibit proficient communication skills (NFPA® 1035, 9.2.1 and 9.2.2).

Chapter 18
JFIS Level I Interventionists: Administration

Case History

A young woman arrives at the local fire station and pleads to a group of firefighters for their help. Obviously distraught, she tells them she has just caught her seven-year-old son setting paper on fire in her bedroom.

The engine company's lieutenant takes the woman into the firehouse office and calms her down. He reassures her that nearly all children exhibit interest in fire and that she has taken an important step to prevent additional fires. According to organizational protocol, the officer collects basic background information about the incident and contact information for the family.

While the woman is still at the firehouse, the lieutenant has the on-call fire prevention officer contact him. He explains the situation to her and has the prevention officer speak directly with the woman. The prevention officer explains the components of the organization's Juvenile Firesetter Intervention (JFI) program. A meeting between the officer and woman is arranged for that afternoon.

The fire prevention officer meets with the woman in person and conducts a formal intake process according to protocol. During the intake process, the fire prevention officer discovers the current episode of firesetting is the third within a two-week period. She also learns that the child has recently been hospitalized for emotional challenges and is being treated by a psychiatrist.

Obviously this case requires specialized attention from trained interventionists. This incident was handled effectively because organizational protocol clearly outlined the sequential actions to initiate when a juvenile firesetting incident is reported.

The Level I Juvenile Firesetter Intervention Specialist (JFIS) operates on the frontline of juvenile firesetting intervention. He or she performs important administrative duties, works directly with juveniles and their families, facilitates interventions, conducts follow-up, and evaluates case outcomes. In performing these duties, the Level I interventionist uses materials and follows program directives that have been developed by a Level II program manager.

Chapters 18 through 20 are dedicated to skill proficiencies expected of a Level I JFIS. This chapter's content includes:

- Explanation of why juvenile firesetting intervention must follow an organized process

- Justification for adhering to established protocols that govern the administration of a juvenile firesetter intervention program

- How to perform specific administrative duties expected of a Level I interventionist

- Explanation of why the firesetter interventionist must exhibit proficient communication skills

Successful Intervention Follows an Organized Process

Mitigating each case of juvenile firesetting should follow an organized process that ascends in logical order. The foundation for addressing a specific firesetting situation includes the following components:

- *Problem identification.* This begins when the situation is reported to a program and steps are initiated to establish contact with the juvenile firesetter and his or her family.

- *Intake process.* The process of collecting initial comprehensive background information from the juvenile's family or caregiver regarding the incident(s) that brought the juvenile to the program.

- *Interview and screening of case.* The process of meeting with the juvenile firesetter and his or her family to determine the severity of the problem. Through use of an approved assessment instrument, the interview functions as a comprehensive screening process to evaluate what level of intervention is appropriate for the juvenile and family.

- *Intervention.* A formal response to the firesetting behavior. Intervention may be limited to education or include a combination of referrals to counseling, medical, or social services. Juvenile justice sanctions are sometimes employed (or required) as part of the intervention process.

- *Follow-up.* Determines if a successful outcome (termination of firesetting behaviors) has been achieved.

- *Program evaluation.* Monitors the overall effectiveness of the intervention. Each juvenile firesetting case should be considered individually and

processed according to need. Following nationally recommended strategies (such as those suggested in this manual) will help interventionists reach successful outcomes.

Program policies and procedures (protocols) are rules that guide how a juvenile firesetting intervention program will be administered. Designing program guidelines is a requisite skill of a Level II JFIS. Guidelines are specific to the local authority having jurisdiction (AHJ) and should be in place before a program is implemented. All interventionists are expected to follow their organization's protocols for firesetting intervention.

Program protocols are often developed in cooperation with the partner organizations that serve juvenile firesetters and their families. Level I interventionists need a clear understanding of these governances (both internal and external) before they begin working with juvenile firesetters. The interventionist must understand the rules of his or her organization and be knowledgeable of the referral process to other agencies. In cases involving criminal activity or abuse, referral is mandatory as is explained at the end of this chapter.

Having an **organizational protocol** helps facilitate consistency of operation. With life safety at stake, the use of standard operating guidelines is strongly recommended. The following examples of recommended policies and procedures should be in place before initiation of a juvenile firesetting intervention program **(Figure 18.1)**:

- *Internal educational component* — Explains the problem of juvenile firesetting and how it impacts the local community. Personnel should also know what the organization is doing to address the issue.

- *Consistent reporting protocol* — Specifies the process to follow if personnel encounter a juvenile firesetting situation.

- *Intake process* — Specifies specialized training on conducting a formal intake of a juvenile into the program.

- *Interview/screening process* — Specifies what qualifications are required of staff who conduct a firesetter interview/screening process. Staff must also have mastery level understanding of when and how to refer a firesetting case to a partner agency.

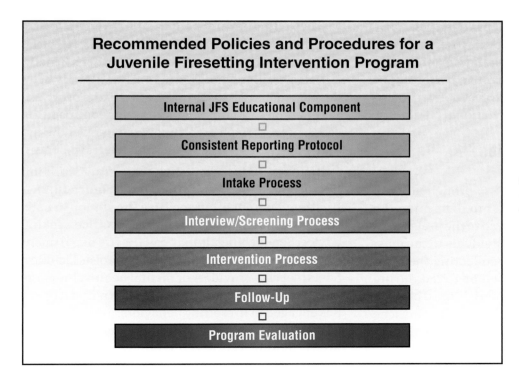

Recommended Policies and Procedures for a Juvenile Firesetting Intervention Program

Internal JFS Educational Component

Consistent Reporting Protocol

Intake Process

Interview/Screening Process

Intervention Process

Follow-Up

Program Evaluation

Figure 18.1 The use of standard operating procedures keeps a program on track and accountable to evaluation.

- *Intervention process* — Specifies what qualifications are required of staff who conduct a firesetting intervention. The policy should also clarify when and how education will be used as a preventive intervention.

- *Follow-up* — Directs when and how the firesetting case follow-up will be performed.

- *Program evaluation* — Outlines when and what type of information will be reported by the Level I interventionist to supervisors so that quality assurance of cases and feedback to staff members can occur.

Rationale for Administrative Proficiencies

Chapter 3 explained why fire and life safety educators (FLSE) must perform administrative duties. These duties include processing requests for service, documenting program activity, and evaluating specific deliveries. While the administrative tasks performed by a JFIS I are similar to those of a FLSE I, the JFIS's level of responsibility is often greater because of the following factors.

The delivery of risk-reduction programs is considered primary (or universal) prevention. Primary prevention is used to help facilitate a safer public through education and skill training. The ultimate goal of primary prevention is to elicit changes in attitudes and behaviors before the occurrence of an incident.

Juvenile firesetting intervention is secondary prevention (also called selective or indicated prevention) initiated after an incident has occurred or because a target population has exhibited behaviors placing them at greater risk from harm. In the context of firesetting intervention, an incident has taken place and the interventionist is being called upon to help prevent future occurrences. Early identification of firesetting behaviors, the intake process, interviewing, screening, interventions, and evaluation are all components of secondary prevention.

In communities where a juvenile firesetter intervention program exists, the fire department often serves as the lead agency. Because juvenile firesetting is a potentially life-threatening behavior, the interventionist accepts a great level of responsibility when addressing firesetting behaviors.

Administrative components of firesetting intervention, such as completed interview/screening instruments and evaluation documents, will often be shared by several professional agencies. Gathering, evaluating, and reporting case information can be a tedious, complex process. Good organizational skills are essential to reach a successful outcome.

While sharing case information is often voluntary and occurs through interagency partnerships, the exchange can be mandated through laws or other court actions. Substandard administrative performance can hamper a referral process, affect delivery of interventions, and damage organizational credibility.

Administrative Proficiencies — Level I JFIS

The Level I JFIS should be able to proficiently use reliable and valid tools in order to determine the needs of juveniles who are referred to the program as well as correctly refer those individuals to the most helpful resource available. By collecting the most relevant data, valuable time can be saved during the beginning of the process when it is most crucial. This section identifies important points that must be addressed in the course of intake activities.

Identifying Juvenile Firesetters

Chapter 7 discussed how to identify and prioritize community risks as part of the Five Step Process to Reduce Community Risk. Only through objective evaluation can a community accurately identify local risk issues and their level of severity. The JFIS component of NFPA® 1035 assumes that a community has already completed this process.

Developing partnerships to address juvenile firesetting at the local level is a skill expected of a Level II program manager. For the Level I reader's benefit, it is also assumed that a program has already been developed and functioning. As part of the program, Level I interventionists will be assigned firesetting cases, process them accordingly, conduct follow-up, and report results to superiors and referral partners.

Requests to intervene in a firesetting situation may originate from several sources **(Figure 18.2)**. A frustrated parent often goes to a fire station or calls the fire department administrative office seeking advice. School officials may call the fire department to report that a small fire was set in one of its facilities. Social service providers or mental health clinicians may ask for assistance after they learn that a client has engaged in firesetting behaviors. Juvenile justice authorities might remand an offender to a Juvenile Firesetter Intervention (JFI) program as part of the process. Regardless of who makes a referral to the program, the organization conducting the intake process must have a reliable mechanism in place.

Referral to a juvenile firesetter intervention program may originate from several sources. The most common include:

- Fire department officials
- Parents and caregivers

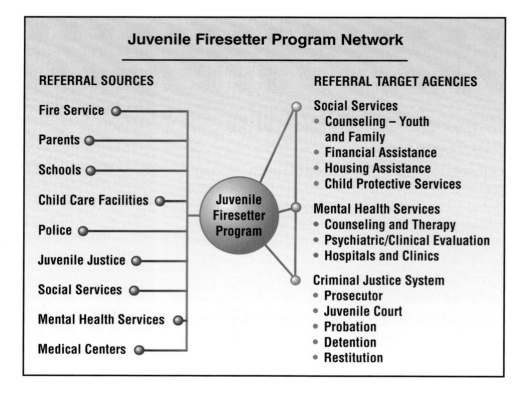

Figure 18.2 Requests for intervention come from many sources.

Juvenile Firesetter Program Network

REFERRAL SOURCES
- Fire Service
- Parents
- Schools
- Child Care Facilities
- Police
- Juvenile Justice
- Social Services
- Mental Health Services
- Medical Centers

Juvenile Firesetter Program

REFERRAL TARGET AGENCIES

Social Services
- Counseling – Youth and Family
- Financial Assistance
- Housing Assistance
- Child Protective Services

Mental Health Services
- Counseling and Therapy
- Psychiatric/Clinical Evaluation
- Hospitals and Clinics

Criminal Justice System
- Prosecutor
- Juvenile Court
- Probation
- Detention
- Restitution

- Law enforcement agencies
- Juvenile justice staff
- Social service providers
- Mental health clinicians
- School officials (teachers, administrators, or behavioral health specialists)

Level II program managers should be proficient at facilitating development of a coalition that will address juvenile firesetting at the local level. The same people or agencies that are likely to report juvenile firesetting are often those best suited to provide intervention services. Formation of a multidisciplinary team represents the best strategy for broad-based mitigation of juvenile firesetting.

Understanding the Intake Process

Intake is the formal process that brings a juvenile into the JFI program. The intake process gathers background information on the juvenile, his or her family, and the event(s) initiating referral to the program. As already explained, referral to a program may be initiated by a variety of sources. All information collected during an intake process is confidential.

The following represents pertinent information to gather during an intake process:

- Identify who is making the referral and why.
- Provide contact information, such as names, address(es), telephone, e-mail, and best contact method and times for the juvenile's family/caregiver so that a reliable communication strategy is established. This is critical when working with at-risk families.
- Identify the juvenile firesetter by name, age, gender, race, nationality, and date of birth.
- Obtain a succinct history of behaviors that precipitate referral of the juvenile to the program. This includes any previous firesetting behaviors and other relevant problematic activities. (**NOTE:** The adult initiating the request for service should be asked for his or her opinion of why the firesetting behavior(s) occurred.)
- Determine the level of intervention (if any) that has already taken place. This includes punishment from parent(s), services from other agencies, or adjudication proceedings.

- Document any special needs of the juvenile and his or her family. Examples include cognitive or behavioral challenges and physical disabilities. Also determine potential family challenges to program attendance, such as transportation issues, shared custody situations, and stability of the home environment.

Gathering an appropriate level of information during the intake process will help interventionists make informed decisions early on about the severity of the situation.

- *Determine what information will be used.* The Level II JFIS is expected to work with the local AHJ and intervention partners to ultimately determine what information will be sought through the intake process. It is also the responsibility of a program manager to secure memorandums of understanding from partner agencies so that case information can be shared contingent to parent or legal guardian approval. More on this topic will be covered in Chapter 23.
- *Immediate reporting.* Certain situations warrant immediate action from the person collecting intake data. Federal law mandates immediate reporting of suspected child abuse or neglect. Local arson laws often require adjudication of juveniles who have damaged property through firesetting activity. Obviously a report of recent and repeat firesetting behaviors signals the need for rapid intervention. The juvenile firesetter intervention program protocol should clearly state what situations require immediate attention and outline expectations of staff members.
- *Rapid and appropriate response.* The rapid and appropriate response to a juvenile firesetting situation will often make the difference between a successful outcome and failure. In certain high-risk situations, the window of opportunity for intervention is often short. This is due, in part, to the sometimes tenuous lifestyles led by many at-risk families. Lack of access to an operational telephone and/or reliable transportation can make long-term connections with high-risk populations a challenge in itself. It is critical to have a thorough and reliable intake system in place so that interventionists may begin mitigation efforts quickly.

Interventionists must be proficient in assembling administrative forms and materials so that an intake process is conducted according to organizational protocol. This applies not only to the Level I interventionist, but anyone who collects intake information.

Depending on organizational determinants, the Level I JFIS may not be the person taking the initial call for service. Administrative staff, station firefighters, or other personnel may serve as a first point of contact. Regardless of who takes the request for service, a system must be in place so that pertinent information is collected by a qualified person and relayed to the JFIS program manager in a timely manner.

If the initial point of contact is not an experienced interventionist, he or she must have baseline understanding of firesetter profiles and how to discern a simple case from that of a complex problematic situation. Staff also must be able to identify which incidents call for immediate attention, such as a crisis situation, abusive environment, or commission of a violent crime. Failure to relay information to interventionists in a timely manner may not only discredit the organization, it may contribute to a lethal delay of intervention services. Every organization with a firesetter intervention program should assign someone to collect initial requests for service and relay pertinent information to the JFIS program manager.

Information collected during the intake phase of a juvenile firesetter intervention case should be maintained in a secure, confidential database. Current and emerging technology simplifies the process. Again, the specifics of how initial contact information will be gathered and the intake process conducted is the responsibility of the Level II JFIS program manager. The Level I interventionist and all approved staff follow the organization's established juvenile firesetter intervention program intake protocol.

Understanding the Interview/Screening Process

The intake process gathers baseline information about the firesetter, his or her family, and the situation that is bringing the juvenile to the intervention program. While the intake process can provide initial insight into the severity of a juvenile firesetter situation, it is not a substitute for the more in-depth process of conducting a comprehensive in-person interview with the firesetter and his or her parents/guardians.

Using a structured interview process allows the interventionist to gain a much broader perspective of why a firesetting situation has occurred. Equally important, it helps the interventionist and inter-

vention team make decisions about the type(s) of intervention needed. The ultimate goal is to create a plan of action that will prevent recidivism (future acts of firesetting) from occurring.

Although agency personnel can be trained to collect intake data, interviewing firesetters and family members should always be conducted by a trained interventionist who uses an approved assessment instrument **(Figure 18.3)**. An assessment instrument helps ensure the following:

- The interview process is conducted in a sequential and organized manner.
- Important demographical information is obtained about the firesetter's family and living environment.
- An in-depth summary of the firesetting event(s) is captured.
- A profile of the cognitive, behavioral, and environmental factors that may have influenced the juvenile's firesetting actions is constructed.

For the benefit of intervention specialists, the United States Fire Administration (USFA) developed two model assessment instruments that can be used as written or adapted to serve local needs. The instruments were developed with professional guidance from nationally recognized juvenile firesetter intervention expert Dr. Ken Fineman.

The first USFA instrument is a screening tool designed to help interventionists succinctly evaluate the severity of a firesetting situation. The instrument features interview components for both adults and juveniles. The second instrument guides the interventionist through a much greater level of evaluation by seeking an in-depth perspective of why firesetting behaviors are occurring. Both tools use a scoring process to determine the level of potential risk for future firesetting behavior.

In addition to USFA's work, several nationally recognized juvenile firesetter intervention coalitions have developed their own instrument(s) after consulting professionals at the local level. Many of the instruments mirror the document designed by Dr. Fineman. The reader is encouraged to network and consult with communities that have experience with the development and use of assessment instruments.

The ultimate aim of an assessment instrument is

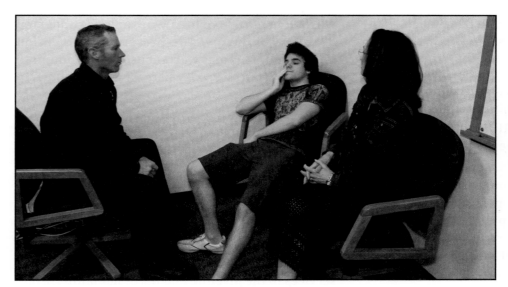

Figure 18.3 A trained interventionist will follow established strategies and collect necessary information for an assessment of the case.

to help the interviewer determine the root cause(s) of firesetting behaviors and gauge the severity of the problem. Only then can a team of trained professionals representing diverse specialties determine a logical course of intervention. (**NOTE:** Comprehensive information on interviewing skills will be covered in Chapter 19.)

Organizing Assessment Tools and Support Materials

In addition to developing a close familiarity with the assessment instruments and their uses and limitations, Level I interventionists must know why, when, and how the following companion documents are used according to program protocol:

- *Participation release form* documents agreement from the parent(s)/legal guardian that the juvenile may participate in the juvenile firesetter intervention program.

- *Release of liability* signifies agreement of parent(s)/guardians that the juvenile firesetter intervention sponsoring agency cannot be held liable should future acts of firesetting (recidivism) be initiated by the juvenile.

- *Release of confidential information* allows the juvenile firesetter intervention program's sponsoring organization to share case information with partner agencies.

- *Risk advisement* clarifies that a juvenile's participation in the juvenile firesetter intervention program is not guaranteed to prevent future acts of firesetting.

Maintaining a Flexible Work Schedule

Information gathered during the intake process can provide interventionists with early insight as to why firesetting behaviors are occurring, family demographics, and special needs that should be considered. This information helps the interventionist estimate the severity of the firesetting situation. High-risk situations often require time-sensitive attention.

Earlier chapters of this manual discussed the need for an educator to maintain a work schedule that is flexible according to need. This is especially true when addressing juvenile firesetting situations. Interventionists should be cognizant of their personal work schedule so interaction with firesetters and their families occurs in a timely manner.

Initiating and maintaining contact with the family of a juvenile firesetter can be a daunting administrative task for the interventionist. To be effective, interventionists must understand that families may have commitments that complicate the scheduling of an in-person interview. This is often the case when working with at-risk families who may already feel overwhelmed with other challenges.

To facilitate preventive action in a timely manner, it may often be the interventionist who must adjust his or her schedule to accommodate the needs of a firesetter's family. While this may be an inconvenience, it may be an action that saves lives by ensuring a family receives intervention when they need it most urgently.

Reporting Case Information

Because Level I interventionists work directly with juvenile firesetters and their families, they are on the frontline of firesetting mitigation. The Level I JFIS collects background information, conducts interviews, facilitates and delivers interventions, and reports results to Level II program managers. These tasks demand competency in both oral and written communication skill.

A Level I interventionist should always follow the organization's protocol for reporting juvenile firesetter case information to superiors. This includes documentation of the intake process, interview/screening, intervention(s), and follow-up evaluation.

Comprehensive written documentation of a juvenile firesetting case is essential for the following reasons:

- A permanent record documenting a level of service that has been provided is established.

- Level II program managers can review the case to ensure organizational protocol has been followed and goals achieved.

- With written permission, practitioners from partner agencies can access a case file to ascertain what actions were taken by the JFIS.

- The interventionist can review a juvenile's case history if long-term follow-up is in order or repeat instances of firesetting occur.

- Courts can summon juvenile firesetter case files as evidence that intervention has been performed to mitigate firesetting behaviors.

In addition to mandating use of intake and interview documents, many juvenile firesetter intervention program protocols call for the interventionist to complete a **written narrative** of actions performed. This narrative, written by the interventionist in third person style, should provide a nonjudgmental overview of the following:

- How and why the juvenile entered the juvenile firesetter intervention program.

- A succinct summary of information gleaned during the interview/screening process. This includes noting root cause(s) of the juvenile's firesetting actions, the profile of firesetting behavior identified using the assessment instrument, and the level of risk for future acts of firesetting (recidivism).

- Interventions and referrals that were recommended and performed. If possible, note the agencies and staff member who provided intervention.

- Documentation of follow-up actions conducted as part of the juvenile firesetter intervention program. This may warrant use of addendums to the narrative in cases where long-term follow-up is required.

NOTE: All the previously listed information should be accompanied by the dates, times, and locations of services provided.

A written narrative can be a vital asset to the juvenile firesetting mitigation process. A good narrative chronicles a timeline of important events (past to present) relevant to the juvenile's firesetting problem. A good narrative is especially helpful in complex firesetting cases as many agencies will likely provide services to the juvenile and his or her family. Upon completion, a written narrative becomes part of the juvenile's case file.

Recording and Securing Data

JFIS interventionists must be proficient at recording and securing juvenile firesetter case information, as defined in the agency's juvenile firesetter intervention program protocol. Recording information is defined as entering juvenile firesetter case information into a collection medium such as a paper-based file or electronic database **(Figure 18.4)**. Doing so preserves the information for future use and statistical analysis. Securing information is defined as using a system of checks to ensure that information is not accessible to unauthorized individuals and helps protect files from being destroyed or used in an inappropriate manner.

Recording Juvenile Firesetter Case Information

Juvenile firesetter case information is the data obtained during the intake, interview, and intervention phases of firesetting intervention. The juvenile's identity and other demographical information such as where, when, how, and why a fire incident occurred is often gathered as part of an official case file.

Recording this information is important for several reasons. First and foremost, the information needs to be easily retrievable for follow-up purposes. This is especially important in problematic firesetting cases where long-term follow-up and referrals to other agencies will be conducted. It is often required by law in cases that are adjudicated by a justice agency.

Figure 18.4 Case information should be stored in an organized and secure file system for future use and statistical analysis.

A second and equally important reason is so that statistical analysis can be conducted to examine and monitor the community's local juvenile firesetter problem. Once a mitigation strategy is developed, data can be used to evaluate the development, delivery, outreach, impact, and outcome of a program.

Chapters 6, 11, and 16 contain extensive information on why, when, and how to evaluate risk-reduction programs. Because all risk-reduction programs should be evaluated, the reader should consider reviewing these chapters. The following levels of evaluation are discussed in these chapters: process, impact, and outcome.

- *Process evaluation* is program monitoring. It is used to track program development, delivery, and outreach.

- *Impact evaluation* examines changes in knowledge levels, behaviors, and living environments.

- *Outcome evaluation* monitors long-term changes in the occurrence of juvenile firesetting incidents within a community. It is also used to track recidivism rates.

The continuous recording of data collected during firesetting mitigation efforts can establish an information base for ongoing statistical analysis. This information can be used by program managers to build profiles of the following:

- Demographics of where, when, how, and why firesetting incidents are occurring

- Age, gender, ethnicity, and special needs of firesetters

- If firesetters received previous fire safety education and from what source

- Types of firesetting cases being handled (curiosity-motivated vs. problematic situations)

- Factors that influence the occurrence of firesetting

- Intervention strategies, referrals, and follow-up services provided by the agency

- Overall disposition of the firesetting case

Having reliable and objective information is essential to developing a juvenile firesetter intervention program that produces a positive long-term outcome. This information gives program managers and team members insight into the scope of the local problem. Good information can also identify program successes and challenges. This information can then be used to help justify resources for future enhancements.

Intake, interviews, and intervention are key components of firesetting mitigation. The long-term success of a juvenile firesetter intervention program demands analysis of program effectiveness and shortcomings. That analysis cannot take place unless information is collected and processed.

While the Level II program manager will choose or design a data collection system, all interventionists are expected to be proficient in data entry. Information to be entered will likely come from intake, interview, and intervention forms that are included in a juvenile's case file. The program manager or juvenile firesetter intervention program coalition will ultimately decide what information is to be collected and entered and how it will be analyzed.

Securing Information

Protecting the private and sensitive information included in a juvenile firesetter's case file is the responsibility of all interventionists. It is also the law, and this applies to all communication media, including conversations.

The **Health Insurance Portability and Accountability Act (HIPAA)** was passed by Congress in 1996. This law was established to help ensure the portability of insurance coverage as employees moved from job to job. In addition to improving efficiency of the health care payment process, it also helps protect a patient's privacy.

Doctors, nurses, pharmacies, hospitals, clinics, nursing homes, and other health care providers are required to follow the HIPAA law. The law also applies to health insurance companies, HMOs, employer group health plans, and government programs that pay for health care such as Medicare or Medicaid. It also applies to information pertinent to a juvenile firesetting situation. Penalties for violating the HIPAA law are severe.

In addition to the need to comply with the privacy guidelines outlined in HIPAA, the following are several other reasons why juvenile firesetter case information must remain private and secure:

- Information on minors is required by several laws to remain confidential and secure.

- Confidentiality promotes a professional, respectful, and ethical environment.

- Unauthorized sharing of information may compromise a current or future criminal investigation.

- Unauthorized sharing of information may influence current or future civil claims and judgments.

Maintaining a Secure Environment

Maintaining a secure environment becomes important when records may be summoned as part of legal proceedings. Law enforcement personnel, such as police officers and fire marshals, are required to maintain copies of written field notes as part of case files. Juvenile firesetter intervention programs should keep a secure paper-based and electronic storage medium **(Figure 18.5)**. Paper-based documents should be kept in a secure filing area that remains locked at all times. Electronic-based information should be pass-code protected. Verbal information exchanges between interventionists discussing a case should be held in private.

Whether paper or electronic-based, all case information should be saved with a duplicate copy maintained at an alternate secure storage area. This action ensures that case files are preserved.

Figure 18.5 Paper-based and electronic files should both have security features enabled.

Every organization with a firesetter intervention program should assign someone to be ultimately responsible for making sure that case files are maintained, duplicated, (backed up), and secure. While a Level I JFIS may be responsible for entering and securing information on cases assigned to them, the program manager is ultimately responsible for ensuring an overall secure environment.

Legal Permissions

During the intake process, it is prudent to obtain written permission from the juvenile's parent/legal guardians to share confidential case information with agencies that are part of a local juvenile firesetter intervention team. The permission-granting document should state that all information will be maintained in a secure environment and shared only with partnering agencies as needed.

Securing this document early in the process may save valuable time should referral to another partner agency be needed. This document should be included as part of the confidential and secure case file.

NOTE: The specifics of how initial contact information will be gathered and the intake process conducted is the responsibility of the Level II program manager. The Level I interventionist and those approved to receive calls for service must follow the organization's established intake protocol.

Chapter Summary

While performing administrative duties may not be as stimulating as working directly with a juvenile or family, these tasks build a foundation that keeps a firesetting mitigation process on track. Mastering these tasks will help the JFIS reach a successful outcome. Chapter 19 will focus on the education and implementation skills required of the Level I JFIS.

Review Questions

1. Why should the intervention of juvenile firesetters follow an organized process?

2. Why is it important to adhere to established protocols governing the administration of a juvenile firesetter intervention program?

3. What are the general duties of a Level I Juvenile Firesetter Intervention Specialist?

4. Why are communication skills important to the JFIS I interventionist?

Key Terms

Health Insurance Portability and Accountability Act (HIPAA) — A congressional law established to help ensure the portability of insurance coverage as employees move from job to job. In addition to improving efficiency of the health care payment process, it also helps protect a patient's/client's privacy. The law also applies to information pertinent to juvenile firesetting situations.

Organizational Protocol — Rules set by the JFIS organization or JFS coalition that guide how a juvenile firesetting intervention program will be administered.

Written Narrative — Chronicles a timeline of important events (past to present) relevant to the juvenile's firesetting problem. The narrative includes events that brought the juvenile into the program, a profile of the firesetting problem, intervention(s) performed, and referrals made.

Chapter 18 Notes

Public Fire Education Planning – A Five Step Process.

Federal Emergency Management Agency. August, 2002.

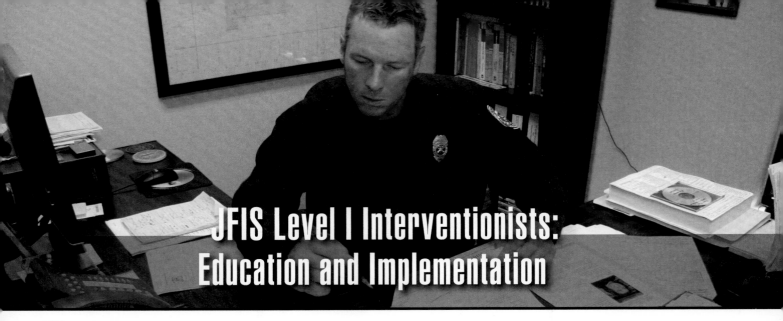

JFIS Level I Interventionists: Education and Implementation

Chapter Contents

Key Terms

Job Performance Requirements

This chapter provides information that addresses the following job performance requirements of NFPA®
1035, *Standard for Professional Qualifications for Fire and Life Safety Educator, Public Information
Officer, and Juvenile Firesetter Intervention Specialist*, 2010 edition.

NFPA® 1035 References

9.4.1

9.4.2

9.4.3

9.4.4

9.4.5

JFIS Level I Interventionists: Education and Implementation

Learning Objectives

After reading this chapter, students will be able to:

1. Explain how to follow a consistent intake process so basic information about the child/youth, family, and firesetting incident is obtained.

2. Explain how to explore a case file so background information is reviewed prior to initiating contact with a juvenile's family (NFPA® 1035, 9.4.1).

3. Describe the process of communicating with a juvenile's family so program benefits/options are explained and an in-person interview is scheduled (NFPA® 1035, 9.4.2).

4. Discuss and demonstrate how to interview juveniles/family members so information pertinent to a firesetting situation is obtained, recorded, and evaluated (NFPA® 1035, 9.4.3).

5. Summarize how to select methods of intervention for firesetting behaviors based on information obtained through use of an approved risk assessment process (NFPA® 1035, 9.4.4).

6. Overview how to implement interventions for firesetting behaviors (NFPA® 1035, 9.4.5).

7. Outline how to facilitate accountability from juveniles/families who are receiving intervention services.

Chapter 19
JFIS Level I Interventionists: Education and Implementation

Case History

As the Juvenile Firesetter Intervention Specialist Program Manager, Janet received a phone call from a social worker named Judy in 2007. Judy said that one of the children in the local Head Start Program was having an issue with setting fires. She stated that 4-year-old Victor, DOB 4/19/02, had lit his hair on fire on 3/14/07. On 3/15/07, she visited Victor's residence and discovered that Victor had also set several fires to his home, his sister's stuffed animals, and two cats, one of which was killed. He'd also punched holes in walls, hid a butcher's knife in his room, and choked himself with a rope.

Victor's parents were at their wits' end because one of them had to stay up at night to keep the family safe from Victor's dangerous behavior. They had contacted Child Protective Services and had been told to lock him in his bedroom at night. When they did this, Victor broke the lock and escaped. Hearing about this behavior, Judy contacted Janet to see if she could find help for the firesetting behavior.

Based on the fact that Victor appeared to be a danger to himself and others, Janet contacted the program manager of the Fire Department's Community Assistance Program (CAP) and related the information from Judy. After some discussion, the CAP Program Manager and Janet arranged to meet Judy at Victor's residence where they met with Victor and his mother, father, and 3-year-old sister.

Janet was tasked with interviewing Victor. When asked to talk about his fires, Victor stated in a flurry of conversation that he lit his hair on fire because, "I didn't know what it was like to be killed." He'd also stabbed his sister in the back because, "I didn't know if she would be killed." He talked about killing both of his cats. Then, he showed Janet where he'd set numerous fires around his residence. In the course of the interview, he also grabbed and broke her fire department identification badge, pushed his sister, and ran around on the furniture while screaming.

Meanwhile, a member of the CAP team was interviewing Victor's mother, who said that a state mental health crisis van had responded to their residence during the evening hours of 3/15/07 after being contacted by Judy. Victor's mother stated that the crisis van took them to a local hospital so

continued on page 436

Case History (Concluded)

Victor could be evaluated. However, after approximately 7 hours at the hospital, the hospital staff said that Victor did not meet the criteria for hospital admittance, and they were sent home. After further investigation into Victor's visit to the hospital, it was found that he was actually taken to the hospital's urgent care and was never psychologically evaluated.

After completing the interview and risk screening with Victor and his parents, it was determined that Victor was an extreme risk for future firesetting and was also deemed to be at great risk for harming himself and others. Because of Victor's young age, the team spent six hours attempting to locate a hospital or mental health facility that would accept Victor. Finally the city's children's hospital agreed to accept Victor and evaluate him. In this case, it was not appropriate or acceptable to provide a juvenile firesetter educational intervention prior to Victor obtaining mental and behavioral health assistance.

Source: Dr. Janet A Boberg, LPC, NCC, Public Education Coordinator, Glendale Fire Department, Glendale, Arizona.

While a JFIS interventionist is tasked with working with health and safety professionals, the interventionist is not a mental health professional. He or she is a specially trained practitioner who collects background information on the firesetting situation, evaluates its severity, and after consultation with a team of professionals, suggests solutions to prevent acts of recidivism **(Figure 19.1)**.

Intake Process and Documentation

The intake phase is a key initial step in the mitigation process. During an intake process, trained staff members collect initial comprehensive background information from a parent, legal guardian, or partnering agency about the incident(s) that brought the juvenile to the program.

The intake information should include a summary of the following:

- Who or what agency is referring the juvenile to the juvenile firesetter intervention program
- Juvenile's history of firesetting behavior
- Cognitive and educational level
- Emotional, social, and physical challenges
- Profile of the juvenile's family structure and living arrangements
- Contact information for parents/legal guardians

Collecting intake information begins the formal process of initiating a juvenile's involvement in an intervention program **(Figure 19.2)**. Once a juvenile firesetter is identified, intervention services should begin quickly. A rapid and well-organized response helps reduce gaps in service that may occur when several agencies must become involved. It also enables the juvenile firesetter intervention specialist (JFIS) to quickly react to situations so that immediate primary prevention activities can occur such as isolating ignition materials and ensuring the presence of working smoke alarm protection. Finally, it creates a mechanism to document that an incident has occurred, who is involved, and what mitigation actions are planned.

Documenting each phase of activity creates an official record of services provided. This becomes especially important should a parent/guardian fail to keep mandated appointments or withdraw a juvenile from the program against professional advice. Information collected during the intake phase of a juvenile firesetting intervention is forwarded to the JFIS II Program Manager and should be secured in a confidential database or paper-based filing system. After reviewing information collected during the intake process, the Level II program manager assigns the case to a Level I interventionist.

Figure 19.1 The interventionist works with a team of professionals to suggest solutions for a community's juvenile firesetting problem. *Courtesy of Chris Mickal, New Orleans (LA) Fire Department.*

In addition to creating an official record of service, documenting and tracking juvenile firesetter case information provides data that can be analyzed to determine the motivations behind acts of firesetting. This information is not only vital to each specific incident, but also to Level II program managers who review case information when considering future program strategies and enhancements.

Reviewing a Juvenile Firesetter Case File

A juvenile firesetter **case file** is an official record that documents, in chronological order, pertinent facts surrounding the juvenile's firesetting history (**Figure 19.3**). It includes personal information that identifies the juvenile, a profile of his or her family structure, and any special needs or circumstances relevant to the situation. If a fire department provided suppression services or conducted an investigation, an official incident report may be included. It summarizes levels of preventive interventions that have been provided by service professionals and the results of any follow-up evaluations.

A well-developed case file is a tremendous asset to the interventionist as it provides a clear summary of what has happened, why, and what intervention strategies have taken place. The file can be used (with written permission from the juvenile's parent or legal guardian) by partnering agencies working

Figure 19.2 Intake information is used to determine the next step in a formal intervention program. *Courtesy of Chris Mickal, New Orleans (LA) Fire Department.*

in tandem to provide services to a juvenile and his or her family. It may also be summoned to legal proceedings when a case is being adjudicated. All information contained in a juvenile firesetter's case file is confidential and must remain secure.

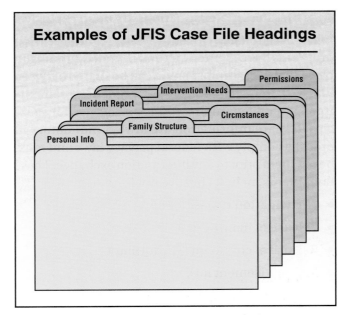

Figure 19.3 A JFIS case file contains personal information about the juvenile's firesetting history.

Collecting information that will be included in a case file begins during the intake process. A trained agency staff member obtains the information and forwards it to a Level II program manager for review and possible referral to partner agencies. Often, the program manager will assign the case to an interventionist for processing. Once a juvenile firesetter interventionist assumes responsibility for a case, it is his or her duty to review all information contained in the file, initiate contact with the juvenile's parent/legal guardian, and begin firesetting mitigation services. The interventionist is also responsible for documenting additional significant information as it is discovered and recording levels of service initiated.

When the interventionist's agency is the first to initiate services for a family (such as in the instance of a first-time incident that is curiosity motivated), a juvenile's case file may not be extensive. At a minimum, an initial case file should include all information that has been obtained during the intake process. The intake process should present the interventionist with an initial foundation of knowledge about the juvenile, his or her firesetting history, family profile, and other pertinent facts.

In complex and problematic situations, a partnering agency may refer a juvenile to receive educational intervention through the juvenile firesetter intervention program. If so, a case file from the partnering agency should accompany the referral. This allows the interventionist to become familiar with the situation before initiating contact with the juvenile's family. Case files in complex situations are often extensive.

It is essential that juvenile firesetter intervention programs have memorandums of understanding in place so that case information can be shared between interventionists and agencies. Signed agreements from parents/guardians giving permission for agencies to share information are always mandatory in order to comply with federal privacy laws and must be obtained prior to any information exchange. These documents include, but are not limited to:

- Participation release form
- Release of liability
- Release of confidential information
- Risk advisement form

Creating these documents and ensuring interagency use is the responsibility of a Level II program manager and will be discussed further in Chapter 23.

The initial review of a juvenile firesetter case file for most first-time curiosity-motivated incidents will usually not be a lengthy process. Complex situations are often more time-consuming because of the amount of information in the file. Regardless of the type of situation being addressed, the interventionist must analyze the background information before making contact with the juvenile's family or legal guardian.

In addition to learning about the juvenile, the interventionist should consider the demographics of the firesetter's family. Having knowledge of who is responsible for the juvenile, his or her intellectual capabilities, potential challenges to communication, and social influences empower the interventionist with information that can be used to facilitate a more effective intervention process.

Making Initial Contact with Parents or Guardians

After reviewing an assigned case file, the next step for the interventionist is contacting the juvenile's parent/guardian to offer mitigation services. The goal is to secure a cooperative relationship with parents so that intervention strategies can be selected and begin quickly. This is a very important task because if contact is not made or services are refused, no interventions will take place.

Because he or she will interact with diverse populations who possess varying ranges of intellectual abilities and cultural influences, the interventionist must be a skilled communicator. He or she must be able to explain the benefits of enrolling a juvenile into the program, the ways in which confidential information will be protected, intervention options, and the level of parental support that is expected.

The interventionist should budget 15 to 30 minutes of uninterrupted time when attempting to contact the parent or guardian. If planning to converse via telephone, it is important to have a quiet and secure environment on both sides. Before initiating contact, it is necessary to have all information collection mediums in place.

Contact information for the juvenile's parents or legal guardian should have been provided as part of the case file. If an intake process has already occurred, the parents or guardian should expect contact from the interventionist. It is always important to adhere to the suggested contact method, time, and location.

Use of Terminology

The terms *parent*, *legal guardian*, and *caregiver* appear frequently in the JFIS chapters of this manual and warrant clarification. In most cases, a juvenile's parent(s) have legal custody of their children. However, certain circumstances (usually surrounding a safety issue) warrant removal of a child from the custody of one or both parents. In these situations, a foster parent or member of the child's extended family may be given legal custody of the juvenile and become the legal guardian. In contrast, a caregiver is defined as a person who provides services, such as temporary periods of supervision, living accommodations, and transportation, to a juvenile. An example of a caregiver may be a grandparent who cares for his or her grandchild but does not have legal custody.

What This Means to You

Initiating contact with a juvenile's parent(s)/guardian may sound easy, but it can sometimes be a challenging process. Many juvenile firesetters reside in households where there is no reliable contact medium (such as an operational telephone or Internet access). In some instances, the parents of firesetters must be contacted in person. If face-to-face contact is necessary, you should consider working with a team member.

Address high-risk situations within 48 hours as the parents' contact medium may change or become unavailable. This strategy ensures a rapid screening of high-risk situations and initiates a timely intervention process.

You may have to keep your schedule flexible when working with high-risk populations. Evening or weekend assignments are often required and should be accommodated.

To facilitate family-interventionist communication, you should maintain multiple contact utilities such as an office phone (with message recording/retrieving capabilities), a cellular phone, and e-mail access. The JFIS team should also provide a mechanism so that families have 24-hour access to an interventionist should further firesetting instances develop.

Due to the confidential nature of juvenile firesetter information, when contact is made with the family member or guardian, the interventionist should confirm that it is a convenient time to exchange information. Juvenile firesetting situations are often a stressful and sometimes embarrassing event for a parent. A parent may be reluctant to discuss details of the situation or hesitant to talk in the presence of other family members. In addition, busy schedules or stressful home environments can create distractions that interrupt information sharing.

When contact is made, the interventionist should introduce him- or herself and explain that the conversation may take 15 to 30 minutes. The parent should be informed that the discussion will focus on explaining the juvenile firesetter intervention program and potential intervention options. If the interventionist is told by the parent that it is not a good time to talk, he or she should attempt to reschedule and possibly relocate the interview.

Once a parent or guardian commits to discussing the firesetting situation, the interventionist proceeds with an in-depth explanation of the juvenile firesetter intervention program. The interventionist should provide a self-introduction that includes his or her position in the organization, education and training levels, and experience working with juvenile firesetting cases. Entry-level interventionists may wish to consider using an outline to help ensure that an appropriate self-introduction and explanation of the program occurs.

After explaining his or her qualifications, the interventionist should provide a detailed explanation of the agency's juvenile firesetter intervention program. At a minimum, the following information should be included:

- *Explanation of why the juvenile firesetter intervention program exists.* Provide a summary of the local juvenile firesetter problem. Parents are often more willing to accept intervention services when they discover that their child is not the only one who has ever started a fire. The interventionist should cite nationally recognized research from the United States Fire Administration.

- *History of juvenile firesetter intervention program.* Explain when the program was created and how many juveniles and families have been served to date. If applicable, cite recidivism rates that occur among program attendees.

- *Who qualifies for the program.* Provide a summary of the types of firesetting behaviors that the agency's program is designed to address.

- *How evaluation of juvenile firesetter behaviors is accomplished.* Provide an explanation of how the root factors of firesetting behaviors are identified. If the program uses an interview and screening process, provide a brief overview of how it is performed.

- *Levels of intervention that are offered through the program.* Clarify that education is used as a core intervention strategy. Explain the other levels of intervention such as clinical support and punitive actions that are often used in tandem with education.

- *How intervention strategies are determined and by whom.* Explain how the interventionist determines appropriate intervention strategies. Identify the partner agencies that are (or may become) involved with the juvenile firesetter case and why. Articulate the goal of involving parents in the decision-making process.

- *Where intervention services are provided and by whom.* Provide an overview of where all components of the juvenile firesetter intervention program will be administered and who may be performing services.

- *How the juvenile's progress will be evaluated.* Clarify the importance of short- and long-term program evaluation. Provide a summary of where and how evaluation of a juvenile's progress will occur.

- *Level of participation required from the juvenile.* Provide a synopsis of what the juvenile will be required to do if he or she is enrolled in the juvenile firesetter intervention program. Offer an estimated amount of time the juvenile will need to commit to the program and activities that will be completed.

- *Levels of support expected from parents.* Summarize the level of involvement that will be needed (and expected) from parents whose child is participating in the program.

While explaining the program, the interventionist should answer any questions the parent or guardian may have about the program. The interventionist should be aware of the cognitive abilities of parents, use appropriate language, and allow adequate time for information to be exchanged and assimilated. The interventionist should not make promises that he or she cannot honor.

After presenting an overview of the program, the interventionist should ask the parent/guardian for permission to enroll his or her child into the program. If an affirmative response is obtained, the interventionist should collect any additional information about the juvenile and family that is required by the agency. If the parent or guardian does not want to enroll his or her child in the program, the interventionist should document the response and offer the parent time to reconsider the offer.

NOTE: If the primary role of the interventionist is to offer education as an intervention strategy, discussion needs to take place regarding the legal ramifications of juvenile firesetter behaviors. If information is discovered that implicates a juvenile in criminal activity, a JFIS I may be required by the AHJ to notify appropriate authorities. While the interventionist should be empathetic toward all situations, he or she must follow all local laws and program guidelines.

Making Secondary Contact with Parents or Guardians: Arranging the Face-to-Face Interview

The interventionist's next task is to arrange an in-person meeting with parents and the juvenile. The parent should be informed that the goal of meeting will be to identify why firesetting behaviors are occurring and how they can be stopped. The JFIS I should also explain that as part of the meeting, he or she would like to interview the parents and juvenile so that more information can be discovered about the firesetting situation. (**NOTE:** In cases where referral is coming from a partner agency, the interview process may or may not have already occurred.)

If the interventionist's agency uses a structured interview procedure to assess firesetting behaviors, explain how the process is accomplished. If an **assessment instrument** is used, explain its purpose. Articulate that the use of a structured interview and screening process is a proven way to identify the root causes of firesetting. Only after root causation has been identified can intervention strategies be recommended. Using a structured interview process and approved assessment instrument is highly recommended.

Being asked to participate in a comprehensive interview can generate anxiety and denial from parents who fear that potentially embarrassing information about their family may be disclosed. They may also be experiencing guilt regarding their child's behavior and their inability to change this behavior through ordinary discipline and guidance. The interventionist can help relieve this apprehension by exhibiting an empathetic demeanor and ensuring that a secure and professional process will be followed **(Figure 19.4)**.

While a parental interview can be conducted via telephone, an in-person meeting is highly recommended. Observing the behavioral dynamics among family members can provide a wealth of insight into factors that may be contributing to a dysfunctional situation. Observing the body language of people being interviewed can provide indicators if a person is providing truthful information.

The decision where to conduct an interview should be decided by the intervention program's coalition and outlined through organizational protocol. Some agencies' standard operating guidelines require interviews to be conducted at the interventionist's office. Larger departments may use the neighborhood firehouse **(Table 19.1, p. 442)**. Still other protocols offer interventionists the option of conducting interviews at the juvenile's residence. Whatever the organization's policy may be, it should be created as part of the program's initial development process and followed by all interventionists.

In cases where protocol is flexible about interview locations, the decision of where to conduct interviews is made by the interventionist after considering several factors. Observing a family in their home environment can provide insight into why firesetting behaviors may be occurring. If a home visit is chosen, consider taking another interventionist along. Many agencies require that home visits be conducted by two interventionists **(Table 19.2, p. 442)**. However, if any doubts exist about the safety of conducting a home visitation, the interventionist should arrange for the meeting to take place at a secure location.

Once a location for the interview is established, a time and date should be selected that is agreeable to all parties. The interventionist should explain to the parent that prompt initiation of the interview will help streamline the screening and intervention process, which often correlates with successful outcomes. The JFIS team should also offer services that fit the needs of busy or stressed families.

Figure 19.4 An interventionist can help parents through the process of intervention by exhibiting empathy and professionalism.

Interviewing Juveniles and their Parents or Guardians

Upon securing cooperation from parents, the next step in the mitigation process is to identify and understand why a juvenile is starting fires. A structured interview process that uses an approved assessment instrument is the recommended strategy to accomplish this goal. An interventionist must be proficient at gathering relevant facts, evaluating information, summarizing findings, and recording data to support the process.

Interviewing the juvenile and his or her parent(s)/guardian is a statistically proven way to identify the root factors associated with firesetting behaviors. It allows the interventionist to develop a fact-based profile of the firesetting situation, screen for specific needs, and consider intervention strategies.

Who Conducts an Interview and Screening Process?

While intake information may sometimes be collected by a trained staff member who is not a formal JFIS team member, an interview process is *always* conducted by a trained interventionist approved

Table 19.1
Potential Benefits and Challenges of Office/Firehouse Interviews

Potential Benefits of Office / Firehouse Interview	Potential Challenges of Office / Firehouse Interview
Potential facilitation and control of a distraction-limited interview environment.	Potential environmental distractions such as office noise, FD radios, incident dispatches, presence of emergency equipment and staff.
Clean, safe environment that includes the presence of witnesses.	Potential lack of transportation to location outside of the home. Practitioner does not experience the "real" living environment of the juvenile / family.
Easier access to educational and other support tools.	Juvenile could potentially perceive the visit to a fire station as a reward to firesetting behavior.
Visual "authority" of a firehouse or FD headquarters.	Juvenile and / or family may find an office or firehouse environment intimidating.

Table 19.2
Potential Benefits and Challenges of Home Interviews

Potential Benefits of Home Interview	Potential Challenges of Home Interview
Can provide the interviewer with a better picture of the "real" home environment.	Overall safety of the practitioner. Potential legal concerns if left alone with parent or juvenile.
Practitioner can provide an in-person home-safety inspection and help facilitate environmental modifications.	Potential chaotic family living environment.
Family does not have to worry about transportation issues.	Potential environmental distractions such as the presence of toddlers and other children.
Family is relaxed and comfortable in familiar surroundings.	Practitioner may not have control over interview environment.

by the local authority having jurisdiction (AHJ). To gain this approval, an interventionist must be aware of the features and limitations of his or her agency's juvenile firesetter intervention program and have strong interviewing skills. These abilities are developed through a combination of education, mentoring from experienced interviewers, and practice. The United States Fire Administration and several other credible sources have published information to help the interventionist become a proficient interviewer.

Why Use an Approved Assessment Instrument?
The success of a juvenile firesetter intervention program depends on its ability to accurately assess each specific firesetting situation. Use of a structured interview process (with approved assessment instrument) represents the most effective way to develop a profile of why a juvenile is starting fires and the risk level for repeat behaviors. Information discovered during an interview can also be used to help make decisions about potential intervention strategies.

A good assessment instrument will help the interventionist obtain and evaluate the following information:

- An overview of the most recent firesetting incident
- History of previous firesetting behaviors
- Motives behind the firesetting events
- Rewards that the juvenile obtains from starting fires
- Family demographics and current living arrangements
- Relationships with family members and peers
- Recent changes in family demographics
- Presence or absence of support systems
- Recent potentially stressful events
- Chronic stressful situations
- Potential social and cultural influences
- Criminal history (if applicable)
- School information
- Level of cognitive function
- Health history (including mental health interventions and medications)
- Special needs of the juvenile and/or his or her family

As noted in Chapter 17, many nationally recognized professionals have invested great effort into developing valid JFIS assessment instruments. For nearly three decades, Dr. Kenneth Fineman has been a catalyst behind the development of tools to help the frontline JFIS I identify why a juvenile is setting fires and his or her risk of repeat behaviors. These instruments, validated by mental health clinicians, use a scoring process to determine levels of risk for repeat behaviors.

Several versions of the instruments developed by Dr. Fineman and his colleagues have been published through the United States Fire Administration. Workshops on the instrument's use have been conducted nationwide. Many communities, with help from qualified local professionals, have adapted or enhanced the tools to fit their specific program's needs. Other juvenile firesetter intervention coalitions have worked with local experts to develop their own assessment instruments.

While this manual cannot suggest use of one instrument over another, it strongly advocates use of a valid assessment instrument to help develop a profile of the firesetting behavior being exhibited. A good assessment instrument will prompt the interviewer to ask questions which will generate responses that can be objectively evaluated through a scoring process. Through this scoring process, a profile of the firesetting situation is created, special circumstances and needs are identified, and the risk probability for potential repeat behaviors noted.

The Comprehensive FireRisk Assessment

Most assessment instruments categorize risk for future episodes of firesetting into three subsets. The Comprehensive FireRisk Assessment, developed for the United States Fire Administration by a team of nationally recognized experts, defines the risk profiles as Low, Definite, and Extreme. These profiles are identified after an interventionist collects information relevant to the following categories:

- Juvenile's health history
- Family structure and possible points of concern
- Peer relationships
- School issues
- Behavior problems
- Fire history
- Recent crisis or trauma
- Characteristics of the firesetting situation
- Personal observations

Juveniles that are identified as being at low risk for starting another fire are usually first-time curiosity-motivated fire starters. According to national studies, a comprehensive fire safety education program is usually very effective at addressing the low-risk firesetting situation.

Those rated at definite risk may be juveniles who have set several curiosity-motivated or peer-influenced fires. Children who have set a single fire after experiencing a moderate level of personal stress are often placed into this category as well. A combination of education, counseling, and sometimes punitive actions are often recommended for this level of firesetting behavior. Final decisions on interventions are made based on the juvenile's age, extent of damage or loss, motivation, and intent **(Figure 19.5, p. 444)**.

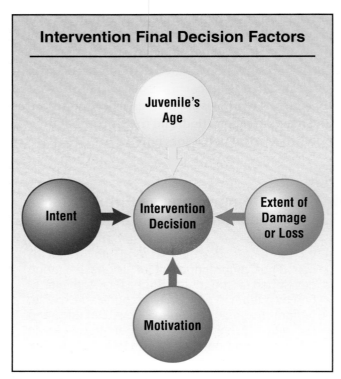

Intervention Final Decision Factors

Juvenile's Age

Intent → Intervention Decision ← Extent of Damage or Loss

Motivation

Figure 19.5 Interventions are decided based on several factors.

The extreme-risk category is reserved for juveniles whose profile indicates he or she will most likely start another fire and shows evidence of various degrees of psycho-pathology within the family. Juveniles who have exhibited several anti-social acts such as aggression toward peers, poor relationships with others, severe obstinacy, and repeated violations of the law are often placed into this extreme-risk category. Juveniles identified as extreme-risk need prompt evaluation from a qualified mental health clinician. In addition, these youth often benefit from an adjudication process that requires placement into a structured learning and living environment.

In 1998, the USFA, in cooperation with Dr. Fineman, the Colorado Department of Public Safety/Division of Fire Safety, and the Colorado Juvenile Firesetter Prevention Program Staff, also published a *Juvenile Firesetter Child and Family Risk Survey (Short Form)*. Like the Comprehensive FireRisk Assessment, the Risk Survey features both a parent and child assessment instrument.

The tool uses a scoring process for evaluation but is shorter and takes less time to administer than the comprehensive evaluation. Questions on the Risk Survey were derived from the Comprehensive FireRisk Assessment. The Risk Survey is intended for use only as a *preliminary* screening tool to assess suitability for fire safety education or mental health program referral. In complex problematic cases, use of the Comprehensive FireRisk Evaluation is recommended. The reader is encouraged to obtain a copy of the Juvenile Firesetter Intervention Handbook published by the United States Fire Administration.[1]

Preparing for the Interview Process

Adequate preparation of the interview site helps facilitate an environment that encourages meaningful communication. If a juvenile, his or her family, or caregivers feel uncomfortable, distracted, or intimidated, an open exchange of information is unlikely to occur. A pre-interview goal for the interventionist should be to create a secure, distraction-free, nonthreatening environment conducive to information sharing.

As previously discussed, the interventionist ultimately decides where the interview and screening process will be conducted. Choices include, but are not limited to, the interventionist's office, neighborhood firehouse, or juvenile's home. The JFIS I may consider a combination of locations if more than one interview session takes place. Regardless of the interview's location, advance planning by the interventionist is needed to help create an appropriate environment. Interventionists should always follow their organization's protocol of how and where interviews are to be conducted.

If the interview is conducted at the interventionist's office or firehouse, it should occur in a quiet, secure area that assures privacy. All electronic communication mediums, telephones, and departmental radios should be silenced. If meeting at the home of the juvenile, enlist the help of parents to secure a similar environment. If the family has other children, the interventionist may wish to ask parents in advance of the meeting to plan for some sort of child care arrangement.

When communicating with parents and juveniles, the JFIS I should always use easy-to-comprehend, nontechnical language. Allow time for information to be received and processed. Check for understanding, encourage questions, and proceed incrementally with additional information. Chapters 5 and 10 provided detailed information about strategies for creating effective learning environments.

Creating an Information-Sharing Environment

While all populations profit from structured learning and information-sharing environments, those with special cognitive needs receive the greatest benefit. If a person does not adequately receive and process information, no meaningful exchanges will occur. Distractions such as people talking, telephones ringing, emergency scanners chattering, or even the sight of fire apparatus can easily divert any person's attention. This type of stimuli can severely affect those who have difficulty maintaining focused attention. Take time in advance of the interview to learn about and address any special needs the juvenile and his or her family may have.

Creating an environment conducive to information sharing also requires knowledge of how people receive and process information. Understanding the stages of intellectual development, learning theory, and age-appropriate communication strategies are essential requisite skills for a JFIS I.

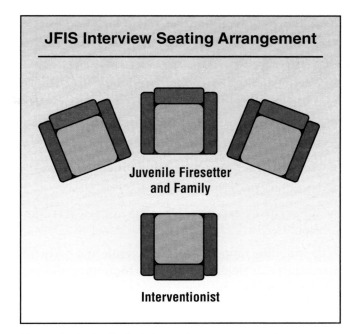

Figure 19.6 The half-circle seating arrangement encourages participation and allows the interventionist to observe body language.

Regardless of where an interview takes place, seating arrangements should be considered carefully. If possible, a half circle seating arrangement is preferred with no barriers (like a desk or table). This invites open participation and presents a less authoritative environment. It also allows the JFIS I to observe body language of the juvenile and his or her parents **(Figure 19.6)**.

When preparing for an interview, the JFIS I should consider his or her personal demeanor or style. While an interventionist's demeanor must sometimes be firm, exhibiting overly authoritative behavior may create an adversarial relationship with a family. Interventionists most successful at identifying the root causation of firesetting behaviors are those who exhibit an honest concern for the family they are assisting. Remember — the interview/screening process is an information gathering activity, NOT the interrogation of a criminal.

In addition to learning the circumstances surrounding the juvenile firesetter case, the interventionist should be mentally prepared to conduct the interview. Many experienced interventionists report that a short period of relaxation prior to the start of an interview helps them develop the focus needed

to conduct a thorough screening process. The JFIS I should also budget enough time so the process is not hurried: budget a minimum of two hours for the interview process.

When the interview's location and environment is controlled by the JFIS I, he or she should prepare the area well in advance of arriving parents. Rearrange the seating in the area selected for the interview if needed. If visiting the juvenile's home, always arrive on time.

The type of clothing worn by the JFIS I to an interview should be determined by his or her organization. Some organizations mandate the wearing of uniforms while others allow flexibility to suit the needs of each situation. Regardless of dress code protocol, the interventionist should exhibit a professional appearance. There is never a second chance to make an appropriate first impression.

Providing a Personal Introduction and Gaining Rapport

When meeting in-person with a family for the first time, always provide an appropriate personal introduction in a nonthreatening, age-appropriate manner so that all family members learn the following information:

- How the interventionist would like to be addressed (Example – "You can call me Firefighter Mike", "Officer Smith", etc.)

- Agency being represented and departmental ID if applicable or required

- Experience as a JFIS I; duties performed

- Purpose and goals of the meeting

- How the interview/screening process will work

- How long the process will take

- What can be expected after the interview is complete

Developing rapport with the juvenile and his or her parents is a critical part of the introduction process. Some juveniles and their parents will be anxious when meeting a JFIS I in person for the first time. This may be especially true when a child is facing criminal charges related to his or her firesetting activities. The JFIS I can help relieve this anxiety by assuring all parties that the goal of the interview/ screening process will be to develop a cooperative strategy (family, juvenile, and interventionist working together) to prevent future incidents. Juveniles and their families are more likely to trust an interventionist they believe is acting as an advocate for them over those who exhibit an authoritative or accusatory demeanor.

Another aspect of the process of developing rapport is the opportunity for the JFIS I to determine if the juvenile is capable of understanding directions from the interventionist. This is especially important when the firesetter is a younger child or exhibits cognitive challenges. The child's ability to understand can be determined in conjunction with gaining rapport by initiating a casual verbal exchange with the child. Appropriate answers to questions such as names of pets, siblings, preferred toys, or favorite clothing are examples of ways to check for understanding. Assessing higher levels of understanding can be done by asking the juvenile to explain why a meeting is about to take place.

JFIS Level II Program Managers can use technology to custom-create presentations that explain the local juvenile firesetter problem and outline actions needed to address the situation. Advancing technology provides the interventionist many options to offer this type of presentation to parents as an introduction to the juvenile firesetter intervention program.

Health Belief Model

Many parents respond favorably to an interventionist's offer to help after learning they are not the only family that has experienced a juvenile firesetter problem. The Health Belief Model, discussed in Chapter 10, proposes that when a person is presented with information on a fire or life safety behavior, he or she may choose to adopt the behavior if specific conditions are satisfied:

- The person is aware that a problem exists as a result of his or her behavior.

- The person understands the problem and the factors contributing to it.

- The person believes they, or someone under their care, are personally at risk from the problem.

- The person believes the benefits to change outweigh any barriers to do so.

- The person believes he or she is capable of successfully making the behavioral change.

- There is a clear understanding of what the person must do to reduce the risk.

- There is an understanding and personal commitment to the reasons for changing the behavior.

- The person has the resources and ability to successfully make the change in behavior.

- There is positive feedback provided when the change is made **(Figure 19.7)**.

Figure 19.7 Positive feedback reinforces desired changes.

Regardless of the medium used, the interventionist must communicate the following information to the family at the outset of the meeting:

- Many motivations exist for juvenile firesetting.

- Discovering the root cause of the problem is essential.

- The intervention program has a multiagency approach to firesetting mitigation.

- The family is being asked to participate as a partner in the intervention process.

- A strong partnership including the juvenile, the involved family, and the interventionist is essential to a positive outcome.

If using a media production, ensure all information is presented in plain non-technical language that everyone (including the juvenile) can understand.

Explaining the Interview Process

The next step is to explain the interview process. This is done in the presence of the parents and child. The JFIS I should explain that conducting a structured interview and screening process is the most effective way of determining root causes of why a juvenile is starting fires; it can usually be completed within the time period of 60 to 90 minutes. The interventionist should explain that he or she will be asking questions to help build a profile of the juvenile, family, living environment, and fires. Answers are given numeric scores that, when summarized, help the interventionist predict if the juvenile is at risk of starting another fire. This process is called screening.

The level of risk identified through screening will enable the interventionist to recommend one or more levels of intervention. Interventions may include, but are not limited to, education, counseling, or justice system referral. Fire safety education usually accompanies all levels of interventions at some point during the process.

The JFIS I should then explain the order in which family members will be interviewed. While all family members come to the same scheduled interview, there is a suggested sequence for interviewing. The following interview sequence is recommended by nationally recognized authorities on juvenile firesetter intervention:

- Step One: Parents are interviewed alone.

- Step Two: Juvenile is interviewed alone.

- Step Three: Family is reconvened and informed of the program's next step.

NOTE: If the firesetter is a preteen or adolescent, he or she should be interviewed first (before the parents are interviewed), if possible. The rationale for this strategy will be explained in the next section.

Conducting Interviews

As mentioned in the previous section, in most cases preteens and adolescents should be interviewed first. This strategy builds rapport by validating their level of maturity and providing them the opportunity to offer a truthful account of the situation prior to parents being interviewed. The following sections are arranged for a juvenile firesetter who is a young child and should be adapted to meet the needs of each situation.

Interviewing Parents

To help facilitate an environment conducive to open communication, it is wise to assign the juvenile a task to perform while parents are being interviewed, in a separate area. Younger children may be asked to draw a picture of their fire so they can better explain to the JFIS I what happened. Older children may be directed to draft a written explanation of the situation that has brought them to the intervention program. In the case of very young children, another family member or adult may be asked to provide supervision in an area separate from the interview.

The interventionist should open the private conversation with parents by commending them for taking action to understand and address their child's firesetting situation. Cite national statistics that 80 percent of juveniles who have set a fire will repeat the behavior if prompt and appropriate intervention is not conducted. It is also important to emphasize that nearly all juveniles exhibit some level of curiosity about fire. Explain that the interview/screening process will help determine why the problem has occurred and the best strategies to prevent future behaviors.

Before asking any questions, assure parents that all information documented during a juvenile firesetter intervention process is confidential and protected from viewing by unauthorized parties. Confirm signatures on all pertinent documents such as release forms, liability waivers, and confidentiality assurances. The interventionist should reiterate the need to be able to share information about the situation with other agencies if a combination of intervention services is required.

Upon commencing the interview, confirm personal and demographical information already recorded about the juvenile and the family. The interventionist can save valuable time by completing the demographical information in advance of the interview. This information should have been obtained during the intake process or when the interventionist contacted the parent/guardian to arrange for an interview. If demographic information is recorded in advance of the interview, all the JFIS I will have to do is confirm its validity.

After confirming all demographical information, parents should be asked to summarize the events that have brought their child to the intervention program. This strategy opens communication with parents and allows for a smooth segue into the actual question/answer component of the interview.

When using an assessment instrument, the interventionist should ask all of the questions as they are written and in the order published. Doing so conforms to the validated protocol of the instrument. In circumstances where parents provide more information than was asked through a published question, use written notes as a supplement to the assessment instrument. While the interventionist should keep the interview process on track, it is important to allow the person being interviewed to tell their version of the situation with the level of detail they are willing to disclose.

After completing the assessment instrument, the interventionist brings closure to the interview by asking parents if they have questions or would like to offer any further information. Many interventionists will also ask the parents for their opinion as to why their child has engaged in firesetting behaviors. As a supplement to the in-person interview, parents may be asked to complete a secondary written assessment instrument while their child is being interviewed. This strategy provides a dual purpose:

- Parents remain occupied during their child's interview.
- Additional information is obtained that can help the interventionist reach a decision regarding intervention options.

Interviewing Juveniles

If possible, juveniles should be interviewed alone and *not* in the company of parents **(Figure 19.8)**. This strategy permits validation of the fire-related events outlined by parents. It also creates an opportunity for the juvenile to disclose information that he or she may not be willing to share in the company of parents. (**NOTE:** In cases involving young children, it may not be practical to interview the child without his or her parents. Interventionist judgment is advised.)

A good juvenile assessment instrument will include a section to help the interventionist develop additional rapport with the child. It will include general non-threatening questions about the juvenile's identity, school, friends, and favorite things to do.

At the outset of the interview, many interventionists will offer a limited amount of self-disclosure about themselves. One idea is to start off by acknowledging that no person is perfect. Everyone (including the

Figure 19.8 When possible, interview juveniles separately from their parents or caregivers.

JFIS I) has done something in his or her life that he or she is not proud of and wishes he or she could take back. It is important to emphasize that people who have made a first-time mistake with fire deserve a chance to correct the behavior. The purpose for the interview is to find out why the mistake happened and how it can be prevented from happening again.

Once rapport has been established and the JFIS I is confident the juvenile is capable of understanding questions that will be asked through the screening process, the interventionist proceeds with the interview. When interviewing juveniles age eight and under, the JFIS I may consider use of ancillary tools such as drawing, games, or puppets to help the child recall and explain events related to the firesetting situation. Regardless of the child's age, the JFIS I should attempt to obtain the information requested by the assessment instrument.

Scoring the Assessment Instrument

An approved juvenile firesetter assessment instrument will use a scoring process to profile the type of firesetting situation being evaluated. Interventionists should follow the directions on the instrument when scoring an interview. In addition to the results of the scoring process, interventionists should consider any other documented information or statements that were made by the juvenile and parents during the interview. The interviewer's personal observations of the behaviors displayed by those interviewed should be considered and documented as well. Use of an assessment instrument, experience, and education will help lead the JFIS I to a decision on possible intervention options.

If a simple firesetting case is obvious, the JFIS I may wish to score the assessment instruments on-site and schedule or perform fire safety education interventions immediately following the interview. In complex situations, the interventionist may choose to schedule a second meeting to discuss intervention options with parents after scoring the assessment instruments privately. This strategy allows the JFIS I to assimilate what he or she has learned about the situation and consult other JFIS team members or agencies as needed.

Reconvening the Family Interview

Once the interview process is completed, the family is reconvened so future program actions can be explained. If educational intervention is the sole medium recommended, the JFIS I may choose to discuss options with the entire family as a group. In complex situations where multiple interventions are possible, it may be prudent to limit the discussion to adults only.

In addition to developing a profile of the firesetting situation, a thorough screening process identifies what a juvenile and his or her family does or does not know about fire. Many juveniles (and often their legal guardians) are unaware of arson laws in their communities. Parents often think that holding a young child's hand near a heat source or using scare tactics are an effective firesetting prevention strategy. Sadly, many television shows and Internet sites condone or sometimes even promote firesetting as a recreational activity. Many juveniles lack vital knowledge of the speed and destructive power of uncontrolled fire.

Regardless of the firesetting profile, nearly everyone (juveniles and adults) will benefit from basic fire safety, prevention, and survival education. In low-risk curiosity-motivated situations, an interventionist may conduct the training immediately after the screening process has been completed. With definite-risk situations it is often performed in tandem with mental health intervention. For extreme-risk cases, it is wise to consult with mental health professionals prior to initiating any levels of intervention. In all cases, the interventionist should ensure that working smoke alarms, less than ten years old, are present on all living levels and bedrooms in the home of a firesetter and that the family has and practices an exit plan in case of a fire.

Facilitating a Productive Interview

An interview is not a conversation per se. It is a voluntary, directed exchange of information to achieve a specific purpose. Good interviewers are able to obtain information through a question and answer process that flows much like a conversation would. This is accomplished through use of both investigative and behavior-provoking questions. Investigative questions allow the person being interviewed to offer their version of an event. Behavioral information is observed as a person communicates with the interviewer.

The interventionist's experience level and knowledge of his or her agency's assessment instrument has a direct influence on how well information is exchanged during an interview. While note-taking is acceptable during an interview, the JFIS I should strive to maintain attentive listening.

Active Listening

Examples of attentive listening are forward posturing, maintaining eye contact with the interviewee, nodding of the head to acknowledge something said, and verbal summarizing of what the JFIS I has heard. The most effective interviewers exhibit a demeanor that indicates a true desire to understand what the interviewee has to say.

Interviewing a juvenile and his or her parents should not be conducted like the interrogation of a criminal. Whereas an interrogation features accusatory questions, an interview seeks voluntary discovery of facts and other pertinent information. Through his or her demeanor, which includes a calm voice, eye contact, and open body language, a proficient interviewer will demonstrate that he or she wants to hear what the juvenile and his or her parents have to say. The interventionist who listens attentively, gathers facts, and analyzes information can help facilitate collaborative family-based solutions to the firesetting situation.

In addition to being a good communicator, listener, and recorder, the JFIS I must be a proficient observer. As part of the evaluation process, interventionists must discreetly assess the truthfulness of responses provided by juveniles and parents. Observing posture, animation, and other body language yields powerful clues about when a person is being truthful or may be ready to offer additional information to a question being asked of them.

Nonverbal Behavior

Nonverbal behavior comprises greater than 50 percent of communication. It often supports or refutes the credibility of an answer. A truthful person generally exhibits a relaxed, casual, and open demeanor. He or she exhibits an upright posture and tends to learn forward. A truthful person uses illustrators such as hand gestures to describe an event or physical activity. Interestingly, however, truthful people often do not use gestures when responding to a question they view as highly important.

Nonverbal behavior can also provide clues indicating possible deception. A deceptive person may exhibit a closed, guarded posture. He or she may appear anxious, exhibit erratic movements, or become defensive. In contrast, some deceptive people are overly polite or seem unconcerned with a situation. Deceptive people often wring hands, chew nails, tap feet, pick lint from clothing, or cover their mouth when speaking. The deceptive person may also avoid eye contact whereas a truthful person will look straight into the eyes of the interviewer. Exceptions to the latter may occur with special needs populations or persons whose culture views direct eye contact as being disrespectful, or with those who are not yet willing to share personal or painful information.

Interventionists should be mindful that many firesetters exhibit special cognitive needs or have disorders that may prompt behaviors like spontaneous movement, toe tapping, and hand wringing. This may lead an interviewer to suspect deception. For this reason, the interventionist should have background information about any special needs that exist before conducting an interview with a juvenile and his or her family. In such cases the interventionist may ask parents to describe normal behaviors their child may exhibit in a situation such as an interview.

Legal Considerations

Resources allow some intervention programs to send two interventionists to the interview. This strategy permits one interventionist to fully engage in the interview while the other observes and records information. It also allows the two interventionists to share opinions on the information and observations gathered during the interview.

As noted earlier in this chapter, if the JFIS I is also acting in the capacity of a law enforcement official and is required to report information disclosed about criminal activity, he should advise the parent/legal guardian and juvenile prior to the start of the interview. Should criminal activity come to light, law enforcement officials are often required by their AHJ to stop the interview and advise the juvenile of his or her legal rights.

A JFIS I not acting in a law enforcement capacity may not be required by his or her AHJ to stop an interview if commission of a crime is disclosed by the interviewee. However, if such an incident occurs, the interviewer should consult with his or her supervisor immediately after the interview to ensure local protocol is followed.

Discovery of any life-threatening situation calls for immediate action from an interventionist.

NFPA® 1035 defines **abuse** as harmful behaviors and/or actions as defined by local law that place an individual at risk and require reporting. Neglect is the failure to act on behalf of or in protection of an individual in ones' care. If at any time during the interview process it is discovered that the juvenile or any family member is in a life-threatening situation, the interview should be stopped and the appropriate authorities contacted.

Determining Intervention and Referral Options

After profiling the type of firesetting situation and classifying risk for repeat behaviors, the interventionist's next task is to determine intervention options. Education programs, counseling services, and justice system involvement should all be considered potential options to explore.

The previously completed interview with the juvenile firesetter and his or her parent/guardian empowers the JFIS I with a general understanding of why the juvenile is engaging in firesetting behaviors. After scoring the assessment instrument and considering other pertinent information provided by interviewees, the interventionist should be able to recommend an appropriate level of intervention.

In cases of first-time curiosity-motivated firesetting where little or no damage occurred, the JFIS I would likely choose education as a sole intervention. For more complex and problematic situations, the interventionist may wish to discuss the assessment instrument's indicators with the JFIS team before recommending potential options.

Selecting Educational Strategies

As part of the interview and screening process, the JFIS I evaluated both the juvenile's and his or her parent's knowledge levels about fire. In many cases, juveniles and adults often lack understanding of the dangers associated with firesetting, local arson laws, and the ramifications of recidivism. A thorough juvenile firesetter intervention program will offer an education component that, as a minimum, focuses on the following topics:

- The importance of fire and its appropriate uses
- Profile of the national juvenile firesetter problem
- National problem contrasted with local juvenile firesetting conditions

- Explanation of why juveniles may choose to start a fire
- Dangers of uncontrolled fire
- Penalties associated with misuse of fire
- Overview of the local intervention program's broad-based mitigation strategy

The timely delivery of age- and intellectually-appropriate education can be a powerful deterrent to recidivism.

> The JFIS selects presentation media and delivers education as a firesetting preventive intervention. NFPA® 1035 states that interventionists who provide this service should meet the qualifications of a Fire and Life Safety Educator I.

NOTE: The following sections discuss age and development levels as factors in educational strategies. Chapters 5 and 10 also include extensive information on how to select and use age-appropriate education materials and should be referenced at need. Specific information about using burned homes as educational props is included in Chapter 10.

Educational Strategies — Young Children

Young firesetters (ages two through five) are at high-risk for dying in a fire they initiate themselves. The younger children of this group are at greater risk because of their limited intellectual development. They often have difficulty understanding why and how things happen. Fire safety messages should be simple and provide a specific direction. Examples include: "If you see lighters or matches, don't touch, tell a grown-up;" "Don't hide, go outside;" and, "Get low under smoke."

Educating young children about the dangers of firesetting can be effectively accomplished if the interventionist uses age-appropriate methodologies. Educational props such as toys, puppets, stories, and mixed media (pictures and video) often work well for this population.

Educational Strategies — Older Children

Most normally developing older children (ages six to ten) are intellectually capable of assimilating the information they receive. This includes understanding good from bad and right from wrong. This age group responds well to direct concrete instruction, reading activities, and stories. Props such as burned objects, pictures, and firefighting tools are often effective used in tandem with the above. Interactive experiences such as touring a burned home are very powerful teaching tools as well.

Educational Strategies — Preteens and Adolescents

The intellectual capabilities of a normally developing juvenile (ages 11 through 18) expand to include the ability to evaluate, reason, and predict future outcomes. Juveniles with these abilities respond well to direct instruction, testimonials, case studies, problem-solving activities, and reality-based experiences. Reality-based experiences for this age group include tours of burned homes, media presentations, and mock-court exercises.

Educational Strategies — Parents, Legal Guardians, and Caregivers

The purpose of educating parents, legal guardians, and caregivers is two-fold:

1. To expand their knowledge base on why and how they are an important partner in the juvenile firesetter intervention process

2. To increase their ability to act responsibly and help prevent recidivism

Since most adults can perform abstract intellectual operations, educational strategies for this group mirror those for adolescents. In addition to the strategies listed for adolescents, adults often benefit from testimonials by professionals, or hearing from other families who have experienced and overcome challenging situations. (**NOTE:** When educating older children, preteens, adolescents, and adults, information on fire science, fire safety, fire survival, and fire prevention should always be integrated into the presentation.)

Use of Extension Activities

All populations, children through adulthood, benefit from extension activities that supplement the educational component of a firesetting intervention program. Extension activities are assigned as part of the intervention program and are performed by the juvenile, often with help from their parents, in their home or community.

Extension activities for younger children may include drawing a picture of a safe home where fire is being used as a tool. Older children may write a story of how a child learned why bad fires must be prevented. Adolescents could perform home fire safety inspections as part of a restitution agreement. Adults are assigned the task of working with their child to collaboratively perform whatever extension assignment has been made.

In addition, all juvenile firesetter educational programs should include a section that teaches overall fire prevention and survival strategies. Prevention strategies, smoke alarm installation and maintenance, and home escape planning should be included as part of the section. While a well-structured intervention program will be successful at mitigating most firesetting behaviors, recidivism is a potential situation that should be considered and prepared for accordingly.

Exploring Mental Health Options

Referral of a firesetting case to a mental health professional should be considered when the interview and screening process indicates that some level of cognitive, psychological, or social dysfunction contributed to the firesetting situation. Mental health professionals such as Licensed Certified Social Workers (LCSW), **psychologists**, and **psychiatrists** are trained to evaluate such situations and provide intensive broad-based intervention services.

Clinical social workers are counselors who work directly with families to determine root factors that contribute to dysfunctional behavior. Psychologists receive a higher level of training to analyze cognitive disorders and suggest treatment options. A psychiatrist is a medical doctor who specializes in treatment of cognitive and psychological disorders. He or she can prescribe medications for use as part of a multifaceted treatment plan.

Chapters 10 and 17 provided comprehensive information on cognitive, psychological, and social challenges that may impact learning. These challenges often contribute to firesetting behaviors. The following section provides a brief overview of why these issues should be identified and evaluated when considering intervention options.

Cognitively Challenged Firesetters

Cognitive challenges can interfere with decision-making processes, impair judgment, and influence behavior. Poor decision making and impulsive behavior are factors that often influence firesetting. The most frequent cognitive challenge exhibited by firesetters is Attention Deficit Hyperactivity Disorder (ADHD). Nearly 60% of juvenile firesetters have a diagnosis of ADHD before their first referral to a firesetter intervention program.

Attention Deficit Disorder can occur alone or in tandem with hyperactivity. When it occurs alone, a person has difficulty staying focused or remaining on task. Hyperactivity influences a person to be in constant motion and often contributes to impulsive behavior. When ADD accompanies hyperactivity, a person has trouble paying attention, moves incessantly, and often makes decisions without thinking of potential consequences. An unsupervised juvenile with ADHD who has access to ignition materials is often a high-risk candidate for firesetting and other potentially dangerous behaviors.

Learning disabilities affect a person's capacity to interpret what they see and hear, and/or to link information from different parts of the brain. Up to 20 percent of the population is challenged by some level of learning disability. In addition, 20 to 30 percent of juveniles with ADHD also have a learning disability. Firesetters with substantive learning disabilities often benefit from combined educational interventions and interaction with a counselor trained to work with special-needs populations.

A juvenile firesetter with ADHD should be screened carefully by the JFIS I. Often the assessment instrument's score will indicate that a mental health referral should occur. Even if it does not, the firesetting situation should be examined closely. If the child's cognitive challenge contributed directly to the firesetting situation or if parents identified their child's behavior as problematic, referral to a mental health professional should be considered.

While many children with ADHD do not take any behavioral medications, those with substantial forms of cognitive challenges may benefit from medical intervention. Sometimes, a firesetter with severe ADHD may not be a candidate for educational intervention because of his or her inability to focus or remain engaged in the learning process. However, once appropriate evaluation and treatment is initiated by a team of clinicians, the child should be able to process information that is presented in a distraction-free structured learning environment.

Psychological Conditions to Consider

There are several other forms of cognitive conditions that qualify as a psychological disorder:

- Anxiety and depression.
- Bi-Polar Disorder with its severe mood swings.
- Autism Spectrum Disorders — diminish a person's ability to communicate and socialize.
- Oppositional Defiant Disorder — characterized by temper outbursts and refusal to obey rules.
- Conduct Disorder — characterized by lying, stealing, fighting, and bullying behavior.

Problematic firesetting involving juveniles with special needs can escalate into incidents that can be difficult to effectively control. If a juvenile is exhibiting several combined behaviors such as aggression, stealing, and firesetting, an antisocial pathology has developed. The term *antisocial* refers to behaviors that are not socially acceptable.

The interventionist should consider consultation with a mental health professional for any firesetter challenged by a psychological disorder prior to making a final decision on intervention options. This is especially critical if multiple anti-social behaviors are being exhibited. In such a case, clinical evaluation occurs first to help ensure that providing education about fire will not exacerbate its inappropriate use. The ultimate aim is to ensure a thorough evaluation process takes place and correct levels of preventive services are provided at the appropriate time and in the appropriate order.

What This Means to You

As a JFIS I, you should possess a strong understanding of clinical interventions used to mitigate firesetting behaviors; however, you are not a mental health professional. Your primary role is to evaluate a firesetting situation and recommend potential solutions based upon an approved screening process. While clinical evaluation may be an option identified through this process, it is always performed by a licensed certified mental health professional who has experience in the field of juvenile firesetter intervention. Tremendous liability and potential violation of laws face a lay person who offers services as a counselor without a license.

Social Challenges That Impact Firesetting Behaviors

Social factors can have direct influence on firesetting behaviors. Family turmoil, a recent crisis situation, or other levels of dysfunction can create stressful home environments. An overall lack of parental support is often noted when evaluating problematic firesetting cases. Many high-risk firesetters reside in homes where daily coping with some form of chaos or crisis is the norm and would benefit from referral to counseling services.

The combination of cognitive, psychological, and social challenges can exponentially increase the risk for repeat firesetting behavior. The screening process, combined with notes collected by the interventionist, should provide an indication that referral to a mental health professional is in order.

Because of the complex and often unstable circumstances surrounding high-risk firesetting cases, rapid access to mental health services is essential. Securing partnerships with clinical and social service agencies helps create a network of support that is critical to achieving success in challenging situations. Developing such a network is the responsibility of the program manager and will be discussed as part of Chapter 23.

Partnerships with Mental Health Agencies

Until two decades ago, only limited research had been conducted on juvenile firesetting. The empirical research conducted by professionals such as Kolko, Fineman, Gaynor, and others not only identified why juveniles were starting fires, it highlighted multi-faceted strategies of how the problem could be mitigated. Strong clinical support was (and remains) noted as a key component. While many communities have strong juvenile firesetter intervention programs that feature collaborative relationships between emergency services, schools, mental health organizations, social services, and juvenile justice departments, still others have none. A strong partnership with local mental health agencies represents one of the most important components of an intervention program.

Legal Consequences of Firesetting

In most jurisdictions, a child exhibiting normal cognitive development that has reached his or her state's **age of accountability** can be held legally responsible for starting a fire. The age of accountability is the minimum age at which state courts have ruled that a child is intellectually capable of understanding right from wrong and the consequences associated with inappropriate behavior. Depending upon the state, the age of accountability may vary, but in most places this age is between seven and thirteen. The specific age is decided by a panel of experts representing child psychologists, education officials, and the state's Supreme Court.

In most communities, the JFIS I is required by his or her authority having jurisdiction to report incidents of firesetting. This is especially true if the child is of age and the fire causes property damage or injury. The JFIS I should be familiar with the local age of accountability and his or her agency's protocol for incident reporting. In some jurisdictions, arson is investigated by a fire marshal's office. In others, local police agencies may be responsible for enforcing fire laws.

The JFIS I should know his or her community's fire laws and enforcement procedure. This is important for several reasons. First, the interventionist needs this knowledge to collaborate professionally with justice system officials. Second, the JFIS I must be able to articulate the penalties of firesetting to juveniles and their parents. Often, juveniles and their parents are shocked to learn of the potential legal consequences (both criminal and civil) that can be imposed as a result of firesetting. While criminal sanctions can be levied against the juvenile, parents can be served with a civil suit to recompense owners of lost property as result of a juvenile-set fire. This is especially true in situations where the firesetter's family is renting property.

Justice officials who have a thorough understanding of juvenile firesetting and its impact on the local community may impose progressive levels of discipline appropriate to the specific firesetting situation. A first-time curiosity-motivated firesetter who started a single fire that caused minimal damages and no injury is often granted probation before judgment (PBJ). PBJ results in no documented criminal record as long as conditions

An Overview of Criminal Charges Against Juvenile Firesetters

While fire and arson laws vary slightly from state to state, the titles of specific offenses and their penalties are relatively consistent. Here is an overview of criminal charges that can be filed against a juvenile who has participated in acts of firesetting. The laws ascend in severity from misdemeanor to felony.

- *Possession/Discharge of Illegal Fireworks.* Violators are usually issued a civil citation but must appear in court to address the offense. Fines may be up to $250.00 per piece of illegal product found in an offender's possession.

- *False Report of Emergency.* The false and malicious report of an emergency situation is a misdemeanor crime. It is punishable by up to five years of incarceration and fines not to exceed $5,000.00.

- *Reckless Endangerment.* Putting other people at risk because of one's actions. This offense is a misdemeanor usually punishable by up to five years in jail and fines not to exceed $5,000.00. This charge is often attached to a case where emergency personnel responded or an incident placed bystanders or other occupants of a building at risk.

- *Malicious Burning.* Setting fire to an abandoned or vacant structure. The offense is punishable in the first and second degrees depending on the amount of dollar loss. First degree malicious burning is a felony in most states. A second degree offense is a misdemeanor. This crime carries up to a five year jail sentence and fines not to exceed $5,000.00.

- *Arson.* The crime of arson involves setting fire to an occupied structure. It is punishable in the first and second degree contingent on the type of occupancy. Both degrees of arson are felonies. First degree arson is charged when a fire is intentionally set in an occupied dwelling where people sleep or a house of worship. This offense is punishable by imprisonment for up to 30 years and a $50,000.00 fine. Second degree arson is committed by setting fire to a business or other type of occupied building excluding a dwelling. It carries up to a 20 year jail sentence and the possibility of a $30,000.00 fine.

- *Threat to Burn.* Making a statement of intent to either burn something or cause something to explode can be rated as either a misdemeanor or felony depending on the circumstances. The offense is punishable by up to ten years incarceration and fines not to exceed $10,000.00.

- *Chemical Devices.* Building, having, or discharging a chemical device is a felony in many jurisdictions. Included in this category are soda bottle and dry ice bombs. Penalties are up to 25 years in jail and fines not to exceed $250,000.00.

- *Guilty By Association.* If a person is willfully in the company of another who commits a crime, he or she is eligible to receive the same penalty as the person who physically performed the act.

of the probation (such as completion of a firesetting intervention program) are completed within a specified timeframe.

Problematic firesetting cases often lead to a combination of ascending sanctions being imposed by the local AHJ. Depending on the circumstances, a combination of education, counseling, community service, restitution, and/or temporary placement in a structured rehabilitative environment may be mandated.

The local justice system's response often directly correlates with the level of outcome that can be expected with firesetting situations. Holding a juvenile responsible for his or her actions has a positive impact on a juvenile's future behavior and reduces the risk of recidivism. Juvenile firesetter intervention programs offering a comprehensive and progressive level of intervention services often have fewer instances of both first-time firesetting and recidivism.

Another excellent benefit of a strong justice system component is that it can be used to leverage a higher level of responsibility and involvement from parents. This strategy helps facilitate responsible adult supervision, isolation of ignition material, and attendance at intervention programs.

Implementing Intervention Options

Implementing a timely, appropriate intervention is the best strategy to prevent or minimize future acts of firesetting. Recidivism has been shown to occur in 80 percent of incidents where a timely intervention is not offered, according to research conducted by Fireproof Children.[2]

As discussed in Chapter 17, challenges of many types and degrees often face the families of juvenile firesetters. The homes of many firesetters are chaotic environments. Population transience, unreliable communication mediums and transportation often complicate both short- and long-term relationships with some families. Partnerships that include the fire service, education, and the clinical and justice systems will provide families with timely access and implementation of services that can produce tangible impact and positive long-term results **(Figure 19.9)**.

An appropriate level of intervention is defined as a series of services that ultimately stop firesetting behaviors. In simple curiosity-motivated cases, comprehensive education may be the sole medium required. In complex and problematic cases, a combination of services employed over a longer period of time is often most successful.

Interventionists implement intervention strategies to mitigate juvenile firesetting. Implementation of intervention strategies is best accomplished when a partnership or coalition providing access to a network of broad-based services exists. If such collaboration is unattainable, implementing programs or making referrals can be a time-consuming endeavor resulting in frustration and service delays.

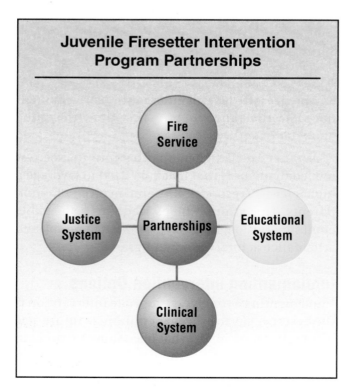

Figure 19.9 Partnerships across several fields will increase options available for juvenile firesetters and their families.

The next sections focus on how to implement three levels of firesetting interventions: education, mental health services, and justice system involvement. These sections represent ascending interventions.

Implementing Educational Interventions

One of the most important tasks conducted during the interview and screening process was to ascertain knowledge about fire behavior held by parents and juveniles. Most experienced interventionists agree that parents and juveniles often lack adequate knowledge of the dangers and penalties associated with firesetting. Education therefore builds a foundation that supports all levels of preventive intervention.

Education also provides information essential for behavioral change to occur. As discussed earlier, the hierarchy of change indicates that a person must:

1. Be aware of a problem.
2. Feel they (or loved ones) are at risk.
3. Understand how to prevent the issue and believe they are capable of taking action.

Arranging for the Intervention

In cases of simple curiosity-based firesetting, some intervention programs offer education as an intervention immediately following the screening process. Other jurisdictions prefer to schedule a second meeting to provide the service. In complex or problematic cases, if and when education is used it is offered after consultation has occurred with mental health partners and/or justice system officials.

Staging the Intervention

Some intervention programs welcome the opportunity to have interventionists interact with a family in their home environment. Others may prefer that the intervention occurs at an agency-sponsored location such as the interventionist's office or a firehouse. Still others use related educational facilities like training academies or safety villages.

Regardless of the intervention's location, proper planning is essential to facilitating a successful outcome. As with preparing to conduct a screening and interview, the JFIS I must ensure the environment surrounding the educational intervention is appropriate. Whether visiting a family's home, using the interventionist's office, or borrowing a firehouse or safety village classroom, the environment must be conducive to learning.

As explained in Chapters 5, 10, and 17 special needs populations require distraction-free learning environments. These chapters should be referenced for an overview explaining how to create an environment suitable for all participants regardless of their specific circumstances.

Preparing for the Intervention

Interactive experiences help enhance a learning environment. Many interventionists use supplementary age-appropriate instructional materials such as toys, puppets, pictures, burned objects, reading/writing activities, and media presentations. Regardless what medium is used, the JFIS I needs to ensure its availability and operability prior to the start of an intervention. A few minutes of preparation can prevent an embarrassing situation that detracts from the serious nature of an intervention. Poor planning damages the professional credibility of the presenter.

The interventionist should also prepare by reviewing the juvenile's case file. The file should include a substantial history of the events surrounding the firesetting situation and actions taken to date. In complex and problematic cases, the JFIS I may need to review the file with interventionists who have already evaluated or provided levels of service for the juvenile and his or her family to clarify details or solidify the planned intervention.

Conducting an Educational Intervention

In addition to calling for comprehensive knowledge of firesetting intervention, NFPA® 1035 states that a JFIS I providing educational intervention to juvenile firesetters and their families must meet the requirements of a Level I Fire and Life Safety Educator — and for good reason. Along with understanding why juveniles set fires and being able to identify and assess firesetter profiles, the JFIS I providing the educational intervention must be a capable educator. To qualify, the JFIS I needs in-depth knowledge of learning theory, stages of intellectual development, and instructional methodology. He or she must also understand the individual needs of all learners and be able to facilitate appropriate learning environments.

The ultimate goal of an educational intervention is to increase the target population's knowledge about the problem and consequences of firesetting and facilitate positive behavioral change. Through the use of age-appropriate strategies, the JFIS I can accomplish this goal.

The two target populations of an educational intervention are the curiosity-motivated juvenile (primary) and his or her parents or legal guardians (secondary). The previous section focused on selecting educational materials and potential delivery media. The following section offers suggestions on how to implement their use. The information is presented in ascending order by specific age groups.

Implementing Educational Interventions with Young Children

Because of their limited attention span and stage of intellectual development, young firesetters (ages two through five) represent one of the most challenging groups to educate. The use of puppets, toys, pictures, and other props can help children remember and act on simple and direct fire safety messages. Stories and age-appropriate media presentations are also effective.

When conducting an educational intervention directed at a younger child, the interventionist may wish to consider the following strategies:

- Younger children often do not feel comfortable when separated from their parents. The JFIS I should consider conducting the intervention with parents present.

- Younger children may be fearful of loud noises or scary situations. Avoid use of props that make loud noise. Avoid graphic media presentations that may scare children or feature tragedy.

- Consider use of puppets, toys, and other props that the child is familiar with and can relate to. Use these props to help tell a story about why fire is important and how a good fire can be used to help adults. Explain how a good fire can become a bad fire. Explain how a bad fire can hurt people, animals, and homes. Explain the consequences of what can happen to children if they try to use fire as a toy.

- Present simple fire safety rules such as: Lighters and matches are tools and not toys. If you see matches and lighters, tell an adult to put them in a safe place. If a fire happens, go outside – do not hide.

- Ask the child to explain his or her fire and why it was a bad situation. Work with the child to collaboratively develop a simple plan that corrects the inappropriate behavior.

- Consider use of an age-appropriate media presentation to review and summarize the main messages of the intervention.

- Keep any presentation within the attention span for this age group; segments of the presentation should last ten to fifteen minutes at the longest. Review key points often.

- Assign extension activities such as working with adults to identify tools that generate heat that are found in the home. Have adults work with the child to create home safety rules about tools that make heat. Have the family evaluate their smoke alarms and make a fire escape plan.

Implementing Educational Interventions with Older Children

Most older children (age six to ten) are intellectually capable of understanding right from wrong and the consequences of inappropriate behavior. They can comprehend why the educational intervention is occurring, the kinds of activities that are going to take place, and what future behavior is expected from them. Here are some suggestions for working with this age group:

- Begin an intervention by asking juveniles to explain why they are participating in the intervention program. Ask them to explain why fire is an important tool and provide examples of its appropriate use. Have them clarify why its use is reserved for adults. This provides an information base to explore simple case studies, current events related to fire, and other age-appropriate media.

- Talk about current real-life fire-related events to create an opportunity for props such as burned objects, pictures, or firefighting tools to be introduced and discussed.

- Because this age group is capable of feeling empathy toward others, interactive experiences (provided in person or through media) are very powerful teaching tools that can be used to appeal to the affective domain of learning. For example, the interventionist may ask older children how they would feel if their home was destroyed by fire or if someone they loved was hurt.

- Have juveniles recount their fire experience and explain what the outcome could have been. This technique provides a good segue to the discussion of penalties related to firesetting.

- In an age-appropriate format, overview local laws and other penalties relating to firesetting. Consider having the juvenile identify which law pertains to his or her situation and explain what sanctions could be imposed.

- Consider use of a case-study (written or media-based) that overviews a juvenile firesetting situation. Have the juvenile examine the case study and provide his or her opinion of what should happen to the person who initiated the problem.

- Assign extension activities like writing a letter of apology to parents, firefighters, and victims. With cooperation of parents, assign a series of home fire safety activities that call for the inspection of heat sources, cooking practices, and smoke alarm presence and operability. Assign the child to create a home fire safety plan that includes practicing a fire drill.

- Consider requiring some form of restitution such as home chores, neighborhood service (safety checks in the homes of trusted family and friends) or helping local firefighters with a task.

Educational interventions for older children can be initiated in the company of parents or privately with the child. Some intervention programs gather several juvenile firesetters and their parents so an interactive experience is created.

Implementing Educational Intervention with Preteens and Adolescents

Preteens and adolescents (ages 11 through 18) can evaluate situations, problem-solve, and predict future outcomes. The following are suggestions for conducting educational interventions with this age group:

- Preteens and adolescents may benefit from individual intervention and/or working in small groups.

- As with older children, conducting an introductory activity works well with adolescents. Many interventionists begin by asking each adolescent to introduce him- or herself and explain things they enjoy doing. This is followed by asking for a brief summary of what situation occurred that led to requiring the adolescent to attend the intervention program. This strategy provides an excellent foundation for a later discussion about the laws and penalties (such as loss of freedom, privileges, and money) associated with violation of the law.

- An age-appropriate summary of the local juvenile firesetter problem may be offered through brief reality-based media such as media clips, digital images, and news articles.

- This group responds favorably to the use of direct instruction interspersed with peer testimonials, case studies, and problem-solving activities.

- If facilitating intervention for a small group of adolescents, consider conducting a value-lines discussion. A value-lines discussion involves examination of a case study followed by an open discussion of what outcome should ensue. (NOTE: This methodology is only recommended for use by educators experienced in value-lines facilitation because disagreements can easily become heated. More information on value-lines discussion can be obtained by conducting an information search on the topic.)

- Because of this group's ability to analyze situations, have empathy toward others, and predict future outcomes, reality-based experiences are very effective and appropriate for this age group. Tours of burned homes, media presentations, and mock-court exercises have been reported by interventionists to work well. (NOTE: Parents of a juvenile firesetter sometimes suggest that their child should tour a burn center or visit with a burn survivor as part of the educational intervention process. While this methodology can be effective, it should be used in an educational context and not as a scare tactic.)

- Adolescents need a clear understanding of local fire laws and their associated penalties. This is best explained through direct instruction. The effectiveness of instruction is heightened when it is presented by an official who has the power to impose penalties (such as a judge or justice system official).

- The analysis of case studies can serve as an excellent review of the program and be used to test for understanding and internalization of information.

- Extension activities for adolescents may include letters of apology to family members, firefighters, and victims affected by the firesetting. Home safety inspections are appropriate for this group. Writing assignments that require a summary of what has been learned as result of the firesetting experience and in the program also work well.

- Completing some form of restitution holds adolescents accountable for their actions and brings a case toward closure. In addition to monetary and community service sanctions, educational extension activities (such as those listed in the previous bullet) can be used as a form of restitution.

Implementing Educational Interventions with Parents/Guardians

The parents/guardians of juvenile firesetters are an essential target population for educational intervention. Studies show that, although significantly influenced by peers and the media, juveniles still rate parents as being their most trusted source of advice. One of the most important tasks for a JFIS I is to empower parents with the knowledge of how their juvenile's firesetting behaviors can be stopped.

As an initial motivator, parents need to gain an understanding of the overall national juvenile firesetter problem and how it affects the local community. This includes the number of incidents, property loss, injuries, deaths, rates of rise, arrest statistics, and other factors that are relevant to their situation. Parents should learn about the three basic profiles of firesetters and how each profile is best addressed. They also need information about local arson laws, categories of offenses, and consequences associated with acts of recidivism. Many intervention programs will provide this information through handout materials or succinct media presentations during the intake or pre-interview phase of the intervention process.

While portions of a comprehensive educational intervention may involve the juvenile working alone with the interventionist or participating with a group of peers, parents must have long-term cooperative involvement with their child. Extension activities that call for parental involvement can be assigned to encourage parents' help in preventing recidivism.

Implementing Referral to a Mental Health Professional

A child's curiosity about fire occurs as a normal part of his or her intellectual development. An episode of purposeful firesetting does not.

Curiosity-motivated firesetting is often mitigated successfully by providing educational interventions. Peer influenced experimentation and delinquency is often resolved through a combination of education and justice system involvement. However, in some cases, firesetting serves as a signal of an underlying problem. Acts of firesetting can be precipitated by a combination of stress, anger, or family dysfunction. Cognitive and psychological disorders can exacerbate the situation.

Use of the comprehensive screening process helps identify firesetters who may have turned to fire to express stress or anger. Rapid and appropriate intervention is essential in such cases. Left unchecked, this type of behavior can lead to development of a pathology whereby a juvenile uses firesetting as a coping mechanism to solve future challenging situations. These firesetters are often challenged by a number of complex factors that ultimately exacerbate the behavior. Evaluation of these situations is beyond the job performance expectations for a JFIS I and must be referred to a mental health professional.

The Mental Health Profession and Juvenile Firesetting

It is important for the JFIS I to understand why and how the mental health profession can serve as a critical partner in firesetting mitigation. The mental health profession specializes in helping people overcome challenges that are negatively impacting behavior. Often, a team of mental health professionals (MHPs) will work collaboratively to design intervention plans specific to a client's needs.

While the JFIS is not expected, or trained, to be a mental health professional, it is important for him or her to have knowledge of interventions that may be implemented after a juvenile firesetter case is referred to a mental health practitioner. The following section explains how some referrals progress and the categories of medical interventions that can be provided.

The Progression of Referrals

When an interventionist refers a firesetting case to a mental health agency, the case file is initially reviewed by a qualified professional. Frontline health professionals such as social workers are trained to assist clients by providing information and a referral to the appropriate mental health specialist. They may also serve as case managers to help people navigate the system of mental health intervention. Social workers interview and counsel clients but cannot write prescriptions.

After an initial screening process is conducted, a diagnostic evaluation to establish a psychiatric diagnosis is performed by trained mental health professionals. This process is often performed in tandem by clinical social workers and a psychologist. A clinical psychologist is a professional with a doctoral degree in psychology who specializes in therapy. He or she can help direct several levels of clinical intervention.

What This Means to You

When a juvenile firesetter intervention case requires a referral to counseling, you may be working in partnership with a mental health practitioner (psychologist, social worker, school counselor, licensed counselor, etc.) who has been trained in working with juvenile firesetters. In such circumstances, you need to be familiar with the protocol used in making the referral to the partner agency or specific health professional.

As part of the evaluation process, mental health clinicians examine the cognitive, social, environmental, and physical factors that may be influencing the juvenile firesetter's behavior. These factors contribute to how the juvenile looks at him- or herself, his or her life, and the other people with whom he or she interacts. The factors also influence how the juvenile handles stress, evaluates personal challenges, explores choices, and makes decisions on how to react. Dysfunction at any level can have a negative impact on a juvenile's mental health and ultimately affect his or her behavior. Firesetting is one such example.

Categories of Medical Interventions

Once the comprehensive evaluation is complete, a clinical treatment plan is developed. A clinical treatment plan is an official course of action that is recommended by certified mental health professionals after they have thoroughly evaluated a patient's adverse behaviors. In the case of firesetting and other disorders, one or more of the following interventions[3] may be initiated:

- *Cognitive Therapy.* Cognitive therapy aims to identify and correct distorted thinking patterns that can lead to feelings and behaviors that may be troublesome, self-defeating, or destructive. The goal is to replace negative thought processes with more balanced views that, in turn, lead to more fulfilling and productive behavior.

- *Behavioral Therapy.* Behavioral therapy focuses on changing a person's unwanted behaviors through rewards, reinforcements, and desensitization. Desensitization, or exposure therapy, is a process of confronting something that arouses anxiety, discomfort, or fear to overcome the negative responses. Behavioral therapy often enlists the cooperation of others, especially family, teachers, and close friends, to reinforce a desired behavior.

- *Cognitive/Behavioral Therapy.* A combination of cognitive and behavioral therapies often helps people change negative thought patterns, beliefs, and behaviors so they can manage symptoms and enjoy more productive, less stressful lives.

- *Interpersonal Psychotherapy.* Through one-on-one conversations, this approach focuses on the person's current life and relationships within the family, social, school, and work environments. The goal is insightful identification and resolution of problems, and building on strengths.

- *Play Therapy.* Geared toward young children, play therapy uses a variety of activities, such as painting, puppets, and dioramas to establish communication with the therapist and resolve problems. Play allows the child to express emotions and problems that would be too difficult to discuss with another person.

- *Group Therapy.* Group therapy involves 4 to 12 people who have similar problems and are already meeting regularly with a therapist. The therapist uses the emotional interactions of the group's members to help them relieve stress and modify their behavior.

- *Family-Centered Services.* Comprehensive clinical and/or social support services designed to meet the specific needs of each individual child and family.

Clinical social workers and psychologists can be thought of as professional communicators, evaluators, and strategists. Problem identification and solving are the hallmark of their profession. These professionals work directly with families to determine and evaluate root factors that contribute to dysfunctional behavior. Once challenges have been identified, they help a family reach collaborative solutions so the factors contributing to the problem can be addressed and resolved.

Most mental health professionals have an office where clients are evaluated and treated. Licensed certified social workers, school-based counselors, and other community-based clinicians who specialize in working with high-risk populations may also offer home visitation.

In situations involving more challenging circumstances, clinical social workers and psychologists may consult with a psychiatrist to create more intensive intervention strategies. A psychiatrist is a medical doctor who specializes in mental health and can prescribe medications to supplement the intervention process.

Behavioral medications are often used to improve attention spans, reduce hyperactivity, or curb sleep disorders. Used as directed and in tandem with a structured clinical intervention process, behavioral medications can have a positive effect on a juvenile's behavior. Unfortunately, if parents fail to follow prescribed directions (as is sometimes the case in dysfunctional situations), behavioral medications can have moderate to no effect. In extreme cases, irregular use of these medications can produce unfavorable outcomes including dangerous side effects.

Facilitating Clinical Services

Families may not have insurance or financial resources to cover counseling expenses if a referral is recommended. It is the responsibility of the JFIS coalition to help facilitate the availability of clinical services – either through agency partnerships, locating supportive funding, or a combination of both.

A **gatekeeper** is often a primary care physician or local agency responsible for coordinating and managing the health care needs of members. Generally, in order for specialty services such as mental health and hospital care to be covered, the gatekeeper must first approve the referral. In communities lacking an organized JFIS coalition or strong inter-agency partnerships, those serving as gatekeepers may lack understanding of the critical need to have immediate access to clinical services. Educating physicians and other staff who act in the capacity of gatekeeper and exploring and addressing insurance challenges as part of developing an organized JFIS program represent the most effective way to facilitate prompt and appropriate levels of services.

In severely challenging situations, a juvenile may benefit from admission to an **inpatient mental health treatment** facility. This is especially true when firesetting has become pathological and fire is consistently being used as a stress or anger release mechanism. Inpatient hospitalization at a specialized mental health treatment facility provides supervised care 24 hours a day. This type of center offers short-term treatment in cases where a child is in crisis and could be a danger to him- or herself or others. It can also provide diagnosis and treatment when the patient cannot be evaluated or treated effectively in an outpatient setting.

Children with serious emotional disturbances receive constant supervision and care at a **Residential Treatment Center (RTC)**. Treatment may include individual, group, and family therapy; cognitive or behavior therapy; special education; recreation therapy; and medical services. Residential treatment is usually more long-term than inpatient hospitalization.

Residential Treatment Centers provide 24-hour care and can usually serve multiple juveniles. A referral to an RTC is typically initiated by the primary mental health professional working with the juvenile firesetter and their family. Sometimes, securing an admission to such a center can be a challenge because an out-of-control firesetter can create a very dangerous situation in such a setting.

Placement into an inpatient or residential treatment center can be either voluntary or mandatory. Voluntary admission occurs when a parent willingly seeks to place their child into a treatment program. Committal is the act of requiring placement into a center. Committal is reserved for situations such as when a juvenile represents a threat to himself or others. Committal is also used in cases of severe delinquency or other criminal behavior.

Treatment Facilities

Unfortunately, many mental health in-patient centers will not accept juvenile firesetters for fear of recidivism during treatment and concern for the protection of their patient population and liability. Further, health insurance coverage (or lack thereof) may restrict access to services. For this reason, it is imperative that JFIS II program managers conduct research into treatment facilities available to juvenile firesetters. Once a potential source has been located, program managers should seek to create a collaborative relationship so that intensive clinical services become available to local firesetters and their families.

Located in South Mountain, Pennsylvania, the Cornell Abraxas Center is a secure residential treatment center specializing in the long-term treatment of firesetters. Juveniles placed at the center receive comprehensive clinical treatment and participate in a highly-structured education program. The center accepts juveniles ages 12 through 18. Students from the National Fire Academy's JFIS Leadership course tour the facility as part of their educational experience.

Initiating Referral to a Mental Health Agency

Where interagency partnerships or a formal JFIS coalition exists, access to trained mental health professionals can be as close as a telephone call or e-mail. A strong JFIS program will include trained professionals from multiple agencies, interagency agreements permitting information sharing, and rapid access to intervention services.

The interventionist should provide a brief summary of the situation to the mental health agency and explain why clinical support is being sought. The interventionist should then forward a copy of juvenile's file to the clinician assigned to the case. The file should include results of the screening process, applicable notes, and the narrative completed by the interventionist. This information allows the clinician to review the case background, together with the interventionists' comments and interventions that have occurred to date. This information is vital to the clinician as he or she designs an intervention strategy.

While some JFIS programs allow interventionists to make initial contact with mental health professionals on behalf of a family, others prefer the parents of a juvenile to perform the action. The benefit of the latter is that it promotes responsible behavior on behalf of the parents. However, if a parent fails to make an appointment for clinical services, no intervention will occur. An alternative approach to circumvent this problem is for the interventionist to contact the mental health agency, advising them to expect a request for service from the respective family. The agency/clinician can then notify the interventionist that a request for service was or was not received **(Figure 19.10)**.

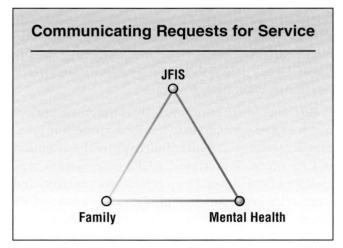

Communicating Requests for Service

JFIS

Family   Mental Health

Figure 19.10 Communication among the interventionist, mental health services, and the family of the juvenile firesetter must take place in order for interventions to be effective.

If, for whatever reason, an educational intervention was not performed by the interventionist prior to referral to a MHP, the JFIS I should request that the clinician follow up with the interventionist to advise when and if educational services should be offered. Even in problematic or complex situations, most juveniles will benefit from educational intervention as long as it occurs in conjunction with supervised clinical support and at an appropriate time. Maintaining an open line of communication with referral agencies helps ensure these parameters are honored and facilitates continuity of service.

Finally, as part of his or her training process, the JFIS I should spend field time with a mental health clinician, and vice-versa. When partnering agencies allow their staff to learn how each group contributes to the mutual goal of firesetting mitigation, everyone benefits.

Implementing Required Legal Actions

Used in tandem with education, enforcement can be a powerful deterrent to the occurrence of risky behavior. While education may enlighten a population about why a specific action is dangerous, the threat of punitive consequences is often the persuading force behind a person's decision to not participate in a behavior they know is against the law.

Holding a juvenile accountable for his or her firesetting behavior by enforcing fire laws has a proven record of reducing both recidivism and first time fire incidents. In fact, the juvenile firesetting problem is often lower in communities that exhibit a no-tolerance policy against destructive behaviors. Communication among juveniles (particularly adolescents) occurs quickly, comprehensively, and often accurately. Even in larger communities, word can get around fast that firesetting is against the law and will not be tolerated. Creating this culture demands leadership from a strong inter-agency partnership or JFIS coalition.

In communities where formal inter-agency relationships are absent, justice system officials may lack adequate understanding of their local juvenile firesetter problem and available solutions. This lack of knowledge may contribute to weak enforcement measures. Weak and inconsistent enforcement can contribute to development of a culture where juvenile offenders view the justice system as being complacent and not a serious threat to inappropriate behavior. A weak system may also offer limited options for placing serious offenders into secure resident treatment centers or juvenile detention facilities.

Creating and maintaining partnerships with justice system officials is the job of a Level II program manager. However, in communities where strong inter-agency partnerships exist, the JFIS I will likely have frequent interaction with juvenile authorities. This is especially true in larger communities. For the sake of the next section, it is assumed that a working partnership or JFIS coalition is in place which includes strong support from the local justice system.

The Juvenile Justice System and Firesetting

An overview of fire laws was provided earlier in this chapter. In most communities, if a child above the age of accountability sets a fire or violates a law, he or she may be held responsible for the actions and referred to the local **Department of Juvenile Justice (DJJ)** for possible adjudication. Because a JFIS I will refer cases to and accept referrals from their local DJJ, the interventionist needs to understand how a juvenile justice system works.

The Department of Juvenile Justice is a branch of state government that enforces laws violated by juveniles. It also coordinates appropriate rehabilitation services and dispenses disciplinary and punitive measures. The juvenile justice system will usually open a case against a juvenile after receiving a referral from a school or public service agency such as police, fire marshal, or social services. In some cases, a frustrated parent may seek disciplinary assistance for a child who has broken laws and where parental intervention has failed.

Upon receipt of a referral, a DJJ intake officer reviews the situation and makes a recommendation on disposition. If adjudication is deemed appropriate, the juvenile and his or her parents must appear at an intake conference. The purpose of the intake conference is to assess the juvenile's level of understanding, review all charges, and seek explanation of why the incident(s) occurred. For minor first-offense cases, the intake officer may grant probation. If terms of the probation are completed, no record of criminal behavior is officially recorded. In more serious cases, or if a juvenile is obstinate, the officer may forward the case to juvenile court for an adjudication hearing.

Juvenile adjudication hearings are usually held in a local courthouse. A local judge presiding over juvenile court hears the case and enters judgment. As with adult crimes, the level of penalty corresponds with the severity of the offense. A first-time offender may receive supervised probation, community service, and be ordered to pay restitution. In the case of fire-related offenses, he or she may also be ordered to complete a JFIS program. For more serious offenses or repeat behaviors, incarceration or placement into a secure and structured rehabilitation facility may be imposed. Serious offenses generate a juvenile criminal record. The record is sealed when the juvenile reaches age 18.

As discussed earlier, juvenile firesetters may reside in homes where environments are chaotic and parental supervision is lacking. Parents who lack responsibility often benefit when behaviors expected of them are mandated by authorities. In cases where parents display serious gaps in responsible behavior, or when any level of child neglect or abuse is suspected, the JFIS I should enlist the assistance of their local Department of Social Services.

Child Protective Services (CPS), or its local equivalent, is a branch of the Department of Social Services. Its mission is to safeguard a juvenile when abuse, neglect, or abandonment is suspected, or when there is no family to take care of the juvenile. CPS can help a challenged family by offering parenting skill and vocational training, financial assistance, homemaker services, and daycare. If in-home supports are insufficient, the department has authority (with court approval) to remove a juvenile from the home on a temporary or permanent basis. In extreme cases, CPS can facilitate placement of a juvenile into foster care or a specialty treatment facility. Ideally however, the goal is to keep the juvenile with his or her family whenever possible.

Because of their potentially dangerous consequences and correlation to family dysfunction, juvenile firesetting incidents often capture the attention of CPS units. Sometimes, a CPS case worker may contact a family even when referral was not initiated from a fire department or public safety agency. CPS has the right to investigate cases of possible neglect or abuse after learning of the situation through any public medium such as press coverage or the review of public safety incident reports.

How to Initiate a Referral to Juvenile Justice Authorities

As with the mental health community, a timely and appropriate level of justice system involvement occurs most frequently in communities where strong inter-agency partnerships or a formal JFIS coalition exists. Referrals to DJJ can be made by telephone, e-mail, or in person. Most DJJ systems utilize an intake process that is similar to juvenile firesetter intervention.

When a referral has been accepted, the JFIS I should forward the juvenile's case file to the DJJ case worker. If he or she has already interacted with the family and established a positive relationship, the interventionist may sometimes choose to accompany the juvenile and his or her parents to the intake conference. This strategy not only shows support for the juvenile, it also reinforces the interventionist's position that a person should be held accountable for their actions.

In more serious circumstances, an interventionist may be called by DJJ or CPS to testify on behalf of the local AHJ. This action may occur as result of recidivism, potential neglect or abuse, or when a juvenile commits other crimes after receiving intervention. In such cases, the interventionist is often subpoenaed to attend a special hearing and produce copies of the juvenile's case file. This, along with many other factors previously discussed, supports the rationale for maintaining complete and accurate case files.

Facilitating Accountability from Juveniles and Families

Holding a juvenile and his or her parents/legal guardians responsible for completing the terms of a JFIS program helps prevent recidivism. Depending on the type and severity of a situation, one or a combination of firesetting interventions may be used as part of a JFIS program. Education is often used alone in situations of first time curiosity-motivated firesetting. In more complex cases, a combination of education, clinical support, and punitive actions may be suggested, or in some cases, imposed.

Performing follow-up allows the interventionist to maintain open communication with the family, monitor an intervention's progress, provide support, and track program impact. Equally important, it sends a message that the JFIS coalition and the community are serious about preventing recidivism. The ultimate goal of follow-up is to ensure all required components of the JFIS program have been completed and recidivism has not occurred.

Juvenile firesetters who show remorse, demonstrate accountability for their actions, and have strong support from their family are more likely to complete the terms of a JFIS program and less likely to exhibit acts of recidivism. This fact is true for most curious firesetters and also in many problematic situations. In cases where a strong support system exists, the terms of completion for the JFIS program are often met in advance of deadlines by cooperative participants.

Unfortunately, not all juveniles and their parents will comply with recommended, or in some cases mandated, interventions. Cognitive, social, and behavioral dysfunction on the part of the juvenile and/or his or her parents may influence levels of compliance. In situations where cooperation and support systems are questionable or dysfunction is suspected, a more intense level and longer term of monitoring should be provided by the JFIS coalition and local AHJ.

The previous section discussed the use of sanctions and other penalties as interventions to mitigate recidivism. If a law has been violated or a juvenile is delinquent, the Department of Juvenile Justice can order specific interventions be completed as part of an adjudication process. If a child is being neglected or abuse is suspected, the Department of Social Service's Child Protective Unit can mandate specific behaviors from parents. If the directives of these agencies are violated, each has the authority to remove a juvenile from his or her home and impose higher levels of justice system involvement.

While most parents will work closely with their child and the interventionist to ensure preventive interventions are completed, the threat of punitive action is a powerful persuader in the case of dysfunctional high-risk situations. Regardless of the intervention medium selected, all parties must understand why it has been chosen, how it will be used, and what behaviors are expected from participants.

Chapter Summary

While education is the foundation of preventive strategies, there are situations where it is used as a secondary intervention. In cases where anger or a crisis situation has motivated firesetting, evaluation by a licensed mental health professional is needed to further examine the root causes behind behaviors. For situations involving juvenile delinquency and violation of laws, justice system intervention may be required prior to educational intervention. Identifying exceptional situations and consulting with JFIS partners will help ensure education is included as an appropriate and timely approach to intervention.

Review Questions

1. What steps should be followed during an intake process to ensure that basic information about the child/youth, family, and firesetting incident is obtained?

2. What is the proper method for reviewing a case file so that background information is analyzed before initiating contact with a juvenile's family?

3. What is the process for communicating with a juvenile's family so that program benefits/options are explained and an in-person interview is scheduled?

4. What is the proper method for interviewing juveniles and family members so that information pertinent to a firesetting situation is obtained, recorded, and evaluated?

5. What is the process for selecting the proper methods of intervention for firesetting behaviors based on information obtained through use of an approved risk-assessment process?

6. What is the procedure for implementing interventions for firesetting behaviors?

7. What is the procedure for facilitating accountability from juveniles/families who are receiving intervention services?

Key Terms

Abuse — Harmful behaviors and/or actions, as defined by local law, that place an individual at risk and require reporting.

Age of Accountability — The minimum age at which State Courts have ruled that a child is intellectually capable of understanding right from wrong and the consequences associated with inappropriate behavior.

Assessment Instrument — A tool to help the frontline JFIS identify why a juvenile is setting fires and his or her risk of repeat behaviors. An assessment instrument should be validated by mental health clinicians and use a scoring process to determine levels of risk for repeat firesetting behaviors.

Case File — A file that includes all documentation from an agency pertinent to a specific juvenile firesetting case.

Child Protective Services — A branch of the Department of Social Services. Its mission is to safeguard a juvenile when abuse, neglect, or abandonment is suspected, or when there is no family to take care of the juvenile.

Clinical Social Worker — A frontline health professional who often serves as a case manager to assist clients with information, referral, and direct help in dealing with the mental health intervention process. A clinical social worker can interview and counsel clients, but cannot write prescriptions.

Department of Juvenile Justice (DJJ) — A branch of state government that enforces laws violated by juveniles.

Gatekeeper — A primary care physician or local agency responsible for coordinating and managing the health care needs of members. Generally, in order for specialty services such as mental health and hospital care to be covered, the gatekeeper must first approve the referral.

Inpatient Mental Health Treatment — Hospitalization in a facility where 24 hour supervised care is present. This type of center offers treatment in cases where a child is in crisis and possibly a danger to him/herself or others.

Psychiatrist — A psychiatrist is a medical doctor who specializes in mental health and who can prescribe medications.

Psychologist — A clinical psychologist is a professional with a doctoral degree in psychology who specializes in therapy. He or she can help direct several levels of clinical intervention.

Residential Treatment Center — Provides 24-hour care and can usually serve several young people at a time. Children with serious emotional disturbances receive constant supervision and care at an RTC. Treatment may include individual, group, and family therapy; cognitive / behavior therapy; special education; recreation therapy; and medical services. Residential treatment is usually more long-term than inpatient hospitalization.

Chapter 19 Notes

1. *Juvenile Firesetter Intervention Handbook*, FA-210 <www.usfa.dhs.gov/applications/publications> Manuals and Reports.

2. *Fireproof Children* www.fireproofchildren.com/>

3. The National Mental Health Information Center.

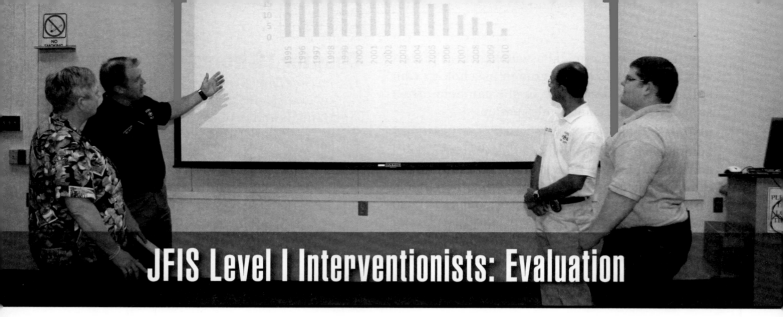

JFIS Level I Interventionists: Evaluation

Chapter Contents

Key Terms

Job Performance Requirements

This chapter provides information that addresses the following job performance requirements of NFPA® 1035, *Standard for Professional Qualifications for Fire and Life Safety Educator, Public Information Officer, and Juvenile Firesetter Intervention Specialist*, 2010 edition.

NFPA® 1035 References

9.5.2

JFIS Level I Interventionists: Evaluation

Learning Objectives

After reading this chapter, students will be able to:

1. Explain why evaluation is an integral component of risk reduction.

2. Describe the levels of program evaluation.

3. Discuss the reasons follow-up evaluation should be performed in all JFS cases (NFPA® 1035, 9.5.2).

4. Summarize the evaluation duties required of a JFIS Level I practitioner.

Chapter 20
JFIS Level I Interventionists: Evaluation

Case History

Steven, a preteen in a residential treatment center, had a hard time understanding the point of the classes he was required to take about juvenile fire facts and consequences. He knew he was under some pressure because his state's protocol mandated that first-offense juvenile firesetters take a fire safety class before being released to their families. Second offenses were treated much more strongly.

Fortunately for him, his treatment center was in the process of adding features to the program with the assistance of the local fire department. The fire department hosted a mini-fire academy in which the firesetters were required to participate. Attendees were ages 13-16, and all had a history of problematic firesetting.

During the course of the academy, students learned fire skills such as donning a full SCBA harness. Students discovered the discomfort of the weight and heat of full gear in the summer heat and realized how much worse it must be working an actual fire.

Follow-up classes included lectures on how much money was required to dispatch a truck as well as the level of danger involved on all calls. Students were empowered with information that they could actively use. Because of the useful nature of this program's features, Steven no longer sets fires to cope with his stress levels. Since the addition of the hands-on interventions included in this program, the effectiveness of the program increased significantly.

Source: Michael McLeieer, Training Coordinator for Juvenile Firesetter Programs; Massachusetts Fire Academy

Evaluation should be an integral component of every community risk-reduction program. At its lowest level, evaluation can provide interventionists with feedback on program delivery methodologies and outreach saturation. Its intermediate stage can statistically validate that a program is producing measurable and positive impact among intended audiences. At its highest level, evaluation can prove that a program is saving lives. As evidence to the importance of evaluation, each level of NFPA® 1035 includes job performance requirements pertinent to the subject. Chapters 6, 11, 16, 20 and 25 of this manual are dedicated to evaluation and should be consulted as needed.

A thorough evaluation is the only way to objectively examine if a program is performing as designed. Statistically measuring the impact of a program involves use of simple mathematics and is well within the capability level of a risk-reduction interventionist.

Three levels of evaluation are used when investigating the performance of a program — process, impact, and outcome.

- Process evaluation examines the development and delivery methodologies of a program.

- Impact evaluation studies how well the program increased participant knowledge and facilitated appropriate behavioral change.

- Outcome evaluation measures if the program is contributing to reducing the occurrence and severity of incidents.

Chapters 6 and 11 provide very thorough explanations of the levels of evaluation that interventionists will perform when examining risk-reduction programs. The following section explains evaluation tasks that will be performed by interventionists. (NOTE: For the best results, it is important to read the information provided in earlier chapters. Some jurisdictions require FLSE I qualification for their JFIS I interventionists.)

How a JFIS I Uses Evaluation

All levels of evaluation require advance planning so the intended data can be appropriately collected and processed into useful information. The evaluation process for any risk-reduction effort should be designed when the program is being planned. Evaluation continues through the life cycle of the program.

Successful evaluation techniques can be effectively learned through educational organizations that teach and practice routine evaluation. The National Fire Academy in Emmitsburg, Maryland, offers an excellent resident course that instructs interventionists how to prove the success of risk-reduction programs. The reader is encouraged to contact the institution for further information about this course.

Process Evaluation

A JFIS will use process evaluation, also known as program monitoring, to track the delivery and outreach of a JFIS program. Process evaluation is also used to examine the strengths and challenges associated with a JFIS program. The Level I interventionist should

collect and record feedback at designated intervals from JFIS program participants after interventions have been provided. When performed, this action is an example of process evaluation.

Process evaluation is nonstrategic in nature and does not provide statistical proof that a program is educating learners or changing behaviors among target populations. Although it is nonstrategic and qualitative in nature, conducting a thorough process evaluation is important because it can identify challenges to a program early in its life cycle. Through accurate and organized record keeping, this level of evaluation should be very easily accomplished.

Significant information can be obtained by soliciting feedback from program participants as to how well they thought the interventionist conducted interviews, delivered educational intervention, and interfaced with the family during referral to other agencies (**Figure 20.1**). Interventionists can use feedback to enhance their interpersonal skills, communication abilities, and instructional proficiencies. The program manager can use it to better match interventionists with target populations. In addition, asking participants their opinion of program materials and intervention methodologies also generates feedback that can be used to enhance an overall JFIS program.

Impact Evaluation

Impact evaluation is the second highest level of evaluation. It is used to measure knowledge gain and behavioral change among participants of a JFIS program. Unfortunately, educators sometimes omit impact evaluation because it involves a lot more time and effort than program monitoring. Impact studies require more planning and effort than process evaluation but they also yield a higher usefulness of evaluation data. Objective baseline statistics must be in place before impact evaluation can be conducted. The only way that accurate impact can be proven is to obtain baseline information on target populations before conducting a program. (NOTE: Refer to Chapter 11 for more information explaining how to develop baseline data.)

Knowledge gain created by a JFIS program can be measured through pretesting and posttesting, verbal or written surveys, and inquiries about services being offered. Behavior change and modifications to a person's living environment or lifestyle can be

Smithville Fire and Life Safety Consortium

We appreciate your feedback. Please take a moment to circle the number that best describes your opinion of the **Juvenile Firesetter Intervention Program**. Your comments are very helpful towards our efforts to continually improve the program.

	Strongly Agree	Agree	Disagree	Strongly Disagree

The staff was courteous and helpful. | 1 | 2 | 3 | 4 | 5 | 6 | 7 | 8 |

Comments: _____
_____

The information presented was age-appropriate and useful. | 1 | 2 | 3 | 4 | 5 | 6 | 7 | 8 |

Comments: _____
_____

The instructors were effective. | 1 | 2 | 3 | 4 | 5 | 6 | 7 | 8 |

Comments: _____
_____

Your one-hour assessment with your son/daughter was comfortable, given the circumstances of the appointment. | 1 | 2 | 3 | 4 | 5 | 6 | 7 | 8 |

Comments: _____
_____

You would be willing to encourage others to use this program. | 1 | 2 | 3 | 4 | 5 | 6 | 7 | 8 |

Comments: _____
_____

Figure 20.1 Feedback about a program provides significant information that may be used by program developers to improve the services offered.

measured through observational surveys and home inspections.

After baseline information is established, interventionists perform follow-up actions to document knowledge gain and behavioral change that have occurred among populations who have received service from a JFIS program. Conducting these actions is a form of impact evaluation.

Outcome Evaluation

Although not in the domain of the JFIS I's duties, all members of a JFIS team should understand that their work contributes to the success of the program as a whole. Outcome evaluation can provide the strongest evidence that a program is working by identifying a reduction in the occurrence of JFIS incidents, injuries, and loss of life and property. When performing outcome evaluation, a program manager uses fire experience data to track statistical and anecdotal evidence collected over a period of time, usually 5

to 10 years. As with measuring impact, baseline risk statistics must be available so comparisons of conditions before a program's inception can be made with those after it has been operating for several years.

Reasons to Perform Follow-Up Evaluation

According to NFPA® 1035, the Level I JFIS Interventionist is expected to be able to perform both process and impact evaluation duties as part of follow-up to each JFIS case they are assigned. **Follow-up** can be defined as the act of maintaining contact with a juvenile firesetter and his or her family over a designated period of time.

There are several compelling reasons why a JFIS should perform follow-up evaluation on all firesetting cases:

- Follow-up can be used to examine if an appropriate and adequate level of program support is being provided to the juvenile and his or her family.

- Follow-up can help identify if the juvenile and family are proceeding with suggested or mandated intervention services.

- Feedback from participants can help identify strengths and challenges associated with the JFIS program.

- Knowledge gain and behavioral change that has been facilitated by the JFIS program can be documented.

- Follow-up evaluation can be used over a longer term to determine if the JFIS program is reducing the occurrence of recidivism.

The ultimate goal of a JFIS program should be to facilitate a continuum of care that ultimately terminates firesetting behaviors. **Continuum of care** is the level and intensity of services needed to facilitate a positive outcome. In the case of simple first-time curiosity-motivated firesetting situations, the continuum of care may only be educational intervention with follow-up services provided by the interventionist. Problematic situations are usually more complex, requiring a broader base of supportive resources employed over a longer period of time and by multiple agencies.

Conducting follow-up with JFIS program participants helps reduce service gaps in the continuum of care. This continuity can be challenging to maintain when multiple agencies are providing services. For example, in complex firesetting situations, a family may be receiving integrated services from a JFIS program and a mental health clinician. Justice system or social service officials may be involved as well. Sometimes, parents become frustrated when trying to coordinate services among several agencies, all of whom have busy staff with large caseloads **(Figure 20.2)**. This frustration can result in a family failing to follow through with interventions.

Chapter 19 discussed the important role that a clinical social worker plays by helping families navigate the mental health system. When the JFIS program is the point of entry for a family, the interventionist should consider acting as a gatekeeper to help clients navigate the overall firesetting intervention system.

Maintaining contact with a juvenile firesetter and his or her family over time helps maintain accountability from all involved parties and agencies. It also proves the interventionist is concerned for the family and serious about ensuring compliance with

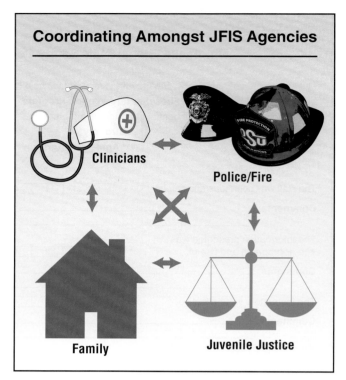

Figure 20.2 Multiple agencies must coordinate with the juvenile firesetter's family in order to provide necessary services.

program standards (whether voluntary or mandated). How long follow-up occurs is a decision usually made collaboratively between an interventionist, the program manager, and when applicable, case workers from referral agencies.

Generally, a primary follow-up is recommended 4 to 6 weeks after intervention. A secondary follow-up should occur 6 to 12 months after exit from the JFIS program. In complex and problematic cases, follow-up should occur more frequently. The specifics of the situation should influence what levels of follow-up are provided.

Collecting and Recording Program Feedback

Soliciting feedback from JFIS program participants occurs as part of process evaluation. As stated earlier, NFPA® 1035 directs the Level I Interventionist to collect and record feedback from program participants at designated intervals as follow-up to the JFIS intervention process. The collection medium is designed by a Level II Program Manager and administered by the Level I Interventionist. Once the desired information has been obtained, it is recorded and forwarded to the program manager.

Several communication mediums exist to collect feedback from JFIS program participants. The most popular include telephone, mail, e-mail, and direct in-person contact.

Telephone interviews represent the easiest follow-up medium to utilize when soliciting feedback on a JFIS program. The interventionist simply contacts the family by telephone and asks a series of predetermined questions pertinent to follow-up of the JFIS program. This strategy is time efficient and results in minimal expense.

Some JFIS programs use postal system mail or e-mail to seek feedback from participants. While these mediums are also low cost, getting parents to return survey forms can sometimes be a challenging process.

While telephone, mail, and e-mail share the advantages of being low cost and easy to administer, all three share a significant disadvantage — the interviewer cannot personally interact with the family in their home environment. Additionally, it is difficult to obtain meaningful written feedback from a child. For this reason, many JFIS programs develop and use a variety of follow-up mediums. This strategy allows the interventionist to select a medium that best fits each specific situation.

Follow-Up on Incidents

Follow-up on simple first-time incidents that are curiosity motivated, telephone or mail contact with parents may be a viable option. However, in problematic or complex situations, it may be prudent to facilitate a direct in-person meeting with the juvenile firesetter and his or her parent or legal guardian. Direct contact allows both the juvenile and parent(s) an opportunity to provide a higher level of feedback on the JFIS program. This is especially helpful when seeking feedback from children. Many programs have developed age-appropriate mediums specifically designed to seek follow-up from children. Conducting in-person follow-up with families also serves a very important function: It allows the interventionist to directly observe family dynamics and living conditions. Both serve as key indicators of behavioral and environmental change.

Measuring Changes in Knowledge and Behavior

Impact evaluation is considered strategic because it requires the gathering of baseline data before intervention. Because of its strategic nature, impact evaluation offers a high level of proof that a JFIS program is facilitating positive change among a target population. To get the most use out of collectable data, the JFIS I should measure behavioral changes that occur among a firesetter and his or her family as a direct result of the JFIS program. Results are then documented in the juvenile's case file and forwarded to the JFIS program manager.

When seeking to evaluate if knowledge, behavior, or environmental changes have occurred among a JFIS program's target population, the researcher must compare circumstances before and after the program was administered. Assessment instruments are developed by Level II program managers and administered by Level I interventionists.

Studying Knowledge Gain

Knowledge gain is a precursor to behavior change. An increase in knowledge helps affect changes in a learner's attitude. A change in attitude, coupled with new knowledge and increased skill level, can lead to modification of one's behavior. Measuring knowledge gain should be included as part of impact studies.

One of the most popular and reliable instruments for measuring changes in knowledge levels is the pretest and posttest. To measure knowledge change, the same test is given to JFIS program participants before services begin and at a designed point (or interval) afterward. Many JFIS programs administer their fire safety knowledge pre-test just prior to the screening process or while other parties are being interviewed. The post-test is administered at some point during follow up.

Tests for knowledge must always be appropriate by age and developmental factors. Many JFIS programs develop written tests specific to age groups: older children, adolescents, and adults. In the case of younger children, verbal tests employing use of pictures or other props may provide more reliable results.

Evaluating changes in human behavior and living environments can be more time-consuming than measuring knowledge gain. However, doing so can provide a greater indication that a JFIS program is producing tangible results.

Studying changes in behavior and living environments can be measured by several mediums. The most popular choices include questionnaires, written surveys, and direct in-person observation. Regardless of the medium used, a study should provide answers to the following questions:

- Has the population made specific behavioral changes related to firesetting prevention as a result of the JFIS program?

- Has the program helped to initiate any modifications to the family living environment conducive to firesetting prevention?

Verbal or written surveys are often used by JFIS programs to solicit information about behavioral change. While these mediums are cost effective and easy to perform, the data they produce can be skewed if respondents do not provide truthful responses. **Skewed data** is inaccurate because of faults inherent to the reporting mediums, bias from evaluators, or false information. When using a questionnaire or survey as an evaluation tool, it is very important to explain why respondents must provide fully truthful information. This applies to tools administered to both adults and children.

Verbal and written surveys can also be used to measure changes made to a person's living environment. Again, while these mediums are efficient by cost and time factors, results may be skewed.

Written documentation from referral agencies can also serve as documentation of impact created by the JFIS program **(Figure 20.3)**. Contingent on the presence of signed parental release forms, referral agencies can share documentation of how well the juvenile and his or her family has complied with the agency's recommended or mandated action plan.

The most powerful proof that behavioral and environmental change has occurred is through direct observation. This type of evaluation is performed by visiting a family in their home to directly observe their behavior and living environment. Many interventionists use home visitation in conjunction with other evaluation mediums:

- An interventionist schedules an in-person follow-up meeting at the home of a firesetter and his family.

- The interventionist secures permission for the juvenile to provide a tour of the home to evaluate

the safety plan that was created as part of the JFIS program. Depending on the circumstances, this activity can be done with all of the family members present or while the adults are completing a follow-up questionnaire.

- As the interventionist tours the home, he or she mentally records examples of behaviors that may have been changed as result of the JFIS program. Examples include isolation of ignition sources, matches and lighters properly secured, stove knob protectors in place, and the presence of working smoke alarms.

Figure 20.3 The documentation received from referral agencies can confirm the JFIS program's impact.

Chapter Summary

Evaluation is an integral component of risk reduction because it provides feedback on the effectiveness of a fire and life safety program. Process evaluation monitors a program and tracks outreach into a community. Impact evaluation measures changes in knowledge, behavior, and living environments. Outcome evaluation studies if a program is reducing the occurrence of incidents.

Every JFIS case should receive follow-up by the assigned JFIS I. Follow-up allows the JFIS I to receive feedback on levels of service provided by the interventionist and JFIS program. The data collected can also be used by program managers to evaluate and enhance the overall JFIS program.

By performing follow-up, the JFIS acts as a supportive advocate for the juvenile and his or her family. Maintaining this level of contact helps ensure an adequate continuum of care is provided to the firesetter and his family. This reduces the potential of recidivism — the ultimate goal of all JFIS programs.

Review Questions

1. Why is evaluation an integral component of risk reduction?

2. What are the levels of program evaluation?

3. Why should follow-up evaluations be conducted for juvenile firesetting cases?

4. What are the evaluation duties performed by a JFIS Level I?

Key Terms

Continuum of Care — The level and intensity of services needed to facilitate a positive outcome.

Follow-Up — The act of maintaining contact with a juvenile firesetter and his or her family over a designated period of time.

Skewed Data — Skewed refers to data that is inaccurate because of faults inherent to the reporting mediums, bias from evaluators, or false information.

JFIS Level II Program Managers: Knowledge and Skills

Chapter Contents

chapter 21

Key Terms

JFIS Level II Program Managers: Knowledge and Skills

Learning Objectives

After reading this chapter, students will be able to:

1. Describe the principal responsibilities of a Level II Juvenile Firesetter Intervention Specialist (JFIS II).

2. Illustrate typical decisions made by a JFIS II that influence the operation of a juvenile firesetting program.

Chapter 21
JFIS Level II Program Managers: Knowledge and Skills

Case History

The Merrimac Lions Club started supporting the local JFIS program when it was presented with documentation proving the reduction in juvenile firesetter cases was a result of the local fire department's JFIS program. The Lions Club understood and valued the importance of that reduction. As a result, the Lions invited the fire department back to its meetings every year to present an update. Over the course of this partnership, the Lions Club has increased its participation and support. Every year, the Lions Club increases the amount of funding it provides for the juvenile firesetter program. As well, the Lions Club has started donating their fund-raising efforts to the program.

The most successful program in the world is one that receives funding. Even if families get free service, it costs money to get help. When one service organization sees positive benefits to its community based on efforts by a related organization, others are more likely to join in.

Source: Michael McLeieer, Training Coordinator for Juvenile Firesetter Programs; Massachusetts Fire Academy

This section of the **Fire and Life Safety Educator** manual introduces the knowledge, skills, and leadership expected of a Juvenile Firesetter Intervention Specialist who meets Level II of NFPA® 1035. This chapter builds a foundation for the discussion of requirements for a JFIS Level II program manager.

The discussion begins with a description of the knowledge and skill levels expected, discusses the principal responsibilities, and culminates with a description of typical decisions made by a program manager. Because most juvenile firesetter intervention programs are led by a local fire agency, it is essential for the fire service to cultivate leaders in this field.

Knowledge and Skill Proficiencies

Because the JFIS II is expected to serve in a leadership capacity, he or she needs to have the following knowledge and skill proficiencies:

- A strong understanding of the motivations and factors that contribute to juvenile firesetting

- The ability to explain how the problem impacts his or her local community

- The skills to be a proficient strategist, organizer, and communicator who can direct the overall process of juvenile firesetting prevention and intervention. This includes the ability to recruit **community stakeholders** who can serve as partners to the process.

The JFIS II must know local laws pertaining to arson and the age of accountability that apply to juveniles in his or her community. He or she must also be able to identify situations that mandate involvement from juvenile justice authorities and how to initiate such actions.

Age of Accountability

In most jurisdictions, a child exhibiting normal cognitive development who has reached his state's age of accountability can be held legally responsible for starting a fire. The age of accountability is the minimum age at which courts have ruled that a child is intellectually capable of understanding right from wrong and the consequences associated with inappropriate behavior. The age of accountability may vary by state or province, but most place this age between seven and thirteen. The specific age is decided by a panel of experts including child psychologists, education officials, and the state's Supreme Court. It is the responsibility of a program manager to ensure that all interventionists are familiar with their area's age of accountability. (Comprehensive information on fire laws was presented in Chapter 19.)

Because he or she acts in a leadership capacity, the Level II JFIS needs to understand the policies and procedures that govern how juvenile firesetting is processed. This knowledge includes how juvenile firesetters are identified and ultimately receive services by the JFIS program.

A JFIS II must also have a clear understanding of how his or her organization's structure may influence delivery of the JFIS program. Determinants such as organizational culture, priorities, budget procedures, and resource allocation will all impact the development of a JFIS program.

The program manager must be proficient in oral and written communication skills. This skill set will be best displayed by his or her ability to mobilize community resources and encourage participation of external organizations. Additionally, the program manager must also be able to develop and manage a budget.

Many of the JPRs for a JFIS I and II are similar to those for a fire and life safety educator. To prevent redundancy, this chapter serves as a guidepost to direct the reader to chapters containing meaningful explanations of information that is summarized here.

Principal Responsibilities of a JFIS II

A JFIS I facilitates the case management of an identified firesetter so that screening, education, and necessary referrals are initiated. Level I interventionists process JFIS cases that have been assigned to them by a Level II program manager **(Figure 21.1)**.

In addition to meeting the JPRs of a JFIS I, the Level II JFIS has several additional duties which require that the program manager be able to skillfully manage the following tasks:

- Develop and lead a juvenile firesetter intervention program.
- Coordinate, supervise, and evaluate JFIS I interventionists.
- Coordinate and evaluate training.
- Define target audiences.
- Establish and maintain interagency networks.
- Coordinate the development of program goals and objectives.
- Develop, deliver, and evaluate education programs and awareness campaigns.
- Maintain and secure records of program components and firesetter case files.

Develop and Lead a Juvenile Firesetter Intervention Program

A common denominator of most successful teams is dynamic leadership. The program manager must develop and clearly articulate juvenile firesetter intervention (JFI) program goals and objectives to team members. The program manager's ultimate responsibility is to facilitate team effort toward reaching the program's goals.

A Juvenile Firesetter Intervention coalition is a formalized network of professionals who agree to meet to address specific community risks and concerns. The coalition develops the operating procedures of a program designed to address the juvenile firesetting behaviors in its community. This kind of program

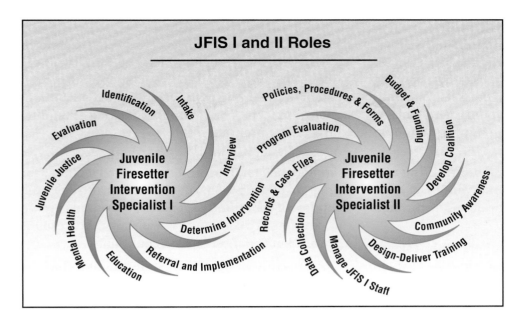

JFIS I and II Roles

Identification · Intake · Evaluation · Juvenile Justice · Mental Health · Education · Referral and Implementation · Determine Intervention · Interview · **Juvenile Firesetter Intervention Specialist I**

Policies, Procedures & Forms · Program Evaluation · Records & Case Files · Budget & Funding · Develop Coalition · Community Awareness · Design-Deliver Training · Manage JFIS I Staff · Data Collection · **Juvenile Firesetter Intervention Specialist II**

Figure 21.1 Interventionists and Program Managers perform many important roles.

is developed through the use of several sets of skills including research and interagency communication. A successful program will show clear results through the application of evaluation.

The JFIS II must be an expert in community risk reduction as it applies to juvenile firesetting behaviors and arson. This expertise includes being able to conduct community risk assessments, develop risk-reduction strategies, and evaluate programs. (These proficiencies were discussed in Chapters 7 and 9.)

An important responsibility of a JFIS II is to recruit partners who share a vested interest in preventing and mitigating fires set by juveniles. The JFIS programs most successful at producing impact are those that employ a broad-based interagency approach to addressing the problem. Logical stakeholders include schools, mental health agencies, social services, and the justice system. (The term *interagency coalition* is often used interchangeably with *network* or *coalition*.)

Because community support is essential to preventing and mitigating a local juvenile firesetting problem, the JFIS II must be prepared to act as coalition leader. Duties associated with this position include organizing, leading, and sustaining a multi-agency firesetting intervention program.

Coordinate, Supervise, and Evaluate JFIS I Interventionists

Recruiting, training, leading, and sustaining a staff of qualified **interventionists** is an important duty of a Level II program manager. In a larger organization,

the JFIS II may lead a staff of career interventionists. In some departments, the JFIS II may lead a team of specially trained field personnel, whether career or volunteer, who agree to serve as interventionists when needed.

One of the most important duties of a Level II program manager is reviewing and supervising the intake of juvenile firesetting cases and assigning them to the interventionist best suited to address the situation. To accomplish this task, the JFIS II must be proficient at distinguishing a **simple firesetting case** from one that is complex or problematic by using parameters explained in earlier chapters. (**NOTE:** Additional information on how to assign and evaluate juvenile firesetter cases will be provided in Chapter 22.)

The JFIS II is responsible for providing support to team members under their command including basic resources such as education, program materials, administrative tools, and transportation to perform their duties. Additionally, it is the responsibility of the JFIS II program manager to evaluate team member performance and provide constructive feedback to Level I interventionists. The most successful program managers are those who recognize an individual's strengths and help them excel in areas of personal interest, yet challenge him or her to explore new interests.

NOTE: Providing leadership and support to team members was discussed in Chapter 7. Evaluating team member performance was covered in Chapter 8. Subject matter specific to program managers will also be presented in Chapters 22 and 23.

Coordinate and Evaluate Training

Coordinating the required training for interventionists is the responsibility of the program manager. All members of a JFIS program need a basic understanding of child and adolescent development, social psychology, learning theory, and instructional methodology. (Chapters 5 and 10 provide some information on these subjects.)

In addition to this manual, more training and information on causation and intervention of juvenile firesetting behaviors may be obtained through a range of sources:

- The National Fire Academy offers both resident and regional delivery of courses designed to help students meet JFIS I and II status.

- Many state training organizations offer training programs.

- Nonprofit organizations such as SOS Fires in Portland, Oregon, as well as a number of fire departments throughout North America have developed excellent resources and systems to provide current information to interventionists and program managers. A listing of juvenile firesetter programs, professionals, and organizations can be found at www.sosfires.org and www.theideabank.com.

The program manager, with input from colleagues, seeks or develops training opportunities for interventionists and other staff who will participate in the intake process. The JFIS II should remain current on emerging training opportunities through ongoing networking with colleagues and review of credible current information sources. Knowing where and how to secure training opportunities, and evaluating the progress of team members' abilities and knowledge gain, are primary duties of the program manager.

> NFPA® 1035 requires interventionists who work with juvenile firesetters to meet the minimum licensing or certification requirements within his or her respective jurisdiction and profession. This includes, but is not limited to, Fire and Life Safety Educator I, fire investigator, law enforcement official, health care provider, social service worker, or educator.

Define Target Audiences

The Level II program manager is expected to perform a strategic analysis of his or her community's juvenile firesetter problem. This includes defining the extent of the problem, its geographic distribution, causation factors, and populations that should be targeted for program services.

The program manager ensures that juvenile firesetters and their families are identified and recruited for program participation. The JFIS II must also enlist the support of community agencies best suited to serve as partners in a community-wide juvenile firesetter prevention and intervention coalition.

A program manager must define populations such as neighborhood groups, property owners, and community leaders who are stakeholders in the local firesetting problem. (Comprehensive information on how to define target audiences was presented in Chapter 9.)

Establish and Maintain Interagency Networks

The program manager leads the process of securing and maintaining interagency networks designed to help prevent and mitigate juvenile firesetting. The goal of such networks is to create rapid accessibility of broad-based intervention services for juvenile firesetters and their families.

To successfully create support networks, the program manager must forge professional relationships and maintain open communication with leaders from partnering organizations. He or she must understand each agency's primary mission and the services each provides to the community.

NOTE: Discussion on how to forge interagency partnerships can be found in Chapters 4, 7, 9 and 14. Information on coalition development was presented in Chapter 14. Additional information specific to JFIS interagency networks will be shared in Chapters 23 and 24.

Coordinate the Development of Program Goals and Objectives

Clear goals supported by measurable objectives are principal building blocks of a JFIS program. The program manager is expected to facilitate the process of developing a comprehensive plan to address juvenile firesetting in his or her community, since developing a plan is best accomplished within the expertise of an interagency partnership.

Any evaluation plan should include an overall goal. The goal must be supported by a series of measurable objectives that direct prescribed actions and provide tangible impact from the overall program. The plan's objectives must be realistic, include deadlines for completion, and state how progress will be evaluated. Each objective should identify a person or group responsible for actions that are expected to be completed.

The program manager is ultimately responsible for evaluating the progress of the plan. It is his or her duty to maintain open communication with those responsible for completing tasks outlined in an evaluation plan. (**NOTE:** This manual has devoted a significant amount of time to the topics of planning and evaluation. Information was presented in Chapters 6, 7, 11, and 14.)

The program manager also shares responsibility for obtaining and allocating resources to support the program. (**NOTE:** Discussion on how to seek and distribute resources to support JFIS programs was included in Chapters 8, 9, and 13. Additional information will be included in Chapter 22.)

Develop, Deliver, and Evaluate Education Programs and Awareness Campaigns

Several considerations must be accounted for during the life cycle of educational programs and awareness campaigns. Establishing the need for a program, developing a program that matches that need, delivering the program to the appropriate audience using time-proven techniques, and evaluating the effectiveness of the program are all essential skills.

Education Programs

The educational component of a JFIS program is most often delivered by fire and life safety educators. Populations targeted to receive intervention are juvenile firesetters and their parents and caregivers. As discussed in Chapter 19, the most common information presented during an educational intervention for a juvenile firesetter includes:

For the juvenile:

- The importance of fire and its appropriate uses
- Explanation of why juveniles may choose to start a fire

- Dangers of uncontrolled fire
- Penalties associated with misuse of fire

For the parents and caregivers:

- The appropriate uses of fire
- Profile of the national juvenile firesetting problem
- National problem contrasted with local concerns
- Explanation of why juveniles may choose to start a fire
- Dangers of uncontrolled fire
- Penalties associated with misuse of fire
- Overview of the local JFIS program's broad-based mitigation strategy

A primary duty of a JFIS I is to deliver and evaluate educational interventions. The JFIS II is responsible for selecting and developing the material presented during interventions. (**NOTE:** Chapter 5 of this manual discussed how to select educational materials that are appropriate for specific target populations. Chapter 10 explained how to develop custom-created materials to support an educational program.)

While serving in a leadership capacity, the JFIS II must retain the ability to deliver educational interventions. This is important because the Level II program manager is expected to model best practices of program delivery and mentor Level I interventionists. Further, the Level II program manager is often called upon to perform intervention services in **complex/problematic firesetting cases**.

In addition to mentoring team members, the Level II program manager is responsible for evaluating the impact created by educational interventions. This task is three-fold:

1. The JFIS II monitors delivery methodologies performed by Level I interventionists.

2. Through impact studies, he or she evaluates knowledge gain that occurs among juvenile and adult populations as a result of educational intervention.

3. Data is researched and evaluated to see if educational intervention helped produce behavioral changes among target groups.

NOTE: Discussion on evaluation may be found in Chapters 6, 11, 16, and 20. Additional information pertinent to the JFIS II will be presented in Chapter 25.

Awareness Campaigns

An **awareness campaign** is a series of marketing strategies designed to inform a community about its local juvenile firesetter problem and potential solutions. A good awareness campaign uses multiple message mediums to reach a broad spectrum of target groups: juveniles, parents, schools, service agencies, investors, and community leaders. The ultimate aim of the campaign is to raise awareness of the problem and rally stakeholders to help create solutions.

While a JFIS II is not expected to develop a comprehensive awareness campaign single handedly, he or she needs to orchestrate the process. Campaigns developed through a collaborative effort of the JFIS coalition and marketing professionals are the most likely to be successful. Once a campaign is developed, a JFIS II is expected to be able to make changes as indicated by the evaluation results in order to reach target populations in the most effective way possible. (**NOTE:** Information on marketing strategies was discussed in Chapters 10, 14, and 15. Material specific to Level II work will be presented in Chapters 23 and 24.)

Maintain and Secure Records of Program Components and Firesetter Case Files

All JFIS educators have an ethical and legal responsibility to ensure that program records and juvenile case files are protected and private. Paper-based records must be secured and electronic documents should be password protected. Program records include information on who has received services through the JFIS program. Case files contain personal information such as the juvenile's identity, address, and family structure. A case file also chronicles events that brought the juvenile into the program, interventions provided, and a summary of progress to prevent acts of recidivism.

While a JFIS I is usually the person who collects data to build a case file, the JFIS II has ultimate responsibility for assuring that records are maintained and information remains secure. Maintenance of records includes making sure program attendance documentation is current and juvenile case files are updated as necessary, and services and referrals are provided.

Typical Decisions Made by a JFIS II

NFPA® 1035 states that a JFIS II, in consultation with an interagency network, sets the mission, goals, and objectives of the juvenile firesetter prevention and mitigation program. This directive implies that a JFIS II must be a proficient leader who can make executive level decisions on behalf of the coalition. Though the program manager does *not* act independently to run the program, he or she must be able to make decisions that affect ongoing program operations. Several of those decisions are explained in the following sections:

- Assign cases to interventionists
- Modify educational intervention strategies
- Modify community awareness campaigns
- Manage the program budget
- Recruit new interventionists
- Expand the JFIS interagency network

Assign Cases to Interventionists

Depending upon how a JFIS case comes to the attention of the fire department, the JFIS II makes the initial and final decisions on the overall disposition of the cases. These decisions are oftentimes made in concert with input from the mental health and law enforcement coalition members (**Figure 21.2**).

The protocol of most JFIS programs calls for a Level II JFIS to review initial requests for service and assign cases to Level I interventionists. This assignment is made after the JFIS II has carefully evaluated the circumstances that prompt referral of a juvenile into the program.

When the JFIS II reviews the initial information, he or she examines factors such as specific behavioral issues, special needs, family demographics, and previous acts of firesetting committed by the juvenile. Analyzing this information allows the program manager to prioritize needs and dedicate resources accordingly. The JFIS II then selects the interventionist who is best suited to serve the juvenile and his or her family. The program manager also helps interventionists make decisions on cases that should be referred to the interagency network for supportive and/or mandated services.

In complex firesetting situations, the JFIS II often consults with specialized members of the JFIS coalition prior to making disposition of how a case will

Figure 21.2 The Program Manager works with other coalition members to make decisions on JFIS cases.

be handled. A complex case is often handled best through collaborative interagency involvement. More information on assigning cases will be provided in Chapter 22.

In addition to other duties, the JFIS II helps interventionists reach decisions on when to declare a case closed or hold it open while multiple levels of intervention take place. While most simple curiosity-motivated cases are relatively short-term events, complex situations may require a lengthy period of time to resolve.

Modify Educational Intervention Strategies

The delivery and impact of the educational intervention component of a JFIS program should be continuously evaluated. Program content must remain current and meet the needs of those being served. Many JFIS programs authorize their program manager or another appropriate individual to make minor modifications to educational intervention strategies on an as-needed basis.

Decisions on lesson plan content, learning or extension activities, program materials, and media presentations are often entrusted to the JFIS II by the coalition. The program manager makes modifications only after reviewing program evaluation results and consulting with fellow team members **(Figure 21.3)**.

Modify Community Awareness Campaigns

The program manager is ultimately responsible for measuring the effectiveness of a community awareness campaign targeting juvenile firesetting. A primary component of this process includes moni-

Figure 21.3 After consulting with coalition members, the Program Manager may make changes to program materials.

toring the number of requests for program services. If program requests fall short of those anticipated by the coalition, the program manager often makes decisions on how to modify marketing strategies.

Manage the Program Budget

A JFIS II should be proficient in budget management. While the JFIS coalition may help develop the overall program budget, the Level II program manager is often granted authority to make decisions on expenditures that support regular operations. To make informed decisions according to program protocol, the program manager must possess the following:

- Understanding of the JFIS program's budget process

- Knowledge of his or her organization's budget process

- An evaluation plan that outlines the program's goals and objectives

- A budget that includes resources and supports the evaluation plan

- Open communication with the coalition and program manager's organization's budget decision-makers

A program budget often includes two components: operating costs and personnel costs. Operating costs are the expenses needed to help create, evaluate, and sustain a risk mitigation strategy. Components of operating costs include the following:

- Program development, implementation, marketing, and evaluation costs

- Supplies and equipment

- Transportation and travel expenses

- Staff training costs

The JFIS II will often make decisions on how resources will be allocated to each of the above-listed areas. He or she must record where the resources were assigned and track budget expenditures for each category.

Personnel costs, including salaries, wages, and benefits, are usually the largest budget expense of an organization. While the participating agencies usually absorb the employee costs of their personnel, some programs use contractual services such as those provided under contract from a private mental health service.

NOTE: Information explaining how to develop and manage budgets was presented in Chapters 8 and 13. Additional information specific to the JFIS II will follow in Chapter 22.

Recruit New Interventionists

The presence of an adequate number of trained interventionists is essential to the success of a JFIS program. A program manager is responsible for monitoring staffing levels and recruiting additional interventionists according to program need.

Before recruiting additional interventionists, the program manager consults with the coalition and develops a job description explaining the scope of work that a Level I JFIS will perform. Required knowledge and skill expectations are listed as well **(Figure 21.4)**. The program manager then markets the opportunity to interested applicants. Upon receipt of applications, the program manager, with assistance from appropriate personnel, selects the best candidate to pursue Level I Interventionist status.

Expand the JFIS Interagency Network

In addition to recruiting and selecting new Level I interventionists, the program manager monitors local needs and makes recommendations on when to expand a JFIS network. As discussed earlier in this chapter, the programs most successful at producing impact are those that utilize a broad-based interagency approach to addressing the local problem.

While the ultimate decision to expand a coalition rests with the membership at-large, it is often the program manager who recommends such action. These decisions are made after evaluating the impact created by the program over time and monitoring occurrences of juvenile firesetting activity.

Chapter Summary

The Level II program manager is responsible for many tasks and decisions that require knowledge, expertise, and experience. Many of the responsibilities and duties performed by a JFIS II are similar to those of a Fire and Life Safety Educator II and III. Knowledge and skill proficiencies are similar as well. It is highly recommended for a JFIS II to pursue FLSE II and III certification. Mastering

Juvenile Firesetter Intervention Specialist (JFIS) I

Duties: The JFIS I is responsible for case management of juvenile firesetters for the purposes of assessment, education, and referral.

Primary Responsibilities:

- Responding to inquiries, reports, or referrals regarding juveniles engaged in firesetting activities
- Scheduling and conducting interviews with juvenile firesetter(s) and their families
- Determining appropriate referral resources as determined by the results of interviews
- Providing appropriate fire and life safety education as determined by interview results
- Collecting data and maintaining JF records
- Determining and implementing appropriate education and referral interventions (after consulting with supervisor) for each assigned JF case

Minimum Qualifications:

Certification/Licensing: Applicable certification and licensing within current profession and jurisdiction, ie: educator, health care provider, social services worker, law enforcement officer, fire investigator, or fire and life safety educator.

Knowledge: Agency and program policies and procedures, basic fire protection systems and devices, data collection systems, emergency reporting procedures, escape planning, family dynamics, fire causes, fire dynamics, fire prevention techniques, fire safety education, firesetter behavior, hazard identification and mitigation, human behavior during a fire, interviewing techniques, juvenile firesetter characteristics, legal issues, mental health opportunities, stages of human development, state/provincial and federal confidentiality laws, and signs or symptoms of abuse or neglect.

Skills: Must be able to communicate in both written and oral forms, employ interpersonal communication skills, apply a variety of interviewing techniques, gather and document case data, properly maintain required data using applicable data collection systems, deliver firesetter intervention educational programs, recognize risk areas, identify and report abuse or neglect, and comply with local or national jurisdiction regarding abuse and neglect.

Education: H.S. diploma/GED; bachelor's degree preferred.

Experience: A combination of work-related experience that demonstrates proficiency in the preceding list of minimum qualifications.

- 24 -

Figure 21.4 A sample job description for a Level I JFIS.

these higher proficiency levels will empower a JFIS II to function as leader and subject matter expert in the field of juvenile firesetting prevention and mitigation.

Review Questions

1. What are the principal responsibilities of a Level II Juvenile Firesetter Intervention Specialist?

2. What are the typical operational decisions made by a Level II Juvenile Firesetter Intervention Specialist?

Key Terms

Awareness Campaign — A series of marketing strategies designed to inform a community about its local juvenile firesetting problem and potential solutions.

Community Stakeholder — Person or group that is affected by or has a vested interest in a specific issue.

Complex/Problematic Firesetting Case — A juvenile firesetting situation that is motivated or exacerbated by cognitive, social, or environmental dysfunction.

Interventionist — A person who works directly with juvenile firesetters and their families to prevent acts of recidivism. The term *interventionist* is used interchangeably with *practitioner*.

Simple Firesetting Case — A juvenile firesetting situation motivated by curiosity and can be addressed effectively though educational intervention.

Chapter 21 Notes

The process of juvenile firesetting prevention/mitigation — National Fire Academy JFIS Curriculum

JFIS Level II Program Managers: Administration

Chapter Contents

chapter 22

Key Terms

Job Performance Requirements

This chapter provides information that addresses the following job performance requirements of NFPA® 1035, *Standard for Professional Qualifications for Fire and Life Safety Educator, Public Information Officer, and Juvenile Firesetter Intervention Specialist*, 2010 edition.

NFPA® 1035 References

10.2.1

10.2.2

10.2.3

10.2.4

10.2.5

JFIS Level II Program Managers: Administration

Learning Objectives

After reading this chapter, students will be able to:

1. Explain program policies and procedures that should be formulated to support JFIS program goals and community needs (NFPA® 1035, 10.2.1).

2. Discuss how to develop a program budget so that operating and personnel costs are determined and justified (NFPA® 1035, 10.2.2).

3. Explain how to select and assign Level I Interventionists to a JFIS case (NFPA® 1035, 10.2.3).

4. Articulate how to supervise a JFIS I so that program policies are followed, performance is evaluated, and ongoing support is given (NFPA® 1035, 10.2.4).

5. Overview how to supervise data collection for JFIS case files so information remains secure and available for official use according to established program policies (NFPA® 1035, 10.2.5).

Chapter 22
JFIS Level II Program Managers: Administration

Case History

Two brothers (ages 8 and 10) in Massachusetts were enrolled in a juvenile firesetter program. Intake screening was not conducted before they were admitted into an education-based program; therefore, there was no way for anyone to know *why* they were setting fires, just that they were.

One day, one of the brothers let slip in conversation that both of them were being molested by their father. The brothers were taken out of the program and the Department of Social Services was contacted. The boys were placed in protective custody so that they did not have to return to an abusive environment.

From the experience with that case, the program was immediately evaluated with a new focus on enhanced screening during the interview and intake process. The program manager required all program members to take refresher courses on intake procedures.

Source: Michael McLeieer, Training Coordinator for Juvenile Firesetter Programs; Massachusetts Fire Academy

The JFIS II Program Manager has many of the same responsibilities as the FLSE III Administrator and must remember that programs, networks, and staff members require consistent monitoring and evaluation. Establishing and reviewing the program policies and procedures in place will reduce the chance that key elements in the risk-reduction process will be overlooked.

Formulating Program Policies and Procedures

Juvenile firesetting can be a problem in any community. The scope of the problem is often influenced by the community's population size and demographics. Juvenile firesetting is influenced by family, social, environmental, and cognitive factors. Firesetting behaviors are often predictable and, in many cases, preventable.

Many U.S. communities have identified and are aggressively addressing their juvenile firesetting problem. JFIS programs most effective at reducing incident occurrence are usually those that have been developed by a multidisciplinary team of stakeholders. Logical stakeholders include representatives from the fire department, education community, social services, mental health agencies, justice officials, and citizens at-large. Once formed, this network should remain in place to serve as an advisory board to the juvenile firesetter intervention (JFI) program.

Primary prevention is a core component of every successful JFI program. The ultimate goal is to prevent a juvenile firesetting incident from happening in the first place. Educational curriculums for preschool to adolescent age groups should target not only students, but include an extension component to enlighten parents on the problem and potential solutions.

Secondary prevention is used to mitigate the effects of an incident that has already taken place. Educating parents and public officials about the local firesetting problem will help create a sense of urgency to address it. In addition, a user-friendly incident reporting system is needed so early detection and intervention of juvenile firesetting occurs. Finally, multiagency agreements that permit open lines of communication, cooperation, and referrals between groups that serve firesetters and their families will expedite interventions.

All juvenile firesetter intervention programs should have policies and procedures that support goals and objectives outlined in the program's action plan **(Figure 22.1)**. Program policies and procedures, referred to in this chapter as *protocols*, are rules that guide how a juvenile firesetting intervention program will be administered. Juvenile firesetter intervention program protocols are often developed in cooperation with the partner organizations (coalition) that serve juvenile firesetters and their families. Protocols are specific to the local AHJ and should be in place before a program is implemented.

Organizational protocols help facilitate consistency of operation. It is a nationally recommended practice that all emergency service organizations develop and follow Standard Operating Guidelines (SOGs) that direct how operations are performed. The National Incident Management System (NIMS) is one example of standard protocol that calls for specific actions to be taken during the mitigation of an incident.

All JFI programs should be governed by a protocol that outlines how each program component is to function. These policies and procedures will help ensure that a standard level and continuum of care is provided to each juvenile and family served by the program.

Once program guidelines are established, the program manager must ensure all interventionists understand and follow their organization's protocols for firesetting intervention **(Figure 22.2, p. 498)**. Interventionists must clearly understand these governances before they begin working with juvenile firesetters. Equally important, the interventionist needs to understand the referral process to other agencies. For example, in cases involving criminal activity or abuse, referral to other partner agencies is mandatory.

The United States Fire Administration, along with other nationally recognized experts, suggests development and use of the following JFIS core program content:

- A mechanism to identify local cases of juvenile firesetting
- An internal JFIS educational component
- Consistent reporting protocols
- A standard intake process
- An interview and screening process that uses approved assessment instruments
- An intervention process that includes multidisciplinary resources
- Follow-up services to each JFIS case
- Comprehensive program evaluation

Because the Level II JFIS helps develop the guidelines of how their organization's JFI program will operate, an in-depth discussion relevant to these components follows and will focus on core policies and procedures that should be developed to support the JFI program.

Problem Identification

Firefighters, police officers, mental health clinicians, social service workers, teachers, school counselors, parents, and the community at-large need to be educated about the problem of juvenile firesetting and how it impacts the local community. For the

Juvenile Firesetter Program

PURPOSE: To establish guidelines for the Juvenile Firesetter Program

SCOPE: Public Education Personnel, Investigations Section

PROCEDURE: Public Education Specialist/Juvenile Firesetter Interventionist Duties

1. A Public Education Specialist/Juvenile Firesetter Interventionist (Certified) is responsible for the duties of managing the Juvenile Firesetter Intervention Program. The Juvenile Firesetter Intervention Program is outlined as follows:

   1.1. Juveniles are referred to this program by a number of people and agencies including, but not limited to: Juvenile Probation, Diversion, Department of Human Services, Pikes Peak Mental Health, parents, schools, school districts, firefighters, and the Investigation Section. Investigators have the authority to arrest juveniles between the ages of 10-17 whereby the court will order the juvenile to attend the Juvenile Firesetter Class.

   1.2. Given that this position and program serves the entire fourth Judicial District, accommodations are made for juveniles and families who live in Teller County. A partnership has been created between Northeast Teller County Fire Protection District and the Colorado Springs Fire Department for the use of office space at its fire station.

   1.3. Once a referral has been made to the Interventionist, contact with the family is made by either telephone or letter to schedule a Juvenile Firesetter Assessment.

   1.4. Once completed, the assessment will determine whether the juvenile should be recommended to the Juvenile Firesetter Intervention Class, to Pikes Peak Mental Health for further assessment, or both.

   1.5. Court ordered offenders must meet all of the requirements set forth by the Interventionist. Juveniles under the age of 10, and noncourt ordered juveniles are recommended for the program only. All court ordered offenders that do not complete the requirements are referred back to probation or diversion for follow-up.

- 15 -

Figure 22.1 An example of a Juvenile Firesetter Program's action plan.

scope of this chapter, it is assumed the JFIS II has already conducted a community analysis, identified the scope of the local problem, and shared the information with the stakeholders listed previously.

Program policy should mandate ongoing evaluation of the local juvenile firesetter problem. Geographic distribution, frequency of occurrence, populations affected, morbidity, mortality, and economic costs should be evaluated at least annually by a qualified interventionist. Protocol should also call for evalua-tion results to be relayed to all stakeholders and the community at-large.

Internal Educational Component

The program manager is responsible for educating all staff members within his or her organization as to the problem of juvenile firesetting and its impact on the local community. All participants should be able to explain the various motivations behind firesetting behaviors, how incident reporting occurs, and services offered by the JFI program.

Figure 22.2 The program manager must ensure that all interventionists are aware of and follow the established program guidelines.

While firefighters, paramedics, or emergency services technicians are not expected to possess the same expertise as the JFIS II responsible for program leadership, the lethal potential of juvenile firesetting behavior mandate that everyone needs a basic understanding of what to do if a juvenile firesetting situation arises. Many fire departments integrate juvenile firesetter information and statistics into their organization's master training schedule. Training records should be documented.

Consistent Reporting Protocol

The JFIS II Program Manager is responsible for creating protocol specific to an AHJ that directs how incidents of juvenile firesetting are reported to the juvenile firesetter intervention (JFI) program. This may involve referral to JFIS team members or to the fire marshal. Unfortunately, many communities have no policy or procedures in place for reporting juvenile firesetting activity. Written protocols facilitate a consistent initial approach to JFIS cases. The protocols should address not only the procedure to follow when a juvenile-set fire is discovered while on an incident scene, but also explain how to handle when a person calls the firehouse or brings an offender to a station.

Collecting basic information about a juvenile firesetting situation helps ensure that a juvenile and his or her family will receive an appropriate

level of intervention. Some organizations train staff from each station on how to conduct a formal intake process. In other departments, protocol calls for an officer to gather basic information and forward it in a timely manner to a JFIS II for assignment.

Regardless of how much initial information is recorded, there must be a policy that directs what actions will be taken when a juvenile firesetting situation is discovered. All reports of juvenile firesetter activity should be documented, secured, and forwarded to the JFI program. Protocol should specify the appropriate timeline for information to be relayed to the JFI program.

In high-risk situations, the window of opportunity for intervention is often short. This is due, in part, to the sometimes transient lifestyles led by many at-risk families. It is critical to have a thorough and reliable reporting system in place so interventionists may begin mitigation efforts in a timely manner.

Intake Process

The intake process gathers baseline information about the firesetter, his or her family, and the situation resulting in referral of the juvenile to the intervention program. This background information is obtained from the juvenile's family or caregiver. Intake information can provide critical initial insight into the severity of a juvenile firesetting situation.

The Level II JFIS, local authority having jurisdiction, and intervention partners ultimately determine what information will be sought through the intake process. (See Chapter 18 for an example of an intake form.)

The JFIS II Program Manager is responsible for selecting and training personnel who will administer an intake process. Protocol should mandate specialized training for those who administer an intake process. Intake staff needs a baseline understanding of firesetter profiles and how to discern a simple case from that of a complex problem. Staff must also be able to identify which incidents call for immediate attention such as a crisis situation, abusive environment, or commission of a violent crime.

Certain situations warrant immediate action from the person collecting intake data. Federal law mandates immediate reporting of suspected child abuse or neglect. Local arson laws often require adjudication of juveniles who have damaged property through firesetting activity. Reports of recent and repeat firesetting behaviors signal the need for rapid intervention. JFIS protocol should outline situations that require immediate attention and possible referral. It should also provide clear direction on actions to initiate in response to a crisis situation.

A juvenile firesetter intervention program should have memorandums of understanding from partner agencies so that case information can be shared quickly and with informed approval from parents and guardians (**Figure 22.3**). Program policy should require that several documents will be explained by interventionists and signed by parents as part of the intake process: Program Participation Release Forms, Release of Liability, Release of Confidential Information, and a Risk Advisement form.

Program policy should also direct that a case file be opened for each juvenile firesetter at the time of intake into a program. This file will include all pertinent information about the juvenile firesetter case from intake through closure. Finally, protocol should dictate where and to whom intake information is to be forwarded, and specify the appropriate timeline for obtaining and referring case information.

Sample Memorandum of Understanding

7.1 Project Data and Information: The data created by the project is intended to benefit the residents of Applebee County and the State of Oklahoma. The measure of such benefits depends to a great extent on the careful collection and use of the data, subject to confidentiality restriction established by the Applebee County Juvenile Firesetters' Program. The Partners will collect data and other information, both for policy analysis and program evaluation. All Partners agree to cooperate with all aspects of the evaluation activities, including, but not limited to, facilitating site visits, providing names and other information about clients needed for the evaluation survey, interviews, and focus groups and provide requested documents, consistent with overall decisions of Partners as provided herein. All local Partners also agree to promptly provide personal data, organizational/outreach data, and other requested information to the Applebee County Juvenile Firesetters' Program coordinator or their designee, on a form approved by the Applebee County Juvenile Firesetters' Program. The Program's form shall permit uniform state and national compilation and analysis. Any use of the data and other information shall be made consistent with the overall policy decisions of the Partners and/or the Applebee County Juvenile Firesetters' Program. In addition, all disclosures shall be made consistent with applicable Oklahoma State and Federal privacy laws.

Figure 22.3 A sample memorandum of understanding for a Juvenile Firesetter Intervention Program.

Interview and Screening Process

The goal of an interview and screening process is to provide an interventionist with a much broader perspective of why a firesetting situation has occurred. It also builds a demographic profile of the firesetter's family and living environment. Finally, information about cognitive, behavioral, and environmental factors that may have influenced the juvenile's firesetting actions is obtained.

The interview and screening process is always conducted by a trained interventionist who uses an approved assessment instrument. Once compiled, results of an interview and screening process can help interventionists make decisions about the type(s) of intervention needed. Protocols should be drafted by the JFIS II Program Manager to support the following components of an interview and screening process:

- Direction on how to use the program's assessment instrument

- Explanation of how the interview and screening process will be conducted

- Selection criteria for interventionists who will conduct interviews

Assessment Instruments

The importance of using an approved assessment instrument to determine the root causes of firesetting behaviors and gauge the severity of the problem was explained in Chapter 18. The JFIS II Program Manager, in cooperation with mental health partner agencies, is responsible for selecting or developing an assessment instrument that fits local program needs.

Many organizations use one, both, or adapted versions of the nationally recognized JFIS screening tool published by the United States Fire Administration. The first version helps interventionists succinctly evaluate the severity of a firesetting situation. It features interview components for both adults and juveniles. The second version guides the interventionist through a much greater level of evaluation by seeking an in-depth perspective of why firesetting behaviors are occurring. Both resources use a scoring process to assess the level of potential risk for future firesetting behavior.

Some JFI programs, with input from local mental health agencies, have developed their own assessment instrument **(Figure 22.4)**. Regardless of the tool chosen or developed, once it has been approved by the JFIS governing body, it should be used by interventionists. All interventionists must receive training on how to administer the assessment instrument(s) used by their local JFI program. If more than one

Figure 22.4 A sample Assessment Instrument.

Common Elements of JFIS Program Assessment Instrument

General Information Section
Child/Youth Name
Date
Interviewer's name
Case #
School and Grade

Rapport Building Section
Do you like your teachers at school?
What classes/subjects do you like/not like?
Who's your best friend(s)?
What do you do for fun?
What computer games do you like?

School Issues Section
Is the youth experiencing any school problems?

Social/Family Relations Section
How does the youth get along with others in the neighborhood?
Does the youth have organized activities or positive alternatives to extra time?
How does the youth get along with parents/caregiver?
How does the youth experience discipline?
Has the child experienced any kind of crisis in the past six months?
Does the youth have any record of criminal activity?

Fire History Section
What was set on fire?
Was there anything significant about the object?
Where was the fire set?
Was there any particular significance to the location of the fire?
How much planning was done prior to the fire?
What was the youth's response to the fire?
How did the youth feel after the fire?
Was the youth supervised when the fire occurred?
How knowledgeable is the youth about fire?
How much does the youth understand about the dangers of fire?
Does the youth use fire for power or control?
Does the youth have a fire history?
How concerned was the youth for accepting responsibility for the fire?

Child/Youth Fire Needs Assessment Score Section
* *Uses a point system and matrix to identify potential intervention approaches (for example: provide fire safety education only, provide fire safety education and referral to behavioral health services, or referral for a crisis evaluation).*

---

instrument is available (as with the USFA materials), criteria should be put in place to guide interventionists on the appropriate instrument selection.

Conducting the Interview and Screening Process

The Level II program manager is responsible for directing how the interview and screening process will be conducted. Protocol should mandate use of the program's approved assessment instruments during all interviews to ensure the process is conducted thoroughly and sequentially.

In addition to outlining how interviews are to be conducted, policy should be in place that clarifies the manner in which the assessment instrument will be used. This includes actions to take based upon the assessment instrument's results. Many programs also have protocols that dictate when a report of the interview/screening process can be shared with parents.

A written narrative, summarizing the information recorded in the assessment instrument, should be submitted as part of the JFIS case file. Written in third person style, it should provide a nonjudgmental overview of services provided by the JFI program. A narrative can include information and observations pertinent to the intake, interview/screening process, assigned intervention(s), and follow-up.

Most professionals in service fields understand the importance of thorough and appropriate documentation. A narrative is one of the best mediums for relaying objective information between interventionists and coalition agencies.

SOS Fires summarizes the importance of a good narrative this way: "If the case is reopened one year from today, what information will be needed to understand the case and the intervention provided?" If documentation, including narratives, of program services can answer that question, it is likely that adequate information has been reported.

Interventionist Selection Criteria

While intake information may sometimes be collected by a trained staff member who is not a JFIS I Interventionist, interviewing and screening is always conducted by a trained interventionist approved by the local authority having jurisdiction. This interventionist must possess mastery knowledge of his or her agency's JFI program components as well as strong communication and interviewing skills.

JFI program policy should outline the education, experience, and skill proficiencies that an interventionist must meet prior to being approved to conduct interviewing and screening. Many programs require successful completion of the National Fire Academy's JFIS curriculum or its state approved equivalent. The didactic material is followed by a probationary period where he or she performs services under direction of a trained mentor.

In addition to formal JFIS training, frontline interventionists should also be knowledgeable in the stages of intellectual development, learning theory, disabilities, and interpersonal skills. Understanding people, family dynamics, and building rapport are critical elements when attempting to engage any family in JFI programs. Interventionists must understand child behavior well enough to interact with all age ranges and be able to effectively communicate with adults.

Intervention Process

Once interventionists have a thorough understanding of why a firesetting situation has occurred, the next step is orchestrating a formal response to the behavior. Services may include education alone or a combination of education, mental health counseling, medical services, social service support, and adjudication by the juvenile justice system. (**NOTE:** See Chapters 17-19 for levels of intervention that have proven successful in mitigating firesetting behaviors.)

The Level II program manager, in cooperation with partner agencies, is responsible for drafting criteria of how interventionists choose intervention strategies. The most appropriate intervention should be based on evaluation of information gathered during the intake, interview, and formal assessment processes, including statements made by juveniles and their parents, and interventionist observations made during family interviews.

Once an intervention strategy has been chosen, protocol should direct how it is to be implemented. While interventionists are often given autonomy to select interventions for low-risk curiosity-motivated firesetting situations, problematic cases usually require multifaceted services and are best addressed by a team of experienced professionals representing multiple disciplines.

A multidisciplinary approach has several important advantages:

1. Juveniles and their families are likely to receive a level of service appropriate to the situation.

2. Frontline JFIS interventionists are not forced to make decisions that are potentially above their level of expertise.

3. A more in-depth level of documentation on the JFIS case is created.

Program protocol should specify, in accordance with the AHJ, who is ultimately responsible for reviewing juvenile firesetter cases. A point person is essential to ensuring an appropriate continuum of care is being provided. Criteria should also be established that defines a situation, how it should be addressed, and an expected time frame for provided services.

JFI programs led by a coalition may have a team of experienced interventionists representing multiple disciplines available on-demand to review cases. In communities lacking a formal JFIS coalition, the Level II program manager must have a strong relationship with school officials, mental health agencies, social services, and the local justice system so a review and referral mechanism is in place.

Follow-Up

Every case of juvenile firesetting should receive follow-up service by the JFI program. Program policy should outline when and how this service should occur. In the case of a low-risk curiosity-motivated situation in which recidivism is unlikely, follow-up may be limited to telephone contact or a single home visit. With complex/problematic situations, several personal contacts may be warranted.

JFI program policy should specify the criteria for performing follow-up services on firesetting cases. Many programs have created a questionnaire or documentation form that is completed by interventionists performing follow-up services. The goal of follow-up services is to inquire about recidivism behavior, evaluate the family's living environment for safety compliance, and obtain feedback on the level of service provided to the family.

Program Evaluation

Statistical measurement of a JFI program's effectiveness is a task of the Level II JFIS. Three levels of evaluation should be conducted proficiently by the JFIS II Program Manager: process, impact, and outcome. These levels were discussed extensively in Chapter 11. The following information is a review of JFI program evaluation.

Process evaluation should be used to track a program's development, outreach into the community, and staff performance. Impact studies should examine changes in juvenile and adult knowledge levels, attitudes, behavior, lifestyles, and living environments. Outcome evaluation should look for changes in the occurrence of juvenile firesetting incidents, related injuries, deaths, and property loss.

Conducting evaluation is essential to determining if the JFI program is effective at reaching target populations, facilitating change, and preventing and reducing incidents.

Protocols should specify what information interventionists are to submit for review by the JFI Program Manager. Process evaluation is supported through records of program attendance, materials used and feedback from parents and juveniles. Impact studies require results from pretesting/posttesting, home visitations, follow-up services, and dialog with attendees. Reports of recidivism are used to evaluate overall program outcome.

Program policy should clarify expected reporting mechanisms and deadlines for data submission. Most programs call for Level I interventionists to provide their program manager with an ongoing report on open cases to ensure that continuity of care is being provided **(Figure 22.5)**. When a case has been officially closed, the entire file should be forwarded to the program manager immediately so it can be securely stored. (Additional information pertinent to JFI program evaluation will be presented in Chapter 25.)

Developing a Program Budget

A juvenile firesetter intervention program needs adequate resources to support its goals and objectives. JFI program resources can include money, people, time, program materials, and other support services. Development of a budget helps define the type and

Figure 22.5 An interventionist should keep the program manager updated on all open cases.

Grants, donations, and in-kind services represent excellent mediums for helping to start a JFI program. To legally receive these resources, it may be necessary that the organization has either nonprofit status or collaborates with an existing nonprofit affiliate who obtains and disperses funds. Chapter 8 featured information on the process of applying for nonprofit status.

Monetary allocation may be overseen by an advisory group or board of directors. In the case of public funds generated through municipal assessments or fees, a commission, board, or council approves all organizational budgets.

Whether a juvenile firesetter intervention program is supported by public funds, private donations, grants, or a combination of sources, its program manager must develop and submit an annual budget **(Figure 22.6)**. Regardless of a JFI program's size, there is a process and timeline for submitting budget proposals. Most municipalities (and sometimes non-

quantity of resources needed for a program and how they will be used.

NFPA® 1035 requires the Level II JFIS Program Manager to exhibit proficiency in creating a JFI program budget. The budget must identify all proposed expenditures, including operating and personnel costs. The program manager must be able to justify the need for all expenditures. Prior to discussing what should be included in a JFI program budget, it is important to review the origin of potential revenue sources and how a **budget cycle** functions. (Further information on this topic was presented in Chapters 7 and 13 and should be consulted as needed.)

Revenue Sources and Approval Mechanisms

Revenues to support a JFI program can be generated in a variety of ways. If the program is managed by a nonprofit coalition, a combination of donations, in-kind contributions, and **grants** may be used to support operations. In larger communities, public funds support program operations. Public funds may be generated through property or sales taxes, charges for services, or a combination of both. They are dispersed by the municipality having jurisdiction. (These kinds of funding sources are discussed in greater detail in Chapter 9.)

Smithville Fire Department
2011 Budget Proposal

Fire Prevention and Education Division:
Juvenile Firesetter Intervention Program

Account	Account Description	Actual FY 2010	Proposed FY 2011
Personnel			
7101	Regular Salaries	$ 137,848.33	$ 148, 108.66
7102	Withholdings and Benefits	$ 65,999.00	$ 72, 638.66
Personnel Total		$ 203,847.33	$ 220,747.32
Supplies and Services			
7351	Other Professional/Technical	$ 1,965.00	$ 2,500.00
7355	Learn Not To Burn	$ 1,728.65	$ 2,200.00
7356	JFI Seminars	$ 4,635.00	$ 5,500.00
7430	Repair and Maintenance Services	$ 562.13	$ 1,550.00
7550	Printing and Binding	$ 967.24	$ 1,500.00
7591	Travel and Training	$ 2,563.59	$ 3,500.00
7599	Memberships and Dues	$ 555.00	$ 750.00
7600	General Supplies	$ 11,019.42	$ 12,000.00
7612	Vehicle Maintenance	$ 2,001.59	$ 2,500.00
7614	Turnouts/Safety Equipment	$ 1,032.76	$ 1,550.00
7615	Clean/Maint: Turnouts/PPE	$ 462.13	$ 500.00
Supplies and Services Total		$ 27,492.51	$ 34,050.00
Administrative and Other			
Administrative and Other Total		$ -	$ -
Capital Outlay			
8040	Machinery and Equipment	$ 1,659.34	$ 3,500.00
Capital Outlay Total		$ 1,659.34	$ 3,500.00
Total Expenditures		$ 232,999.18	$ 258,297.32

Figure 22.6 An example of an annual budget proposal.

profit organizations) require budget proposals to be submitted several months in advance of the actual fiscal starting date.

Connect Budget Proposals to an Evaluation Plan

As explained in Chapters 7 and 11, the foundation of any risk-reduction budget proposal is the program's evaluation plan. The evaluation plan includes a problem statement, the program's goal, and a series of measurable objectives that outline how the plan will be carried out.

Developing a budget that corresponds with the JFI program's specific objectives allows decision-makers to see how the resource will impact overall outcome. It also helps justify why the expense should be funded.

Creating a budget for a JFI program is similar to developing an evaluation plan for addressing a risk issue. The proposal should articulate what is to be accomplished, how funds will be spent, and how results will be demonstrated. Most JFIS budget proposals include the following:

- Rationale explaining why the JFI program should be funded
- Scope of the JFI program
- Explanation of local problems and proposed interventions
- Estimate of program costs to include:
  — Staffing and training
  — Supplies, equipment, and transportation
  — Implementation and marketing
  — Evaluation

Understanding Operating and Personnel Costs

Whether under public or private supervision, most JFI program budgets will outline proposed program expenditures within a category entitled operations expenses. This topic is covered in depth in Chapter 13. Operations expenses include two sections: operating and personnel costs.

Operating costs are the resources needed to develop, operate, and evaluate a JFI program. Examples of operating costs include:

- *Staff training.* Resources that permit staff to gain subject matter expertise through higher education opportunities. Tuition, educational materials, and travel per diem costs are examples of staff training costs.

- *Program development and implementation.* Monies requested for developing, piloting, and implementing a new JFI program or enhancements to an existing program.

- *Program marketing.* Resources dedicated to increasing community and inter-agency awareness of the local JFIS problem. Costs may include purchase or development of both print and broadcast media. They may also include expenses associated with convening a group of stakeholders to collaborate on potential solutions to the local JFIS problem.

- *Supplies and equipment.* Funds to purchase supplies and equipment that support operation of a JFI program. These costs include purchase and/or development of materials used as part of the actual JFI program. Materials that support intake, interview, and intervention components are included in this line item. Equipment required to deliver the JFI program is also included in this section. Preventive maintenance and funds set aside for long-term replacement can be included in this category.

- *Transportation costs.* Resources that enable staff to deliver program services within the community. Fuel, maintenance, and insurance costs for department-owned vehicles are part of this line item. It can also include per diem mileage reimbursement for civilian or contractual employees who deliver program services.

- *Contractual services.* Some JFI programs have mental health providers or other agencies under contract to provide clinical intervention services for juvenile firesetters and their families. Services are used as needed and compensation provided according to contractual agreement. Because the program or agency in this case is providing contracted services, employee benefits are not required. This type of expense is an operating, *not* personnel cost.

- *Evaluation costs.* Fifteen percent of a total JFI program budget should be dedicated to evaluation. This practice will help ensure that adequate resources exist to support process, impact, and outcome evaluation. The cost of this line item is determined after a draft of the proposed overall budget has been developed. It is then added to the overall budget prior to submission.

Personnel costs are salaries, wages, and benefits paid to employees for services provided. Personnel costs are usually the largest expense of municipal government or any agency that pays for services provided by people.

A full-time person costs an organization more than what is paid in salary or wages. Not only are full-time employees due benefits, there are other costs associated with hiring a person to perform a service. The cost of employing a person often includes:

• Federal, state, and local taxes

• Social Security and Medicare contributions

• Insurance and workers compensation coverage

• Sick leave

• Holiday and vacation time

• Retirement, pensions, and deferred compensation options

In cases where the organization or nonprofit institution requires personnel costs to be identified or justified, the Level II JFIS is expected to perform these duties. (**NOTE:** Chapters 8 and 13 provided a detailed explanation of how to serve in this capacity when supervising fire and life safety programs.)

Assigning Interventionists for the Interview/Screening Process

Once a juvenile firesetter incident has been reported, the JFIS II program manager is responsible for assigning an interventionist to the case. Interventionist selection may therefore occur before or after an intake process has occurred. In some cases, the same interventionist may perform intake, interview, and screening tasks. For the scope of this section, it is assumed that the intake process has been completed and information forwarded to the program manager.

The Level II program manager should assign a JFIS I Interventionist to conduct an intake and interview process according to program protocol **(Figure 22.7)**. As outlined earlier in this chapter, policy should also require the use of an approved assessment instrument.

Figure 22.7 A program manager should assign each case to a trained interventionist.

The use of an assessment instrument, combined with the interviewing skills of the interventionist, can determine why a firesetting situation has occurred, thereby guiding the interventionist as to the type(s) of intervention needed. Selecting the interventionist best suited to each specific JFIS case is an important responsibility of the JFIS II Program Manager.

Review Intake Information

The JFIS program manager should always review intake information collected about a firesetting situation before assigning an interventionist to the case. A good intake process will have gathered information about the juvenile's current and past firesetting experience and interventions that may have occurred to date. It will also provide baseline information on the juvenile's cognitive level, special needs, and family demographics.

While reviewing intake information will not provide the depth of knowledge attained during the more comprehensive screening process, it can help differentiate a low risk case from a problematic situation. Having this level of information prior to assigning interventionists is very helpful in complex cases.

Match Interventionists with Cases

The goal of the interview/screening process is to identify why a firesetting situation exists, its level of severity, and interventions that prevent recidivism. This can sometimes be a challenging task for interventionists.

Many factors can contribute to juvenile firesetting behaviors. Chapter 17 lists several and discusses the cognitive, social, and environmental influences that often exacerbate firesetting situations.

Prior to assigning an interventionist to a JFIS case, the Level II program manager should consider the complexity of the situation and the knowledge and skill level of the interventionist. The program manager should strive to match the abilities of his or her staff with the needs of the juvenile and family to be served. To accomplish this goal, the program manager must possess mastery understanding of firesetter profiles and the special needs often exhibited by juveniles and their families. Equally important, the program manager must know the capabilities and talents of every interventionist under his or her command.

Good interpersonal skills are a trademark of expert interviewers. Active listening, coupled with the use of probing, open-ended questions, optimize fact collection. Exhibiting empathy, compassion, and patience with juveniles and stressed families helps build an environment of trust that can open lines of communication.

Many JFI programs use a mentoring process that partners experienced interventionists with those in training. New interventionists often begin by performing interviews and screenings on lower-risk curiosity-motivated cases. Once proficient at this level, the junior interventionist ascends under supervision to begin work on more complex and problematic situations.

By matching interventionist skill level with the needs of a situation, the JFIS II Program Manager serves an important role in the mitigation of firesetting activity. Discussion on how to supervise Level II interventionists will continue in the next sections.

Supervising Program Staff Members

A program manager must ensure that interventionists collect a consistent body of information on all JFIS cases. The information should be obtained according to program protocol and forwarded to the program manager in a timely manner. Upon reviewing case information, the program manager evaluates interventionist performance and provides regular feedback.

Review Case Files According to Protocol

Program protocol should mandate a case file be created for every juvenile that enters the JFI program. The case file is created/opened at the time of intake and is updated during each phase of service. The JFIS case remains active/open until program services are terminated and the file is sealed.

Program policy should specify the breadth of documentation expected from interventionists and team members during each phase of service. The JFI Program Manager should review each juvenile's case file at intervals specified by program protocol to evaluate the documentation of services provided by interventionists. This strategy not only enlightens the program manager on interventionist performance, it allows for ongoing review of each case by the program manager, the most experienced JFIS.

Review Feedback from Senior Interventionists, Mentors, and Parents

All JFI programs should have a training mechanism for both new and experienced interventionists. Many programs require a new interventionist to work in tandem with a skilled interventionist to gain experience serving juveniles and their families. A new interventionist may work with clinicians from other agencies to learn advanced interviewing and screening skills. The program manager should create a means to document interventionist training and record feedback from instructors and mentors.

The Level I interventionist is to conduct a follow-up on each case they are assigned. The primary purpose of follow-up is to assess program effectiveness at preventing recidivism. As a subset of this process, interventionists must solicit feedback from participants so program components and staff performance can be evaluated. Many programs have a questionnaire that is completed by families and forwarded to the JFI Program Manager for review.

Communicate Regularly with Interventionists

A primary responsibility of the program manager is to continually evaluate the program's operation and facilitate improvements as indicated. Part of this process includes reviewing interventionist performance and providing constructive feedback on a regular basis. Communication between the program manager and each interventionist is essential to a successful process that results in personal growth and a stronger JFI program.

The JFI Program Manager should communicate regularly with staff, both as a team and individually. Overall program performance and information pertinent to the team is shared among the group. Constructive feedback specific to a interventionist is always discussed privately with the staff member.

For additional information on leadership, see Chapters 1 and 7. For information on evaluating staff member performance, see Chapter 8.

Maintaining Case Files

Due to the often sensitive nature of firesetting cases, privacy laws, ethics, and potential legal issues, the maintenance of case files warrants significant attention. Chapter 18 includes additional information on security topics regarding case files and documentation.

Components of a Case File

The Level II program mlanager is responsible for ensuring that all JFIS case files are created, maintained, and secured in accordance with protocol established by the local AHJ. Protocol should call for a case file to include intake records, results of the interview/screening process, interventions recommended and performed, and documentation of follow-up evaluation. Narratives developed by interventionists should also be part of the file.

Consistent and Accurate Documentation

Incident data can help identify leading risk issues, root causation factors, and resulting loss. In many localities, funding may be withheld from an organization that fails to report on the occurrence of emergency incidents. The importance of accurate and thorough documentation cannot be overstated since an incident report may be referenced in a court case.

Additionally, consistent and accurate documentation helps the program manager ensure that interventionists deliver an appropriate continuum of care. *Continuum of care* is an uninterrupted ascending level of services delivered through multiagency participation and partnership.

Consistent reporting means that the same type and breadth of information is collected on each juvenile referred to the program. Every JFI program should establish a policy stating what data is to be collected and a procedure for how to do so. Protocol should direct a specific level of reporting on each step of the process.

Accurate documentation means that all information pertinent to a JFIS case is factual and collected objectively without bias. Consistent use of data collection instruments ensures a standard approach to all JFIS cases by all staff members. Examples of documentation forms include intake forms, interview/screening tools, and records of follow-up. Narratives, written in third person, documenting intervention services provided are also categorized as data collection instruments.

Mandated Reporting Guidelines

A JFI program policy should outline what situations require mandatory reporting to an external agency. For example, federal law mandates immediate reporting of suspected child abuse or neglect. Local arson laws often require adjudication of juveniles who have damaged property through firesetting activity. The JFIS II Program Manager is responsible for ensuring that JFIS protocol clearly states what situations require immediate attention. The expectations of team members should also be enumerated.

The JFI Program Manager is responsible for working with the lead agency's departmental leadership so that a uniform reporting protocol is in place and understood by all personnel. In addition, the JFIS II should encourage and assist partnering agencies in developing a protocol whereby all reports of firesetting activity are forwarded to the JFI program.

Protecting and Securing Case Files

The Level II JFIS Project Manager is responsible to ensure the privacy of the juvenile's case in accordance with federal law. The JFIS case file is a confidential legal document that must be protected from destruction, unauthorized viewing/use, or public discussion. Federal laws, such as the Health Insurance Portability and Accountability Act (HIPAA), are in place to protect a person's privacy as they receive health care. Services provided through a JFI program meet the criteria for HIPAA oversight. Chapter 18 includes a review of what information should be protected, why, and how.

Figure 22.8 Paper-based documents must be kept in a secure filing area.

The program manager is responsible for establishing protocol that outlines how JFIS case information will be protected and secured. Thus, paper-based documents must be maintained in a secure filing area that remains locked at all times **(Figure 22.8)**. Electronic-based information must be pass-code protected. Verbal information exchanges between interventionists discussing a case must be held in a secure, private location.

Chapter Summary

The Level II JFIS Program Manager is ultimately responsible for ensuring that program protocols are developed and followed to keep a firesetting mitigation process on track and functioning within the intended scope of operation. New interventionist training and supervision, budget development, and the security of all program documents are important tasks performed by the program manager.

Review Questions

1. What program policies and procedures should be created to support a JFI program's goals?

2. What are the steps to developing a budget that identifies and justifies a program's operating and personnel costs?

3. What is the procedure for selecting and assigning Level I interventionists to a case?

4. What methods can a supervisor use to ensure program policies are followed, performance is evaluated, and ongoing support to personnel is provided?

5. What methods or procedures can be used to ensure that JFIS case file information remains secure and is available for use according to established program policies?

Key Terms

Budget Cycle — Specific timelines used by organizations and communities to receive and act on requests for resources to support general operations.

Grants — Gifts of money to a nonprofit, tax exempt organization or to a government organization.

JFIS Level II Program Managers: Planning and Development

Chapter Contents

chapter 23

Key Terms

Job Performance Requirements

This chapter provides information that addresses the following job performance requirements of NFPA® 1035, *Standard for Professional Qualifications for Fire and Life Safety Educator, Public Information Officer, and Juvenile Firesetter Intervention Specialist*, 2010 edition.

NFPA® 1035 References

10.3.1

10.3.2

10.3.3

10.3.4

10.3.5

JFIS Level II Program Managers: Planning and Development

Learning Objectives

After reading this chapter, students will be able to:

1. Summarize the steps necessary for developing an interagency network for the specific purpose of juvenile firesetting intervention, including the development of a mission statement, goals, agreements, and services to be provided (NFPA® 1035, 10.3.1).

2. Create or adapt the forms necessary for the agency's JFI program, including forms to be used for intake, interview, referral, and follow-up (NFPA® 1035, 10.3.2).

3. Create a training program for the program's personnel so that individuals working within the JFI program will be able to properly perform intake, interview, follow-up, and evaluation (NFPA® 1035, 10.3.3).

4. Create an advertising program within the community, so that individuals know of the existence of the intervention program and how they can access its services (NFPA® 1035, 10.3.4).

5. Design a system for the collection of data for the community's JFI program (NFPA® 1035, 10.3.5).

Chapter 23
JFIS Level II Program Managers: Planning and Development

Case History

In July 2008, four-year-old Dion died as a result of a fire that started in a pile of clothes in the basement. Dion was hiding behind the couch and would not respond to the calls of his family or neighbors. It is thought that Dion believed he was in trouble with his parents.

Dion had a history of playing with matches. Even though there were no matches or lighters found in the charred basement, fire investigators believe that Dion started the fire that led to his death. Dion had been alone in the basement of his North Linden (OH) home.

The community where Dion and his family lived had a firesetter program, but either the family did not see the need or did not have knowledge of the program. As with many parents, it is possible that Dion's family did not understand the potential danger involved in Dion's unsafe behavior.

Source: The Columbus Dispatch, July 20, 2008

Many children demonstrate a fascination with fire. Curiosity is a manifestation of intelligence and learning. At the same time, children are not always able to understand or control the products of their curiosity. The dangerous number of child-set fires is the primary focus of the Juvenile Firesetter Intervention (JFI) program, and the reduction of those fires is its reason for existence.

The JFIS II Program Manager must make many decisions about the design of the program and its policies and procedures. The program design may be modeled after programs in other communities, or it may be entirely developed locally. Whatever the design decision, the JFIS II should seek out other agencies in the community for their assistance.

This is done through the creation of an interagency network. This multidisciplinary approach will lend itself to ensuring the success of the program.

Along with the development of the coalition, forms must be designed and program must be advertised. In addition, those participating as instructors or leaders in the program, such as agency representatives, must be trained in the day-to-day operations of the program.

One of the more important functions of the JFIS II is to ensure the proper and appropriate documentation for the program. Proper documentation can lead to meaningful and accurate evaluation. Without evaluation, there is no evidence that the program is successful in deterring firesetting behavior.

This chapter discusses these facets of the JFIS II responsibility for the development and administration of the intervention program. This attention to detail is paramount in proving the success of the program, in seeking additional funding, and ensuring its continuation.

Building an Interagency Coalition

It is the responsibility of the JFIS II Program Manager to develop and oversee the various components of the program. As opposed to the JFIS I Interventionist, who acts as the delivery agent of the program's components, the JFIS II Program Manager must create the program, determine what policies and procedures are needed, and evaluate the administration of the program.

One of the first, and perhaps most important, components of the program is the interagency network or multidisciplinary coalition. No single agency in a community has the skills and resources necessary to solve the juvenile firesetting problem. It takes a broad variety of professional and community organizations working together to make a difference. While most firesetter programs are housed within the local fire agency, this does not mean that the fire department has all the necessary resources to properly conduct the intervention program.

All successful community-based programs require a champion. For juvenile firesetting intervention, this is usually a representative of the fire agency, such as the JFIS II Program Manager. This champion and the lead agency are responsible for coordinating and directing the work of the coalition. This work includes performing administrative tasks, organizing activities, maintaining the interest and motivation of the members, and recruiting new members for the network **(Figure 23.1)**.

Steps to Creating a Juvenile Firesetter Intervention Coalition

The following sections discuss the steps involved in creating a JFI coalition. There are many steps which are similar to the process taken to determine a community's level and types of risk and will be familiar to the program manager. (Other topics related to the development of a coalition are discussed in Chapters 4, 9, and 14.)

Identify Potential Partners in the Coalition

The same people and agencies that are likely to provide referrals to the firesetter program should be included in the initial coalition. This multiagency or multidisciplinary approach to the juvenile firesetting problem will provide the best groundwork for success for the program. An initial network should include representatives from the following community agencies:

- Law enforcement
- Juvenile justice department
- School system
- Social services

Figure 23.1 Recruitment is one task assigned to the Level II program manager.

- Child protective services
- Mental health
- Fire department

Include in the initial core group other individuals or organizations in the community that are already working on the issue of firesetting. Look for those individuals who have a strong interest in the issue and will make sure that the coalition, and therefore the intervention program, is successful. It may be appropriate to also include community leaders who have influence or power, or are part of the community's political network.

Gather a Core Group of Agencies

It is important to start with a small core group. Each of the agencies listed in the section above plays a pivotal role in the success of an intervention program, and this group must coordinate and work together before widening the membership. As the program develops and grows, the coalition can be expanded to include other community representatives, such as neighborhood groups, youth interest groups, childcare providers, healthcare providers, and other interested parties.

Organizing the interagency network for firesetter intervention is a process similar to organizing a coalition for the purpose of risk reduction. (Chapter 14 includes more information on that topic.) As was indicated earlier, coalitions do not come together naturally or by accident. It takes an organized leader, such as the program manager, to successfully bring such a diverse group of individuals together for a single purpose.

Initially, the program manager must solicit the involvement of the core group of representatives and their agencies. Most community agencies and organizations understand the problems associated with fire, unintentional injuries, and other risk issues, but few agencies understand the special nature of juvenile firesetting. It will be necessary for the program manager to educate representatives of the core agencies on the firesetting problem and the unique nature of the interventions needed.

In enlisting the representatives from the various agencies, it is important that a need be shown for such a program. The JFIS II should have local or regional data available about juvenile firesetting to help develop a picture about the problem to justify each agency's involvement. The collection of local data will be critical in showing the need for a firesetter intervention program in any community.

A one-on-one meeting with key individuals at each agency can be time consuming, but it is very effective in seeking their commitment for participation. The JFIS II needs to learn how each agency works and what resources they can bring to the intervention program. By meeting face-to-face, the program manager can easily build relationships with the agency staff, allow for more open conversation, and provide an opportunity for discussion.

Plan and Hold an Informational Meeting

Once the essential agencies are on board with the program, it is time to bring everyone together for an organizational meeting. This will provide an opportunity for agency members to get to know each other. This initial meeting could take the form of a workshop or an informal gathering.

Present the Data

The program manager should be prepared to provide an overview of the problem both locally and nationally, an overview of local efforts to date, and a review of the successes of intervention programs in other communities. Open discussion should be encouraged. Strengths and weaknesses of the program should be explained, with suggestions for changes being willingly accepted. Funding sources may be identified as a part of this initial planning meeting.

The organizational meeting should have a specific agenda. Items to include on the agenda should be the following:

- *Introduction of the group.* Everyone at the meeting should give a brief introduction of themselves, including their organization, and the nature of their personal or professional interest in juvenile firesetting and the intervention program.

- *Define the issues.* The coalition should develop a statement of the issues around which it is being developed. This is where data collection becomes very important. Whether national data or local, information about the problem of firesetting must be gathered and presented to this core group for a clear definition of the issues.

- *Structure of coalition.* The group should discuss the coalition's organizational structure and processes. If the JFIS II is the champion for the intervention program, he or she should be prepared to take charge of the coalition and provide the necessary leadership.

Identify the Vision and Mission

After the structure is explained, the direction the program is going should be discussed:

- *Discuss the vision.* This will begin the process of developing a mission statement and vision statement that will guide the group's work.

- *Discuss procedures.* This should include the formation of the organizational action plan. It may also include the acceptance of the overall intervention program as designed by the program manager and provide the opportunity for suggestions or changes for improvement.

- *Schedule the next meeting and review action items.* A regular meeting schedule may be established or at least the date and time for the next meeting set. In addition, those attending should leave the meeting with a sense of accomplishment and purpose, with actions to be taken prior to the next meeting.

This initial meeting of the coalition should not be considered the training workshop, as will be discussed later in this chapter. Coalition members should be active participants in the training workshop and may desire to bring coworkers or supervisors to the training. The initial coalition meeting is a chance for the participants to begin to work together, get to know each other, and set about designing the inner workings of the intervention process.

Considerations for Creating a Successful Coalition

As was previously indicated, members should address the development of a mission statement for the work of the coalition. A well-written mission statement will aid in creating solidarity among the agencies and individual representatives involved. It can also serve as a publicity tool to advertise the existence of the coalition and attract the involvement of other interested parties.

Design a Structure for the Coalition

Operating principles and procedures describe how the coalition will do its work. While some of those operational procedures may be inherent in the design of the intervention program, all operating principles should be clearly stated so that there is no misunderstanding. The roles of each individual and each agency should be clearly delineated. In addition, the coalition needs to agree on a list of operating principles that will govern the work of the coalition and the intervention program. With multiple agencies involved, it is important that there is consensus on one set of principles and policies for everyone. Yet it is also important to the successful participation of all representatives that the principles and policies are not in conflict with any existing policies and regulations that govern the day-to-day operations of the individual agencies.

Effective leadership is imperative to the success of the coalition and the intervention program. As the champion of the intervention program, the JFIS II may be designated to lead the coalition, at least during the organizational phase. The coalition's leader must make everyone feel a part of the group and recognize each individual for his or her contribution. While coalition maintenance will be covered in the next chapter, strong leadership of the coalition is an essential element to its long-term existence.

Determine What Resources Are Needed

If the intervention program is to be successful, each organization must be committed to the problem of juvenile firesetting and work together to solve the problem. Each organization must be willing to commit the time and resources required, recognizing that each individual and agency is key to the successful intervention of firesetting behavior. Each organization must realize that every other organization has a vital role to play in solving the firesetting problem. Commitment is needed from all participating organizations and their representatives for open, respectful communications. It may be helpful for the coalition to create a **memorandum of understanding** or other form of written agreement to make sure that each member is aware of the importance of his or her participation and cooperation. (A Web search for MOU templates will yield examples that may be used to begin the process of developing the necessary formal agreement. Also, a sample form can be found on page 499.)

Once the structure and operational principles are determined, the coalition can begin its work. Many successful intervention programs have established regular meeting times while others meet on an as-needed basis. It is important that the program manager keeps all coalition members informed and involved. Maintaining an effective coalition will be covered in Chapter 24.

Creation of Program Forms

Intake forms, referral forms, and assessment instruments are a few examples of the forms needed for a successful JFIS program. It is the responsibility of the JFIS II to collect and develop the forms that are necessary for the program. This task may be in coordination with the work of the interagency network, but it is the duty of the program manager to see that all forms needed are properly used by the program participants.

The design of any form must meet the needs of the program and the interventionists. The number and type of forms can be determined as the program is developed. Forms from other firesetter programs may be adapted, or new forms may be developed. Some forms are longer than others; some ask for more detailed information. There is no rule of thumb about the design of any form. However, the forms should allow interventionists to gather all the necessary information to make the appropriate referral. In addition, the forms used by the JFI program must fall within the legal parameters of the authority having jurisdiction (AHJ), and any state or federal statutes. A professional should review the assessment instrument for validity and reliability **(Figure 23.2)**. When developing forms for the program, it is highly recommended that the program manager or the coalition as a whole consult local legal and mental health professionals for their input on all forms.

Intake Forms

Intake forms are used to gather information about the firesetter and the firesetting incident. Some programs refer to this type of form as a program referral form, or an incident form. Whatever its name, it is the form that gathers the initial intake information about the juvenile, his or her family, and the firesetting incident(s) being discussed. The form can also provide demographic information about the child and his or her family. This form can be very simple, or it can be used to gather in-depth information. It must meet the needs of the community and its program design. This form is not used for screening purposes. It is simply an information-gathering form

Figure 23.2 Program materials should be reviewed by a professional to ensure their quality.

that may be used by a variety of individuals, including administrative staff, line firefighters, teachers, and law enforcement officials.

Other Important Forms

One of the major forms that will be used by intervention specialists is the assessment instrument, or *interview form*. JFIS II Program Managers, in cooperation with the local interagency coalition, are responsible for developing an assessment instrument that fits local program needs. For the benefit of intervention specialists, the United States Fire Administration developed two model assessment instruments that can be used as written or adapted to serve local needs. The forms were developed with the professional guidance from nationally recognized JFI expert Dr. Ken Fineman.

- The first USFA form was designed to help interventionists succinctly evaluate the severity of a firesetting situation. The instrument features interview components for both adults and juveniles.

- The second version guides the interventionist through a much greater level of evaluation by seeking an in-depth perspective of why firesetting behaviors are occurring.

Both forms use a scoring process to assess the level of potential risk for future firesetting behavior.

In addition to USFA's work, several nationally recognized JFI coalitions have developed their own forms after consulting professionals at the local level. Many of the forms mirror the document designed by Dr. Fineman. Program managers and team members should network and consult with communities that have experience with the development and use of assessment instruments.

While the purpose of this manual is not to recommend use of one assessment instrument over another, the JFIS II Program Managers should consider the following points:

- When designing forms for the local program, the JFIS II should conduct research and obtain several assessment instruments used by credible organizations.

- Each assessment instrument should be evaluated for its applicability to local need. Team partners such as mental health clinicians, social services, justice officials, and schools should provide input into the form's design.

- If an assessment instrument used by another organization fits local needs, be sure and obtain permission to use it. Even if a form is going to be modified for use with a local agency, ask for permission to adapt it to fit local needs.

- There may be situations when local needs dictate the development of a custom assessment instrument. Consultation with local professionals will be critical in the validation and reliability of the form's use.

- The ultimate aim of an assessment instrument is to help the interviewer determine the root cause of firesetting behaviors and gauge the severity of the problem. Only then can a team of trained professionals representing diverse specialties determine a logical course of intervention.

Intake and assessment forms are only two examples of forms that are needed for a successful intervention program. The following forms may be needed as well:

- Release of Liability
- Waiver/Consent (consent to release information and liability, consent to interview the child)
- Parent Questionnaire

- Parent/Child Contract
- Post Interview
- Referral
- Follow-Up Survey (for short-term and long-term follow-up) **(Figure 23.3)**

There are also a variety of letters that can be drafted for use as forms to invite parents to participate in the program, to confirm meeting dates for interviews and educational classes, and to inform parents of the recommendations for intervention.

It is up to the program manager, the interagency network, local agency policies, and local legal counsel to decide what forms are necessary for the intervention program. At a very minimum, of course, there must be an intake form, an assessment instrument, and a follow-up survey.

Summary of Accurate and Timely Program Documentation

- Everything must be documented, including all phone calls, meetings, no-shows, and follow-up.

- If a form is needed to ensure that these steps are completed, then one should be created.

- Each and every form should have a purpose and there should not be needless gathering of information or form completion.

- Information gathered should be for a specific purpose in the intervention activities for the firesetter.

- Each individual who is a part of the intervention process should be trained in the proper completion of the forms.

- The JFIS II program manager must provide quality assurance for the accurate completion of all forms pertinent to the program.

Designing a Training Program

It is the program manager's responsibility to ensure that those who will be working with the intervention program receive the proper training. This includes the sponsoring agency's staff and members of the interagency coalition. Individuals must be trained on the philosophy surrounding the program, its operational procedures, and the policies and regulations that apply.

Smithville Fire and Life Safety Consortium
JUVENILE FIRESETTER FOLLOW-UP FORM

CHILD'S NAME: _____

CALLER'S NAME: _____

CASE NUMBER: _____ DATE: _____

DATE OF ENTRY INTO SYSTEM: _____

1. Has your child had any fire incidents since your last meeting with Portland Fire & Rescue?
   _____ Yes (continue to #2)   _____ No (skip to #6)

2. What type of fire incident was it?
   _____ Fireplay (lighting of matches/lighters)   _____ Firesetting (intent to do harm or damage)

3. What form of ignition did it involve?
   _____ Matches   _____ Lighters
   _____ Other (explain) _____

4. Were there any injuries?
   _____ No
   _____ Yes (explain) _____

5. What was done as a consequence of the fireplay or firesetting?
   _____ Parental Punishment   _____ Mental Health Referral
   _____ Fire Department Referral   _____ Juvenile Justice
   _____ Other (explain)

6. In what way do you think your child benefited from the first visit with the Smithville Fire
   and Life Safety Consortium (SFLSC)?
   _____
   _____
   _____

7. During your first visit with the SFLSC, was your child referred to counseling?
   _____ Yes (continue to #8)   _____ No (skip to #9)

8. Did you go to counseling?
   _____ Yes
   _____ No (why not) _____

9. Please rate the following factors: POOR   GOOD
   Methods of Education   1   2   3   4   5
   Educational Effectiveness   1   2   3   4   5
   Overall Program Rating   1   2   3   4   5

10. In what ways do you think we can improve the program?
   _____
   _____
   _____

11. Do you have any other comments or criticisms of the Juvenile Firesetting Program?
   _____
   _____
   _____

Figure 23.3 A sample post interview follow-up form.

In Chapter 15, the process for designing training programs for new educators was discussed. While the skills needed for a competent and able intervention specialist are somewhat different than those needed for a fire and life safety educator, the process for developing the training is very similar. In this instance, however, not only are in-house personnel being trained but individuals from other fields and disciplines will also be included. The training must be of service to all the different agencies and affiliations in order to be effective.

Interventionist Workshop

In order to properly develop a training workshop for certified interventionists, the program manager must identify each and every component of the program, including but not limited to the following:

- An understanding of the community's juvenile firesetting problem

- A description of the unique nature of working with juvenile firesetters

- The importance of the interagency network in the program's success

- The purpose of the intake process and how to correctly conduct an intake interview
- The purpose of the assessment process and how to correctly conduct both a parent and child interview
- The rating process and the proper procedure for referrals
- Procedures for case follow-up and evaluation
- Child development, child abuse and neglect, delinquency, legal issues, and confidentiality requirements

Topics presented during a training workshop should focus on helping interventionists understand their respective roles in providing services connected with the intervention program. Interventionists should be provided with a document outlining the parameters of the program, copies of all the forms and assessment instruments used in the program, and an outline of the policies and procedures related to the program, its documentation, and legal requirements.

Sample Training Topics
- Characteristics of juvenile firesetters
- How to identify juvenile firesetters
- Developing and managing a juvenile firesetter program
- Screening/assessment techniques
- Interviewing and educating the juvenile firesetter
- Referral and follow-up
- Normal child development
- Juvenile delinquency
- Child abuse/neglect
- Legal issues

The interventionist must develop a certain skill set to be effective in his or her work. One of the most important skills is interviewing. Interviewing does not come naturally and is a skill that needs to be developed with practice. It will most likely not be possible to cover all aspects of interviewing techniques during the initial workshop. It is up to the JFIS II to secure this training for all interventionists who will be performing the assessment function.

Coalition Member Workshop

Regardless of their background, all program personnel should receive training in juvenile firesetting issues. This includes members of the interagency coalition, and others that may be involved in the referral and/or intervention process. Administrative personnel who will be involved with the program will need to be trained. This may be administrative support staff who answer the telephone as well as other individuals within the risk-reduction division who may not have any direct responsibilities with the JFI program.

Program orientation must also be conducted for fire department personnel, particularly those in operations, upper level command staff, and those performing fire cause investigations. This may be done in the form of an in-service training or a one-day seminar. If possible, fire personnel should be included in the training workshop conducted for all program personnel. Fire service personnel should be aware of the program and the services it provides. In addition, personnel should have an understanding of the procedures used to refer a firesetter to the program.

Coalition Training Follow-Up

Once personnel have been properly trained on the program procedures, it is the responsibility of the JFIS II Program Manager to ensure that each and every component is properly conducted and recorded. Quality assurance is important, and the JFIS II Program Manager should be the one who oversees the intake and assessment processes. The JFIS II also must ensure that the policies and procedures established for the program are being followed.

Ongoing training opportunities should be available for existing coalition members and interventionists so they can stay abreast of program issues and updates. Opportunities for training should exist for new coalition members, new fire department members, and/or new JFIS interventionists. Furthermore, a protocol for the evaluation of training should be established and followed.

Creating Community Awareness

Once the program is in place, the coalition is organized, and personnel have been trained, it is time to "open the doors," so to speak, of the intervention program. The program is ready to begin accepting referrals, and it is up to the JFIS II to create an awareness program to inform the community about this new and important service.

The purpose of the JFIS awareness program is two-fold:

- One purpose is to educate the community on the extent of the firesetter problem. Many individuals are unaware that there is a problem, or there may be myths and misunderstandings about what can happen to a child when parents seek assistance.

- The second purpose is to inform the community that a program exists to assist with the firesetter issue. The JFIS II has a responsibility to the community to inform them that a program is available to assist juvenile firesetters.

The focus of this awareness effort is slightly different than the one discussed in Chapter 14. For the fire and life safety educator, an awareness program for a fire or life safety issue involves changing the behavior and attitudes of individuals. With the juvenile firesetter intervention program, community awareness involves advertising the program and the services that it provides. With this particular program, the fire department and the interagency network are providing a specific service to the community, and one that it needs to know exists. Behavioral messages can be included as a part of the awareness program, but its main purpose is to provide information about the interventions to the people who will be affected by it.

When the program manager or the coalition decides it is time to advertise the program, there are some decisions that need to be made about this publicity effort:

- *What are the goals of the advertising effort?* The scope of the publicity program must be specified.

- *What outlets will be used to advertise the program?* These include radio/television, print, press conferences, and general communications. Radio and television can include interviews, public service announcements, and talk shows. Print media includes newspapers and magazines. Press conferences can utilize a press kit, which is an organized promotion for a variety of media. General communications are facts sheets, press releases, and presentations. Each of these carries a different type of strategy and target audience **(Figure 23.4, p. 522)**.

- *What is the target audience?* The target audience may be the entire community, or it may be limited to a particular high-risk area. There may be areas where more child-set fires are occurring, or where children are more apt to become involved in firesetting activities.

- *What activities will be included in the awareness campaign?* The campaign strategies and activities can include:
  — Brochures **(Figure 23.5, p. 523)**
  — Posters
  — News Releases
  — Public Service Announcements (PSAs)
  — Presentations
  — Letters
  — Newsletter

This list is not meant to be all-inclusive. Each community has its own resources and the JFIS II should be familiar with the various outlets for providing information to the community.

At a very minimum, juvenile firesetter intervention programs should have a simple brochure to describe the program and provide contact information for parents and other community members. The material should be simple and briefly highlight the service of the JFI program and how individuals can avail themselves of this service. These brochures can be distributed to daycare centers, preschools, pediatricians, social services, and all community organizations and agencies that work with children.

Posters can be developed as a means of advertising the program, and even as a means for encouraging fire safe behaviors. They can be designed for and placed in strategic locations such as schools, municipal buildings, government offices, retail establishments, and fire stations.

The news media is certainly an important avenue for advertising the program. In most communities, this is probably the most effective way to publicize the program. It is beneficial to have a member of a local media outlet as a part of the interagency coalition. Local newspaper, television, radio, and internet services are able to inform the public about the firesetter problem and the intervention program in a timely fashion **(Figure 23.6, p. 523)**.

Figure 23.4 A sample media fact sheet.

Smithville Fire Department

MEDIA FACT SHEET
Children and Fire

Smithville Fire Dept.
911 Post Drive
Smithville, Indiana
000-555-1234
www.smithville.gov/firedept

Smithville Statistics
- Between January 2000 and December 2005, 351 children were referred to the Smithville Fire Department for firesetting behavior.
- The fires set by these children caused over $1.9 million in damages.
- During this time, 171 children participated in the Smithville Fire Department's Fire Stoppers Program.

National Statistics
- Nationally, children cause about 13,900 fires each year resulting in over 210 deaths, 1,250 injuries, and $339 million in property damage (source: From NFPA's® Children Playing with Fire, by John R. Hall, Jr., March 2005)
- Most of the people killed in child-playing fires are under 5, and such fires are the leading cause of fire deaths among preschoolers.
- The FBI Crime Index reports that 55% of all arson arrests in the U.S. are children under 18. Nearly half of these are age 15 and under. The crime of arson has the highest rate of juvenile involvement.
- The bedroom is the area of the home where most juvenile-set fires originate, and matches are the most prevalent ignition sources.

Safety Precautions
- Keep matches and lighters out of sight, out of reach and away from children.
- Teach young children to tell an adult if they see matches or lighters, and teach school-age children to immediately bring any matches or lighters they find to an adult.
- Set an example of safety when lighting candles, fireplaces, campfires, and barbecues. Children learn from the adults around them through watching, rather than listening.
- Take steps to get help and don't ignore the obvious. When children play with or misuse fire, the results can be serious. Resources are available to help address this issue. In Smithville, contact the Fire Department's Education Office at 000-555-5637 for more information.

Having a working smoke alarm dramatically increases your chances of surviving a fire. And remember to practice a home escape plan frequently.

The JFIS II must be proactive and aggressive in seeking out media representatives to assist with advertising the JFI program. Visits to the radio and television stations, telephone calls to reporters, editors, and producers are ways to get the attention of the media. The program manager will have to sell the story and it is imperative to have some type of fact sheet or clear, consistent messages about the program.

One way to get the media's attention about the program is when a juvenile firesetting incident occurs. Interest is certainly heightened after an incident. A description of the program and its service can serve as a sidebar for the news story. The JFIS II must make sure that when child-set fires are reported to the media, the firesetter intervention program is mentioned as well.

Most radio and television outlets donate airtime for public service announcements (PSAs). These are advertisements that are not selling a product, but discussing a community problem or program. Some fire departments and national organizations have developed generic PSAs for juvenile firesetter intervention programs that allow local fire departments to customize them. For departments wishing to develop their own PSAs, it must be noted that this can be an expensive venture. Seeking outside funding or donations may be necessary. In addi-

Figure 23.5 Informative literature is one component of an awareness campaign.

tion, it may be beneficial to seek out the assistance of professionals in the media field to make sure that the proper medium is used based upon the target audience and that the messages are appropriately designed for that audience.

Community presentations are a good way to provide information to community members. Many local service organizations seek out speakers for their meetings. The JFIS II should contact local organizations such as civic groups, parent-teacher groups, service organizations, and other community agencies to provide such a program. Some communities have developed speakers' bureaus comprised of representatives from the interagency coalition that can speak on the subject of juvenile firesetters and the intervention program.

Letters of introduction can be sent to agencies and organizations in the community. School principals or other school administrators not included in the coalition should be informed of the program and the services that can be provided. Introductory letters should be sent to the various childcare centers in the community. Adults working with organized youth groups, such as the Boys & Girls Club, should be informed about the program and the process

Figure 23.6 The news media can offer a timely means of public information.

for making a referral. Church groups, civic groups, health care providers, and even local merchants should be targeted in this advertising campaign. Some of these organizations may be able to provide referrals to the program as well as financial support or in-kind donations.

Many communities that have firesetter programs have designed titles or names for their program and accompanying slogans. This is another way to advertise the program. The program name and slogan can be used in designing posters or letterhead that can promote the name of the program and its services. Several departments, such as Gainesville (FL) Fire and Rescue Department, have coined the phrase, "Operation Extinguish," as the title for their program and have used it as a means of promoting the program.

It may be prudent for the JFIS II to form partnerships with local businesses and community organizations for the sole purpose of promoting the intervention program. Organizations and businesses can provide personnel, equipment, and money for the purpose of creating, developing, and implementing advertising strategies in the community. Stressing the fact that juvenile firesetting is a community problem is certainly one way to appeal to those local businesses for their assistance.

NOTE: Juvenile firesetter programs must be prepared and ready to handle the requests for information and the referrals once the publicity campaign has started. The program should not be publicized until all components are in place. If the program advertises services that it is not ready to provide, it will lose credibility quickly. This is particularly true if a parent or other caregiver is seeking assistance and the family must be placed on a waiting list.

Documentation and Data Collection

Previously in this chapter there was a discussion about the forms needed for documentation of activities and events in the firesetter program. A juvenile firesetter intervention program must document its day-to-day operations. Program policies and procedures should describe this documentation process, and all those working with the intervention program should be familiar with these procedures. As the program manager, the JFIS II is responsible for designing and overseeing the documentation process.

Accurate documentation of the JFI program is a valuable practice for several reasons. The data can be used to sustain or increase the program's budget. The information can be used to categorize the individuals receiving services from the program for targeting efforts. It can also be used to identify future audiences for fire and life safety education programs within the community. Information from the data management system can help monitor caseloads, track cases, determine final dispositions, and provide valuable information about the successes of the program for evaluation purposes.

National Uniform Juvenile Firesetter Database

According to a recent report written for the National Fire Academy, one of the major issues that affect juvenile firesetter intervention specialists is the collection of data. It was found that, on a statewide basis, the collection of data relating to juvenile firesetters was minimal. This situation has come to the attention of the National Association of State Fire Marshals, and at the time of publication, the benefits and challenges of a Mandatory National Juvenile Firesetter Database were being explored. The main sources of data about juvenile firesetting at the national level are the Federal Bureau of Investigation and the National Fire Incident Reporting System (NFIRS). Most states do not collect statewide data about their firesetter problem. In truth, most local jurisdictions have not done a good job at collecting this data as well. Some states, such as Oregon and Massachusetts, require local jurisdictions to report their firesetter statistics to a state agency, usually the State Fire Marshal's Office, for compilation.

While it may be the task of the JFIS II as the program manager to oversee the documentation of the program, it is the responsibility of each agency involved in the program to provide information about their involvement with the youths participating in the program **(Figure 23.7)**. The data collection process should not be burdensome. Simple reports can be developed for case tracking and disposition.

At intake, each case should be assigned an identifying case number. This will allow each individual file to be tracked through the system, similar to a fire department's incident response report number. This will also allow for easy accounting of the number of cases presented during a specific time period.

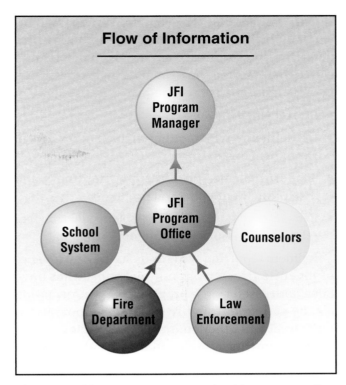

Flow of Information

Figure 23.7 The program manager should encourage all participating agencies to regularly provide information about the program's impact on participants.

Using case numbers also aids in maintaining the confidentiality of those involved in the program. A confidential master file will need to be maintained that cross-references the case number with the name of the firesetter and his or her family.

Information gathered from the program can be divided into two different categories. Curriculums from the National Fire Academy have identified demographic information and case management information as two categories that are vital to the successful evaluation of the program.

Demographic Information

Demographic information is data that reports the general circumstances of an event and information about the participants. Demographic data cannot be connected back to an individual. Demographic data that is pertinent to the JFI program includes:

- Source of referral
- Age, sex, race, and family status of the firesetter
- Name of school attended by the firesetter and grade level
- Details of the firesetting incident

- Prior firesetting incidents
- Initial assessment after screening (level of risk)

This information is pertinent in determining if there is a local community profile for a firesetter, that is, if children are from a particular neighborhood, school, age bracket, or family status. Information about the firesetting incident can assist fire and life safety educators in their primary prevention efforts in the community. Of course, this information will only be as good as the information gathered and recorded during the initial intake and assessment. For this reason, it is imperative that individuals conducting these functions of the program have an understanding of the importance of the accuracy of the information.

Case Management Information

Case management information is data that is specific to an individual firesetter and his or her family. This might include names, addresses, specific incident numbers, and the like. This information is critical in tracking the individual case through the program. However, collection and maintenance of this information must be done carefully as it has the potential to breach confidentiality requirements if shared outside of the program.

Types of Data Monitoring and Collection Systems

The Federal Emergency Management Agency (FEMA) has identified the following basic types of data monitoring and collection systems for a juvenile firesetter intervention program:

- Management information
- Evaluation
- Incidence reporting

These systems serve different purposes, depending upon the information they contain and how that information will be used. Evaluation systems are simply an extension of management information, while incidence reporting systems provide a different set of data to be examined.

Management Information System

A **management information system (MIS)** includes demographic information, as well as dates of key events and the final disposition of the case. An MIS provides a means for tracking information about the program, for summarizing and analyzing the program's caseload, and securing data for annual reports and evaluations. It is also used as a tool to monitor individual cases and ensure that needed interventions have been completed.

Management information systems include information on case characteristics, such as the demographic information outlined above. It also will provide information on the services rendered, such as dates and length of educational sessions, the number and type of counseling sessions, and details of any other services that might be provided. These might include mentoring, community services, and restitution.

Management information systems will also provide information on case disposition. Information about the dates and outcomes of services rendered and the status of any case in the justice system are considered to be part of the case disposition information in the MIS.

A management information system should be able to provide answers to the following questions:

- How many cases have been handled this year relative to last year?
- What are the individual and family characteristics of the juveniles who were assessed?
- What are the characteristics of the fires that were set by the juveniles involved in the program?
- Which referral agencies are used the most?
- How long, on average, are juveniles and families in treatment?

There may be additional information that is needed by an individual jurisdiction. Just as with the assessment instruments and other forms, the management information system can be tailored to meet the needs of the local jurisdiction.

Evaluation System

An evaluation system is simply an extension of the MIS. An evaluation system includes all of the data from the MIS, including follow-up data on recidivism or other delinquency and school or family problems. This information comes from routine follow-up with the families of firesetters and the referral agencies. This information is key in an objective evaluation of the program. If the rates of firesetting recidivism are high or the firesetter is experiencing issues in other areas, the planned interventions may need to be reevaluated.

Data gathered for the evaluation system will include follow-up information about activities with police, fire, prosecution, courts, and probation agencies. Other information to include in the evaluation documentation system includes:

- Firesetting recidivism
- Delinquency, which might include other acts of vandalism or stealing
- School problems, such as truancy, tardiness, and disciplinary or behavioral problems
- Personal and interpersonal problems, such as peer relationship issues or behavioral problems

Incident reporting systems include all incidences of juvenile firesetting, not just those that have been addressed by the program. This information can be gathered from fire department operations personnel and other community agencies. An incident reporting system will include all known or suspected juvenile firesetting incidents, even if they are not reported to the fire department. If the family declines participation in the intervention program, an incident report would still be completed and this case documented.

Incidence Reporting Systems

Incidence reporting systems provide valuable information about the entire problem of juvenile firesetting in a community. An incidence reporting system specifically for juvenile-set fires will provide information about the nature of the problem in the community. Having this information also provides the ability to determine the effectiveness of primary prevention programs, such as fire and life safety programs that are conducted in the schools.

As previously indicated, information for the incidence reporting system will come from operations personnel in fire departments, school resource officers, and other law enforcement and community agencies. This information will include fires that are extinguished without the assistance of the fire department and not reported. Another effective means of gathering the data is to survey the children themselves. An anonymous survey among school children can yield a lot of information about firesetting behaviors. Of course, anonymity must be assured in order for the survey to be effective and truthful.

Building a Documentation Program

When building a documentation program, the JFIS II must ensure that there is full cooperation and coordination from all agencies involved in the intervention program. The responsibilities of each agency should be spelled out at the outset of the program. All issues concerning confidentiality, policies, and regulations should be worked out to everyone's satisfaction prior to the commencement of the program. Everyone should be in unison on the procedures for collection of the data and the amount of time involved in the process. All concerns about confidentiality should be addressed to the satisfaction of all organizations and agencies involved in the program.

System for Collection and Maintenance of Data

The system for collection and maintenance of the data will be dependent upon the capabilities and resources of the fire agency. A simple spreadsheet may suit the needs of one agency, while another may need the creation of a database specifically for firesetter information. Whatever system is used, it must meet the needs of the program and the people using it. As was stated earlier, any data collection program must be simple and easy to use.

System for Monitoring Programs

All juvenile firesetter intervention programs, no matter what the size, need to have some type of system for monitoring cases. Without this system, cases can get lost, forgotten, or neglected. Systems for monitoring cases should have some kind of reminder or calendar component so that the cases are not overlooked, and each case is handled in a timely manner. Whatever system is designed for case management, it can provide valuable information such as case status, the status of the program itself, and evaluation results as to its effectiveness. As the program manager, it is the responsibility of the JFIS II to ensure that documentation and monitoring of each case is handled according to the policies and procedures established by the interagency network. The JFIS II must also ensure that the program itself is appropriately monitored for effectiveness and success.

Confidentiality of Information

Much of the information gathered during the intervention process can pertain to psychological and legal status of minors. This information is highly sensitive and is subject to strict confidentiality issues. Questions about confidentiality and who has access to the information should be given careful consideration by the JFIS II and the interagency network. The JFIS II should consult with the appropriate individuals, such as legal counsel for the agency, medical professionals, school officials, and others to determine the appropriate means for maintaining confidentiality of information while seeking to assist the juvenile and his or her family. The JFIS II must stay abreast of legal decisions and laws that may affect how the information is gathered, maintained, and recorded as those tasks relate to the confidentiality of information.

Chapter Summary

When it comes to the planning and development of a juvenile firesetter intervention program, many tasks and activities are crucial to the success of the program. In addition to the development of the overall program, the JFIS II as program manager must ensure that the necessary agencies and organizations are included in the program and that everyone is on board with its policies and procedures. Training of all personnel involved is crucial to the program. Even in the best planned and designed program, if the personnel responsible for the implementation and execution of the program are not properly trained in its processes and procedures, the effectiveness of the interventions can be compromised. Informing the community of the services available to the community is paramount to the program as well.

When speaking about the success of the program, it is not enough to simply reference whether firesetters are accurately assessed and educated; it is about the long-term success for the community. The goal of the juvenile firesetter intervention program is to reduce the number of child-set fires in the community, thereby reducing the number of deaths, injuries, property damage, and arrests that result from this community issue.

Review Questions

1. What are the steps for developing an interagency network for the purpose of juvenile firesetting interventions?

2. What forms are necessary for a juvenile firesetting intervention program including the intake, interview, referral, and follow-up tasks?

3. What should be addressed in a training program for personnel who work within an established juvenile firesetter intervention program?

4. What elements should be addressed in an advertising program with the goal of informing community members about the local juvenile firesetter intervention program?

5. What should be included in a data collection system for a community's juvenile firesetter intervention program?

Key Terms

Case Management Information — Data that is specific to an individual firesetter and his or her family. This might include names, addresses, specific incident numbers, etc. This information is critical in tracking the individual case through the program.

Demographic Information — Data that reports the general circumstances of an event and information about the participants. This information is pertinent in determining if there is a local community profile for a firesetter.

Incidence Reporting System — Database used to track reported incidents of juvenile firesetting that will provide valuable information about the entire problem of juvenile firesetting in a community. An incidence reporting system specifically for juvenile-set fires will provide information about the nature of the problem in the community.

Intake Form — A form used to gather information about the firesetter and the firesetting incident.

Management Information System (MIS) — Provides a means for tracking information about the program, for summarizing and analyzing the program's caseload, and securing data for annual reports and evaluations.

Memorandum of Understanding — Form of written agreement created by a coalition to make sure that each member is aware of the importance of his or her participation and cooperation.

Chapter 23 Notes

Federal Emergency Management Agency (1994). National Juvenile Firesetter/Arson Control and Prevention Program. Emmitsburg, MD.

Federal Emergency Management Agency (2002). Juvenile Firesetter Intervention Handbook. Emmitsburg, MD.

Fireproof Children (2006). Juvenile Firesetting: A Community Guide to Prevention and Intervention. Pittsford, NY.

JFIS Leadership Module: Data Collection Paper prepared for the National Fire Academy. Gerri Penny, M.Ed.

National Fire Academy (2006). *Juvenile Firesetter I and II: Leadership,* Student Manual.

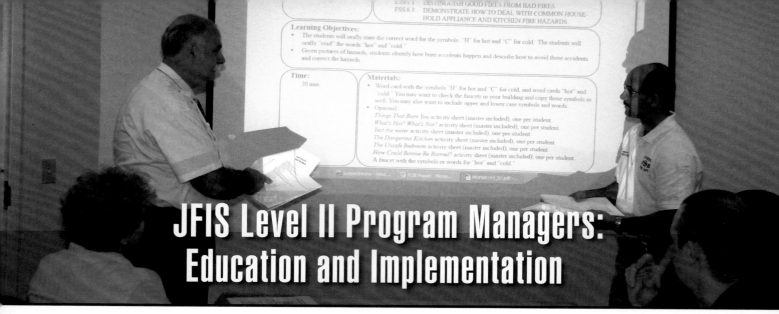

JFIS Level II Program Managers: Education and Implementation

Chapter Contents

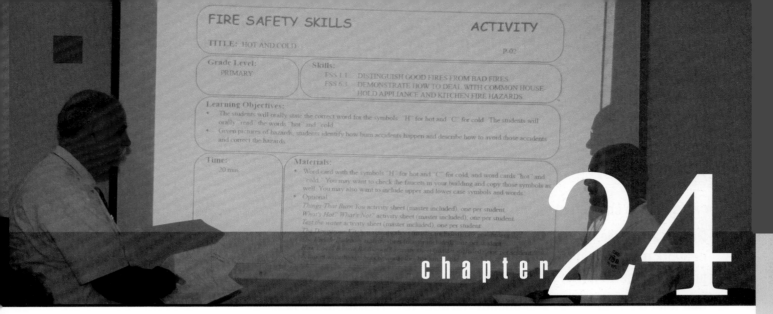

Key Terms

Job Performance Requirements

This chapter provides information that addresses the following job performance requirements of NFPA® 1035, *Standard for Professional Qualifications for Fire and Life Safety Educator, Public Information Officer, and Juvenile Firesetter Intervention Specialist*, 2010 edition.

NFPA® 1035 References

10.4.1

10.4.2

10.4.3

Learning Objectives

After reading this chapter, students will be able to:

1. Deliver a juvenile firesetter intervention training program for program personnel and interagency network members in order to support the program and provide for the proper identification of juvenile firesetters (NFPA® 1035, 10.4.1).

2. Maintain the established interagency network (NFPA® 1035, 10.4.2).

Chapter 24
JFIS Level II Program Managers: Education and Implementation

Case History

In a rural Georgia town, firefighters were confronted with a juvenile firesetter issue. Three children were involved with a fire that caused property damage but no injuries. The property owner requested that charges be filed because of previous problems with the children. The three children were taken to the police station to be processed, but were released to their parents.

This community had no juvenile firesetter program. Some training had been conducted with one of the firefighters who was interested in starting a program, and he wanted to pursue the situation. However, a firesetter program was an unknown option to community members, law enforcement, and even the fire service itself.

Fortunately a nearby community had an established intervention coalition and was willing to extend the partnership to another fire department. All local firefighters were referred to that program to learn the process involved in juvenile firesetter intervention.

Source: Lt. Michael J. Kufrovich, Hahira (GA) Fire Department

The individual serving in the position as the JFIS II is considered the program manager. This individual is responsible for overseeing all aspects of the intervention program, which includes organizing the interagency coalition, compiling reports, and providing quality assurance or control for the work of the program's personnel.

In the previous chapter, the development of the interagency network (or coalition) was discussed in detail. Steps were provided for making the initial contact with agencies and agency personnel and for bringing this group together for the important work of the juvenile firesetter intervention program.

Once the coalition has been developed, it is up to the JFIS II to maintain the interagency network. People will come and go from agencies, responsibilities will be shifted, and the JFIS II must ensure that the interagency network maintains the balance of skills and areas of expertise that is needed to provide the best services with the program.

The development of the necessary training for program personnel was also discussed in the previous chapter. However, development is only half of the training process. There is still much work to be done that can ensure that the training is meaningful and well received. In this chapter, information is provided on the delivery of the training sessions and the need for continuing education.

As the coordinator of the JFI program, the JFIS II must oversee the various components of the program and determine the needs of program personnel and the interagency coalition. By ensuring excellence in these areas, the excellence and success of the program will be ensured as well.

Training for Program Personnel and Coalition Members

As was discussed in the previous chapter, the design of a training program for firesetter intervention program personnel is based upon the community's specific program and the audience being trained. The purpose of a particular training workshop may be to train program personnel on the specific steps of intake, assessment, and referral. Another training event may be for fire service personnel and will focus on the identification and intake aspects of the intervention program. Yet another may focus on community members who may come in contact with firesetters who are in need of the program's services.

In addition to receiving training on the specific steps and procedures of the program, the JFIS I interventionist or other program personnel should receive training in **interpersonal skills**. These individuals should be trained to interact well with children and to communicate effectively with adults.

Professionals from outside the fire service, such as mental professionals and teachers, should be trained in the role of the fire service in child-set fires. This portion of the training must be tailored to the particular program that has been developed and implemented in a specific community.

Fire service personnel, particularly frontline firefighters and fire investigators, need to receive an overview of the program components and the philosophy behind the program. For some firefighters, this may be a new way of addressing juvenile firesetters. It is important that any child-set fires to which the fire department responds be handled correctly.

The JFIS II needs to be mindful of the variety and numbers of individuals who need to be trained in the program policies and procedures. For some individuals, the training may only need to provide an overview of the program and its components. Other program participants may need more extensive training on the use of the forms used in the intervention program **(Figure 24.1)**. Others may need to receive in-depth training on interviewing techniques, the assessment process, or simply interpersonal communications skills. It is up to the JFIS II, as coordinator of the training process, to determine the needs of the program's personnel. Ample and adequate training must be provided to meet those needs.

It is the responsibility of the JFIS II program manager to design and deliver the training, regardless of the audience. This is not to say that the JFIS II program manager has to be the one who actually conducts all the training sessions. A wide array of national experts can provide their expertise in the training of program personnel. However, the team-teaching approach is extremely valuable in that the JFIS II can assist a national expert by providing knowledge of the local issues and program design. It is often beneficial to have individuals from social services, mental health, and juvenile justice contribute to the training as well.

A number of decisions surround the planning and delivery of the training program. These decisions can be broken down into three major parts:

1. What is done before training?

2. What is done during training?

3. What is done after the training?

Before Training

Before planning and delivering the training session, the JFIS II must establish a budget for the training. The training budget will be based upon funds available for the intervention program. There may not be any funds available, but that does not mean that the training can be cancelled. Prior to planning the delivery of the training session, the JFIS II needs to know what funds, if any, can be used.

Logistical decisions need to be made such as the location and length of the training and the most appropriate and convenient time. The JFIS II should consult with the interagency network to determine what would be in the best interest of the entire group. Some workshops are held at the location of the lead agency, while others may be conducted off-site due to space limitations. While most workshops are conducted in one day, others are half-day, or they may be extended to two days in length.

Figure 24.1 The program's personnel and other participants should be kept up-to-date on the forms that they should be using.

When looking at the location for the training, the following should be considered:

- *Accessibility of the location.* Is it user-friendly and ADA compliant? Is it centrally located? Is there adequate parking available?

- *Seating type.* Are there enough chairs? Can they be arranged to meet the needs of the training session? How comfortable are the seats?

- *Cost of location.* Is there a cost in renting this particular location? Is this cost within the budget of the coalition?

- *Equipment.* Is there audio-visual equipment available? Will it have to be brought in? Is there a cost associated with using the equipment?

As coordinator of the training, the JFIS II must determine which individuals and agencies should be included in a particular training session, especially the initial training program. A multidisciplinary audience is preferred because it is important that each member of the program understands the importance of the contributions of each agency to the success of the program. Participants may be chosen based upon their length of involvement with juvenile firesetters and prevention programs, pre-vious training, and the extent of their involvement in the firesetter program. Whatever the makeup of the audience, the training must be guided by the needs and learning styles of the participants in the workshop.

Before the training, the following duties must be accomplished:

- Photocopy or duplicate the materials that are used during the training **(Figure 24.2, p. 536)**.

- Gather all training supplies, such as markers, easel charts, and pens for transport to the training area.

- Send participants invitations to the training event and include specific directions to the training location.

- Send reminders approximately a week before the training date.

- Always provide specific and clear directions; never assume that people know how to get to the location.

- Provide the training participants with training materials two weeks before the training session.

- Remind the participants to bring the materials with them to the training session.

Figure 24.2 Training materials should be organized before the training session begins.

During Training

Different training formats can be used during the training sessions. The JFIS II should be cognizant of learning styles and plan to use a variety of instructional skills and methodologies. If the JFIS II is not the individual who is actually conducting the training, he or she may want to discuss with the trainer which formats will be used to ensure an appropriate variety to meet all needs.

When presenting information on the development of the JFI program and its procedures, the JFIS II can employ several different teaching strategies:

- A straightforward lecture-discussion that outlines the steps of the program.

- A computer-based slide presentation that provides the steps in order could be used as a visual aid.

- A panel discussion with individuals who have established an intervention program in their community. These individuals can share their experiences and challenges with setting up a community-based program. The individual in charge of the training can guide this discussion and identify program planning and development tasks.

When discussing the interview and assessment portions of the program, a mental health professional can be a great instructional resource. It is important that program personnel understand the psychological characteristics of the different categories of firesetters. The lecture-discussion teaching methodology can certainly be effectively employed for this portion of the training. In addition, participants can be given a hands-on activity using the interview and assessment materials.

The discussion on the three different intervention processes is an important part of the training. The focus of the training will depend upon the makeup of the audience:

- If the participants are mainly fire service personnel, then the focus will be on the educational intervention.

- If the participants are primarily mental health personnel, then the focus will be on the counseling and social services intervention.

Once again, this topic lends itself easily to a lecture-discussion teaching methodology.

On the day of training, the JFIS II should perform the following duties:

- Arrive at the location early to check the organization of the room and test the audiovisual equipment **(Figure 24.3)**.

- Have someone greet the training participants as they arrive. Depending upon the number of participants, a registration table may be needed.

- Distribute an agenda to the training participants before the training. The session should follow the agenda as much as possible.

During training, the training coordinator should perform the following:

- Identify and promote the referral agencies within the community.

- Spotlight representatives of these agencies in the training program.

- Allow representatives a few minutes to introduce themselves and their agencies and to describe the role they play in helping juvenile firesetters and their families.

After Training

At the end of the training, participants should be asked to provide input on the quality of the training session. The preferred method for evaluation is a written evaluation form (**Figure 24.4**). Individuals can be encouraged to complete it at that time, or they can return it at a later date. The usefulness of the information collected will be greater if the evaluation is completed immediately. The participants should be asked to evaluate the trainer, the location, the materials presented, the training methodologies, and suggestions for improvements for future training sessions.

Figure 24.3 A program manager should ensure that the training room is adequate for the needs of the scheduled activity.

Participants should leave the training armed with the information that they need in order to perform their function in the intervention program. Training sessions should do more than just deliver information. Participants should gain the knowledge of how their agency fits into the intervention program, what their role is in the program, and how to apply the information that they have been provided.

The JFIS II should always remember to thank those who assisted with the training. Those assisting might include funders, trainers, volunteers, and donors. The JFIS II should conduct a debriefing with those who worked at the session to talk about the positive aspects of the training, the challenges, and the improvements that can be made.

The behind-the-scenes details will make the training successful and beneficial. If everything runs smoothly at the training session, participants will focus on the material being presented and will leave with the knowledge and skills necessary to participate in the intervention program.

Follow-Up Training

The interagency coalition should establish training goals for the program personnel. This might include continuing education in the field of juvenile firesetting or in developing skills for working with children and parents. Many conferences, workshops, and seminars are conducted around the country and can provide additional training for firesetter program personnel. The JFIS II should provide information

Figure 24.4 Written evaluation forms are the preferred type of feedback after a training session.

on these trainings and conferences to program personnel and be prepared to assist individuals with obtaining the proper authorizations to attend such training sessions. The JFIS II may need to seek funding on behalf of those attending such training.

In order to provide up-to-date services, the program personnel and management must stay current with new information in the field of juvenile firesetting and arson. This will require that these individuals regularly participate in continuing education training. There are classes at the National Fire Academy that update JFI personnel on new ideas and emerging trends. National organizations, such as the International Association of Arson Investigators (IAAI) and the National Fire Protection Association® (NFPA®) hold annual meetings during which juvenile firesetting may be a topic. Several states, such as Massachusetts and Oregon, conduct annual conferences and seminars for juvenile firesetter intervention program personnel. Additionally, the Internet offers a wide range of Web pages and sites for personnel to seek new ideas and information in the field.

Whatever source of information and training is used, it must be understood by all program personnel that the life of the intervention program depends on the community's ability to offer the highest standard of services. In order to do this, program components must be based upon the most current knowledge and information available in the various disciplines that are involved in the program.

Maintaining the Interagency Network

In the previous chapter, the process for developing an interagency coalition or network was discussed. Forming the coalition is only half the process. The coalition must be maintained for it to move forward and develop sustainability. Because the learning environment and community demographics are always changing, the interagency network must be flexible and change as needed. The coalition needs to maintain its optimal functioning level to provide consistent and effective intervention services to its clients.

As the program coordinator, the JFIS II is responsible for maintaining the interagency network. Maintenance of the interagency coalition

Workshop Versus Training Session

There may be times when a workshop may be beneficial to the intervention program. What is the difference between a **training session** and a **workshop**?

- Workshops are generally small (6-15 participants) where training sessions may have many more participants.

- Workshops may be more participatory than a training session. Due to the small size, there is more opportunity to practice skills and techniques.

- Workshops are more informal than a training session. There may be a lot of discussion in a workshop, rather than just a trainer presenting information.

- Workshops are usually shorter in time than a training session.

For the intervention program, a training session will be necessary to provide the program participants with all the procedures and processes of the program, while the topic for a workshop might be interviewing skills and techniques.

means that the program manager must continually foster relationships with coalition members and possibly serve as their advocate with management to secure their continued involvement in the program. The program manager must also encourage fire department personnel who work with the program to join the coalition and make meaningful contributions.

There are a variety of ways that the program manager can work to maintain the interagency coalition. These include:

1. *Grooming others for leadership positions.* Coalition leadership may change over time. A planned rotation will help provide new insight, as well as curb any burnout on the part of the program manager who is serving as the coalition's leader. It is up to the JFIS II to develop staff members or other program personnel to run the JFI program's interagency coalition.

2. *Including the community.* Community involvement and support is important for the successful work of the coalition and the JFI program itself.

3. *Conducting regular, effective meetings.* Effective meetings are those in which peoples' time is used wisely and which make those attending feel that they want to continue to participate. The JFIS II, as the leader of the coalition, must provide members with the opportunity to socialize and bond, reflect on achievements, update each other, propose new ideas and initiatives, and decide on the next steps for proceeding with the program. Effective meetings require the following:

- A clear agenda, which is shared with all members prior to the meeting **(Figure 24.5)**

- Good facilitation skills on the part of the coalition leadership (See Chapter 9 for a listing of skills that lead to effective facilitation)

- Starting and ending on schedule

- Identifying members who will follow up on already assigned tasks, or those to whom tasks may be assigned

- Refreshments

After the meeting, it will be imperative that the coalition's leader prepare an official summary of the meeting to be shared with the coalition's membership, including members in good standing who did not attend the meeting.

4. *Establishing the coalition's organizational structure.* In order for the interagency coalition to have long-term existence, leadership should be established within an agency that will have a long-term interest in the intervention. This will provide for continuity of leadership. In addition, the program itself, as well as coalition membership, will become a permanent part of that agency. Most often this will be the fire agency, but it certainly does not have to be.

5. *Reviewing successes often.* Coalition members, and their respective agencies, need to see results. People need to know that their time is being spent wisely and that the objectives of the program are being met. Coalition members also need to see that regular progress is being made.

Communication Within a Coalition

Communication within any coalition is an important aspect of maintaining the cohesiveness of the group. Minutes of each meeting should be distributed among all the coalition members. There should be constant communication among members, particularly as questions or situations arise that need input from one or more of the group's members. Other features of good coalition maintenance and communication include:

- Continually involving all members in some way in the JFI program and the work of the group. This promotes ownership in the program and in the coalition. The more the members feel ownership, the harder they will work for the success of the coalition.

- Continually reviewing and updating the mission and objectives established by the membership. If goals are set for the group, they should be reevaluated on a regular basis. The group may wish to seek funding from a particular source or grant or may desire to establish their name in the community. Goals such as these can be adapted and changed as needed.

- Being realistic and keeping promises. Be sure that what is promised can be achieved and gets done. All members should be held accountable for their commitments and the work they have agreed to do.

Smithville Fire and Life Safety Consortium

Weekly Meeting Agenda

Date: Wednesday, April 26, 2011
Time: 9:00 a.m. to 11:00 a.m.
Location: Smithville Fire Station #1 Conference Room

1) Call meeting to order
2) Review and approve previous meeting minutes
3) Old Business
   a. FIRE Grant funds
   b. New partnerships
4) New Business
   a. Allocation of funds for new JFI public service announcements
   b. Discuss case #11-012
   c. Discuss case #11-015
5) Review discussions
6) Adjourn meeting

Figure 24.5 An example of a clear agenda for a weekly meeting.

- Continually praising and celebrating successes and mile markers. The first family that successfully completes the program is a success. Even the first referral should be considered a success, as this means the program is being recognized in the community. Celebration of achievements can certainly help the coalition continue to work and develop.

The integrity of the coalition can also be maintained in a very informal fashion. Ways to conduct informal maintenance might include:

- *Requesting feedback at scheduled meetings.* This is as simple as asking the group about how they feel things are going and if they are pleased with the accomplishments of the group. This might also include requesting suggestions for improvement, whether it is the process of the coalition or the program itself.

- *Feedback by e-mail or telephone.* Sending a postcard or e-mail to members asking them for feedback on certain aspects of the coalition and its performance is an excellent way to conduct informal maintenance. Again, ask for suggestions on ways to improve the processes surrounding the intervention program and its components.

- *Special meetings.* Provide the opportunity to meet away from the coalition's regular meeting place and time. This is beneficial when the coalition is considering changes in the program or is wishing to redesign the procedures of the program. This might be a weekend meeting or dinner meeting. This will also allow for interaction among coalition members that might not otherwise take place.

Barriers to a Successful Coalition

Several barriers were discussed in Chapter 14 that could affect the creation of a successful coalition. These barriers may also be a hindrance to maintaining the coalition as well. Some barriers to successful coalitions include turf issues, politics, and leadership issues.

Turf Issues

Some individuals or agencies may feel that they are not getting the recognition that they deserve or that they feel is warranted for either themselves or their organization. It is up to the JFIS II as the facilitator of the group to ensure that no single individual or

organization takes precedence over another. It is imperative that the group takes on its own identity separate from its component agencies and that the group as a whole receives recognition and praise.

Politics

At times political issues may arise among different agencies that are outside of the control of the coalition members. These issues will most likely have nothing to do with the intervention program or the work of the coalition. It will be the responsibility of the JFIS II to keep the coalition members focused on the tasks at hand and working for the good of the program.

Leadership Issues

Leadership for the coalition is an important component in keeping the group together and functioning. These issues can take several forms:

- *Domination by the JFIS II.* While the JFIS II may feel that it is his or her responsibility to lead the coalition, others may perceive this as domination. The JFIS II may need to "pass the torch," so to speak, to other coalition members. This does not mean that the JFIS II turns over complete control of the program but allows someone else to lead the coalition.

- *Weak leadership.* When the leadership role is passed on to others, it opens up the possibility that someone who is not as strong could become the leader. Those in leadership positions must be carefully chosen, and individuals should be groomed to take over the leadership role.

- *Domination by professionals or other individuals.* Members of a firesetter intervention coalition will possess a variety of backgrounds, education, training, and expertise. Some individuals may feel that because of their background, they possess superior information or expertise in the field of juvenile firesetting. At the outset, the JFIS II, as the coalition coordinator, must make it understood that each individual is important to the group, each brings a certain level of expertise in their field, and everyone must work together for the success of the program.

Forming a coalition is oftentimes the easiest part of the process. Maintaining the coalition takes work and effort on the part of the leadership and each individual coalition member. The JFIS II, as the program manager, must understand what is needed to create a strong bond and partnership with a variety of agencies.

Chapter Summary

Much of the work of the JFIS Level II Program Manager revolves around the day-to-day operations of the program. Maintaining the integrity of the interagency network and providing appropriate training opportunities are just several examples of what needs to be done to ensure the success of the program. The program must be maintained to be successful. This includes ensuring that program personnel receive proper training in all aspects of the program, from the paperwork involved to interpersonal skills. It also requires that that the coalition keeps moving forward and working together. The JFIS II must provide the necessary leadership for these tasks to be accomplished in a timely, efficient, and effective manner.

Review Questions

1. What are the considerations when preparing to deliver a training program for personnel involved in the juvenile firesetter intervention program?

2. What steps can be taken to maintain an established interagency network?

Key Terms

Interpersonal Skills — JFIS I interventionist or other program personnel should be trained to interact well with children and to communicate effectively with adults.

Training Session — For the intervention program, a training session provides the program participants with all the procedures and processes of the program.

Workshop — Beneficial to the intervention program. Workshops are generally small, participatory, informal, and generally short. Topics for each workshop may vary according to need.

Written Evaluation Form — The preferred method for evaluation. At the end of the training session, participants are asked to provide input in writing on the quality of the training, the trainer, the location, the materials presented, the training methodologies, and suggestions for improvements for future training sessions.

Chapter 24 Notes

Community Tool Box. University of Kansas.

FEMA. *National Juvenile Firesetter/Arson Control and Prevention Program.*

National Fire Academy. *Juvenile Firesetter I and II: Leadership curriculum.* (September, 2004).

FEMA. *Juvenile Firesetter Intervention Handbook.* January 2002.

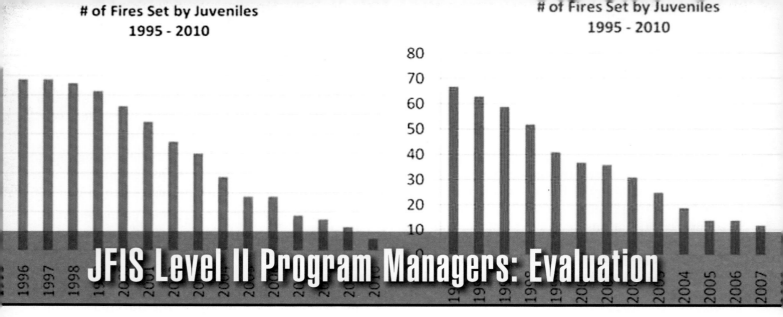

# of Fires Set by Juveniles
1995 - 2010

# of Fires Set by Juveniles
1995 - 2010

JFIS Level II Program Managers: Evaluation

Chapter Contents

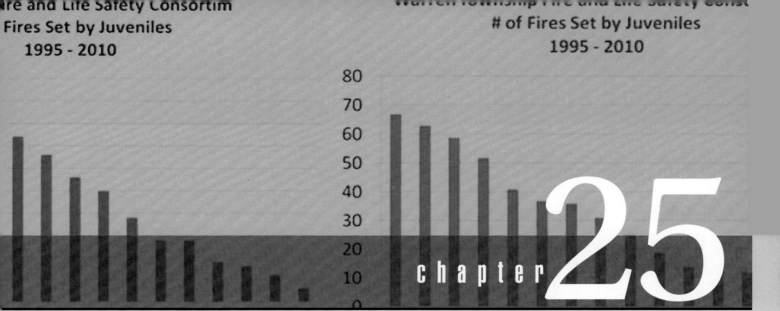

re and Life Safety Consortim
Fires Set by Juveniles
1995 - 2010

# of Fires Set by Juveniles
1995 - 2010

chapter 25

Key Terms

Job Performance Requirements

This chapter provides information that addresses the following job performance requirements of NFPA®
1035, *Standard for Professional Qualifications for Fire and Life Safety Educator, Public Information
Officer, and Juvenile Firesetter Intervention Specialist*, 2010 edition.

NFPA® 1035 References

10.5.1

10.5.2

10.5.3

Learning Objectives

After reading this chapter, students will be able to:

1. Evaluate the juvenile firesetter intervention program to determine if program outcomes are being met (NFPA® 1035, 10.5.1).

2. Determine if the juvenile firesetter intervention program is effective in reducing the incidence of child-set fires (NFPA® 1035, 10.5.2).

3. Prepare a report for the community and the interagency network describing juvenile firesetter intervention program results and outcomes (NFPA® 1035, 10.5.3).

Chapter 25
JFIS Level II Program Managers: Evaluation

Case History

Prior to 1992, interesting yet unintended results were found in preschool fire safety education programs in Portland, Oregon. In 1992, Portland began using the Learn Not to Burn® preschool curriculum in its Head Start programs. This program was well received. After the Learn Not to Burn® curriculum was implemented in Portland elementary schools, there was a decrease in the overall number of child-set fires in the community. In 1994, another preschool fire safety program, Play Safe! Be Safe!, was distributed to 175 child-care facilities.

Portland Fire Bureau understood the importance of the education of these young children, but they did not expect the educational programs to have an effect on their child-set fires. In ten years, the department saw a 50 percent drop in the number of referrals of curious firesetters in the 3-5 year age range, the target age for the educational program.

Outcome evaluation takes a long time and may demonstrate unintended results. The importance of documentation and evaluation of documentation cannot be overstated: Without proper documentation, evaluation is simply not possible.

Source: Don Porth, Portland (OR) Fire and Rescue

Once the juvenile firesetter intervention program is established and serving the community, the JFIS II must monitor the operations of the program. Information about the number of cases handled, the types of firesetters and their families, and the variety of services rendered will allow the program's manager to determine the impact the program is having in the community.

For those working with the program, having information about the outcome and effectiveness of the program are of the utmost importance. As with prevention programs, evaluation can provide hard data that the intervention program is effective in deterring and preventing the number of fires set by children. Evaluation can also uncover areas of the program that need to be revised or adjusted to increase their effectiveness. Evaluation can also provide information that can lead to continued or added support from funders both in the department and in the community.

Evaluation of a Firesetter Intervention Program

The JFIS II needs a means for demonstrating that the intervention program is reaching its goals and that the goals of the program are contributing to the achievement of the department's goals. Being able to capture the effectiveness of the intervention program is critical to the long-term goals of the program and the support of the community. It also provides a mechanism for evaluating the current program practices and for making needed changes to achieve the desired outcome.

The evaluation of a firesetter intervention program occurs on several levels:

- *Evaluation of the program.* This includes the process used for intake, interview, and intervention as well as the policies, practices, and procedures.

- *Evaluation of the effectiveness of the interventions.* The effectiveness can be determined by examining recidivism rates of those involved in the program.

- *A long-term evaluation of the overall effectiveness of the program in reducing the number of child-related fires in the community* (**Figure 25.1**). Evaluation of the overall intervention program can involve a number of facets of the program.

- *Evaluation of the educational intervention component to determine the educational gain of the participants.* The number of individuals who completed the program can provide data about the reduced risk to the families and other community members. A decrease in the number of child-related fires in the community indicates a reduction in the loss due to child-set fires.

The program's evaluation procedures should be determined during the initial planning stages of the program's development. The identification of the categories of data and other information needed to

properly evaluate should take place as the program is being designed.

The evaluation process for the firesetter intervention program is similar to the evaluation of fire and life safety education programs. Process, impact, and outcome evaluation strategies are all applicable to a firesetter program and necessary to determine the program's success.

Program Evaluation: Review and Application

Throughout this publication, there have been many discussions about the various levels of evaluation and the assorted means and methods of the evaluation process. While this chapter covers the evaluation process for the intervention program, it is suggested that the reader review the previous chapters relating to evaluation of educational programs for more extensive information (**Figure 25.2**).

Implementation and Data Collection: A Review

Demographic information and case management data provide information about the procedures related to the program and individuals cases. (See Chapter 23 for more information on documentation, data collection, and systems of organization.) Information about educational gain, behavioral changes, and recidivism rates should be collected and documented as a part of an evaluation information system. Incident reporting systems gather data related to the rates of child-set fires and injuries in

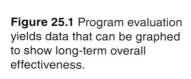

Figure 25.1 Program evaluation yields data that can be graphed to show long-term overall effectiveness.

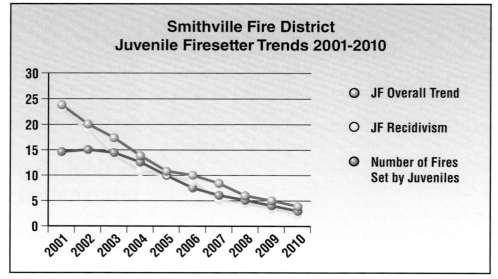

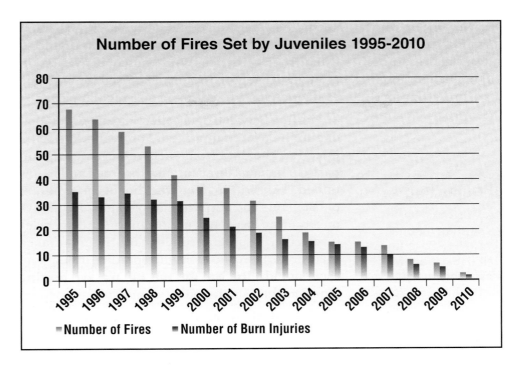

Number of Fires Set by Juveniles 1995-2010

Number of Fires   **Number of Burn Injuries**

Figure 25.2 Outcome evaluation is collected over a period of many years.

the community. Because the data collection systems are crucial to evaluation of the intervention program, a review of the basic types of data monitoring and collection systems is necessary.

- *Management information systems.* This type of data collection system includes demographic information as well as case information. Evaluators can use this information to determine how many cases were handled, assess details about the families involved in the program, review the disposition of the cases, and find out the length of each intervention type. This type of data provides information about the procedures and policies of the intervention program. MIS programs are more often used to generate a picture of current trends than to examine individual cases.

- *Evaluation system.* The information from the evaluation system provides data regarding recidivism and other school or family problems. This system can also provide data about knowledge gain from educational interventions and information gathered from any mental health professionals or other involved agencies. This gathered information will allow evaluation of the program's components and their effect on the firesetting behavior.

- *Incident reporting system.* This data collection system provides information about the overall firesetting problem in the community. It addresses the nature of the juvenile firesetting problem. This informa-

tion not only involves the intervention program, but it also helps to determine the effectiveness of primary prevention programs conducted in the schools and community. It uses information from fire department reporting systems, as well as schools, law enforcement, and other community agencies.

Data Collection System	Level of Evaluation
Management Information System (demographic and case information)	Process Evaluation
Evaluation System (follow-up data)	Impact Evaluation
Incident Reporting System (overall community problem)	Outcome Evaluation

Geographic Information Systems (GIS)

A **geographic information system (GIS)** integrates hardware, software, and data for capturing, managing, analyzing, and displaying all forms of geographically referenced information. The GIS can be useful in identifying locations of juvenile firesetters or areas of concern in a community. This system allows individuals to view, understand, question, and visualize data in many ways that can assist in working with community members and organizations. Using GIS can help to identify trends or patterns in firesetting within a community or a particular neighborhood. GIS can also help record locations of firesetting incidents and locations of families that are participating in the JFI program.

National Fire Incident Reporting System (NFIRS)

One of the reporting modules of the National Fire Incident Reporting System (NFIRS) is an **Arson Module**. This module (NFIRS-11) allows departments to track information on intentionally set fires. It is used in conjunction with the Basic, Fire, and/or Structure Fire Modules, and it is an optional component. The 2008 version of NFIRS 5.0 allows the user to track information about fires set by juveniles. The information includes:

- Demographic data such as age, gender, and race

- Family type, including single-parent, foster, two-parent, or extended

- Motivation and risk factors, including curiosity, history of firesetting, history of stealing, and diagnosed/suspected ADD and ADHD

- The module also allows the user to record whether the child was referred to the JFIS program, arrested, released to parent or guardian, or referred to a treatment program.

At the time of publication, use of the Arson Module is not a required component at the federal level, but may be required by individual states. The component is designed to interface with the Arson and Explosives National Repository of the Bureau of Alcohol, Tobacco, and Firearms once the information is transmitted to the National Fire Data Center. (For more information on NFIRS and the Arson Module, please visit the NFIRS Web site.)

Source: FEMA's *National Fire Incident Reporting System,* January 2008

The Process of Evaluation

In order to provide for a valid and reliable evaluation of the firesetter intervention program, the accuracy of any data collected must be ensured. When the intervention program is in the development stage, the data collection system and evaluation process should be determined and designed. Process and impact evaluation should take place at regularly established intervals. While outcome evaluation is a long-term process, any data used for outcome evaluation must be gathered on a regular basis.

The link between data collection and evaluation cannot be overemphasized. For evaluation to be effective, the data from each and every program participant must be accurately recorded and maintained. This will involve tracking of the program participants and performance of follow-up surveys on a routine basis. It is important that all agencies involved in the program understand the importance of accurate data collection and reporting. In addition, they should adhere to the collection and reporting requirements established at the onset of the program.

In the evaluation of JFI programs, special attention must be paid to the results received from the different categories of firesetter. That is, those children classified as curiosity firesetters may have different evaluation results than those classified as more severe. More success may be seen with curiosity firesetters, simply because it is easier to curb firesetting behavior in these circumstances than with more severe or delinquent cases. In fact, curious firesetters may have a lower recidivism even without intervention. Additionally, not only must the category of "child-set fires" be examined when looking at recidivism, the category of "arson" must be examined as well. Evaluation measures must take into account the definitions of those categories and how fire causes are categorized when dealing with children and fires.[1]

The interagency network should establish the frequency of the different levels of evaluation. Again, this should be determined during the planning and development process. In the beginning, it may be necessary to conduct process and impact evaluations frequently. Monthly or quarterly evaluations may be prudent. The frequency may depend on the number of families involved in the program. Even a lack of participation in the program is a form of process evaluation and would indicate the need for changes. Perhaps alterations need to be made to the program's publicity and advertisement in the community. Information about families who do not participate in the program when asked needs to be included in the evaluation process, as well as those who drop out or do not complete the program. This information can assist the interagency network in making changes to the program to promote ease of use or in marketing the program.

Just as it is with risk-reduction programs, evaluation is a key component in any juvenile firesetter intervention program. The evaluation process should be simple, flexible, reliable, and timely. Without data collection and the accompanying evaluation process, the program's effectiveness is unknown.

Reporting the Results of the Program's Evaluation

Sharing the results of the intervention program's evaluation process is an important component of success **(Figure 25.3)**. As results are gathered, stakeholders should be informed of the progress of the program and any adjustments that are made. Stakeholders include those individuals who are directly involved with the program, those having an interest in the outcome of the program, and community members.

All members of the fire agency should be informed of the results of the evaluation process. There is certainly a vested interest among the leaders of the organization in the effectiveness of the program in curbing firesetting behavior. Departmental leadership also needs to know that resources, such as time, money, and equipment, are being used successfully in meeting the goals and objectives established for the program. Additionally, all members of the fire

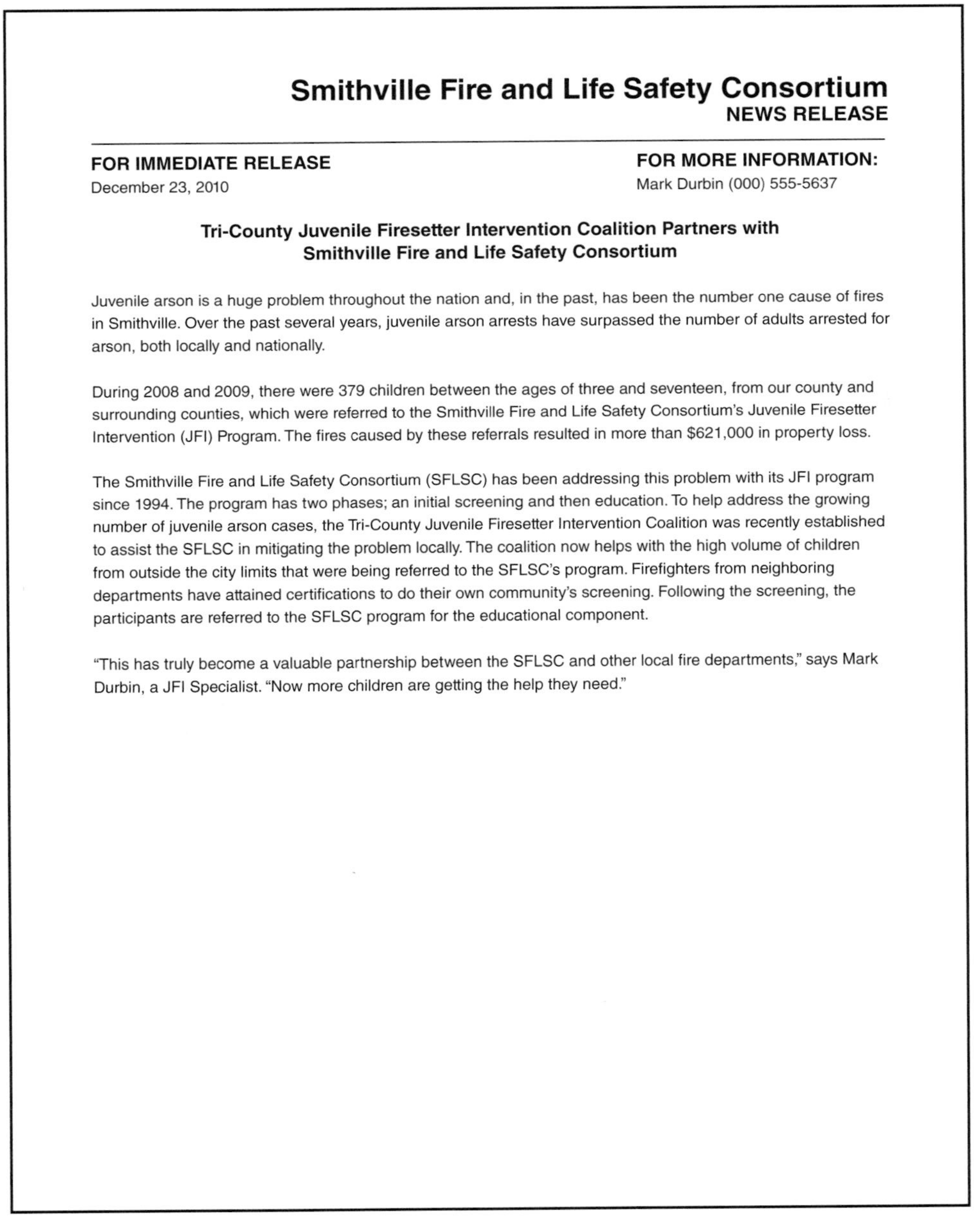

Smithville Fire and Life Safety Consortium
NEWS RELEASE

FOR IMMEDIATE RELEASE
December 23, 2010

FOR MORE INFORMATION:
Mark Durbin (000) 555-5637

Tri-County Juvenile Firesetter Intervention Coalition Partners with Smithville Fire and Life Safety Consortium

Juvenile arson is a huge problem throughout the nation and, in the past, has been the number one cause of fires in Smithville. Over the past several years, juvenile arson arrests have surpassed the number of adults arrested for arson, both locally and nationally.

During 2008 and 2009, there were 379 children between the ages of three and seventeen, from our county and surrounding counties, which were referred to the Smithville Fire and Life Safety Consortium's Juvenile Firesetter Intervention (JFI) Program. The fires caused by these referrals resulted in more than $621,000 in property loss.

The Smithville Fire and Life Safety Consortium (SFLSC) has been addressing this problem with its JFI program since 1994. The program has two phases; an initial screening and then education. To help address the growing number of juvenile arson cases, the Tri-County Juvenile Firesetter Intervention Coalition was recently established to assist the SFLSC in mitigating the problem locally. The coalition now helps with the high volume of children from outside the city limits that were being referred to the SFLSC's program. Firefighters from neighboring departments have attained certifications to do their own community's screening. Following the screening, the participants are referred to the SFLSC program for the educational component.

"This has truly become a valuable partnership between the SFLSC and other local fire departments," says Mark Durbin, a JFI Specialist. "Now more children are getting the help they need."

Figure 25.3 An example of a news release.

department should be informed about the program and the evaluation results. This will keep individuals interested in supporting the program and its various components.

Members of the interagency coalition and their respective agencies should be kept up-to-date on the program's progress and evaluation. Regular reporting is important to coalition members not just on the activities taking place, but on their outcome as well. Evaluation reports should be given to organizations involved with the program even if they are not a part of the coalition.

Additionally, community members need to be informed of evaluation results for the program. This keeps the community informed and also serves as a publicity tool. Once positive outcomes for the program are reported, families whose children are involved in firesetting will be more likely to seek the intervention services being offered. Individuals interested in working with the program or organizations wishing to provide needed resources will want to see that the program is successful before making such a commitment.

The format of the evaluation report and the information contained therein will differ according to the intended audience for the report. Evaluation information reported to the community should be general and describe the overall results. Reports submitted to the fire agency should be more detailed and include information regarding expenditures of time and money. Evaluation reports for other agencies may include expenditure information, but should certainly include more specific results relating to the firesetter cases, the interventions provided, and the outcomes.

Once evaluation results are compiled and reported, the interagency coalition must critique the results. The results should be compared to the program's objectives and any benchmarks set for the program. If there are processes or components of the program that are not successful or have not reached the desired goal, they should be evaluated and adjusted accordingly. Members of the coalition should look at those areas of the program needing improvement to determine what the best course of action might be for adjustment:

- The educational intervention is not producing the expected results. Evaluate that portion of the program to determine where the problem might be.

Format for Reporting

Chapter 16 covers formats for evaluation reports. A short review is presented below.

1. *Face-to-face meetings.* This works best for smaller groups and would be appropriate for reporting to the interagency coalition and fire agency leaders.
2. *Public presentations.* This reporting would be appropriate for community groups or other large gatherings.
3. *Written reports.* This allows for in-depth information to be presented but should be geared toward the intended audience.
4. *Video reports.* This is appropriate for news reports or public access channels. This type of evaluation report might include a family that has successfully completed the program.
5. *Mass media.* This format would be appropriate for the community in the form of news stories.
6. *Journal articles.* This is an appropriate reporting format for peers and other professional groups.

- Some educational programs may not be well attended. It may be necessary to alter the day and time of the program to meet the needs of those needing to attend.
- There may be people who have transportation issues. It may be necessary to change the location of the training to make it more accessible **(Figure 25.4)**.

Without evaluation results, support and enthusiasm for the program will dwindle. Successes should be shared and celebrated, and evaluation allows for regular opportunities to discover new things to celebrate.

Chapter Summary

Congratulations on demonstrating an interest and proficiency in a field that is constantly proving its worth in many communities. By developing and discovering useful communication and evaluation skills, a successful educator at any level will be able to gain definitive answers to important questions, instead of having to guess. Sharing those skills improves the quality of life for everyone.

Smithville Fire and Life Safety Consortium
2010 Annual Report

6. Juvenile Firesetter Intervention Program

6.1 Findings and Recommendations

6.1.1 Findings

1) Overall, the program is well administered.
2) The diversity of the program partnerships continues to be a highlight of this program.
3) Program staffing and funding are adequate with one exception.
4) Limited staffing in recordkeeping continues to impair information dissemination.
5) Analysis has shown a slight increase in the number of JF fires in the past year.
6) Parental involvement in the JF intervention program remains low.

6.1.2 Recommendations

1) At least one more person should be hired to assist with recordkeeping functions.
2) Continue to monitor the increase in JF fires to identify trends that may suggest new approaches to the problem.
3) Seek new opportunities to involve parents of juvenile firesetters in the intervention program.

Pg. 8 of 15

Figure 25.4 An annual report gives coalition members a clear view of program successes and problems.

Review Questions

1. What is the process for evaluating a juvenile firesetter intervention program to determine if program outcomes are being met?
2. What process should be used to determine if the juvenile firesetter intervention program is effective in reducing the incidence of child-set fires?
3. What is the procedure for preparing a report to the community and the interagency network on juvenile firesetter intervention program results and outcomes?

Key Terms

Arson Module — The Arson Module consists of two parts: a local investigation module that permits a fire department or arson investigation unit to document certain details concerning the incident; and a juvenile firesetter section that identifies key items of information that could be used for local, state, and national intervention programs.

Geographic Information System (GIS) — Integrates hardware, software, and data for capturing, managing, analyzing, and displaying all forms of geographically referenced information. This type of system can be useful in identifying locations of juvenile firesetters or areas of concern in a community.

Chapter 25 Notes

FEMA. *Juvenile Firesetter Intervention Handbook.* January 2002.

FEMA. *National Juvenile Firesetter/Arson Control and Prevention Program.* June 1994.

National Fire Academy. *Juvenile Firesetter I and II: Leadership curriculum.* (September, 2004).

1. National Fire Protection Association®. *Fire Protection Handbook, Twentieth Edition.* (2008)

Appendix A

Appendix A
Chapter Correlation to NFPA® Requirements

NFPA® 1035 Competencies	Chapter References	Page References
5.1.1	2	30-52, 66-71
5.1.2	3	81-88
5.2.1	3	81-85
5.2.2	3	81-85
5.2.3	3	85-88
5.2.4	4	96-103
5.3.1	4	96-106
5.4.1	5	143-146
5.4.2	5	140-146
5.4.3	5	136-140
5.4.4	5	136-140
5.4.5	5	147-153
5.4.6	5	147-153
5.5.1	6	163-176
5.5.2	6	170-176
6.1.1	7	184-185
6.1.2	7	185-189
6.2.1	8	196-199
6.2.2	8	199-201
6.2.3	8	201-203
6.2.4	8	203-206

Continued

NFPA® 1035 Competencies	Chapter References	Page References
6.3.1	9	213-221
6.3.2	9	221-227
6.3.3	9	227-232
6.4.1	10	250-251
6.4.2	10	252-257
6.4.3	10	257-267
6.4.4	10	267-271
6.4.5	10	271-276
6.5.1	11	282-286
6.5.2	11	287-288
6.5.3	11	288-302
7.1.1	12	309-310
7.1.2	12	320-341
7.2.1	13	320-323
7.2.2	13	324-330
7.3.1	14	336-339
7.3.2	14	345-349
7.3.3	14	339-341
7.3.4	14	349-351
7.3.5	14	351-356
7.4.1	15	364-366
7.4.2	15	367-376
7.4.3	15	368-376
7.4.4	15	369-372

Continued

NFPA® 1035 Competencies	Chapter References	Page References
7.4.5	15	376-377
7.5.1	16	390-393
7.5.2	16	386-387
9.2.1	18	422-423
9.2.2	18	426-427
9.2.3	18	427
9.2.4	18	428
9.2.5	18	428
9.4.1	19	437
9.4.2	19	438-440
9.4.3	19	441, 447-451
9.4.4	19	451-452
9.4.5	19	456-465
9.4.6	19	460-462
9.5.1	20	474
9.5.2	20	475
10.2.1	22	495-502
10.2.2	22	502-505
10.2.3	22	505-506
10.2.4	22	507-508
10.2.5	22	506-507
10.3.1	23	514-517
10.3.2	23	517-518
10.3.3	23	518-520

Continued

NFPA® 1035 Competencies	Chapter References	Page References
10.3.4	23	520-524
10.3.5	23	524-527
10.4.1	24	534-538
10.4.2	24	538-541
10.4.3	24	533-539
10.5.1	25	545-546
10.5.2	25	545-547
10.5.3	25	549-550

Concluded

Glossary

Glossary

A

Abuse — Harmful behaviors and/or actions, as defined by local law, that place an individual at risk and require reporting.

Adjudication — To hear or settle a case by judicial procedure.

Affective Domain of Learning — Affective learning is demonstrated by behaviors that indicate attitudes of awareness, belief, and responsibility. Affective learning appeals to attitude change and behavior modification.

Age of Accountability — The minimum age at which state courts have ruled that a child is intellectually capable of understanding right from wrong and the consequences associated with inappropriate behavior.

Alarm Check Valve — Type of check valve installed in the riser of an automatic sprinkler system that transmits a water flow alarm when the water flows in the system.

American Paradigm of Fire — A belief held by many people that fire cannot or will not happen to them.

Applied Learning — Making information relevant so that the proposed learner understands why she or he should receive and process the material.

Arson Module — The Arson Module consists of two parts: a local investigation module that permits a fire department or arson investigation unit to document certain details concerning the incident; and a juvenile firesetter section that identifies key items of information that could be used for local, state, and national intervention programs.

Assessment — A structured process by which relevant information is gathered for the purpose of determining specific juvenile or family intervention needs.

Assessment Instrument — A tool to help the frontline JFIS identify why a juvenile is setting fires and the risk of repeat behaviors. An assessment instrument should be validated by mental health clinicians and a scoring process used to determine levels of risk for repeat firesetting behaviors.

Attention Deficit Disorder (ADD) — Chronic inability to maintain attention to specific stimulus for an extended time period. ADD occurs as result of a combination of neurological, biochemical, social, and cognitive factors.

Attention Deficit Hyperactivity Disorder (ADHD) — Chronic nonpurposeful excessive movement combined with inability to sustain meaningful attention. ADHD sometimes coexists with learning disabilities.

Attention Seeking Firesetters — Juvenile who starts a fire in an attempt to bring attention to a stressful life situation such as depression, anger, or abuse.

Authority Having Jurisdiction (AHJ) — An organization, office, or individual responsible for enforcing the requirements of a code or standard, or for approving equipment, materials, an installation, or a procedure.

Awareness Campaign — A series of marketing strategies designed to inform a community about its local JFS problem and potential solutions.

B

Backdraft — Explosively rapid combustion that occurs with an increase in ventilation in an environment with high heat, large volumes of smoke, and limited oxygen.

Baseline Data — Data collected before a lesson or program is implemented.

Baseline Knowledge — What a person knows about a topic before a presentation is conducted.

Brainstorming — Identifying as many ideas as possible in a relatively short period of time.

Budget Cycle — Specific timelines used by organizations and communities to receive and act on requests for resources to support general operations.

C

Case File — A file that includes all documentation from an agency pertinent to a specific juvenile firesetting case.

Case Management Information — Data that is specific to an individual firesetter and his or her family. This might include names, addresses, specific incident numbers, etc. This information is critical in tracking the individual case through the program.

Census Data — Demographical information about people and communities that is collected by the U.S. Census Bureau every ten years.

Census Tracts — Defined geographical areas within a city, town, county, or village. Each tract carries a numerical identification.

Chain of Command — Pathway of responsibility from the highest level of the department to the lowest.

Child Protective Services (CPS) — A branch of the Department of Social Services. Its mission is to safeguard a juvenile when abuse, neglect, or abandonment is suspected, or when there is no family to take care of the juvenile.

Clinical Social Worker — A frontline health professional who often serves as a case manager to assist clients with information, referral, and direct help in dealing with the mental health intervention process. A clinical social worker can interview and counsel clients, but cannot write prescriptions.

Clinician — A degreed health professional who is licensed to perform specific services.

Coaching — When used in reference to training or instruction, it refers to an intensive tutoring given to subordinates regarding a particular activity.

Coalition — An alliance that comes together for some specific purpose, particularly among those who share common goals.

Cognitive Domain of Learning — Core domain of learning that involves knowledge recall and use of intellectual skill. Examples of cognitive process include how a person comprehends information, organizes subject matter, applies knowledge, and chooses alternatives.

Collaboration — Partnering with one or more person to accomplish a specific project.

Collaborative Partnership — Plans implemented by a partnership of agencies working to reduce risks of common interest and concern.

Combustion — An exothermic chemical reaction that is a self-sustaining process of rapid oxidation of a fuel, that produces heat and light.

Common Fire Hazards — Those that are prevalent in almost all occupancies and encourage a fire to start.

Community Analysis — The process of creating a risk profile that identifies leading risks, who is affected, and where problems are occurring.

Community Emergency Response Teams (CERT) — Groups of people within neighborhoods, community organizations, or the workplace who are trained by the emergency services in basic response skills.

Community-Risk Reduction — The process of addressing the larger issue of preventable injury that is occurring in a community. The process involves identifying leading risks and creating mitigation strategies through use of integrated prevention interventions.

Community Stakeholder — Person or group that is affected by or has a vested interest in a specific issue.

Community-Based Program — Activities that support an overall risk-reduction strategy and occur throughout a community.

Compensatory Time — Often referred to as "comp time." Work time earned by an individual that is space-banked by the employer. This time off may be used by the employee in place of vacation, holiday, and sick leave.

Complex/Problematic Firesetting Case — A JFS situation that is motivated or exacerbated by cognitive, social, or environmental dysfunction.

Concrete Operational Stage of Intellectual Development — Third stage of intellectual development; spans ages 7 to 11 years. Learner can perform "operations" and do something logically with information, so long as it can be applied to specific or concrete examples.

Confidentiality — A principle of law and professional ethics that recognizes the privacy of individuals.

Consensus — Group agreement on a topic.

Continuum of Care — The level and intensity of services needed to facilitate a positive outcome.

Cooperative Learning — Activity-based instruction that seeks to involve all students in the learning process.

Cost/Benefit Analysis — Examination of the proposed expense of an effort and deciding if the overall benefit is worth the investment of money and/or time.

Curiosity-Motivated — The curiosity-motivated firesetter is a child who is exploring his or her interest in fire through experimentation.

Curriculum — Broad term that refers to the sequence of presentation, the content of what is taught, and the structure of ideas and activities developed to meet the learning needs of learners and achieve desired educational objectives; also the teaching and learning methods involved, how learner attainment of objectives is assessed, and the underlying theory and philosophy of education.

D

Decay Stage — Stage of fire development in which the heat release rate is declining and the amount of fire diminishes as the fuel diminishes.

Delinquent Firesetter — Starts fires because of boredom or peer or media influences. Fires may also be set to commit destruction of property, conceal a crime, or as a rite of passage into a group.

Demographic Information — Data that reports the general circumstances of an event and information about the participants. This information is pertinent in determining if there is a local community profile for a firesetter.

Demonstration — Instructional/teaching method in which the instructor/educator actually performs a task or skill, usually explaining the procedure step-by-step.

Department of Homeland Security — Created by the Homeland Security Act of 2002, this agency serves to mobilize and organize America to secure the country from terrorist attacks.

Department of Juvenile Justice (DJJ) — A branch of state government that enforces laws violated by juveniles.

Determinants — Internal and external factors that influence how an organization develops and operates.

Direct Inspection — Used when an evaluator wants to physically examine an environment in search of proof that behavioral change has occurred.

Discussion — Instructional method in which an instructor generates interaction with and among a group. There are several formats of discussion: guided, conference, case study, role-play, and brainstorming.

Dry-Pipe Sprinkler System — Fire sprinkler system that consists of closed sprinklers attached to a piping system that contains air under pressure.

E

Economic Incentives — Used to support the prevention interventions. An example of positive incentives include reduced insurance premiums for buildings having fire-resistive construction, sprinklers, and automatic notification systems. An example of negative incentives includes fines for violating fire codes.

Education Interventions — Designed to raise awareness, provide information, impart knowledge, and ultimately produce a desired behavior. Education provides a foundation for the entire prevention intervention system.

Education Program — A series of lessons and activities designed to impact a specific risk-reduction outcome. Several programs are often used in tandem to support a broader based risk-reduction strategy.

Educational Materials — Printed matter, audiovisual materials, and "props" that an educator uses to enhance delivery of a lesson.

Emergency Response — Because risk will never be completely eradicated, communities must have an adequately staffed, trained, and equipped emergency response system.

Enforcement Interventions — All the ways in which people are required to act to mitigate risk. Examples related to fire safety include ordinances, laws, and building codes that require the installation of smoke detection and sprinkler systems.

Engineering Interventions — Modifications made to vehicles, products, materials, and processes to make them less hazardous, or to alter an environment to make it safer.

Environmental Change — Change in a learner's surroundings, particularly the home or workplace, following a fire and life safety outreach activity.

Epidemiologist — A professional who scientifically analyzes the occurrence of morbidity and mortality.

Epidemiology — The scientific study of the causes, distribution, and control of diseases among populations.

Evaluation — (1) Systematic and thoughtful collection of information for decision-making. It consists of criteria, evidence, and judgment. (2) Last of the four teaching steps in which the fire and life safety educator finds out whether the educational objectives have been met. (3) Process that examines the results of a presentation or program to determine whether the followers have learned the information or behaviors taught; consists of criteria, evidence, and judgment.

Evaluation Instrument — An instrument designed to collect data so that changes in knowledge, behaviors, environments, and lifestyles can be evaluated.

Evaluation Plan — Component of an intervention strategy that includes the problem statement, goal, and a series of measurable objectives that support the goal.

Evaluation Strategy — Plan that details how a risk-reduction program will be examined for effectiveness.

Executive Summary — A condensed single page synopsis of the written narrative.

External Organizations — Groups from outside the organization to which the educator is associated.

F

Fair Labor Standards Act — Federal law requiring employers to compensate employees at a pay/comp rate of time and a half for services performed off duty in the local community on behalf of the agency where the individual is employed.

Family Dynamics — The structure and characteristics of a person's living environment(s), including relatives, caregivers, other relationships and their interactions with each other.

Family Medical Leave Act — Federal law requiring employers to allow employees specific use of personal sick leave to care for an ill spouse or other immediate family member.

Fire and Life Safety Educator I — Those who have demonstrated the ability to coordinate and deliver existing educational programs and information.

Fire and Life Safety Educator II — Those who have demonstrated the ability to prepare educational programs and information to meet identified needs.

Fire and Life Safety Educator III — Those who have demonstrated the ability to create, administer, and evaluate educational programs and information.

Fire and Life Safety Strategy — A series of activities, programs, and initiatives designed to reduce identified risks within a community

Fire Corps — A national program in which citizen advocates assist fire departments with nonoperational roles.

Fire Department Connection (FDC) — Point at which the fire department can connect into a sprinkler or standpipe system to boost water flow in the system.

Fire Hazard — A condition that encourages a fire to start or increase the extent or severity of the fire.

Fire Tetrahedron — Heat, oxygen, fuel, and the self-sustained chemical reaction.

Fire Triangle — Heat, oxygen, and fuel: the components of fire.

Firesetters with Special Needs — Firesetters who suffer from some level of cognitive disability or challenge such as ADHD. Any level of firesetter may have a special need that should be considered during a screening process.

Firesetting — Any unsanctioned incendiary use of fire, including both intentional and unintentional involvement, whether or not an actual fire and/or explosion occurs.

Five-Step Planning Process to Address Community Risk — A nationally recognized process proven to be successful in guiding risk-reduction efforts.

Flashover — Rapid transition between the growth and fully developed fire stages during which all surfaces and objects within a space have been heated to their ignition temperature and flame breaks out almost at once over the surface of all objects in the space.

Flesch Reading Ease and Flesch-Kincaid Grade Level Index — Strategies to evaluate readability based on a 100-word passage of the written material being studied. Grade level and reading ease are matched to each other.

Follow-Up — Act of maintaining contact with a juvenile firesetter and his or her family over a designated period of time.

Formal Operational Stage of Intellectual Development — Fourth and highest stage of intellectual development, usually occurs between ages 11 and 15. Learners can think systematically to develop hypotheses about why something is happening the way it is. They can then test the hypotheses with deductive reasoning.

Full Thickness Burns (Third-Degree) — Those involving all the layers of skin and may damage the muscle, bone, or underlying organs.

Fully Developed Stage — Stage of fire development in which all combustible materials in the compartment are burning and releasing the maximum amount of heat possible.

G

Gatekeeper — A primary care physician or local agency responsible for coordinating and managing the health care needs of members. Generally, in order for specialty services such as mental health and hospital care to be covered, the gatekeeper must first approve the referral.

General Municipal Fund — The largest and most important accounting activity managed by a community or organization. The fund provides revenue and expenditures of unrestricted municipal purposes and all financial transactions not accounted for in any other fund.

Geographic Information System (GIS) — Integrates hardware, software, and data for capturing, managing, analyzing, and displaying all forms of geographically referenced information. This type of system can be useful in identifying locations of juvenile firesetters or areas of concern in a community.

Grants — Gifts of money to a nonprofit, tax-exempt organization or to a government organization.

Growth Stage — Stage of fire development in which the fire is developing within the compartment, drawing air into the plume above the fire, and spreading heat to other fuels in the compartment.

H

Health Insurance Portability and Accountability Act (HIPAA) — A congressional law established to help ensure the portability of insurance coverage as employees move from job to job. In addition to improving efficiency of the health care payment process, it also helps protect a patient's/client's privacy. The law also applies to information pertinent to juvenile firesetting situations.

Home Safety Council (HSC) — A national nonprofit organization solely dedicated to preventing home-related injuries. HSC helps facilitate national programs and partnerships to educate people of all ages to be safer in and around their homes.

I

Illustration — Instructional method that uses the sense of sight. The instructor or educator provides information coupled with visuals such as drawings, pictures, slides, transparencies, video clips, models, and other visual aids to illustrate a lecture and help clarify details or processes.

Impact Evaluation — Measuring knowledge gain, behavioral change, and modifications to living conditions or lifestyles.

Incidence Reporting System — Provides valuable information about the entire problem of juvenile firesetting in a community. An incidence reporting system specifically for juvenile-set fires will provide information about the nature of the problem in the community.

Incipient Growth Stage — Stage of fire development in which the fire is developing within the compartment, drawing air into the plume above the fire, and spreading heat to other fuels in the compartment.

Initiative — A fire or life safety program that targets a specific issue and audience(s) and is terminated when program goals are achieved.

In-Kind Contributions — Donations of services, time, or products.

Inpatient Mental Health Treatment — Hospitalization in a facility where 24-hour supervised care is present. This type of center offers short-term treatment in cases where a child is in crisis and possibly a danger to himself/herself or others.

Inspection — Formal examination of an occupancy and its associated uses or processes to determine its compliance with the fire and life safety codes and standards.

Institutionalized Behaviors — Collective support shown for a project by an organization. This includes the investment of time, people, money, and equipment to support the project.

Intake — Process of collecting the comprehensive background information from the juvenile's family or caregiver regarding the incident(s) that brought the juvenile to the program.

Intake Form — A form used to gather information about the firesetter and the firesetting incident.

Integrated Prevention Interventions — Process of combining education, technology, codes, standards, and supporting incentives to address community risk. Commonly referred to as the Five Es of Intervention.

International Fire Service Training Association (IFSTA) — An association of personnel dedicated to upgrading the training and skills of emergency services personnel and allied professionals.

Interpersonal Skills — JFIS I interventionist or other program personnel should be trained to interact well with children and to communicate effectively with adults.

Intervention — Formal response to firesetting behavior. It may include education alone or be combined with referral to counseling, medical, or social services. Juvenile justice sanctions are sometimes used (or required) as part of an intervention process.

Intervention Strategy — Action plan that describes how a risk-reduction initiative will be implemented and evaluated.

Interventionist — A JFIS Level I who is qualified to perform a specific task. This person works directly with juvenile firesetters and their families to prevent acts of recidivism.

Interview — Process of meeting with the juvenile firesetter and the family to determine the severity of the problem.

Ionization Smoke Alarm — Smoke detection device that uses a very small amount of radioactive material to ionize air molecules as they enter the detection chamber.

J

Job Performance Requirement (JPR) — A statement that describes a specific job task, lists the items necessary to complete the task, and defines measurable or observable outcomes and evaluation areas for the specific task.

Juvenile Firesetter — A person up to the age of 18 (or as defined by the authority having jurisdiction) who is involved in the act of firesetting.

Juvenile Firesetter Intervention Specialist I — Individual who has demonstrated the ability to conduct an intake/interview with a firesetter and his or her family using prepared forms and guidelines. The individual, based on program policies and procedures, determines the need for referral for counseling.

Juvenile Firesetter Intervention Specialist II — Individual who has demonstrated the ability to manage juvenile firesetting intervention program activities and the activities of the Juvenile Firesetter Intervention Specialist I.

L

Learning Activity — Any component of a lesson designed to enhance knowledge, attitude, or skill development. Activities are used to facilitate achievement of learning objectives.

Learning Disability — Cognitive disorder that diminishes a person's capacity to interpret what they see and hear and/or to link information from different parts of the brain.

Learning Objectives or Outcomes — Description of the minimum acceptable behaviors that students must display by the end of an instructional period.

Lecture — Instructional method using one-way communication in which an instructor or educator provides material verbally by telling, talking, and explaining but allows no exchange of ideas or verbal feedback.

Lesson Plan — The road map providing general guidance for how a presentation is to be delivered. It contains information and instructions on what will be taught and the teaching procedures to be followed. It covers lessons that may vary in length from a few minutes to several hours.

Liability of Injury — Legal responsibility and accountability for an act or process related to a program.

Lobbyists — People compensated by an organization to influence decision-makers to favor the special interests of the sponsoring organization.

Long-Term Memory — A large cognitive storage area where information can be processed and applied.

M

Management Information System (MIS) — Provides a means for tracking information about the program, for summarizing and analyzing the program's case load, and securing data for annual reports and evaluations.

Mean — Term that refers to the "average" of a set of scores and is calculated by adding all of the set of scores (values) and dividing by the total number of scores.

Median — Middle score in a set of scores (values) that are arranged or ranked in size (order) from high to low.

Memorandum of Understanding — Form of written agreement created by a coalition to make sure that each member is aware of the importance of his or her participation and cooperation.

Milestone Budget Dates — Dates by which municipalities are required to initiate actions on budget proposals. Governances usually require municipalities to submit a balanced budget by a specific date.

Mission Statement — The mission statement is about the present state of the risk-reduction division. It provides a meaning for the existence of risk-reduction work and allows the entire organization to understand the importance of the work being performed.

Mode — Most frequent score (value) in a set of scores.

N

National Fire Academy (NFA) — Federal agency that offers courses and programs to enhance the ability of emergency service providers and allied professionals to deal more effectively with fire and related emergencies.

National Fire Incident Reporting System (NFIRS) — National fire incident data collection system managed by the United States Fire Administration. Local fire departments forward incident data to a state coordinator. The coordinator collates statewide fire incident data and reports information to the USFA.

National Fire Protection Association® (NFPA®) — A private, nonprofit organization that works to reduce the worldwide burden of fire and other hazards. The organization develops and advocates use of consensus codes, standards, research, training, and education.

Neglect — Failure to act on behalf of or in protection of an individual in one's care.

Networking — Process of meeting others and determining resources that others have that can assist with the accomplishment of the risk-reduction initiatives.

NFPA® 1035 — Document outlining the Job Performance Requirements that can be used to determine whether an individual possesses the skills and knowledge to perform as a public or private fire and life safety educator.

Nonstructured Question — Question that does not offer a list of answer choices. Respondents are simply asked to write their response to the question.

Nontraditional Partnerships — Forming alliances with groups from outside the organization to which the educator is associated. The collaboration may be extended into venues not previously sought or even considered.

O

Objective Reporting — Ensuring those who report data to a collection system utilize an agreed upon standardized reporting methodology.

Observational Survey — Used when evaluators want to observe if behavioral, environmental, or lifestyle changes are occurring among a target population.

Operating Costs — The expenses needed to help create, evaluate, and sustain a risk-mitigation strategy.

Organizational Protocol — Rules set by the JFIS organization or JFS coalition that guide how a juvenile firesetting intervention program will be administered.

Outcome Evaluation — Measures changes in the occurrence of incidents over time. It also involves documenting anecdotal success stories of how prevention efforts impacted community risk.

P

Partial Thickness Burns (Second Degree) — Burns involving several layers of skin.

Partially-Structured Question — Used in cases where the researcher has some idea of potential responses that may be generated by respondents.

Partner — A person, group, or organization willing to join forces and address a community risk.

Partnerships — Joining forces with other groups to address common interests.

Pathological Firesetting — Firesetters who have transcended through the firesetting profiles whereby they are now setting fires as a way to release stress.

Pathology — Manifestation of a problem into a deviating condition.

Peer Assistance — Refers to the process of having employees of equal status assist others in the training process.

Percentage — Part of a whole expressed in hundredths.

Personal Fire Hazards — Common hazards that are caused by unsafe acts of individuals.

Photoelectric Smoke Alarm — Smoke detection device that uses a photoelectric cell coupled with a light source to detect smoke particulate.

Pilot Testing — Testing a specific intervention for effectiveness.

Place — In a social marketing campaign, it may refer to barriers that prevent the target audience from adopting the behavior. Place refers to accessibility of the supports that provide the target audience with the ability to make the change.

Practitioner — A person who is qualified to perform a specific task such as juvenile firesetter intervention specialist. Also one who works in a frontline agency to prevent or reduce risk.

Preoperational Stage of Intellectual Development — Second stage of intellectual development; occurs from age two to seven. Learners represent the world with words, images, and drawings.

Presentation — (1) Second of the four teaching steps in which the educator teaches a class or individual and transfers facts and ideas. (2) Lesson plan component at which point an instructor provides to, shares with, demonstrates to, and involves the followers in the lesson information. *Also see* Lesson Plan. (3) Single delivery of fire and life safety information. Also called *lesson* or *delivery.*

Pretest/Posttest — A test administered prior to and after a lesson or program has been conducted.

Prevention Intervention — Using a component of education, technology, fire codes, standards, supporting incentives, or emergency response to reduce risk.

Price — One of the four basic principles of any marketing campaign. Simply put, this is the cost of the product. Price in a social marketing campaign is not always easy to quantify, but it is still a determining factor for the target audience.

Primary Prevention — Prevention phase that promotes the well-being of an already healthy population through activities designed to prevent events that might result in injuries or property loss. It also seeks to enhance well-being by reinforcing healthy behaviors and discouraging lifestyles that may eventually lead to injury or illness.

Primary Stakeholder — People, groups, or organizations that have vested interest in a specific issue.

Problem Firesetter — Includes the profiles of intentional firesetting and firesetters with special needs.

Problem-Related Data — Statistics that can be used to analyze incident occurrences, develop a risk profile, prioritize problems, and identify at-risk populations.

Process Evaluation — Documenting the creation of prevention efforts, monitoring program activity, and tracking outreach into the community.

Product — The product is what is being marketed. In commercial campaigns, this is usually an item or service that the target audience will purchase or use. For social marketing, the product is the behavioral change that is the focus of the risk-reduction initiative.

Program Revision — Enhancement of a program so that it is accurate, current, and effective in helping to achieve intended outcomes.

Promotion — Advertising that is done to create awareness of the issue and provide the solution.

Psychiatrist — A medical doctor who specializes in mental health and can prescribe medications.

Psychologist — A professional with a doctoral degree in psychology who specializes in therapy. He or she can help direct several levels of clinical intervention.

Psychomotor Domain of Learning — Domain of learning in which the learner uses physical movement, coordination, and use of motor skills to develop proficiency of a skill.

Public Fire and Life Safety Educator's Canon of Ethics — Professional and ethical behaviors that should be exhibited by a fire and life safety educator.

Public Information Officer — Those who have demonstrated the ability to conduct media interviews, prepare news releases, and advisories.

Public Policy — A system of laws, regulatory measures, courses of action, and funding priorities by a government entity or its representatives. Public policy is often created through a legislative process at either the federal, state, or local level.

Purchase Order (PO) — A written document generated by the purchaser that allows vendors to invoice for monies owed. This action serves as an official record that the organization and vendor/contractor have conducted financial business.

Pyrolysis — Chemical decomposition of a substance through the action of heat.

Q

Qualitative Analysis — Nonstatistical subjective analysis of educational materials that relies on a developer's experience, judgment, and interpretation of the material.

Quantitative Analysis — Statistical analysis of educational materials involves formal testing of the products for ease of readability.

R

Recidivism — Recurrence of firesetting behavior.

Referral — An act or process by which an individual and/or family gain access to a program or community resources.

Reliability — A condition of validity; the extent to which a test or test item consistently and accurately shows the same results or scores given to a set of learners on different occasions or marked by different assessors or by the same assessors on different occasions.

Reliable Data — Statistics that come from an organization with proven expertise in collecting and disseminating fire experience data.

Request for Proposal (RFP) — A document sent to a vendor that specifies exactly what the purchaser wants a product or service to do. The proposed vendor is expected to meet the specification and provide an itemized bid for the product or service.

Requisite Knowledge — Fundamental knowledge one must have in order to perform a specific task.

Residential Treatment Center (RTC) — Provides 24-hour care and can usually serve several young people at a time. Children with serious emotional disturbances receive constant supervision and care at an RTC. Treatment may include individual, group, and family therapy; cognitive/behavior therapy; special education; recreation therapy; and medical services. Residential treatment is usually more long term than inpatient hospitalization.

Riser — Vertical water pipe used to carry water for fire protection systems aboveground.

Risk-Reduction Program — Comprehensive strategy that addresses fire and life safety issues via educational means.

Risk-Reduction Strategy — A series of integrated programs designed to impact a common goal.

Role-Playing — Discussion in which a group acts out various scenarios.

Rule of Nines — Method for approximating the extent of burns in the field.

S

Safer Cigarettes — Smoking materials that will self-extinguish if not inhaled upon by the user over a specific amount of time.

School-Based Program — Activities that support specific outcome objectives of a curriculum presented within a school system.

Secondary (or Selective) Prevention — Prevention phase that seeks to mitigate or modify events to reduce their severity. It targets high-risk conditions and populations.

Sensorimotor Stage of Intellectual Development — First stage of intellectual development; occurs from birth to age two. Learner constructs understanding of the world by coordinating sensory experiences (seeing/hearing) with motor actions (doing).

Service Learning — Educational trend that tries to connect young people to the community in which they live through community service projects.

Short-Term Memory — Information storage area with a finite amount of space. Information not acted upon or used by the learner will be replaced within a relatively brief time period.

Simple Firesetting Case — A JFS situation motivated by curiosity and can be addressed effectively though educational intervention.

Skewed Data — Skewed refers to data that is inaccurate because of faults inherent to the reporting mediums, bias from evaluators, or false information.

Skills Test — Evaluation instrument used to assess the individual's ability to perform a specific physical behavior; also called a performance test.

Social Marketing — Refers to the application of commercial marketing strategies and techniques to health issues and social problems. While the focus of commercial marketing is to change people's behavior for the benefit of a producer or merchant, the focus of social marketing is to change people's behavior to benefit themselves, the community, or society as a whole.

Special Fire Hazards — Those that arise from or are related to the particular processes or operation in an occupancy.

Sprinkler (or Sprinkler Head) — Water flow device in a sprinkler system.

Stages of Intellectual Development — Stages of intellect that build upon one another in sequential order.

Stagnant Organizational Culture — A group of people satisfied with the status quo of an organization and not interested in engaging in progressive change.

Stakeholders — People, groups, or organizations that have vested interest in a specific issue.

Standard Operating Procedures (SOPs) — Standard methods or rules in which an organization or a fire department operates to carry out a routine function. Usually these procedures are written in a policies and procedures handbook and all firefighters should be well versed in their content.

Structured Question — A question that offers the respondent a closed set of responses from which to choose.

Superficial Burns (First Degree) — Burns involving only the outer layer of skin.

Survey — Evaluation instrument used to identify the behavior and/or attitude of an individual or audience both before and after a presentation.

Survey Questionnaire — Survey that uses a series of questions to obtain data from respondents.

T

Target Hazards — Those properties where there is a great potential for loss of life or property loss if a fire erupts.

Team Teaching — Instructional method in which a group of two or more instructors work together. They combine their individual content, techniques, and materials in presenting information, demonstrating skills, and supervising practice of a class or several classes.

Training Session — For the intervention program, a training session provides the program participants with all the procedures and processes of the program.

U

United States Fire Administration (USFA) — Federal agency works to reduce death and economic losses due to fire and related emergencies. The organization provides public education, training, technology support, and data initiatives to educators and the public at large.

Unity of Command — Management system in which an individual reports to only one supervisor.

V

Validity — Extent to which a test or any assessment technique measures the learner qualities (knowledge and skills) that it is meant to measure.

Vision Statement — A description of the ultimate results of the work of fire and life safety educators. The first step in developing goals, procedures, or policies for fire and life safety activities.

W

Warning — Term used to signify that the event has been sighted or will occur soon.

Watch — Term used to indicate that conditions have developed that make the event possible; Watches are often issued for weather conditions such as tornados and floods.

Wet-Pipe Sprinkler System — Fire-suppression system that is built into a structure or site; piping contains either water or foam solution continuously; activation of a sprinkler causes the extinguishing agent to flow from the open sprinkler.

Workshop — Beneficial to the intervention program. Workshops are generally small, participatory, informal, and generally short.

Written Narrative — Chronicles a timeline of important events (past to present) relevant to the juvenile's firesetting problem. The narrative includes events that brought the juvenile into the program, a profile of the firesetting problem, intervention(s) performed, and referrals made for program participants with all the procedures and processes of the program.

Written Evaluation Form — The preferred method for evaluation. At the end of the training session, participants are are asked to provide input in writing on the quality of the training, the trainer, the location, the materials presented, the training methodologies, and suggestions for improvements for future training sessions.

Index

newspapers, 152–153
print media, 152–153, 247
promotion of community programs, 147
public information officer, 147
public service announcement, 147, 151, 522
publicity and informational items, 153
radio, 151–152
    awareness publicity, 522
    program education and implementation, 151–152
    programming summary, 151
    public service announcement, 151
relationships with, 153
social marketing, 154, 351
soft news, 151
television
    awareness publicity, 522
    Children's Television Workshop, 119
    functions, 152
    program education and implementation, 152
    programming summary, 152
trading cards, 153
Median, defined, 172
Memorandum of understanding, 499, 516
Memory
    long-term memory, 240
    random access memory, 240
    short-term memory, 240
Mental health options for firesetters
    cognitively challenged firesetters, 453–454
    Cornell Abraxas Center, 462
    criminal activity, 455
    funding, 462
    implementing intervention options, 455–456
    inpatient mental health treatment facility, 462
    legal consequences, 454–455
    medical interventions, 461–462
    mental health professionals, 460
    professionals, 452
    psychological conditions to consider, 453
    recidivism, 462
    referrals, 460–461, 462–463, 465
    Residential Treatment Center, 462
    social factors, 454
Mentoring, 374–375
Message
    adapting for the audience, 366
    creating, for risk reduction, 364–366
    defined, 365
    message medium saturation, 251, 275
Microsoft Access®, 300
Microsoft Excel®, 300
Microsoft PowerPoint®, 264
Middle school. *See* Adolescent learning
Milestone budget date, 320
Mims, Tilda, 366
MIS (management information system), 525–526, 547
Mission statement
    fire and life safety educators, 20
    FLSE Level III administrator, 368
    JFIS Level II program managers, 516
Mode, defined, 172
Modifications to programs, 394

Monitoring programs
    FEMA data monitoring and collection, 525–526
    Pregnancy Risk-Assessment Monitoring System, 392
    systems for, 527
Monthly activity report, 84
Mothers Against Drunk Driving (MADD), 105
Motivation
    in the learning process, 116
    A Study of Motivational Psychology Related to Fire Preventive Behavior in Children and Adults, 8
Motor vehicle crashes. *See also* Vehicles
    alcohol-related, 57
    child occupant protection, 57
    older adults, 54–55
    reenactments, 127
MOWAA (Meals on Wheels Association of America), 131
Multidisciplinary coalition, 514
Multiple choice tests, 166, 176

N

National Association of State Fire Marshals, 524
National Board on Fire Service Professional Qualifications (ProBoard), 18
National Burn Information Exchange, 64
National Center for Health Marketing, 353
National Center for Health Statistics (NCHS), 216
National Center for Injury Prevention and Control (NCIPC), 216
National Electronic Injury Surveillance System (NEISS), 216
National Fire Academy (NFA)
    Executive Fire Officer curriculum, 370–371
    Health Belief Model, 247
    history of fire and life safety education, 8
    JFIS data collection, 524–525
    JFIS leadership courses, 415–416
    organizational change, 370–371
    Solutions 2000-based education curriculum, 11–12
    training about juvenile firesetting, 484
National Fire Data Center, 214, 548
National Fire Incident Reporting System (NFIRS)
    Arson Module (NFIRS-11), 548
    history of fire and life safety education, 8
    history of NFIRS, 214
    juvenile firesetting data, 524
    objectives, 214
    voluntary membership, 214
National Fire Protection Association® (NFPA®). *See also specific NFPA*
    annual meetings, juvenile firesetting topics, 538
    Center for High Risk Outreach, 11
    evaluation curricula, 302
    fire database, 215–216
    Fire Service Inventory file, 215
    FLSE Level I educator, 29
    FLSE Level II manager, 30
    FLSE Level III administrator, 30
    history of fire and life safety education, 8
    juvenile firesetting, 403
    Learn Not to Burn™, 8, 270
    NFPA Journal®, 216
    predeveloped school- and community-based life safety programs, 325
    residence fire fatalities, 45

Index by Nancy Kopper